THE SELECTED PAPERS OF
E.S.PEARSON

EGON SHARPE PEARSON

THE SELECTED PAPERS OF E. S. PEARSON

ISSUED BY
THE BIOMETRIKA TRUSTEES
TO CELEBRATE HIS 30 YEARS
AS EDITOR

CAMBRIDGE
AT THE UNIVERSITY PRESS
1966

PUBLISHED BY
THE SYNDICS OF THE CAMBRIDGE UNIVERSITY PRESS
Bentley House, 200 Euston Road, London, N.W.1
West African Office: P.M.B. 5181, Ibadan, Nigeria

LIBRARY OF CONGRESS CATALOGUE
CARD NUMBER: 66–15940

First printed in Great Britain at the University Press, Cambridge
Reprinted by lithography in Great Britain by
John Dickens & Co Ltd, Northampton

CONTENTS

FOREWORD

At the end of 1965 Professor Egon S. Pearson retired from the Managing Editorship of *Biometrika*, a position he has held with distinction for nearly thirty years. Professor Pearson has shown exceptional zeal and skill in carrying out the functions of the editor of a scientific journal, and the high position *Biometrika* holds in the world of science is largely owing to this. The financial stability of the journal also owes much to his wise and efficient management. The Trustees of *Biometrika* wish to express their high appreciation of this work and this they do by sponsoring the publication of this volume.

Professor Pearson's direct contributions to statistics are of major and widely-acknowledged importance and the Trustees felt that the reissue of his papers in collected form would be of value to statisticians and students and would be a worthy way of celebrating his editorship. Some of his most important contributions were made jointly with Professor Jerzy Neyman between the years 1928 and 1938, and these are being issued in a separate volume. The present volume contains a selection of Professor Pearson's own papers, of which many of the earlier items are closely associated with this joint work. A few of the papers were written in collaboration with other authors.

L. H. C. TIPPETT
Chairman of Biometrika Trustees

ACKNOWLEDGEMENTS

The Trustees of *Biometrika* thank the Council of the Royal Statistical Society, the Institute of Mathematical Statistics and the U.S. Army Research Office, Durham, North Carolina for permission to reproduce papers No. 17, 18 and 21, respectively, which originally appeared in their publications. They also wish to thank Mrs Gena Wilks for agreeing to the inclusion of Professor Pearson's joint paper with the late Professor S. S. Wilks, as well as the following authors for agreeing to the inclusion of their joint papers: N. K. Adyanthāya, C. Chandra Sekar, B. A. Maguire, Maxine Merrington and A. H. A. Wynn.

THE DISTRIBUTION OF FREQUENCY CONSTANTS IN SMALL SAMPLES FROM SYMMETRICAL POPULATIONS

THE DISTRIBUTION OF FREQUENCY CONSTANTS IN SMALL SAMPLES FROM SYMMETRICAL POPULATIONS.

(Preliminary Notice.)

By EGON S. PEARSON, D.Sc., assisted by N. K. ADYANTHĀYA.

It is hoped that the following preliminary results may be of some interest to practical workers, both in showing the extent to which the tests developed for the case of samples from a normal population are valid, and also in suggesting modifications of these tests when required. The range of symmetrical populations from $\beta_2 = 1{\cdot}8$ to $7{\cdot}1$ has been covered by adding to the theoretical values for the Rectangular and Normal Populations three sets of experimental sampling results as indicated below.

Population Curve	β_2 of grouped distribution	Samples	S.D. of population in terms of grouping unit
Type II	2·500	1000 of 2, 500 of 5, 500 of 10	6·3249
		500 of 20	10·5404
Type VII	4·122	1000 of 2, 500 of 5 500 of 10, 500 of 20	5·6672
Type VII	7·069	1000 of 2, 1000 of 5 500 of 10, 500 of 20	6·4482

The sampling was carried out with the help of Tippett's Random Numbers*, the population frequencies being obtained from "Student's" Tables of t†.

Suppose the variates of a sample of n to be arranged in order of magnitude, and u to be the highest and v the lowest value. Then the *Range* is $u - v$ and the *Centre* is $\frac{1}{2}(u + v)$. If n be odd the *Median* is the $\frac{1}{2}(n + 1)$th observation, and if even is taken as the mid-point between the $(\frac{1}{2}n)$th and $(\frac{1}{2}n + 1)$th. In Tables I and II theoretical values are given in italics; these were obtained as follows:—

Rectangular Population. $\beta_2 = 1{\cdot}8$.

Range; from formulae in *Biometrika*, Vol. XX^A. p. 217.

Centre, G; from equation (xl) of the same paper it follows that

$$\sigma_G = \sigma \sqrt{\frac{6}{(n+1)(n+2)}}.$$

Median; it is found that, n odd $\sigma_M = \sigma \sqrt{\frac{3}{n+2}}$,

$$n \text{ even } \sigma_M = \sigma \sqrt{\frac{3n}{(n+1)(n+2)}}.$$

* *Tracts for Computers*, No. XV.

† *Metron*, Vol. V. p. 114.

Normal Population $\beta_2 = 3{\cdot}0$.

Range; from Table VIII, *Biometrika*, Vol. XVIII. p. 192.

Centre; $\sigma_G = \sigma_u \sqrt{\frac{1}{2}(1 + r_{uv})}$, where σ_u and r_{uv} have been given by Tippett, *Biometrika*, Vol. XVII. p. 364 *et seq.*

Median; obtained up to $n = 5$ only, from the integrals computed by quadrature and given on p. 178, *Biometrika*, Vol. XVIII.

The figures obtained experimentally are of course subject to errors of sampling, but if the whole series of values of mean and standard error of range and of standard error of centre are plotted either to n or to β_2, it will be seen that they change comparatively smoothly so that an interpolation adequate for many practical purposes can be obtained for any value of n between 2 and 20 or of β_2 between 1·8 and 7·1. As the definition of the median is different according to whether n be odd or even, interpolation for n is not in this case easy. The results may be considered briefly in order.

1. *The Distribution of Range.*

The mean and standard errors of Table I are given in terms of the population standard deviation. It will be seen that the mean changes very little with β_2 for samples of 10 or less, but that at 20 there is a somewhat greater change. The standard error of range changes however very considerably with β_2, increasing steadily as the population becomes more leptokurtic*. No useful interpolation can be made from the values of β_1 and β_2 for range, but the following points are of interest. If we define as "positively skew" a sampling curve with its longer tail towards increasing range, then, (*a*) for the Rectangular Population, the range distribution at $n = 2$ is a sloping straight line with positive skewness, at $n = 3$ it is a symmetrical platykurtic curve, while for $n > 3$ we have curves of increasing negative skewness; (*b*) at $\beta_2 = 2{\cdot}5$ the curves are platykurtic, almost symmetrical, but positively skew; (*c*) as the population β_2 increases the range curves for a given n become more and more positively skew; (*d*) for a given population and changing n, there is the same tendency as was observed in the normal case†, for the (β_1, β_2) point of the range curve to approach the normal point (0, 3) as n increases up to about 10, and then to recede.

For practical purposes it is necessary to know the chance of drawing a sample with a range greater than certain multiples of the population standard deviation. It would therefore be desirable to fit curves to the distribution of range; this has not yet been done, but the results given in Table II will give an adequate idea of the position. Here the permilles for the experimental sampling groups have been found by rough smoothing from the data; the rectangular results follow from equation (xxxix), *Biometrika*, Vol. XX^A. p. 210, while for the normal we are indebted to "Mathetes" who has lent the data used in computing the curves for

* At $\beta_2 = 4{\cdot}12$, chance sampling fluctuation appears to cause some irregularity at $n = 5$ or 10.

† See the diagram on p. 191, *Biometrika*, Vol. XVIII.

"Student's" paper on Routine Analysis*. The great length of the tails of the range curves obtained in sampling from leptokurtic populations will be seen at a glance. This is of considerable importance. "Student" has found, for example, that leptokurtic error systems are common in routine analysis*, and a value of $\beta_2 = 7{\cdot}0$ is probably not unduly exceptional. The analyst must decide therefore whether he should reject extreme observations as excessively improbable deviations on "normal theory," or accept them as perhaps rare but perfectly genuine variants in a leptokurtic system.

2. *The Distribution of Centre.*

The standard error of centre given in Table I is expressed as a multiple of $\sigma/\sqrt{n}$, the standard error of the mean. The centre is theoretically the best estimate of the mid-point of the rectangular population. The figures suggest that the standard error of the mean equals that of the centre for a population with $\beta_2 = 2{\cdot}2$ approximately, and that after this the ratio of the latter to the former steadily increases above unity. For samples of 5 or less, the centre is not so bad an estimate of the mid-point even when $\beta_2 = 4{\cdot}1$, but for larger samples it becomes very unsatisfactory.

3. *The Distribution of Median.*

Just as the centre is at its best as an estimate at $\beta_2 = 1{\cdot}8$, and the mean at $\beta_2 = 3{\cdot}0$, so the median begins to gain upon the latter as β_2 increases, and for the extreme sampling series, $\beta_2 = 7{\cdot}1$, we find that for $n = 10$ and 20, the standard error of median is less than that of mean. Further, in this case the sampling distribution of the median is possibly less leptokurtic than that of the mean, which if confirmed would be a point in favour of the former. We find

	$n=5$	10	20
β_2 of distribution of means (theory)	3·81	3·41	3·20
β_2 „ „ „ medians (experiment)	3·62 (·42)	3·13 (·27)	3·40 (·42)

where the standard errors are given in brackets. By using the median and taking account of the presence, but not of the exact value of the extreme variates, the large sampling errors arising from their inclusion on calculating the mean may be avoided. In problems, therefore, where it is known that the population is leptokurtic, the use of the median rather than the mean as a central estimate certainly appears to be worth consideration. As Table I shows, it is not a satisfactory estimate in the case of platykurtic distributions.

We are very grateful to Mr A. E. Stone for taking all but 400 of the 8000 samples involved.

* *Biometrika*, Vol. XIX. pp. 151—164.

TABLE I.

Distribution Constants.

Size of Sample.

β_2	—	2	3	4	5	10	20
1·80	Range: Mean	*1·155*	*1·732*	*2·078*	*2·309*	*2·834*	*3·134*
	Range: S.E.	*·816*	*·775*	*·693*	*·617*	*·386*	*·217*
	Range: β_1	*·320*	*·000*	*·082*	*·219*	*·773*	*1·265*
	Range: β_2	*2·400*	*2·143*	*2·357*	*2·625*	*3·648*	*4·569*
	Centre: S.E.	*1·000*	*·949*	*·894*	*·845*	*·674*	*·510*
	Median: S.E.	*1·000*	*1·342*	*1·265*	*1·464*	*1·508*	*1·612*
2·50	Range: Mean	1·158	—	—	2·343	3·024	3·604
	Range: S.E.	·850	—	—	·786	·713	·549
	Range: β_1	—	—	—	·110	·008	·039
	Range: β_2	—	—	—	2·869	2·884	2·705
	Centre: S.E.	*1·000*	—	—	1·062	1·101	1·266
	Median: S.E.	*1·000*	—	—	1·319	1·231	1·312
3·00	Range: Mean	*1·128*	*1·693*	*2·059*	*2·326*	*3·078*	*3·735*
	Range: S.E.	*·852*	*·888*	*·880*	*·864*	*·797*	*·729*
	Range: β_1	*·991*	*·417*	*·273*	*·217*	*·156*	*·161*
	Range: β_2	*3·869*	*3·286*	*3·188*	*3·169*	*3·22*	*3·26*
	Centre: S.E.	*1·000*	*1·042*	*1·092*	*1·142*	*1·362*	*1·691*
	Median: S.E.	*1·000*	*1·160*	*1·092*	*1·198*	—	(→*1·253*)
4·12	Range: Mean	1·118	—	—	2·360	3·085	3·961
	Range: S.E.	·890	—	—	1·010	·893	1·029
	Range: β_1	—	—	—	·614	·335	·603
	Range: β_2	—	—	—	4·748	3·377	3·693
	Centre: S.E.	*1·000*	—	—	1·182	1·569	2·411
	Median: S.E.	*1·000*	—	—	1·145	1·126	1·141
7·07	Range: Mean	1·020	—	—	2·245	3·034	3·905
	Range: S.E.	·892	—	—	1·100	1·229	1·300
	Range: β_1	—	—	—	9·042	2·228	2·633
	Range: β_2	—	—	—	19·280	6·898	7·970
	Centre: S.E.	*1·000*	—	—	1·372	2·015	2·947
	Median: S.E.	*1·000*	—	—	1·049	·979	·970

N.B. The Mean and Standard Error of Range are expressed in terms of the Population Standard Deviation, σ. The Standard Errors of Centre and Median are given as multiples of the Standard Error of the Mean, $\sigma/\sqrt{n}$. Figures in italics are theoretical, the others are obtained from experimental sampling.

TABLE II.

Permille of Samples with Range greater than Multiples of Population Standard Deviation.

Range greater than

Size of Sample	Population β_2	1σ	2σ	3σ	4σ	5σ	6σ	7σ	8σ	9σ	10σ	11σ
	1·80	*506*	*179*	*18*	—	—	—	—	—	—	—	—
	2·50	501	174	27	3	—	—	—	—	—	—	—
2	3·00	*480*	*157*	*34*	*5*	—	—	—	—	—	—	—
	4·12	468	154	36	8	3	1	—	—	—	—	—
	7·07	396	119	37	10	3	2	—	—	—	—	—
	1·80	*973*	*701*	*136*	—	—	—	—	—	—	—	—
	2·50	968	646	190	34	—	—	—	—	—	—	—
5	3·00	*956*	*619*	*211*	*38*	*4*	—	—	—	—	—	—
	4·12	922	609	240	62	8	4	2	2	—	—	—
	7·07	922	521	201	72	16	4	3	2	2	1	1
	1·80	*1000*	*966*	*396*	—	—	—	—	—	—	—	—
	2·50	998	926	495	90	2	—	—	—	—	—	—
10	3·00	*1000*	*922*	*515*	*127*	*15*	*1*	—	—	—	—	—
	4·12	1000	898	501	154	28	6	—	—	—	—	—
	7·07	994	831	436	154	68	30	16	4	2	2	—
	1·80	*1000*	*1000*	*769*	—	—	—	—	—	—	—	—
	2·50	1000	1000	861	235	4	—	—	—	—	—	—
20	3·00	*1000*	*998*	*856*	*349*	*55*	*4*	—	—	—	—	—
	4·12	1000	998	833	421	156	44	8	2	—	—	—
	7·07	1000	995	775	422	170	74	21	14	8	6	2

N.B. Figures in italics are theoretical, the others are obtained from experimental sampling.

In the case of $\beta_2 = 1{\cdot}8$ no sample range as great as 4σ is *possible.* For $\beta_2 = 3{\cdot}0$ the permilles beyond the last figure shown are less than unity; while for the other three cases no samples with range greater than the value indicated by the last figure in each row were *observed.*

THE DISTRIBUTION OF FREQUENCY CONSTANTS IN SMALL SAMPLES FROM NON-NORMAL SYMMETRICAL AND SKEW POPULATIONS.

2nd Paper: The Distribution of "Student's" z.

BY EGON S. PEARSON, D.SC., ASSISTED BY N. K. ADYANTHĀYA, B.SC. AND OTHERS.

CONTENTS.

1. THE USE OF "STUDENT'S" z-TEST WITH POPULATIONS NOT NORMAL.

One of the most important problems with which the mathematical statistician is faced is that of bringing his theoretical structures into some degree of correspondence with the situations of practical experience. This is no doubt hardest when the samples are small, for here he will often be faced with two difficulties. In the first place his populations may not be completely stable; the sample when drawn may be a random one, but owing to difficulties in control or to some changing time factor he cannot be sure that it will be quite the same population with which he will be concerned in further work And then, even if he is sure of the stability of his population, it will generally be impossible for him to obtain any certain estimate of its exact form. For purposes of inference he may calculate from the sample one or more statistical measures, but the first difficulty will make him hesitate to lay too much stress on the exact value of the figures found on entering his probability table, while the second may make him wonder whether there is after all any appropriate table in existence.

The questions of stability and randomness of sampling can only be dealt with in each problem as it arises, but though the statistician may be prepared to accept these conditions as approximately true, he is still faced with the second problem. "The majority of tests dealing with small samples," he may say, "have only been worked out for the case in which the population distributions are normal. I do not know whether my distribution is normal, although from my general experience in the past I do not think that it is likely to be excessively skew or leptokurtic. How sensitive are the 'normal theory' tests to changes in population form? May I use some with less hesitation than others?"

In the present paper an attempt will be made to answer this question as far as it concerns some of the tests connected with "Student's" Type VII distribution of z, the two fundamental tests considered being those dealing with the mean of a single sample and the difference between the means of two samples. It may be well to illustrate the problem by taking a concrete example. A commercial firm, let us suppose, is considering whether to introduce a new method of production, which may be of advantage perhaps either through a saving of time or because it seems likely to lead to an improvement in the quality of the article produced. A series of experiments is carried out in which some variable quantity x is carefully observed under both methods. As a result two samples are available, one of n_1 values of x with a mean $\bar{x}_1$ and standard deviation s_1, the other of n_2 with $\bar{x}_2$ and s_2. In this case the most useful answer that statistical analysis could give would perhaps be as follows: "The exact difference that would be found to hold in the long run between the average values of x arising from the two methods cannot of course be determined, but the odds are k to 1 that this difference lies between d_1 and d_2." With such an answer as this before it the firm could decide whether the innovation showed an improvement of sufficient significance to be commercially profitable, or if the question remained in doubt whether it seemed worth the expense of undertaking further experiments in order to narrow down these limits, d_1 and d_2. But unfortunately an answer in so precise a form cannot be given without serious assumptions which at once destroy the precision.

If the samples are small we may use R. A. Fisher's two-sample z-test* and calculate

$$z = \frac{\bar{x}_1 - \bar{x}_2 - d}{\sqrt{n_1 s_1^2 + n_2 s_2^2}} \sqrt{\frac{n_1 n_2}{n_1 + n_2}} \quad \text{......................} \quad (1).$$

Then choosing a suitable value of α, such as ·01, and entering "Student's" tables, we may find the values of d_1 and d_2 corresponding to $z = \pm z_\alpha$ for which $P_z = 2\alpha$, where

$$P_z = 2\int_z^\infty c_0 (1 + z^2)^{-\frac{n_1 + n_2 - 1}{2}} dz \quad \text{......................} (2).$$

On the assumption that the two distributions of x are normal and have the same variance, we can then say that if the difference between the population mean values of x were (1) as low as d_1, or (2) as high as d_2, then the chance would be α of obtaining in pairs of random samples of n_1 and n_2: (1) a positive deviation of z, or (2) a negative deviation of z as great or greater than that observed. But it is not possible to speak in any exact sense of the odds being $1 - 2\alpha$ to 2α that the difference in means lies between d_1 and d_2. Such a use of the inverse probability would involve an assumption regarding the *à priori* probability distributions of the

* *Metron*, 1925, Vol. v. No. 3, p. 7; *Statistical Methods for Research Workers*, 1928, p. 107.

The relation of this and the single sample z-test to the criterion of likelihood was discussed by Neyman and Pearson in *Biometrika*, Vol. xx^{A}. pp. 190 and 207. The symbol z will be used throughout this paper. "Student's" later tables in *Metron*, Vol. v. are entered with $t = z\sqrt{n' - 1}$, and the t-notation is that used by Fisher. In equation (2) c_0 has the value $\Gamma(\frac{1}{2}(n_1 + n_2 - 1))/\{\Gamma(\frac{1}{2}(n_1 + n_2 - 2))\sqrt{\pi}\}$.

population means and standard deviations; and further in the case where it is not even certain that these populations are exactly normal a more complex *à priori* assumption still must be introduced, so that any approach to an exact solution in terms of inverse probability becomes impossible. The difficulty and one method of treating it was discussed briefly by "Sophister" in the last number of this Journal* in dealing with the distribution of z found on sampling from a skew population. With the fuller results now available it will be possible to analyse the situation a little more in detail than he was able to do last year.

It is true that it may be more helpful for the practical worker to look at his problem from the inverse point of view, and to obtain some measure of the odds for or against the population parameters lying within certain limits. But a little reflection suggests that unless he is prepared to grapple with *à priori* probability, his justification in the use of any such rough and ready guide must depend on the validity of employing the probability tables of the z-distribution in dealing with the following questions:

(*a*) There is a sample of n individuals measured for a certain character. We wish to test the probability of the hypothesis that this sample has been drawn from a population whose mean is at a distance $m = \bar{x} - a$ from the sample mean $\bar{x}$.

(*b*) There are two samples of n_1 and n_2, and on the assumption that they come from populations with the same variance, we wish to test the hypothesis that the means in these populations differ by d† (d of course will often be zero).

In discussing the various experimental results we shall therefore be concerned chiefly with the adequacy of the "normal theory" in testing these two fundamental hypotheses. There are many cases in which the problem presents itself in almost exactly one or other of these forms, but the reader should find no difficulty in interpreting the tables given in any manner which seems more applicable to the particular form of problem with which he is concerned.

In practice an hypothesis will be accepted or rejected with a varying degree of confidence; no precise line between acceptance or rejection can be drawn. Yet some light is thrown upon the problem if it is supposed for the moment that this vague edge of uncertainty can be given precision, the statistician being compelled to make a definite decision one way or the other; he will reject the hypothesis when $P_z \leqslant 2\alpha$ ‡ and accept it when $P_z > 2\alpha$, where the value of α used will depend upon the nature of his problem. If this be so errors in judgment cannot be avoided, and it is seen that they will be of two kinds:

(1) The hypothesis is rejected when it is in fact true.

(2) It is accepted when it is false.

* *Biometrika*, Vol. xx^A. p. 421.

† The question of finding the probable limits d_1 and d_2 in the commercial problem suggested above seems really to consist at bottom in testing the second of these hypotheses for varying values of d. We can then get a good appreciation of these limits without attempting to assign numerical odds to the chance that the difference in population mean lies between them.

‡ In the case of two samples P_z is as in equation (2) above. For the single sample hypothesis

$$P_z = 2\int_z^\infty c_0 (1+z^2)^{-\frac{n}{2}} dz, \text{ where } c_0 = \Gamma(\tfrac{1}{2}n)/\{\Gamma(\tfrac{1}{2}(n-1))\sqrt{\pi}\}.$$

It is impossible to estimate the relative proportions in which these two types of error occur, as it will depend upon the kind of problems to which the statistician applies his tests, but we can analyse separately each type.

If the populations sampled are all of a form such that z follows "Student's" distribution, then the source of error (1) may be completely controlled. In the long run such errors will be committed in $100 \times 2\alpha\,°/_{\circ}$ of the cases in which the hypothesis tested was really true, and the statistician may choose α according to the risk he is prepared to take of making this form of error of judgment. From this point of view, $|z|$* is as good a criterion as z. Suppose that $\pm z_\alpha$ are the deviations

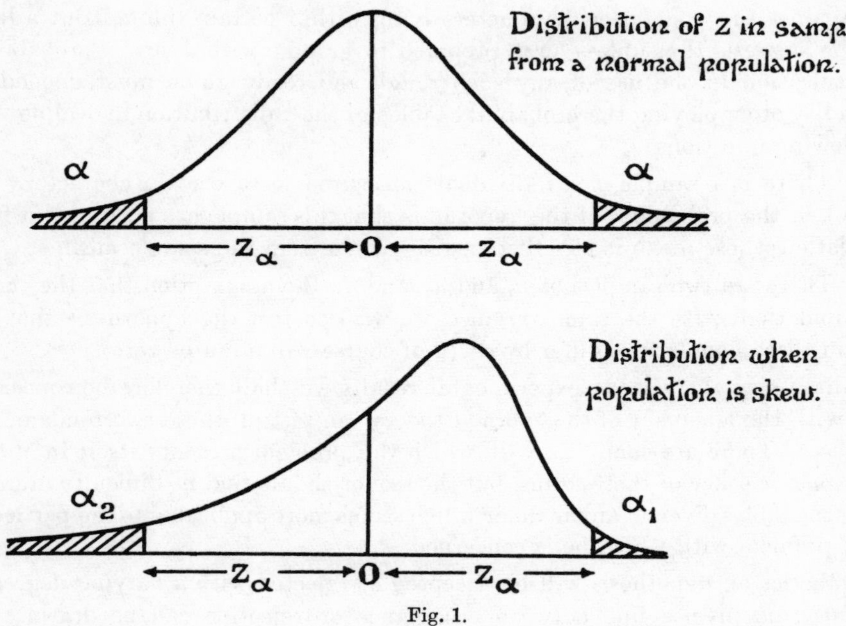

Fig. 1.

corresponding to tail areas of α when "Student's" tables are entered, but that in fact, as the population is not normal, the distribution of z in repeated samples follows a certain skew curve. The tail areas beyond $\pm z_\alpha$ are now α_1 and α_2 which are not equal. But if we know that $\alpha_1 + \alpha_2 = 2\alpha$ (or very nearly so) and this for a wide range of values of α†, then our control of the first source of error will be as good in sampling from the non-normal population as from the normal one.

We shall therefore first consider below how far $|z|$ follows "Student's" distribution in samples from a variety of non-normal populations‡. We may note here, incidentally, that any other statistical constant, z', for which the sampling

* The expression $|z|$ indicates that the numerical value of z is to be given a positive sign.

† Say between $\alpha = \cdot 100$ and $\cdot 005$.

‡ Previous experimental work in this direction has been carried out by Shewart and Winters, *Journal of the American Statistical Association*, Vol. XXIII. pp. 144—53; Neyman and Pearson, *Biometrika*, Vol. XX^A. pp. 197—207, using Church's sampling data; "Sophister," *Biometrika*, Vol. XX^A. pp. 408—21, and Rider in the present volume, pp. 124—43.

distribution of $|z'|$ is as invariable for changing populations as $|z|$, will be of equal value as a criterion *in so far as the control of source of error* (1) *is concerned.*

When, however, we consider the second type of error, the position is somewhat different. It will not generally in practice be of serious consequence if we accept the hypothesis tested when in fact the mean of the sampled population differs by some small quantity, τ, from the supposed value a; nor in the case of two samples, if the population means differ by $d+\tau$ instead of by d. This cannot be avoided, but we should like to have some appreciation of the rapidity with which the untrue hypotheses are rejected as τ, or rather the ratio of τ to the population standard deviation, increases. If we accept the hypothesis when $P_z > 2\alpha$, are we likely to be doing so when really the true population mean is at a distance of σ or perhaps even 2σ from its supposed position? Or in the second test, when the means of the two populations really differ by $d+\sigma$ or even $d+2\sigma$? We are concerned now with what may be termed the sensitivity of the test in the rejection of false hypotheses, and this will depend upon (*a*) the size of the sample, (*b*) the form of the population sampled, and (*c*) the sign of τ. It has been pointed out that in testing any given hypothesis there will be an indefinite number of criteria which will ensure the control of the first source of error, but it seems probable that for each type of population there will be one of these which is more efficient than any other in controlling the second error. This point will be examined in more detail below in connection with the experimental results, and the sensitivity of "Student's" z and of the ratio z' = sample centre/(half sample range)* will be compared for samples of 5 and 10 from a variety of populations.

2. THE POPULATIONS SAMPLED.

No experimental programme could possibly cover all the populations likely to be met in common experience, but a variety of types of frequency form have been represented by taking samplings from Pearson-curves of the following nature:

TABLE I.

Population Curve	β_1 and β_2 of grouped distribution	Samples	S.D. of population in terms of grouping unit
Type II	0, 2·50	1000 of 2	63·25
		500 of 5, 500 of 10	6·32
		500 of 20	10·54
Type VII	0, 4·12	1000 of 2	56·67
		500 of 5, 500 of 10, 500 of 20	5·67
Type VII	0, 7·07	1000 of 2	64·48
		1000 of 5, 500 of 10, 500 of 20	6·45
Type III	·20, 3·30	1000 of 2	50·00
		1000 of 5, 500 of 10	5·00
		500 of 20	6·67
Type III	·50, 3·73	1000 of 2	50·00
		1000 of 5, 500 of 10, 1000 of 20	5·00

* The use of the "centre" or mid-point between extreme observations in the sample as an estimate of the population mean was discussed in *Biometrika*, Vol. xx^A. pp. 212 and 358.

The sampling was carried out with the help of Tippett's Random Numbers*. Certain results obtained from the sampling of the three symmetrical populations have already been published†. The samples of 5 and 20 from the skewer of the two Type III populations are those obtained by "Sophister"‡, who has kindly placed his data unreservedly at our disposal. To these we have added samples of 2 and of 10, and have taken a fresh Type III population to fill in the gap between his population and the normal population.

In drawing samples of 2 from a grouped population distribution, both individual values will occasionally fall in the same group so that the value of z becomes indeterminate. And even if the values fall into groups, one or two units apart, considerable uncertainty must exist as to the true value of z if it be supposed that the population distribution is really continuous. By taking a very fine grouping, i.e. 50 or more groups to the population standard deviation, this difficulty was reduced to a minimum. Only about 10 cases occurred in the 5000 samples of 2 in which both individuals fell in the same group; these cases were discarded and fresh samples taken, and it was assumed that no serious systematic error would arise in other cases if z were calculated on the assumption that the variates had mid-group values.

TABLE II (*a*).

Frequencies of z in 1000 *Samples of* 2.

$\lvert z \rvert$ greater than		Populations Sampled						
		$\beta_1=0{\cdot}00$ $\beta_2=1{\cdot}80$	$\beta_1=0{\cdot}00$ $\beta_2=2{\cdot}50$	$\beta_1=0{\cdot}00$ $\beta_2=3{\cdot}00$	$\beta_1=0{\cdot}00$ $\beta_2=4{\cdot}12$	$\beta_1=0{\cdot}00$ $\beta_2=7{\cdot}07$	$\beta_1=0{\cdot}20$ $\beta_2=3{\cdot}30$	$\beta_1=0{\cdot}50$ $\beta_2=3{\cdot}73$
0·0		*1000·0*	1000	*1000·0*	1000	1000	1000	1000
0·5		*666·7*	682·5	*704·8*	716·5	723·5	731·5	699
1·0		*500·0*	487	*500·0*	512	526	509·5	487·5
1·5		*400·0*	373	*374·4*	374·5	372·5	376·5	355
2·0		*333·3*	308·5	*295·2*	296·5	272	290·5	280·5
2·5		*285·7*	249·5	*242·2*	233·5	204	226	231·5
3·0		*250·0*	222	*204·8*	199·5	173	188	196
3·5		*222·2*	193	*177·2*	170·5	147	152·5	168·5
4·0		*200·0*	178	*156·0*	156	131	134	150
4·5		*181·8*	162	*139·4*	147	113	119·5	126
5·0		*166·7*	145	*125·6*	132	109	106·5	116
6·0		*142·8*	119·5	*105·2*	112	97	84	101
7·0		*125·0*	99	*90·4*	100	88	74·5	88·5
8·0		*111·1*	90·5	*79·2*	87·5	76	67·5	78·5
9·0		*100·0*	80	*70·4*	79	68	64	71
10·0		*90·9*	73·5	*63·4*	69·5	62·5	57	61
15·0		*62·5*	50	*42·4*	42	42	39·5	36
20·0		*47·6*	31·5	*31·8*	30	29·5	28	26·5
Goodness of Fit	$\lvert z \rvert$ P	—	·137	—	·684	·006	·394	·871
	$\lvert z \rvert$ n'	—	17	—	17	17	17	17
	z P	—	—	—	—	—	·242	·022
	z n'	—	—	—	—	—	26	26

* *Tracts for Computers*, No. xv. A fresh sampling was carried out for each of the 20 sets, and the columns of the sampling book and the number scale were frequently altered so as to ensure as far as possible complete independence between the different sets.

† *Biometrika*, Vol. xx^A. pp. 356—60.

‡ *Biometrika*, Vol. xx^A. pp. 389—423.

3. THE SINGLE SAMPLE TEST.

Tables II (*a*), (*b*), (*c*) and (*d*) give the results of the sampling. In the first place they show the number of samples in which $|z|$ lay beyond the limit given in the leading column. The figures in italics are theoretical values, the others

TABLE II (*b*).

Frequencies of z in 500 Samples of 5.

$\|z\|$ greater than		Populations Sampled						Normal distribution with S.D. $=1/\sqrt{2}$
		$\beta_1=0{\cdot}00$ $\beta_2=2{\cdot}50$	$\beta_1=0{\cdot}00$ $\beta_2=3{\cdot}00$	$\beta_1=0{\cdot}00$ $\beta_2=4{\cdot}12$	$\beta_1=0{\cdot}00$ $\beta_2=7{\cdot}07$	$\beta_1=0{\cdot}20$ $\beta_2=3{\cdot}30$	$\beta_1=0{\cdot}50$ $\beta_2=3{\cdot}73$	
0·0		500	*500·0*	500	500*	500*	500*	*500·0*
0·1		432	*425·6*	436	430	422·5	433	*443·8*
0·2		355	*354·8*	376	371·5	360·5	357·5	*388·6*
0·3		284	*290·4*	296	305·5	302	291·5	*335·7*
0·4		216·5	*234·3*	235	254	246	231·5	*285·8*
0·5		179	*187·0*	186·5	203·5	192	183	*239·8*
0·6		147	*148·2*	146	158·5	153	150	*198·1*
0·7		121	*117·1*	113	123·5	121	117	*161·1*
0·8		95·5	*92·4*	81	88	92	88	*128·9*
0·9		76	*73·1*	65	70	73	71·5	*101·6*
1·0		65·5	*58·1*	50	51	58	60·5	*78.7*
1·1		55	*46·3*	38	39·5	50	50·5	*59·9*
1·2		43	*37·2*	30	30·5	42·5	41	*44·9*
1·3		32	*30·0*	26	24	35	31·5	*33·0*
1·4		26	*24·4*	22	19·5	28·5	23	*23·9*
1·5		22	*20·0*	19	14·5	22	21	*16·9*
1·6		20	*16·4*	18	13	18·5	16·5	*11·8*
1·7		20	*13·6*	14	8	16·5	14·5	*8·1*
1·8		14	*11·4*	13	7·5	14	12·5	*5·5*
1·9		11	*9·6*	8	5	12·5	10	*3·6*
2·0		8·5	*8·1*	6·5	3·5	10	9·5	*2·3*
Goodness of Fit	$\|z\|$ P	·629	—	·634	·057	·678	·407	—
	$\|z\|$ n'	15	—	15	18	18	18	—
	z P	—	—	—	—	·182	<·001	—
	z n'	—	—	—	—	30	28	—
Mean z		− ·0268	*0* S.E. *·0224*†	− ·0247	+ ·0066	− ·0244	− ·1283	—
σ_z		·7273‡	*·7071*	·6556	·6447	·7235	·7005	—

experimental. Thus to take Table II (*a*), we find among 1000 samples of 2 the following numbers having $|z| > 5{\cdot}0$, that is to say with z outside the limits $-5{\cdot}0$ and $+5{\cdot}0$:

* Figures in these columns reduced from results for 1000 samples.

† Standard error of Mean z for 1000 samples from a normal population. The standard error of σ_z would be theoretically infinite were the sampled population truly normal.

‡ This value of σ_z has been calculated, omitting one very divergent value of z of $-8{\cdot}5$; including it $\sigma_z = {\cdot}8193$.

Rectangular Population, 166·7 (theory)*; Symmetrical Platykurtic Population ($\beta_2 = 2·5$), 145; Normal Population, 125·6 (value from "Student's" tables); Symmetrical Leptokurtic Population ($\beta_2 = 4·1$), 132; etc.

TABLE II (c).

Frequencies of z in 500 Samples of 10.

$\|z\|$ greater than		Populations Sampled							Normal distribution with S.D. $=1/\sqrt{7}$
		$\beta_1=0·00$ $\beta_2=2·50$	$\beta_1=0·00$ $\beta_2=3·00$	$\beta_1=0·00$ $\beta_2=4·12$	$\beta_1=0·00$ $\beta_2=7·07$	$\beta_1=0·22$ $\beta_2=3·16$	$\beta_1=0·20$ $\beta_2=3·30$	$\beta_1=0·50$ $\beta_2=3·73$	
·00		500	*500·0*	500	500	500†	500	500	*500·0*
·05		435	*442·1*	446	446		433	438	*447·4*
·10		370	*385·5*	390	388	381·5	380	379	*395·7*
·15		312	*331·6*	349	335		330	332	*345·7*
·20		265	*281·7*	307	294	270	287·5	273	*298·4*
·25		224	*236·2*	269	246		239	245	*254·2*
·30		186	*195·8*	218	209	185	207	200	*213·7*
·35		153	*160·5*	180	168		172	167	*177·2*
·40		121	*130·4*	137·5	138	124	145	139	*145·0*
·45		95	*105·0*	104	108		123	112	*116·9*
·50		78	*83·9*	82	86	83	99·5	96	*92·9*
·55		64	*66·7*	62	71		80	73	*72·8*
·60		51	*52·7*	51	57	44·5	59	60	*56·2*
·65		41	*41·5*	38	41		41	49	*42·7*
·70		35	*32·6*	34	30	31	37	41	*32·1*
·75		29	*25·5*	25	24		33	35	*23·6*
·80		26	*19·9*	19	19	21·5	29	31	*17·1*
·85		20	*15·6*	17	15		26	29	*12·2*
·90		15	*12·2*	11	13	12	19	22	*8·6*
·95		11	*9·6*	8	11		16	19	*6·0*
1·00		9	*7·5*	8	7	7·5	11	11	*4·0*
Goodness of Fit	$\|z\|$ P	·867	—	·219	·935	·195	·334	·066	—
	$\|z\|$ n'	16	—	16	16	11	16	16	—
	z P	—	—	—	—	·033	·071	·005	—
	z n'	—	—	—	—	18	26	26	—
Mean z		+·0007	*0* S.E. *·0169*‡	−·0226	+·0208	−·0120	+·0022	−·0556	—
σ_z		·3763	*·3780* S.E. *·0151*‡	·3808	·3815	·3709	·4112	·3992	—

The last columns of Tables II (b), (c) and (d) give the corresponding frequencies obtained on the assumption that the distribution of z is normal, with a standard deviation of $1/\sqrt{n-3}$ or $1/\sqrt{2}$, $1/\sqrt{7}$ and $1/\sqrt{17}$ respectively.

* For samples of two, z is the same as z', or the ratio, centre/($\frac{1}{2}$ range), for which the distribution $y=\frac{1}{2}(1+|z'|)^{-2}$ was given in *Biometrika*, Vol. xx[A]. p. 211.

† Figures in this column reduced from results for 1000 samples.

‡ Standard errors of Mean z and σ_z for 500 samples from a normal population.

In the lower part of Tables II (a), (b), (c) and (d) are given:

(1) The result of applying the (P, χ^2) test for Goodness of Fit, the theoretical distribution being in each case that of the Type VII z-curve of "normal theory." In the test for $|z|$, corresponding positive and negative values of z have been combined, or the z-curve was doubled over about $z = 0$; in that for z the positive

TABLE II (d).

Frequencies of z in 500 *Samples of* 20.

$\|z\|$ greater than		Populations Sampled $\beta_1=0{\cdot}00$, $\beta_2=2{\cdot}50$	$\beta_1=0{\cdot}00$, $\beta_2=3{\cdot}00$	$\beta_1=0{\cdot}00$, $\beta_2=4{\cdot}12$	$\beta_1=0{\cdot}00$, $\beta_2=7{\cdot}07$	$\beta_1=0{\cdot}20$, $\beta_2=3{\cdot}30$	$\beta_1=0{\cdot}50$, $\beta_2=3{\cdot}73$	Normal distribution with S.D. $=1/\sqrt{17}$
·00		500	*500·0*	500	500	500	500*	*500·0*
·05		415	*414·9*	402	409	412	413	*418·3*
·10		333	*333·9*	324	317	323	332·5	*340·0*
·15		253	*260·5*	251	244	240	261	*268·1*
·20		182	*197·1*	196	176	194	198·5	*204·8*
·25		136	*144·7*	147	125	145	150	*151·4*
·30		101	*103·3*	103	84	98	105	*108·0*
·35		69	*71·8*	80	54	65	74·5	*74·5*
·40		46	*48·7*	51	38	52	57	*49·6*
·45		35	*32·3*	32	21	36	37·5	*31·8*
·50		26	*21·1*	20	11	25	26	*19·6*
·55		20	*13·5*	15	6	12	16·5	*11·7*
·60		13	*8·5*	10	1	11	10·5	*6·7*
·65		7	*5·3*	3	1	7	7	*3·7*
·70		6	*3·3*	1	1	5	6	*2·0*
Goodness of Fit	$\|z\|$ P	·535	—	·618	·487	·172	·797	—
	$\|z\|$ n'	11	—	11	11	11	13	—
	z P	—	—	—	—	·022	·049	—
	z n'	—	—	—	—	20	20	—
Mean z		+ ·0006	*0* S.E. *·0108*†	− ·0056	+ ·0135	− ·0217	− ·0223	—
σ_z		·2439	*·2425* S.E. *·0084*†	·2409	·2187	·2436	·2494	—

and negative values were kept separate. n' is the number of groups used in applying the test.

(2) For samples of 5, 10 and 20, Mean z and σ_z are given‡. The results have been represented graphically in Figures 2 (a), (b), (c) and (d). The continuous

* Figures in this column reduced from results for 1000 samples.

† Standard errors of Mean z and σ_z for 500 samples from a normal population.

‡ Here and throughout this paper the standard error of a standard deviation has been taken as $\frac{1}{2}\sigma\sqrt{\frac{\beta_2-1}{N}}$, where σ and β_2 are the constants of the theoretical distribution of the variable, and N is the number of samples upon which the value of the standard deviation has been based.

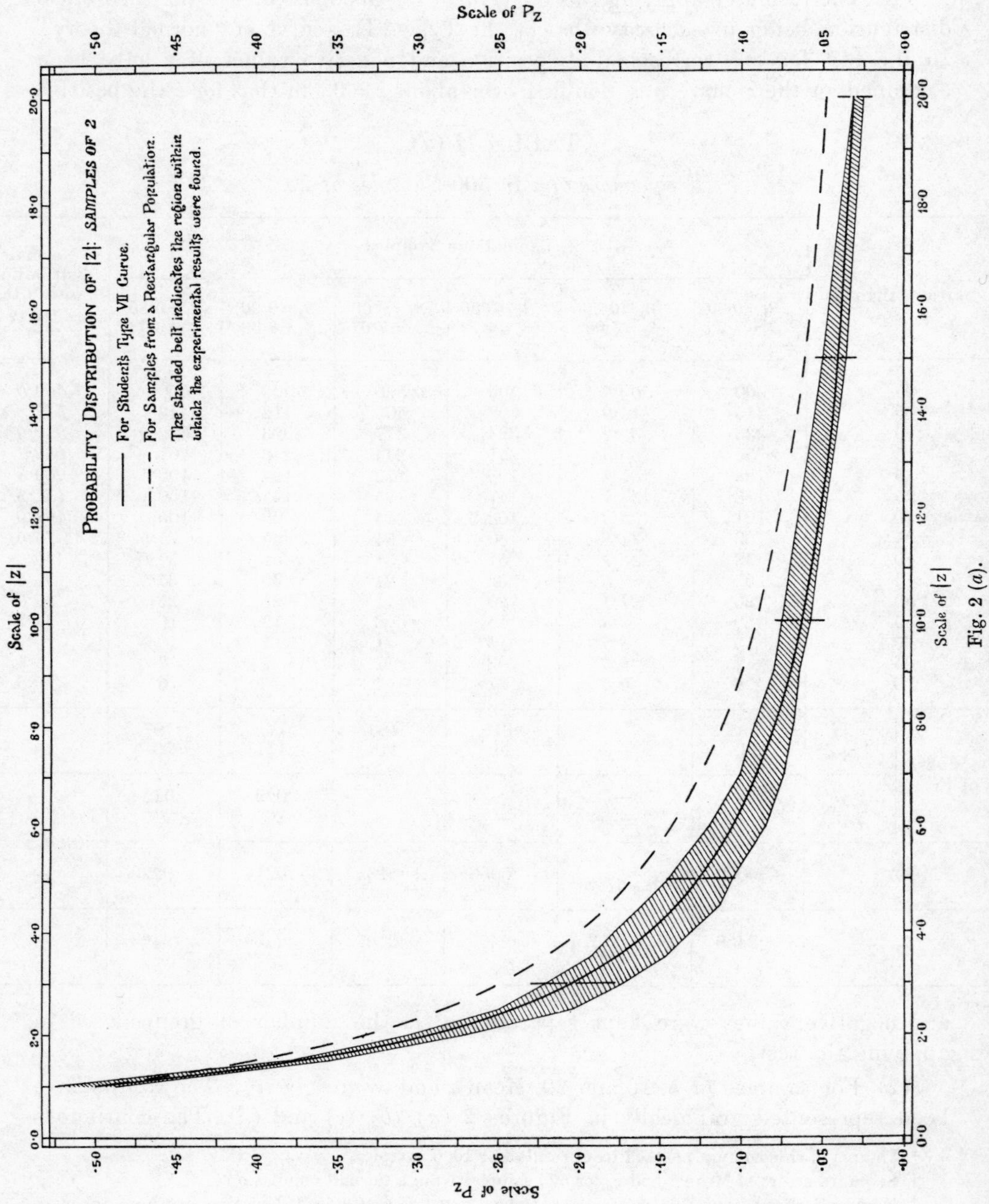
PROBABILITY DISTRIBUTION OF |z|: SAMPLES OF 2
For Student's Type VII Curve.
For Samples from a Rectangular Population.
The shaded belt indicates the region within which the experimental results were found.
Scale of |z|
Scale of Pz
0·0 2·0 4·0 6·0 8·0 10·0 12·0 14·0 16·0 18·0 20·0
·00 ·05 ·10 ·15 ·20 ·25 ·30 ·35 ·40 ·45 ·50

Fig. 2 (*a*).

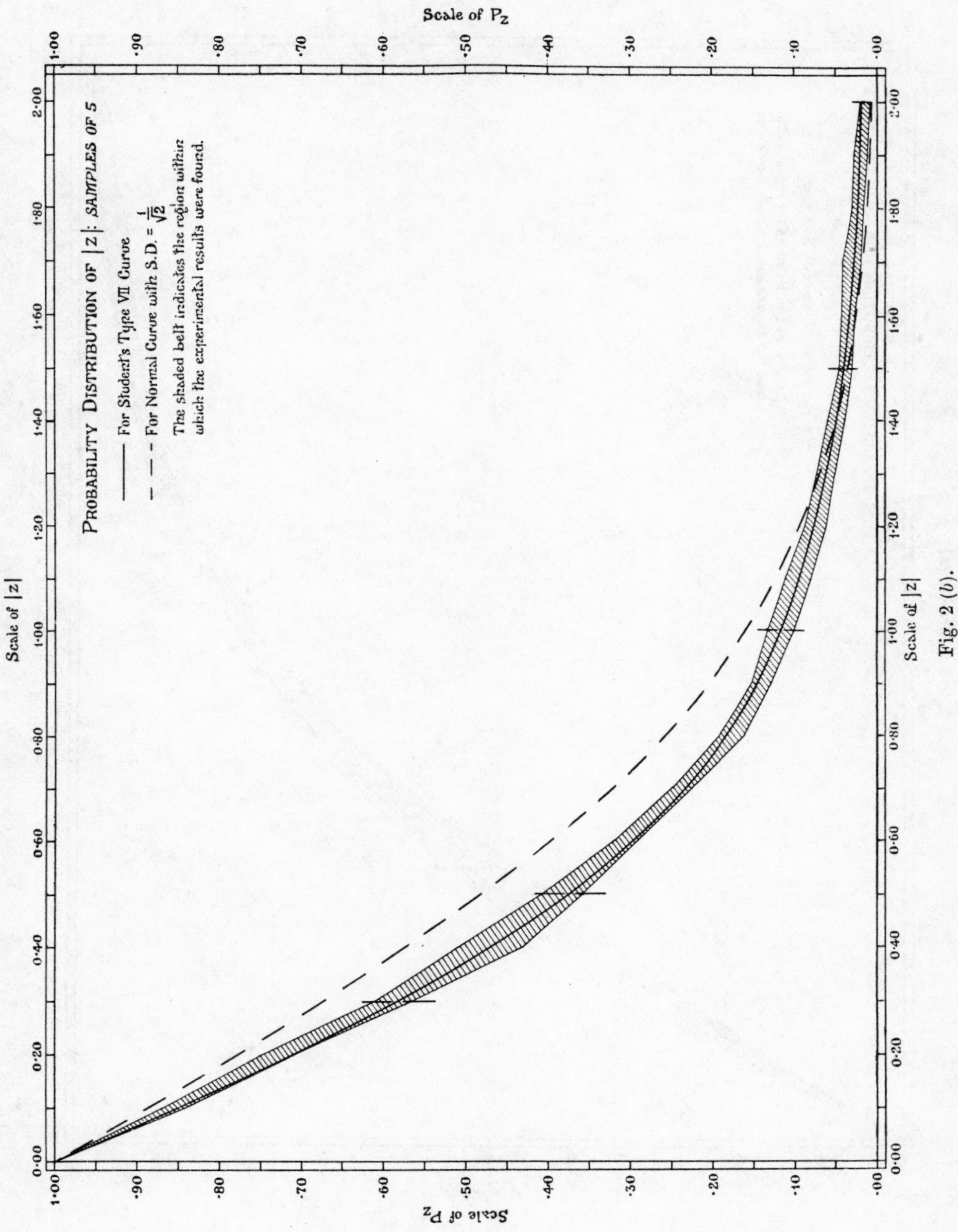
Scale of P_Z
Scale of |z|
PROBABILITY DISTRIBUTION OF |z|: SAMPLES OF 5
—— For Student's Type VII Curve
— — For Normal Curve with S.D. = 1/√2
The shaded belt indicates the region within which the experimental results were found.
0·00 0·20 0·40 0·60 0·80 1·00 1·20 1·40 1·60 1·80 2·00
1·00 ·90 ·80 ·70 ·60 ·50 ·40 ·30 ·20 ·10 ·00

Fig. 2 (b).

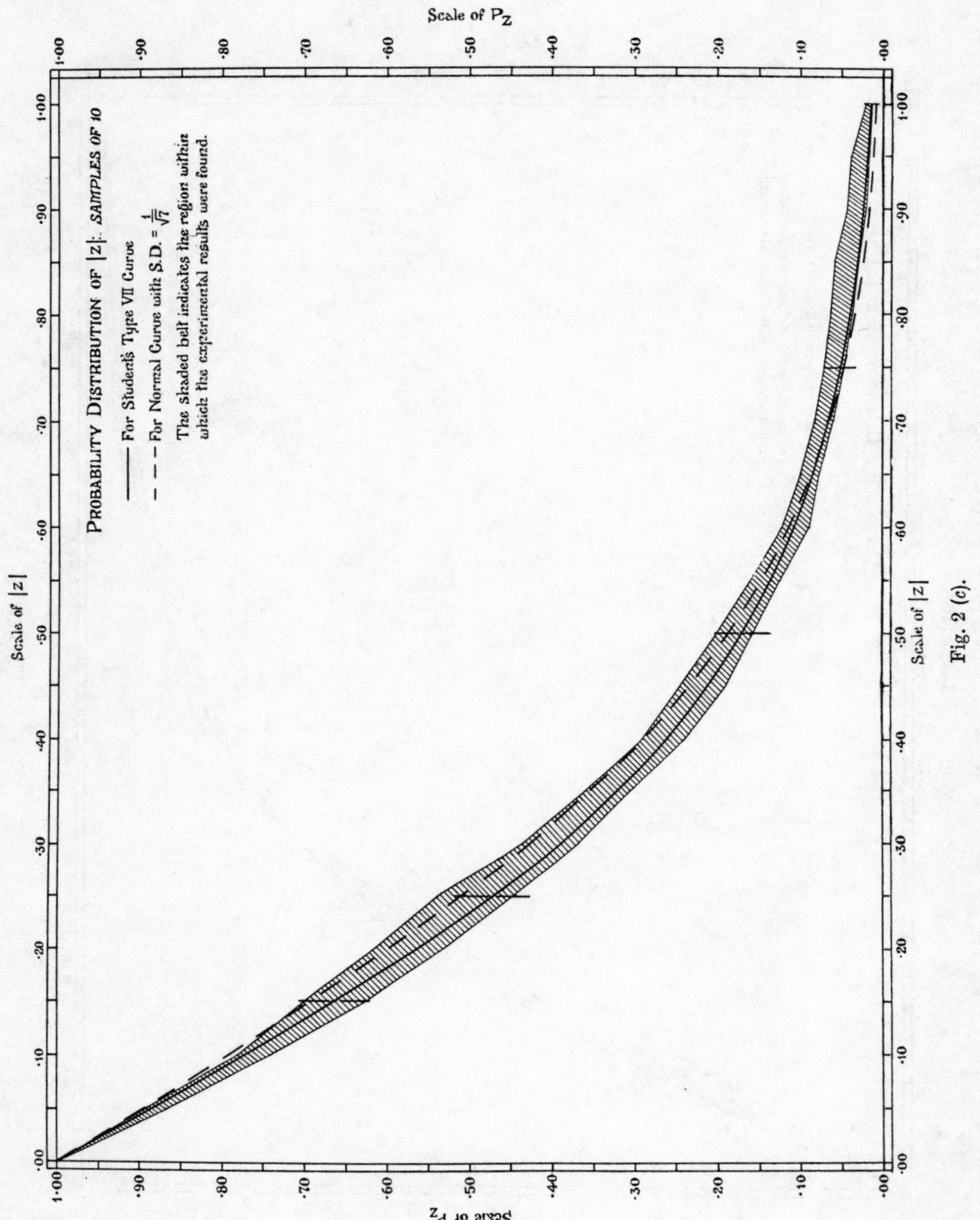
PROBABILITY DISTRIBUTION OF |z|: SAMPLES OF 10
—— For Student's Type VII Curve
– – – For Normal Curve with S.D. = $\frac{1}{\sqrt{7}}$
The shaded belt indicates the region within which the experimental results were found.
Scale of |z|
Scale of P_Z

Fig. 2 (*c*).

curve shows the change in the P_z of "normal theory" as $|z|$ increases, and the upper and lower limits of the shaded belts represent the highest and lowest observed frequencies of the corresponding row of Table II when divided by 500 or 1000 as the case may be. To give some indication of the sampling variation that might be expected to arise at different points on the z-scale if the true distribution

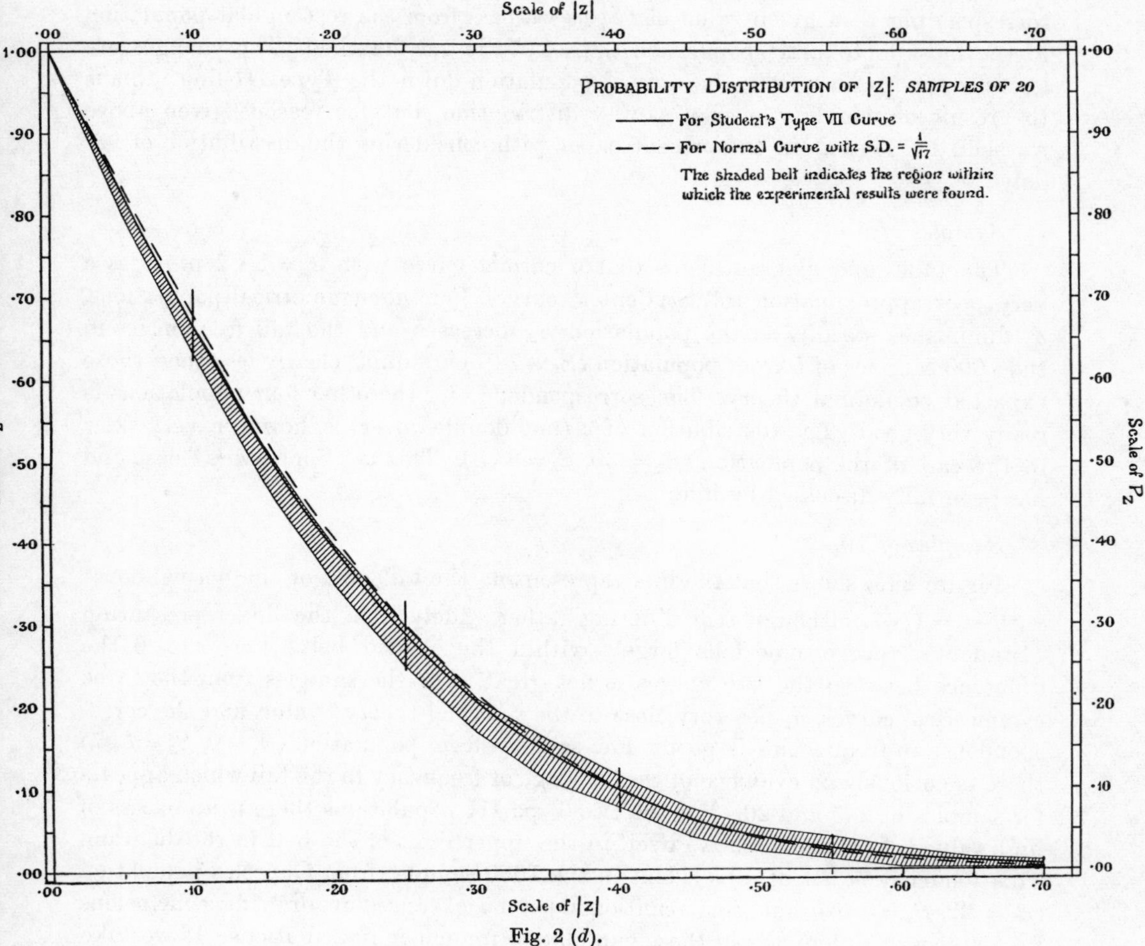

Fig. 2 (*d*).

followed "Student's" curve, lengths equal to twice the standard error of these reduced frequencies have been plotted on either side of the continuous curve*. But of course the systematic manner in which the frequencies differ in certain cases from "normal theory," as shown in the tables, makes it clear that the width of the shaded belt has at any rate sometimes a real significance. Owing to the

* If P_z is as defined in the footnote to p. 261 above, then the standard error of the proportion of N samples in which $|z|$ is greater than a certain value is $\sqrt{P_z(1-P_z)/N}$.

inevitable sampling fluctuations too much stress cannot be laid on any single difference taken alone, but in combination the results support one another. We shall consider them briefly in order.

Samples of 2.

Taking the symmetrical populations, the progressive change in the frequencies corresponding to a given value of $|z|$ as we pass from the rectangular population to the most leptokurtic population ($\beta_2 = 7{\cdot}07$) is very marked. The changes are less clear in passing from the normal population down the Type III line; this is the result of doubling over a skew z-distribution, but for reasons given above we shall be content in the present paper with considering the distribution of $|z|$ only*.

Samples of 5.

The table and diagram show that a normal curve with $\sigma_z = 1/\sqrt{2}$ provides a very poor approximation to "Student's" curve. For the symmetrical populations, σ_z diminishes steadily as the population β_2 increases, and the tail frequencies in the 1000 samples of 5 from population ($\beta_2 = 7{\cdot}07$) are quite clearly less than those expected on normal theory. The correspondence for the other four populations is really very good. The distribution of z (not doubled over) is, however, very skew in the case of the population ($\beta_1 = {\cdot}50$, $\beta_2 = 3{\cdot}73$). This is "Sophister's" case and has been fully discussed by him.

Samples of 10.

Figure 2 (*c*) shows that the line representing the tail area of the normal curve with $\sigma_z = 1/\sqrt{7}$, although still differing rather widely from the line representing "Student's" curve, now falls largely within the shaded belt. For $|z| > {\cdot}6$ the difference between the two curves is not great. For the samples from the three symmetrical curves, σ_z lies very close to the "normal theory" value, and the correspondence in frequencies is good. For samples from population ($\beta_1 = 0$, $\beta_2 = 7{\cdot}07$) there is curiously no evidence of the shortage of frequency in the tail which appears for samples of 2, 5 and 20. For the two Type III populations there is an excess of high values of $|z|$ which shows itself in the upper limit of the belt in the diagram. This tendency is not at all evident in the 1000 samples from Church's population ($\beta_1 = {\cdot}22$, $\beta_2 = 3{\cdot}16$), but great caution must be exercised in drawing conclusions from apparent differences in these cumulative frequency distributions. If we take the distribution of $|z|$, (*a*) for the 500 samples from the Type III population ($\beta_1 = {\cdot}20$, $\beta_2 = 3{\cdot}30$), and (*b*) for the 1000 samples from Church's population ($\beta_1 = {\cdot}22$, $\beta_2 = 3{\cdot}16$), and apply the (P, χ^2) difference test, we obtain for 11 groups a P of ${\cdot}592$; that is to say the observed differences which look large in the columns of Table II (*c*) are not inconsistent with a common theoretical law of distribution for $|z|$.

* That the distribution of z for samples from the skewest population is also skew, is shown by the drop in value of P from ${\cdot}871$ (test for $|z|$) to ${\cdot}022$ (test for z) in the goodness of fit tests.

The distribution of z (not doubled over) for samples from "Sophister's" population ($\beta_1 = {\cdot}50$, $\beta_2 = 3{\cdot}73$) is definitely negatively skew.

Samples of 20.

Figure 2 (*d*) suggests that we have now reached a size of sample where the normal curve with standard deviation $1/\sqrt{n-3}$ represents the z-distribution very well. The observed distributions of $|z|$ are quite closely represented by "normal theory" in all cases except that of the extreme leptokurtic population. Here there is again a shortage of high values of $|z|$, although judged by the test of goodness of fit this difference is not exceptional. For the Type III populations the distributions of z are again skew.

A completely satisfactory analysis of the position will only be possible when the theoretical distribution of z in samples from any non-normal population has been found. But in the meantime these results enable a good appreciation to be formed of the extent of variation from "normal theory" that may be expected in sampling from a fairly wide variety of populations*. They suggest that within this range there will not in practice be a danger of any serious loss of control of the source of error (1), if $|z|$ be assumed to follow "Student's" law. The least satisfactory agreement occurs among the samples from the very leptokurtic population ($\beta_2 = 7{\cdot}1$). Taken together, we find that the 21 tests of goodness of fit for $|z|$ give a mean value of P of ·463; even if the variations were all due to chance we should only expect a value of ·500.

In Table III a comparison is made at about the level $P_z = {\cdot}04$ of the chances, theoretical and observed, of obtaining $|z|$ greater than the values indicated in the 2nd column. The observed frequencies have been divided by 500 or 1000 according to the number of samples, and the figures are therefore subject to sampling errors. But even if they represented the true values of P_z in sampling from the corresponding populations, the differences between them and the "normal theory"

TABLE III.

Comparative values of P_z near ·04.

		Population						Normal distribution with
n	$\lvert z\rvert$	$\beta_1=0{\cdot}00$ $\beta_2=2{\cdot}50$	$\beta_1=0{\cdot}00$ $\beta_2=3{\cdot}00$	$\beta_1=0{\cdot}00$ $\beta_2=4{\cdot}12$	$\beta_1=0{\cdot}00$ $\beta_2=7{\cdot}07$	$\beta_1=0{\cdot}20$ $\beta_2=3{\cdot}30$	$\beta_1=0{\cdot}50$ $\beta_2=3{\cdot}73$	S.D. $=1/\sqrt{n-3}$
2	15·0	·050	*·042*	·042	·042	·039	·036	—
5	1·5	·044	*·040*	·038	·029	·044	·042	*·034*
10	0·8	·052	*·040*	·038	·038	·058	·062	*·034*
20	0·5	·052	*·042*	·040	·022	·050	·052	*·039*

* Certain incomplete results suggest that the population skewness cannot be increased much further without beginning to modify the distribution of $|z|$ appreciably.

values, as shown in the 4th column, are hardly large enough to lead to any serious errors in inference.

With characteristic intuition "Student" anticipated the adequacy of his test in sampling from symmetrical leptokurtic systems more than twenty years ago in his original paper*; the idea of the "doubling over" in the case of skew populations lies also to his credit.

4. The Two Sample Test.

We may now examine the adequacy of Fisher's two sample z-test in controlling the source of error (1) when sampling from non-normal populations. If two independent samples of n_1 and n_2 are drawn from the same normal population, then

$$z = \frac{\bar{x}_1 - \bar{x}_2}{\sqrt{n_1 s_1^2 + n_2 s_2^2}} \sqrt{\frac{n_1 n_2}{n_1 + n_2}} \qquad \text{.............................(3)}$$

is distributed according to the law

$$y = \text{constant} \times (1 + z^2)^{-\frac{n_1+n_2-1}{2}} \qquad \text{.....................(4).}$$

Equation (4) is the distribution of z in the single sample problem with $n_1 + n_2 - 1$ written for n. It does not, however, necessarily follow that when sampling from a non-normal population the distribution of $z = m/s$ for $n = 14$, let us say, will be the same as that of the z of (3) when $n_1 = 5$, $n_2 = 10$. This fact is illustrated in the case of sampling from the leptokurtic population ($\beta_1 = 0$, $\beta_2 = 7{\cdot}07$); there is here a considerable positive correlation between the values of m and s in a sample. Large deviations in mean tend to be associated with large deviations in standard deviation, and as a result the preceding tables have suggested that the ratio, z, is slightly less variable than on "normal theory." But if we combine the samples of 5 and 10, taking $n_1 = 5$, $n_2 = 10$, and calculate the z of (3), the most variable term in the numerator is $\bar{x}_1$, the mean of the smaller sample, while the most important term in the denominator is $10 s_2^2$, which is quite uncorrelated with $\bar{x}_1$. There is not compensation, therefore, as in the previous case, and as a result the z is somewhat more variable than that of "normal theory."

Tables IV (*a*), (*b*) and (*c*) show the result of pairing together samples of (*a*) 5 and 10, (*b*) 5 and 20, and (*c*) 10 and 20, from the three populations (0, 2·5), (0, 7·07) and (·50, 3·73). Results for the other two populations sampled are not yet available†. The tables show the observed and theoretical frequencies lying beyond certain values, not of $|z|$, but of a multiple of $|z|$ (as shown at the head of the leading column), which was a simpler ratio to obtain in the computation. The values of Mean z and σ_z are, however, given below, as well as the results of testing the doubled-over distribution for goodness of fit. The skewness and goodness of fit of the undoubled-over z-distributions have not yet been examined. The final columns of each table contain the frequencies found from a normal curve with standard deviation equal to $1/\sqrt{n_1 + n_2 - 4}$; even for samples of 5 and 10

* *Biometrika*, Vol. vi. p. 19.

† See Addendum, p. 285.

these frequencies never differ very widely from those of the true "normal theory" z-curve. The sampling results as they stand do not suggest that the distribution of $|z|$ varies in any simple way as the sampled population changes. But this could hardly be expected owing to the complex structure of the ratio, in which $\bar{x}_1$ is correlated with s_1^2, and $\bar{x}_2$ with s_2^2, but with no cross correlation. It seems justifiable,

TABLE IV (a).

Distribution of z in Pairs of Samples of 5 and 10.

Frequencies in 500 pairs.

$\sqrt{1\cdot5}\,\lvert z\rvert$ greater than	Populations Sampled				Normal distribution with S.D. $=1/\sqrt{11}$
	$\beta_1=0\cdot00$ $\beta_2=2\cdot50$	$\beta_1=0\cdot00$ $\beta_2=3\cdot00$	$\beta_1=0\cdot00$ $\beta_2=7\cdot07$	$\beta_1=0\cdot50$ $\beta_2=3\cdot73$	
·00	500	*500·0*	500	500	*500·0*
·05	447	*442·6*	459	443	*446·1*
·10	402	*386·6*	399	390	*393·3*
·15	352	*333·0*	341	337	*342·3*
·20	297	*283·0*	295	277	*294·0*
·25	235	*237·4*	256	232	*249·2*
·30	196	*196·4*	222	197	*208·3*
·35	157	*160·8*	184	156	*171·6*
·40	131	*130·0*	153	130	*139·4*
·45	106	*104·0*	121	99	*111·5*
·50	86	*82·5*	102	85·5	*87·9*
·55	67	*64·7*	86	72	*68·2*
·60	44	*50·4*	67	53	*52·1*
·65	34	*39·0*	61	44	*39·2*
·70	23	*30·0*	49	33	*29·0*
·75	15	*22·9*	35	23	*21·1*
·80	12	*17·4*	23	18	*15·1*
·85	9	*13·2*	19	14	*10·7*
·90	9	*10·0*	18	10	*7·4*
·95	7	*7·5*	10	9	*5·0*
1·00	7	*5·7*	7	6	*3·4*
Goodness of Fit P	·161	—	·034	·591	—
Goodness of Fit n'	16	—	16	16	—
Mean z	− ·0116	*0* S.E. *·0135*	+ ·0141	− ·0071	—
σ_z	·3019	*·3015* S.E. *·0110*	·3317	·3024	—

however, to conclude, after examining the tables, that the practical worker will be led to make no very serious error of judgment if he refers the value of z to "Student's" tables (or even to the normal tables with $\sigma_z = 1/\sqrt{n_1+n_2-4}$) when examining the difference between the means of pairs of small samples, taken from moderately skew, leptokurtic or platykurtic populations. Possibly the position might be less satisfactory if n_1 and n_2 were below the values of 5 and 10.

The average of the nine values of P found in the goodness of fit tests is now ·332. The standard errors given for Mean z and σ_z are for 500 samples from a normal population.

TABLE IV (b).

Distribution of z in Pairs of Samples of 5 and 20.

Frequencies in 500 pairs.

$\frac{1}{2}\sqrt{5}\,\lvert z\rvert$ greater than	Populations Sampled				Normal distribution with S.D. $=1/\sqrt{21}$
	$\beta_1=0{\cdot}00$ $\beta_2=2{\cdot}50$	$\beta_1=0{\cdot}00$ $\beta_2=3{\cdot}00$	$\beta_1=0{\cdot}00$ $\beta_2=7{\cdot}07$	$\beta_1=0{\cdot}50$ $\beta_2=3{\cdot}73$	
·00	500	*500·0*	500	500	*500·0*
·05	411	*416·0*	412	417·5	*418·8*
·10	332	*336·0*	340	340·5	*340·9*
·15	255	*263·2*	274	260	*269·3*
·20	198	*199·9*	224	183·5	*206·2*
·25	143	*147·3*	162	139	*152·8*
·30	106	*105·4*	123	101	*109·4*
·35	64	*73·4*	82	72·5	*75·7*
·40	49	*49·8*	53	47	*50·6*
·45	33	*33·0*	36	30·5	*32·6*
·50	23	*21·4*	23	18	*20·2*
·55	13	*13·6*	16	8	*12·1*
·60	7	*8·5*	10	4	*7·0*
·65	6	*5·2*	4	1·5	*3·9*
·70	2	*3·2*	3	0·5	*2·1*
·75	2	*1·9*	3	—	*1·1*
·80	2	*1·1*	2	—	*0·5*
Goodness of Fit P	·610	—	·397	·085	—
Goodness of Fit n'	11	—	11	13	—
Mean z	−·0094	*0* S.E. *·0098*	+·0099	−·0058	—
σ_z	·2175	*·2182* S.E. *·0074*	·2280	·2088	—

5. Examination of the Second Type of Error.

Suppose that on finding a value of z such that $P_z > 2\alpha$ (say, $>$ ·10 perhaps), it is decided to accept the hypothesis that the mean of the sampled population has a value b. How often is this likely to occur when in fact the true population mean lies at a instead of b? In such a case "Student's" tables will have been entered with $\zeta = (\bar{x} - b)/s$ instead of with $z = (\bar{x} - a)/s$, and the error in judgment will arise because the test is not sensitive enough to detect this fact. What we require is to have, for different values of $(a - b)$, some appreciation of the chance that $-z_\alpha < \zeta < +z_\alpha$*, for the smaller the chance the more effective is the control of this source of error.

* z_α being, as above, the value of z giving $P_z = 2\alpha$.

The position may be explored with the aid of the experimental sampling results. We have fixed in the first place on two different values of α, ·05 and ·01, which backward interpolation in "Student's" tables shows to correspond to deviations (z_α) of 1·066 and 1·873 for $n=5$, and of ·611 and ·941 for $n=10$. We have then chosen out randomly for each of the five sampled populations, and also for a normal population*, 100 of our samples and have given in succession to $(a-b)$ the values

TABLE IV (c).

Distribution of z in Pairs of Samples of 10 *and* 20.

Frequencies in 500 pairs.

$\sqrt{1\cdot5}\,\lvert z\rvert$ greater than	Populations Sampled				Normal distribution with S.D. $=1/\sqrt{26}$
	$\beta_1=0\cdot00$ $\beta_2=2\cdot50$	$\beta_1=0\cdot00$ $\beta_2=3\cdot00$	$\beta_1=0\cdot00$ $\beta_2=7\cdot07$	$\beta_1=0\cdot50$ $\beta_2=3\cdot73$	
·00	500	*500·0*	500	500	*500·0*
·05	411	*415·3*	410	416	*417·5*
·10	310	*334·5*	329	330	*338·6*
·15	239	*261·1*	258	273	*266·2*
·20	174	*197·4*	196	216	*202·5*
·25	124	*144·6*	144	155	*149·0*
·30	97	*102·7*	105	119	*105·8*
·35	75	*70·8*	76	82	*72·5*
·40	51	*47·4*	55	59	*47·9*
·45	32	*30·9*	31	34	*30·5*
·50	25	*19·7*	19	19	*18·7*
·55	16	*12·2*	12	8	*11·0*
·60	12	*7·4*	8	3	*6·2*
·65	8	*4·4*	5	3	*3·4*
·70	4	*2·6*	4	—	*1·8*
·75	1	*1·5*	2	—	*0·9*
Goodness of Fit P	·104	—	·917	·092	—
Goodness of Fit n'	11	—	11	11	—
Mean z	·0000	*0* S.E. *·0088*	– ·0036	– ·0085	—
σ_z	·1947	*·1961* S.E. *·0066*	·1972	·1997	—

$\sigma/\sqrt{n}$, $2\sigma/\sqrt{n}$, $3\sigma/\sqrt{n}$, ..., etc. ($n=5$ and 10), where σ is the standard deviation of the population sampled. $(a-b)$ has then been added in each case to the observed deviation in the sample mean and the result divided by s, the corresponding sample standard deviation, to give ζ. In samples from a normal population, if $(a-b)$ were zero, the percentage of values of $\zeta(=z)$, which should lie in the long run within the limits $\pm z_\alpha$, should be 90 for $\alpha=\cdot05$ and 98 for $\alpha=\cdot01$. For the non-normal

* One hundred random samples of 5 and 10 were specially drawn from a normal population for this purpose.

population, the results discussed in Section (3) above suggest that these percentages will also be fairly nearly approached. As $(a-b)$ is increased from zero the number of values of ζ found between these limits will decrease and will represent the percentage of false hypotheses accepted. The situation can be explained most clearly by turning to Table V.

This table shows the percentage of samples for which $-z_\alpha < \zeta < +z_\alpha$ when different multiples of $\theta = \sigma/\sqrt{n}$ have been added to or subtracted from the sample mean. Suppose for instance that we have a sample of 10 from the population ($\beta_1 = 0, \beta_2 = 7{\cdot}07$) and wish to test the hypothesis that the population mean lies at b, and decide to accept it if $|z| = |(\bar{x} - b)|/s < z_\alpha$. Then the experimental results suggest that

(1) if the true population mean were to lie at $a = b \pm 2\sigma/\sqrt{10} = b \pm {\cdot}63\sigma$ instead of at b, we should in repeated sampling accept 38 % of these false hypotheses if we took $\alpha = {\cdot}05$ as the critical level, and 67 % if we took $\alpha = {\cdot}01$;

(2) if the true population mean were to lie at $a = b \pm 4\sigma/\sqrt{10} = b \pm 1{\cdot}26\sigma$ we should accept in repeated sampling only 2 % of these false hypotheses in taking $\alpha = {\cdot}05$, and 9 % with $\alpha = {\cdot}01$.

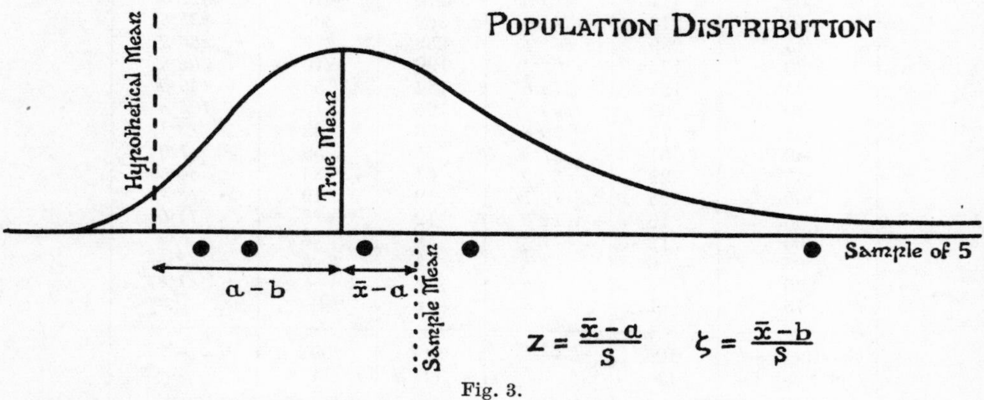

Fig. 3.

The table therefore shows the sensitiveness of "Student's" test in rejecting false hypotheses when applied to samples from various populations. We may comment on the results briefly as follows:

(a) For symmetrical populations the test will be equally sensitive whether $(a-b)$ be positive or negative. Multiples of $\sigma/\sqrt{n}$ were therefore only *added* to the observed samples*.

(b) There is extremely little difference in the degree of sensitiveness among the samples from the four symmetrical populations, the percentages being of course subject to sampling errors.

(c) The Type III populations were both positively skew, and the position is represented diagrammatically in Figure 3. An examination of Table V shows that

* For convenience in comparison with the results for the skew populations the figures for the normal population have been repeated on the negative side.

TABLE V.

z-Test. Table showing Percentage of False Hypotheses accepted when the True Population Mean lies at Increasing Distances $(a-b)$ *from its Supposed Position.* $(\theta = \sigma/\sqrt{n}.)$

Values of $(a-b)$.

	$-11, 10, 9\theta$	-8θ	-7θ	-6θ	-5θ	-4θ	-3θ	-2θ	$-\theta$	Population β_1	Population β_2	$+\theta$	$+2\theta$	$+3\theta$	$+4\theta$	$+5\theta$	$+6\theta$	$+7\theta$	$+8, 9, 10\theta$
Samples of 5, $\alpha=\cdot05$, $z_\alpha=1\cdot066$										0	2·50	75	57	28	7	2			
						7	24	48	70	0	3·00	70	48	24	7				
										0	4·12	73	49	23	6	1			
										0	7·07	71	42	20	7	2	1		
			1	1	4	7	16	38	67	·20	3·30	84	54	14	3				
					4	12	27	45	73	·50	3·73	84	50	21	3				
Samples of 5, $\alpha=\cdot01$, $z_\alpha=1\cdot873$										0	2·50	93	80	65	47	22	10	4	1
			1	9	20	39	56	76	86	0	3·00	86	76	56	39	20	9	1	
										0	4·12	94	78	61	45	18	10	4	1
										0	7·07	86	73	49	35	17	8	2	2, 1, 1
	1, 1, 1	3	4	7	12	26	55	73	81	·20	3·30	96	88	63	39	11	4		
	1	2	6	14	24	38	53	75	89	·50	3·73	99	88	66	38	12	6	1	
Samples of 10, $\alpha=\cdot05$, $z_\alpha=\cdot611$										0	2·50	74	39	13	3				
						1	10	44	69	0	3·00	69	44	10	1				
										0	4·12	74	42	21	4				
										0	7·07	68	38	9	2				
						3	18	46	84	·20	3·30	72	31	9	1				
					1	8	14	42	66	·50	3·73	80	45	8	1				
Samples of 10, $\alpha=\cdot01$, $z_\alpha=\cdot941$										0	2·50	92	71	41	11	3			
					3	12	40	67	89	0	3·00	89	67	40	12	3			
										0	4·12	93	73	47	22	4			
										0	7·07	88	67	34	9	2			
				2	4	18	48	82	95	·20	3·30	93	67	31	10	1	1		
			1	2	10	15	40	62	85	·50	3·73	95	77	46	9				

for these two populations the test is quicker in rejecting false hypotheses when the true population mean is, as shown in the figure, to the right of its supposed position than when it is in the other direction.

(*d*) For values of $(a-b)$ with the same sign as the population skewness the test appears to be slightly more sensitive in rejection than in the normal case. But for the opposite sign the position is distinctly less favourable when the populations are skew. In other words when dealing with skew populations there is more danger of failing to detect a faulty hypothesis when the long tail of the true population distribution points towards the position of the supposed mean than when the steep tail does. In certain problems the direction of the skewness, if not its exact magnitude, may be clear; in such cases we shall know that the chance of error is less completely controlled in one direction than in the other.

(*e*) The control of what has been termed the first source of error is as good for small samples as for large, provided that the population is such that $|z|$ follows approximately "Student's" law. It is in dealing with the second source of error that small samples are at a disadvantage. Suppose for example we are dealing with normal populations and on obtaining a sample $(\bar{x}, s)$ decide to accept the hypothesis that the population mean lies at b whenever $\zeta=(\bar{x}-b)/s<z_\alpha$ or $P_z>2\alpha=\cdot 10$, say. Then a rough interpolation in Table V suggests that for samples of 5 we may be accepting the hypothesis in as many as about 42 % of cases where the true population mean differs from b by as much as the population standard deviation; while in samples of 10 this will happen only in about 9 % of such cases*. For samples of 20 the risk would be almost negligible. There is nothing new in this except perhaps the method of approach; it is the old tale that no conceivable method of statistical analysis will enable differences below a certain limit to be detected from the evidence of a single small sample.

6. An Alternative Test.

In a recent paper† it was shown that in sampling from a rectangular population the appropriate criterion to use in testing a hypothesis regarding the position of the mean, a, was not z but the ratio $z'=(G-a)/\frac{1}{2}R$, where

u and v are the highest and lowest values of the variable in the sample,

G is the sample "centre," $=\frac{1}{2}(u+v)$,

R is the sample range, $=u-v$.

The theoretical distribution of z' in samples of n from this population was obtained, and it was suggested that perhaps it might be of wider application, just as "Student's" z-distribution has been found to be adequate for populations differing considerably from the normal. Further analysis, however, soon showed that the

* For $n=5$, $\alpha=\cdot 05$ we have interpolated roughly between the columns $a-b=2\theta=2\sigma/\sqrt{5}=\cdot 894\sigma$ and $a-b=3\theta=3\sigma/\sqrt{5}=1\cdot 342\sigma$, i.e. between the percentages 48 and 24. For $n=10$ we interpolate between $a-b=3\sigma/\sqrt{10}$ and $a-b=4\sigma/\sqrt{10}$.

† *Biometrika*, Vol. xx^A. p. 212.

" rectangular theory " z'-distribution would not be appropriate for samples from the populations of common statistical experience. That this is so is suggested at once by an examination of the values of $\sigma_{z'}$ found from the sampling experiments and given in Table VI. The whole form of the curve also changes.

TABLE VI.

Comparison of Observed Distribution of z' with Empirical "Normal Theory."

Populations.

n		$\beta_1=0{\cdot}00$ $\beta_2=1{\cdot}80$	0·00 2·50	0·00 3·00	0·00 4·12	0·20 3·30
	Goodness of Fit $\left\{\begin{array}{l}P\\ n'\end{array}\right.$	— —	·472 12	— —	·558 12	·175 15
5	Mean z' S.E.*	0 —	− ·0103 ·0242	0 —	− ·0224 ·0242	+ ·0274 ·0171
	$\sigma_{z'}$ S.E.*	*·5773*† —	·5515 ·0309	·5418 —	·5150 ·0309	·5651 ·0218
	Goodness of Fit $\left\{\begin{array}{l}P\\ n'\end{array}\right.$	— —	·003 13	— —	·063 13	·007 13
10	Mean z' S.E.*	0 —	+ ·0160 ·0132	0 —	+ ·0034 ·0132	+ ·0737 ·0132
	$\sigma_{z'}$ S.E.*	*·1890*† —	·2629 ·0103	·2947 —	·3169 ·0103	·3246 ·0103

It seemed, however, worth undertaking the following research :

(*a*) Find experimentally the distribution of z' in samples of 5 and of 10 from a normal population, and by fitting the data with curves obtain empirically " normal theory " z'-curves.

(*b*) Test the adequacy of these curves to represent the distribution of z' in the samples from the three neighbouring non-normal populations, with β_1 and β_2: (0, 2·5), (0, 4·1), (0·2, 3·3). That is to say examine the adequacy of these distributions in controlling the error (1).

(*c*) As in the case of z, examine the sensitiveness of the z'-test in rejecting false hypotheses (control of error (2)).

(*d*) Make a comparison of the sensitiveness of the z- and z'-tests for samples of 5 and 10 from the same populations.

* Standard errors for samples of 500 or 1000 if the distribution law of z' were of the empirical " normal theory " form.

† These are theoretical values obtained from equation (xliii), *Biometrika*, Vol. xx[A]. p. 211.

Let us take these steps in order:

(*a*) Mr L. H. C. Tippett very kindly placed at our disposal the 1000 samples of 5 and of 10 from a normal population which he had used in his work on the Distribution of Range*. He also undertook some preliminary computation. The distribution of z' must clearly be symmetrical; the following values were obtained by using the 2nd and 4th moment coefficients about $z' = 0$.

$$n = 5 \quad \sigma_{z'} = \cdot 5418 \quad \beta_2 = 7\cdot 5225,$$
$$n = 10 \quad \sigma_{z'} = \cdot 2947 \quad \beta_2 = 3\cdot 4342.$$

Type VII curves were fitted to the observations and gave on applying tests for goodness of fit, for $n = 5$, $P = \cdot 715$; and for $n = 10$, $P = \cdot 491$. These curves were taken to represent the standard z'-curves of "normal theory," and the chance of exceeding any given value of z' could be obtained by interpolating in "Student's" Tables of t (*Metron*, Vol. v. No. 3, p. 26).

(*b*) The two curves were then doubled over and fitted to the observed distributions of $|z'|$ for the three non-normal populations with the result shown in Table VI. The fits appear quite reasonable for samples of 5, but are no longer satisfactory when $n = 10$. That is to say it would appear that the "normal theory" z'-curves will only represent the distribution of $|z'|$ from moderately non-normal populations in very small samples. It did not seem worth while attempting the fitting in the more extreme cases of sampling from the populations with β_1 and β_2 (0·00, 7·07) and (0·50, 3·73). The table shows how, for symmetrical populations, $\sigma_{z'}$ decreases with β_2 for $n = 5$ and increases for $n = 10$. For samples from the skew Type III population the distributions of z' are negatively skew, and Mean z', at any rate for $n = 10$, differs quite significantly from zero. In dealing of course with a skew population the mean value in repeated samples of G, the "centre," is no longer at the population mean but at a point which changes as n is increased.

(*c*) The sensitiveness of the test in the control of error (2) was examined in precisely the same manner as for the z-test. The error arises because on taking $P_{z'} = 2\alpha$ as the limiting probability†, we find $-z_\alpha' < \zeta' < +z_\alpha'$, where $\zeta' = (G - b)/\frac{1}{2}R$ has been calculated instead of $z' = (G - a)/\frac{1}{2}R$, the supposed population mean being at b, the true one at a. Table VII gives the observed results based as before on 100 samples in each case. The following appear its most important features:

(1) For the symmetrical populations the test becomes less sensitive the more leptokurtic the population. This is not connected with the change in $\sigma_{z'}$, which, as we have seen, takes place in opposite directions for $n = 5$ and 10, but arises because the z' criterion becomes less and less efficient in controlling error (2) as we move away from the rectangular population for which it is theoretically most suitable.

* *Biometrika*, Vol. XVII. pp. 364—87.

† $P_{z'} = 2\int_{z'}^{\infty} f(z')\,dz'$. Using the empirical distribution referred to above it was found that

for $\alpha = \cdot 05$, $z_\alpha' = \cdot 852$ when $n = 5$ and $z_\alpha' = \cdot 482$ when $n = 10$,

for $\alpha = \cdot 01$, $z_\alpha' = 1\cdot 404$ when $n = 5$ and $z_\alpha' = \cdot 710$ when $n = 10$.

TABLE VII.

z'-Test. Table showing Percentage of False Hypotheses accepted when the True Population Mean lies at Increasing Distances $(a-b)$ from its Supposed Position. $(\theta = \sigma/\sqrt{n}.)$

Values of $(a-b)$.

	-10θ	-9θ	-8θ	-7θ	-6θ	-5θ	-4θ	-3θ	-2θ	$-\theta$	Population β_1	Population β_2	$+\theta$	$+2\theta$	$+3\theta$	$+4\theta$	$+5\theta$	$+6\theta$	$+7\theta$	$+8\theta$	$+9\theta$
Samples											0	2·50	77	60	28	11	1				
of 5						7	14	29	52	77	0	3·00	77	52	29	14	7				
$a = \cdot 05$											0	4·12	82	54	35	15	7	4			
$z_a' = \cdot 852$					1	5	13	28	63	82	0·2	3·30	72	51	21	3					
Samples											0	2·50	91	82	67	42	26	9	3		
of 5			4	7	15	23	39	61	78	87	0	3·00	87	78	61	39	23	15	7	4	
$a = \cdot 01$											0	4·12	96	79	59	45	27	15	7	4	2
$z_a' = 1\cdot 404$			2	5	13	22	42	67	81	92	0·2	3·30	92	77	62	35	17	2			
Samples											0	2·50	80	56	29	9	1				
of 10						7	13	29	59	81	0	3·00	81	59	29	13	7				
$a = \cdot 05$											0	4·12	75	57	33	17	6	3	1		
$z_a' = \cdot 482$			1	1	4	9	20	44	66	80	0·2	3·30	67	46	25	6	1				
Samples											0	2·50	93	82	58	31	15	3			
of 10				2	7	15	36	60	79	95	0	3·00	95	79	60	36	15	7	2		
$a = \cdot 01$											0	4·12	92	76	57	37	20	7	4	2	1
$z_a' = \cdot 710$	1	1	2	6	12	24	45	67	80	91	0·2	3·30	91	74	50	27	5	2			

(2) In sampling from the skew population, the control is slightly better than in the normal case when $(a-b)$ is positive, but worse when this difference has a negative sign. Exactly the same effect was observed in the case of z.

(d) We shall conclude with a comparison between z and z'. For the second type of error, this can be obtained by comparing Tables V and VII, but for convenience the results for the case $\alpha = \cdot 05$ have been placed together in Table VIII. The figures give the percentages of false hypotheses accepted for increasing values of $(a-b)$. It will be seen that for samples of 5 the z-test is not very much more sensitive than the z'-test, but that when n has increased to 10 the former has a very marked advantage. The difference is least for the platykurtic population.

TABLE VIII.

Comparing the Efficiency of the z- and z′-Tests in Rejecting False Hypotheses. $(\theta = \sigma/\sqrt{n}.)$

	$n=5$										$n=10$									
β_1 β_2	0·0 2·5		0·0 3·0		0·0 4·1		0·2 3·3				0·0 2·5		0·0 3·0		0·0 4·1		0·2 3·3			
							Positive θ		Negative θ								Positive θ		Negative θ	
$a-b$	z	z'	z	z'	z	z'	z	z'	z	z'	z	z'	z	z'	z	z'	z	z'	z	z'
θ	*75*	77	*70*	77	*73*	82	*84*	72	*67*	82	*74*	80	*69*	81	*74*	75	*72*	67	*84*	80
2θ	*57*	60	*48*	52	*49*	54	*54*	51	*38*	63	*39*	56	*44*	59	*42*	57	*31*	46	*46*	66
3θ	*28*	28	*24*	29	*23*	35	*14*	21	*16*	28	*13*	29	*10*	29	*21*	33	*9*	25	*18*	44
4θ	*7*	11	*7*	14	*6*	15	*3*	3	*7*	13	*3*	9	*1*	13	*4*	17	*1*	6	*3*	20
5θ	*2*	1	—	7	*1*	7	—	—	*4*	5	—	1	—	7	—	6	—	1	—	9
6θ	—	—	—	—	—	4	—	—	*1*	1	—	—	—	—	—	3	—	—	—	4
7θ	—	—	—	—	—	—	—	—	*1*	—	—	—	—	—	—	1	—	—	—	1
8θ	—	—	—	—	—	—	—	—	—	—	—	—	—	—	—	—	—	—	—	1

The figures for z have been printed in italics to aid the eye in comparison.

We have available, therefore, the distribution of two criteria in samples from a normal population, one (of z) known exactly and the other (of z') found empirically. That of the former, which is in theory ideal at the normal point, has been shown to be still applicable for a very considerable variety of population forms. But the distribution of z', while providing complete control of the first type of error at this point, begins to lose this control much more quickly than does that of z as the population form is modified. And further the z' criterion is less sensitive than the other in the detection of false hypotheses regarding the position of the population mean. Were the populations of experience clustered round the rectangular point the situation would almost certainly be reversed.

Owing to the simplicity in calculation it seems, however, possible that in problems where the population is known to be approximately normal, the criterion

$$z' = (u + v - 2a)/(u - v)$$

may be of value in providing a rapid method of testing the validity of a hypothesis regarding a population mean from a knowledge of the two extreme individuals in the sample only. This would be in cases where n is not greater than, say, 7 or even 10; for $n=2$ of course $z=z'$. It is therefore hoped to provide shortly brief tables of the empirical "normal theory" probability integral of z'.

Elsewhere in statistical theory there may well be cases of two criteria, for both of which the frequency distributions in sampling from a given population are known. In the case of z and z' the method of likelihood expresses in simple logical form the reason for the choice of z at the normal point and of z' at the rectangular point. This method should be applicable in other cases, and its value in picking out the right criterion is supported by the conclusions of this paper which have been reached by a quite different process of argument. In any case, however, the sensitiveness of the tests to changes in population form could not have been gauged except by the present form of experiment or by surmounting certain stubborn obstacles in the mathematical theory of sampling.

In conclusion, it is necessary to emphasise the extent to which this paper is a result of co-operation. The labour of sampling and computation is far too great to have been undertaken by a single individual. Mr N. K. Adyanthāya has been entirely responsible for this and other work on the symmetrical population with $\beta_2=4{\cdot}1$. As has been stated above, the results for samples of 5 and 20 from the skewest of the populations have been taken from "Sophister's" paper, and acknowledgments have also been made to Dr A. E. R. Church and Mr L. H. C. Tippett. Far the greater part of the remaining computing has been courageously undertaken by Mrs L. J. Comrie, while other computers have been Miss Marie H. Anderson, Mr A. B. Thomson and Mr Ernest Martin. To Mr A. E. Stone we are indebted for some 11,000 samples, and the diagrams are the work of Miss Ida McLearn. To all these the chief author is exceedingly grateful.

ADDENDUM: *Distribution of z in 500 Pairs of Samples from Population $\beta_1=0{\cdot}20$, $\beta_2=3{\cdot}30$.*

Samples of 5 and 10			Samples of 5 and 20			Samples of 10 and 20		
$\sqrt{1{\cdot}5}\,\lvert z\rvert$ ater than	Observation	Normal Theory	$\frac{1}{2}\sqrt{5}\,\lvert z\rvert$ greater than	Observation	Normal Theory	$\sqrt{1{\cdot}5}\,\lvert z\rvert$ greater than	Observation	Normal Theory
·00	500	500·0	·00	500	500·0	·00	500	500·0
·15	361	333·0	·10	340	336·0	·10	342	334·5
·30	204	196·4	·20	200	199·9	·20	203	197·4
·40	135	130·0	·30	121	105·4	·30	119	102·7
·50	88	82·5	·40	59	49·8	·40	64	47·4
·60	52	50·4	·50	23	21·4	·50	25	19·7
·70	29	30·0	·60	9	8·5	·55	15	12·2
·80	14	17·4	·65	6	5·2	·60	8	7·4
·90	6	10·0	·70	3	3·2	·65	6	4·4
1·00	5	5·7	·75	2	1·9	·70	5	2·6
P	·337		P	·441		P	·185	
n'	16		n'	12		n'	11	
σ_z	·3023	·3015	σ_z	·2204	·2182	σ_z	·1983	·1961

The above results correspond, in somewhat abbreviated form, to those of Tables IV (*a*), (*b*) and (*c*) above. The values of σ_z show very close agreement with "normal theory," and the frequencies do not appear to differ seriously.

For the population $\beta_1 = 0{\cdot}00$, $\beta_2 = 4{\cdot}12$ the result for samples of 5 and 10 alone is available. Testing goodness of fit to "normal theory" it is found that $P = {\cdot}350$, while $\sigma_z = {\cdot}3111$ against the normal value of ·3015. The distribution of z is somewhat too variable, but not as much so as in the case of samples from the extremely leptokurtic population ($\beta_2 = 7{\cdot}07$).

SOME NOTES ON SAMPLING TESTS WITH TWO VARIABLES.

By E. S. PEARSON, D.Sc.

CONTENTS.

(1) Introductory.

Suppose that we are considering the distribution of a single variable, x, and that the population sampled is divided into a groups such that in the rth group x is normally distributed with standard deviation σ about a mean $\tilde{x}_r$. In general $\tilde{x}_1, \tilde{x}_2, \ldots \tilde{x}_a$ are not equal, although in a special case they may be so. A sample of N is now drawn in which n_1 individuals are taken randomly from the first group, n_2 from the second, and so on, where

$$n_1 + n_2 + \ldots + n_a = N \qquad \text{.............................(1).}$$

Estimates $X_1, X_2, \ldots X_a$ are made from the sample of the true population group means $\tilde{x}_1, \tilde{x}_2, \ldots \tilde{x}_a$, and

$$u = \underset{r=1}{\overset{a}{S}} \left\{ \underset{t=1}{\overset{n_r}{S}} (x_{rt} - X_r)^2 \right\} \Big/ \sigma^2 \qquad \text{..........................(2)}$$

is calculated. Then if the quantities X_r have been obtained in a suitable manner, it can be shown that the distribution of u in repeated samples of N* follows the Type III law

$$f(u)\, du = \text{constant} \times u^{\frac{N-c-2}{2}} e^{-\frac{1}{2}u} du \qquad \text{....................(3),}$$

where c will depend upon the method of estimation of the X's. For example, if X_r is the mean of the n_r values of x sampled from the rth population group

$$(r = 1, 2, \ldots a),$$

then $c = a$; or if in the population $\tilde{x}_1 = \tilde{x}_2 = \ldots = \tilde{x}_a$, and we take $X_1 = X_2 = \ldots = X_a$ = mean of the N sample values of x, then $c = 1$. It will be noted that (3) gives

$$\text{Mean } u = N - c, \quad \sigma_u = \sqrt{2(N-c)}.$$

* That is to say, samples in which n_r individuals are drawn randomly from the rth population group ($r = 1, 2, \ldots a$), n_r remaining fixed.

Dr R. A. Fisher has based a number of simple but important statistical tests on the equation (3), which he classes under the heading of "Analysis of Variance*." The expression

$$\overset{a}{\underset{r=1}{S}} \left\{ \overset{n_r}{\underset{t=1}{S}} (x_{rt} - X_r)^2 \right\} \Big/ (N-c) = u\sigma^2/(N-c) \quad \text{.................(4)}$$

he describes as an estimate of the population variance, σ^2, based upon $N-c$ degrees of freedom; its mean value in repeated samples is seen to be σ^2.

The expression u, containing as it does the population σ^2, is not of much direct value if this quantity be unknown, but in a number of problems the appropriate criterion to use is the ratio $\theta = u'/u$, where u' is a quantity similar to the u of (2) but based upon an independent estimate of σ^2, such that

$$f(u')\, du' = \text{constant} \times u'^{\frac{N'-c'-2}{2}} e^{-\frac{1}{2}u'} du' \quad \text{..................(5).}$$

θ is now independent of σ^2 and, as Fisher has shown (also it may be easily proved from (3) and (5)), if u and u' are uncorrelated, then in repeated sampling θ is distributed according to the Type VI law

$$f(\theta)\, d\theta = \text{constant} \times \theta^{\frac{N'-c'-2}{2}} (1+\theta)^{-\frac{N+N'-c-c'}{2}} d\theta \quad \text{.........(6).}$$

Here the constant term is independent of σ^2. In dealing with this distribution Fisher uses the transformation

$$z = \frac{1}{2} \left\{ \log_e \frac{u\sigma^2}{N-c} - \log_e \frac{u'\sigma^2}{N'-c'} \right\} \quad \text{........................(7),}$$

that is to say he takes z as half the difference of the natural logarithms of the two estimates of variance. He has given tables showing for different values of $n_1 = N-c$ and $n_2 = N'-c'$ the value of z, the chance of exceeding which is ·05 and ·01†. It will be noticed that by writing $\zeta = \theta/(1+\theta)$, (6) may be transformed into the Type I distribution

$$f(\zeta)\, d\zeta = \text{constant} \times \zeta^{\frac{N'-c'-2}{2}} (1-\zeta)^{\frac{N-c-2}{2}} d\zeta \quad \text{..............(8),}$$

whose probability integral depends upon the Incomplete Beta Function.

The various tests based upon the frequency law (6) depend upon the variables being normally distributed. As soon as non-normality is introduced the distribution of θ will be modified in a direction varying with the particular test. Not only may (3) and (5) be no longer applicable, but u and u' will in certain cases be correlated where previously they were independent. In the present paper it is proposed to examine how far deviations from normality are likely to affect one of Fisher's tests, that for the goodness of fit of regression curves. The experimental results used to illustrate this point will also help to throw some light on the distribution of the correlation coefficient in small samples from non-normal populations.

* A description of these tests is given in a paper entitled "On a Distribution yielding the Error-Functions of several well known Statistics," read before the International Mathematical Congress at Toronto in 1924 but only recently published. The methods of application without the mathematical framework are given in Dr Fisher's *Statistical Methods for Research Workers*, 1925 and 1928, pp. 178 *et seq.*

† Table VI, *Statistical Methods for Research Workers*. This z must be distinguished from the original z of "Student's" test which Fisher writes as $t/\sqrt{n}$.

(2) THE APPLICATION OF THE PRINCIPLE OF LIKELIHOOD.

In two recent papers an attempt has been made by Dr J. Neyman and the author to connect together the various tests that are applied in different sampling problems by deducing from a common basis the criterion appropriate in each case*. It will perhaps be of interest to illustrate the use of this method in a further instance. The problem of the goodness of fit of regression curves presents itself commonly in the following form. We have before us a sample, Σ, and wish to know whether it is likely that this has been drawn from a population, Π, for which the curve of regression of y on x, let us say, follows a law

$$Y_x = F(x;\ \alpha_1, \alpha_2, \dots \alpha_c) \qquad (9),$$

where F is of given form but the constants α are unspecified. That is to say, we are testing what has been described as a "composite hypothesis"; it would become a "simple hypothesis" only if the values of α were specified in advance. What is the appropriate criterion to use? In the case where $c=1$, and we suppose that in the population Y_x is constant, should we take the correlation ratio η_{y_x}? And when in the population Y_x is supposed to lie on a sloping straight line ($c=2$), should we consider $\eta - r$ or $\eta^2 - r^2$ or even (as one of Blakeman's alternatives†) the ratio of η to r? The general problem in which the array distributions may be of any form would probably be extremely difficult to solve, at any rate for small samples, but the solution in one important case—that in which the arrays of y for constant x are homoscedastic normal curves—can be obtained. And here the principle of likelihood appears to provide a method of finding the appropriate criterion.

Σ is a sample of N in the form of a correlation table, for which the marginal totals, the means, and the standard deviations in the a y-arrays are respectively n_x, $\bar{y}_x$, and s_x ($x=1, 2, \dots a$). The set Ω‡ of all possible populations from which Σ may have been drawn is that in which the y-arrays are homoscedastic normal curves, but the regression of y on x as well as the distribution of the x-arrays and of both marginal distributions may be of any form whatever§. The sub-set ω of Ω contains the populations for which the regression of y on x is given by the law (9). As a step in measuring the probability that Σ is a sample from a member of ω we shall find the likelihood of this composite hypothesis. Let Π be a member of Ω for which the standard deviation in the y-arrays is σ, and the proportions in the marginal totals of these arrays are $p_1, p_2, \dots p_a$, where of course

$$p_1 + p_2 + \dots + p_a = 1 \qquad (10).$$

* "On the Use and Interpretation of Certain Test Criteria for Purposes of Statistical Inference," *Biometrika*, Vol. xx^A. pp. 175—240 and 264—294.

† *Biometrika*, Vol. IV. pp. 332—350.

‡ This terminology was explained in *Biometrika*, Vol. xx^A. pp. 263—265.

§ There is no need for the x-variate to be continuous; in fact, if it be, the distribution in the y-arrays is only likely to be normal if the number of arrays, a, be fairly large. If, for example, dx be the breadth of a y-array and we are dealing with a bivariate normal surface, then the array distributions will only be strictly normal in the limit as dx tends to zero.

Then the chance of drawing from Π a sample

(1) in which n_x individuals come from the xth array ($x=1, 2, \dots a$),

(2) where within the array the observations lie between the limits $y_{tx}-\frac{1}{2}h$ and $y_{tx}+\frac{1}{2}h$ ($t=1, 2, \dots n_x$, $x=1, 2, \dots a$),

will be in the limit as $h \to 0$ asymptotic to

$$C=\frac{N!}{n_1! \dots n_a!}(p_1)^{n_1}\dots(p_a)^{n_a}\frac{1}{(\sqrt{2\pi}\sigma)^N}e^{-\frac{1}{2\sigma^2}\underset{x}{S}\underset{t}{S}(y_{tx}-Y_x)^2}h^N \text{.........(11).}$$

Taking logarithms we find

$$\log C=\text{constant}+\overset{a}{\underset{x=1}{S}}(n_x\log p_x)-N\log\sigma-\frac{1}{2}\left\{\overset{a}{\underset{x=1}{S}}(n_x s_x^2+n_x(\bar{y}_x-Y_x)^2)\right\}\Big/\sigma^2,$$

where the constant term is a function of h and the sample frequencies only. To determine Π (Ω max) we maximise $\log C$ with regard to the variables σ, Y_x and p_x ($x=1, 2, \dots a$). The result gives

$$\left.\begin{aligned}\sigma^2&=\overset{a}{\underset{x=1}{S}}(n_x s_x^2)/N\\ Y_x&=\bar{y}_x,\ (x=1, 2, \dots a)\\ p_x&=n_x/N,\ (x=1, 2, \dots a)\end{aligned}\right\} \text{........................(12),}$$

and hence as $h \to 0$,

$$C(\Omega\text{ max})=\frac{1}{(\sqrt{2\pi})^N}e^{-\frac{1}{2}N}\left\{\frac{S(n_x s_x^2)}{N}\right\}^{-\frac{N}{2}}\frac{N!}{N^N}\frac{n_1^{n_1}}{n_1!}\dots\frac{n_a^{n_a}}{n_a!}h^N \text{......(13).}$$

To determine Π (ω max) we maximise $\log C$ with regard to σ; $\alpha_1, \alpha_2, \dots \alpha_c$; $p_1, p_2, \dots p_a$; where the α's are the c undetermined parameters contained in the expression (9). The solution is now

$$\sigma^2=\overset{a}{\underset{x=1}{S}}\{n_x s_x^2+n_x(\bar{y}_x-Y_x)^2\}/N \text{.......................(14),}$$

$$p_x=n_x/N,\quad (x=1, 2, \dots a) \text{..............................(15),}$$

and for Y_x we have the values obtained by the solution of the equation

$$\overset{a}{\underset{x=1}{S}}\left\{n_x(\bar{y}_x-Y_x)\frac{\partial Y_x}{\partial\alpha_t}\right\}=0,\quad (t=1, 2, \dots c) \text{ ....(16),}$$

which are the same as those found by minimising $\overset{a}{\underset{x=1}{S}}\{n_x(\bar{y}_x-Y_x)^2\}$, or from fitting (9) by least squares to the observations. Inserting these values into (11) we obtain an expression for C (ω max) identical with (13) except that the sample array means and standard deviations occur in a term of form

$$\overset{a}{\underset{x=1}{S}}\left\{\frac{n_x s_x^2+n_x(\bar{y}_x-Y_x)^2}{N}\right\}^{-\frac{N}{2}}.$$

It follows that the likelihood of the composite hypothesis becomes

$$\lambda=\frac{C(\omega\text{ max})}{C(\Omega\text{ max})}=\left\{1+\frac{\overset{a}{\underset{x=1}{S}}n_x(\bar{y}_x-Y_x)^2}{\overset{a}{\underset{x=1}{S}}(n_x s_x^2)}\right\}^{-\frac{N}{2}} \text{..............(17),}$$

the values of Y_x being obtained by fitting (9) to the weighted sample array means by the method of least squares. Following a common notation, if s_y be the standard deviation in the y-margin of the sample, we may write

$$\left.\begin{aligned}\overset{a}{\underset{x=1}{S}}(n_x s_x^2) &= N(1-\eta_{yx}^2)\,s_y^2\\ \overset{a}{\underset{x=1}{S}}\{n_x(\bar{y}_x - Y_x)^2\} &= N(\eta_{yx}^2 - R^2)\,s_y^2\end{aligned}\right\}\quad\text{.................(18)},$$

so that

$$\lambda = \left\{1 + \frac{\eta_{yx}^2 - R^2}{1-\eta_{yx}^2}\right\}^{-\frac{N}{2}} = \left\{\frac{1-R^2}{1-\eta_{yx}^2}\right\}^{-\frac{N}{2}} \quad\text{.................(19)}.$$

The hypothesis to be tested is most likely to be true when $R = \eta_{yx}$ and $\lambda = 1$, and becomes more and more improbable as λ decreases. The completion of the solution depends upon finding the distribution of λ in sampling from a member of ω. This has been done by R. A. Fisher and is a special case of his general distribution (6) given above (p. 338). The quantity whose distribution he has obtained is not λ, but a function of λ which we may call θ, defined by the relation

$$\lambda = (1+\theta)^{-\frac{1}{2}N},$$

or

$$\theta = \frac{\eta_{yx}^2 - R^2}{1-\eta_{yx}^2} = \frac{\overset{a}{\underset{x=1}{S}}\{n_x(\bar{y}_x - Y_x)^2\}}{\overset{a}{\underset{x=1}{S}}(n_x s_x^2)} \quad\text{.....................(20)}.$$

As λ varies from 1 to 0, θ varies from 0 to ∞. If we divide the denominator of the expression for θ by $N-a$, it will be seen that it becomes the ratio of the weighted sum of the squares of the deviations of the sample array means from the fitted regression curve to a weighted estimate of the population array variance. Without therefore introducing the idea of likelihood, θ appears to be a natural criterion to use in judging the deviation of the observed regression from expected type.

(3) THE SAMPLING DISTRIBUTION OF θ.

The proof has been given by Fisher in somewhat condensed form*. It may be divided into the following steps:

(a) The set of all possible samples, Γ, from a population Π can be divided into a number of sub-sets within any one of which, say γ, the totals of the y-arrays have a fixed series of values $n_1, n_2, \ldots n_a$. The chance of drawing a given sample Σ from Π can then be represented by the product of (1) the chance that Σ belongs to γ, or $C_\gamma = \dfrac{N!}{n_1!\ldots n_a!}(p_1)^{n_1}\ldots(p_a)^{n_a}$, and (2) the chance of obtaining the observed value of the variates on drawing a random sample of n_1 from the first population array, n_2 from the second, and so on. The solution is simplified immensely by first obtaining the distribution of θ among the samples of a single sub-set.

* *Journal of the Royal Statistical Society*, Vol. LXXXV. pp. 597—611.

(*b*) Take $$k = \overset{a}{\underset{x=1}{S}} \{n_x (\bar{y}_x - Y_x)^2\}/\sigma^2 \quad \text{.........................(21).}$$

Then within the samples of the sub-set γ, if $\tilde{y}_x$ be a true population array mean, $\sqrt{n_x}(\bar{y}_x - \tilde{y}_x)$ is a quantity normally distributed about zero with standard deviation σ. The sum contains the squares of a such quantities. The effect of using Y_x, found by fitting a regression curve to the observations, instead of $\tilde{y}_x$, can be shown, at any rate in certain important cases, to give for the distribution of k a curve of the form of (3), where $N = a$, the number of arrays, and c is the number of constants in the fitted regression curve (9)*. That is to say we have

$$f(k)\, dk = \text{constant} \times k^{\frac{a-c-2}{2}} e^{-\frac{1}{2}k} dk \quad \text{..................(22).}$$

(*c*) Take $$q = \overset{a}{\underset{x=1}{S}} \left\{ \overset{n_x}{\underset{t=1}{S}} (y_{xt} - \bar{y}_x)^2 \right\} \Big/ \sigma^2 = \overset{a}{\underset{x=1}{S}} (n_x s_x^2)/\sigma^2 \text{..................(23).}$$

This is the special case arising from equations (2) and (3) referred to on p. 337 above, where X_r is the mean of the group of n_r observations. The distribution of q is of form (3); there are N observations and the number of groups is a, hence

$$f(q)\, dq = \text{constant} \times q^{\frac{N-a-2}{2}} e^{-\frac{1}{2}q} dq \quad \text{..................(24).}$$

(*d*) Finally within γ, as the population y-arrays are normal, k and q are independent, the first depending only on the variation in means, the second on that of standard deviations. It is therefore easy to obtain from (22) and (24) the distribution of $\theta = k/q$, namely,

$$f(\theta)\, d\theta = \text{constant} \times \theta^{\frac{a-c-2}{2}} (1+\theta)^{-\frac{N-c}{2}} d\theta \text{..............(25).}$$

This distribution is not only independent of σ but also of the array totals $n_1, n_2, \ldots n_a$. It will therefore hold within all sub-sets γ, and hence for the aggregate of all possible samples Γ. The probability integral of (25) provides in fact the means of testing the hypothesis regarding the form of the regression curve. Various methods of obtaining this probability integral will be considered below.

(4) The Effect of Non-normality.

Dr Fisher's test can be used in examining the goodness of fit of linear and non-linear regression curves, but it has involved two large assumptions, first that the distributions in the y-arrays are normal, and next that they have the same standard deviations. In cases of non-linear regression it is often found that the array standard deviations change, while the form of the curve may pass from symmetry through increasing degrees of skewness. With linear regression the assumptions are more likely to be justified. As the population diverges from normal form the test will become less and less efficient, partly because the criterion

* This result appears to be exact provided that the constants $a_1, a_2, \ldots a_c$ appear in (9) in *linear* form; for example, if the curve be a parabola, or even a hyperbola of type $Y_x = a_1 + \frac{a_2}{x} + \ldots + \frac{a_c}{x^{c-1}}$. In the more general case it may perhaps be only true as an approximation.

θ is no longer the most appropriate one to use, and partly because its sampling distribution will cease to conform to (25), but it would be almost impossible to say at what point it becomes invalid. The practical situation seems, however, to be this; the statistician who is not dealing with very large samples has often no means of judging the exact form of his population distribution. It is therefore of first importance that he should feel some confidence that moderate deviations from normal homoscedasticity will not make worthless any conclusions which he may draw by referring z to Fisher's tables or $\theta = k/q$ to the distribution (25). The problem is a large one, seeing in how many directions non-normality may arise, but a simple illustration will throw some light upon it.

Suppose that the distributions in the y-arrays of the population are homoscedastic non-normal curves with the frequency constants σ, β_1 and β_2. If the means of the population arrays, $\tilde{y}_x$, were known, we could calculate

$$k' = \overset{a}{\underset{x=1}{S}} \{n_x (\bar{y}_x - \tilde{y}_x)^2\}/\sigma^2 = \overset{a}{\underset{x=1}{S}} (v_x^2)/\sigma^2 \quad \text{......................(26).}$$

Within the sub-set of samples, γ, defined on p. 341 above, v_x will vary about zero with standard deviation σ and with a second "beta coefficient" defined by

$${}_xB_2 = 3 + (\beta_2 - 3)/n_x.$$

It follows that in repeated sampling within γ,

$$\text{Mean } k' = a,$$

$$\text{Mean } (k')^2 = \left\{ \overset{a}{\underset{x=1}{S}} (\text{Mean } v_x^4) + 2S' (\text{Mean } v_x^2 v_{x'}^2) \right\} \Big/ \sigma^4 \text{*}$$

$$= \overset{a}{\underset{x=1}{S}} ({}_xB_2) + 2S' \{\text{Mean } v_x^2 \times \text{Mean } v_{x'}^2\}/\sigma^4$$

(since within γ, v_x and $v_{x'}$ are uncorrelated)

$$= \overset{a}{\underset{x=1}{S}} ({}_xB_2) + a(a-1) = a^2 + 2a + (\beta_2 - 3) \overset{a}{\underset{x=1}{S}} \left(\frac{1}{n_x}\right).$$

Hence $$\sigma_{k'}^2 = \text{Mean } (k')^2 - (\text{Mean } k')^2 = 2a + (\beta_2 - 3) \overset{a}{\underset{x=1}{S}} \left(\frac{1}{n_x}\right) \quad \text{.........(27).}$$

It is seen that the mean value of k' is the same whatever form be the population array, but (27) shows that the variability of k' depends upon β_2, and further is not the same within each of the sub-sets γ, varying according to the marginal totals n_x. The second term of (27) will usually, however, be very small compared with the first, and we may conclude that unless the population arrays are extremely leptokurtic or the sample very small, the distribution of k' will not differ seriously from that of "normal theory." The quantity with which we are really concerned is the k of (21), obtained by using the Y_x's of the fitted regression curve; its variability would appear harder to determine, but it seems likely that just as for k' the equation (22) will represent its sampling distribution with fair accuracy provided the sample is not very small or the array β_2 large.

* S' implies the summation for all possible pairs out of the a-arrays.

We may now consider the modifications connected with the q of (23). Within the sub-set γ, we know that

$$\begin{cases}\text{Mean}\,(s_x^2) = (n_x - 1)\,\sigma^2/n_x, \\ \text{Mean}\,(s_x^4) = (n_x - 1)\,\{(n_x - 1)\,\beta_2 + (n_x^2 - 2n_x + 3)\}\,\sigma^4/n_x^3 * .\end{cases}$$

Hence $$\text{Mean}\,q = \overset{a}{\underset{x=1}{S}}\,\{n_x\,\text{Mean}\,s_x^2\}/\sigma^2 = \overset{a}{\underset{x=1}{S}}\,(n_x - 1) = N - a,$$

$$\text{Mean}\,q^2 = \overset{a}{\underset{x=1}{S}}\,\{n_x^2\,\text{Mean}\,s_x^4\}/\sigma^4 + 2S'\,\{n_x n_{x'}\,\text{Mean}\,s_x^2 \times \text{Mean}\,s_{x'}^2\}/\sigma^4,$$

as within γ, s_x^2 and $s_{x'}^2$ are uncorrelated. Substituting the values for Mean s_x^2 and Mean s_x^4 it is found after reduction that

$$\text{Mean}\,q^2 = (N-a)^2 + 2\,(N-a) + (\beta_2 - 3)\left\{N - 2a + \overset{a}{\underset{x=1}{S}}\left(\frac{1}{n_x}\right)\right\},$$

or $$\sigma_q^2 = 2\,(N-a)\left\{1 + (\beta_2 - 3)\frac{N - 2a}{2\,(N-a)} + \frac{\beta_2 - 3}{2\,(N-a)}\overset{a}{\underset{x=1}{S}}\left(\frac{1}{n_x}\right)\right\} \quad \text{......(28)}.$$

Again the mean value of q is independent of the population array form, but σ_q differs from the "normal theory" value of $\sqrt{2\,(N-a)}$. Although the third term within the brackets in (28) may be small, the second term will often not be negligible compared to unity. For example, if $\beta_2 = 4$, and we are dealing with very large samples, this second term will be of the order of 0·5. We must conclude therefore that if the population array distributions are distinctly platykurtic or leptokurtic, the variability of q will be affected and the "normal theory" law (24) begin to fail, although still giving the correct mean for q. The denominator of the ratio $\theta = k/q$ is in fact more sensitive to changes in population form than the numerator. If the array curves are skew, another feature is introduced owing to the correlation between deviations in mean and variance; that is to say $\bar{y}_x$ and s_x will be correlated. This will lead to a correlation between k and q which, provided that it is positive†, should have in the ratio θ somewhat the same compensating effect as in "Student's" ratio z when the population is not normal‡.

(5) Sampling Experiments.

To illustrate further the result of non-normality in this and certain other problems two series of sampling experiments have been carried out. The first, in which the arrays were both normal and homoscedastic, does no more than confirm the unquestioned accuracy of "normal theory" as set out in equations (22), (24) and (25), but it will be of more value in connection with the distribution of r. In the second experiment the standard deviation in the arrays was varied and the distributions were taken to be Type III curves.

* This value for the mean of the square of the variance is taken from Dr Church's paper in *Biometrika*, Vol. XVII. p. 81.

† If the array distributions are leptokurtic this correlation will presumably be positive. If, however, they were for instance "rectangular," large deviations in $\bar{y}_x$ would be associated with low values of s_x^2, leading to a negative correlation between k and q which would tend to increase the variability of θ.

‡ See *Biometrika*, Vol. XXI. p. 259 *et seq.*

Experiment I.

The population contained three arrays ($a = 3$) with proportions $p_1 = \cdot 40$, $p_2 = \cdot 35$, $p_3 = \cdot 25$. The three array distributions were normal and homoscedastic, and the regression of y on x was linear, the coefficient of correlation being $\rho = \cdot 5346$. The sampling was carried out with the help of Tippett's Random Numbers*, the grouping unit for y being $\frac{1}{5}$ of the array standard deviation. 200 random samples of 20 were taken and k, q and θ, as defined above, calculated in each case. In fitting a sloping regression straight line to each sample we are using a law (9) of form

$$Y_x = \alpha_1 + \alpha_2 x \qquad (29),$$

that is to say $c = 2$, while $N = 20$, $a = 3$.

Distribution of k.

Equation (22) becomes

$$f(k)\, dk = \text{constant} \times k^{-\frac{1}{2}} e^{-\frac{1}{2}k}\, dk \qquad (30),$$

which is the distribution of χ^2 with $n' = 2$. The following results were obtained:

Mean k; Theory 1·000, Observation 1·109, Standard Error† 0·100.
σ_k; „ 1·414, „ 1·538, „ 0·187.

The Goodness of Fit Test, using 11 groups, gave $P = \cdot 416$.

Distribution of q.

Equation (24) becomes

$$f(q)\, dq = \text{constant} \times q^{\frac{15}{2}} e^{-\frac{1}{2}q}\, dq \qquad (31),$$

or the distribution of χ^2 with $n' = 18$. The following results were obtained:

Mean q; Theory 17·000, Observation 17·035, Standard Error 0·412.
σ_q; „ 5·831, „ 5·586, „ 0·339.

The Goodness of Fit Test, using 16 groups, gave $P = \cdot 982$.

Distribution of $\theta = k/q$.

Equation (25) becomes

$$f(\theta)\, d\theta = \text{constant} \times \theta^{-\frac{1}{2}} (1 + \theta)^{-9}\, d\theta \qquad (32).$$

Using the transformation $\zeta = \theta/(1 + \theta)$ we obtain the Type I distribution

$$f(\zeta)\, d\zeta = \text{constant} \times \zeta^{-\frac{1}{2}} (1 - \zeta)^{\frac{15}{2}}\, d\zeta \qquad (33),$$

whose probability integral depends on the Incomplete Beta Function. For the general distribution (25),

$$\text{Mean } \theta = \frac{a - c}{N - a - 2}, \quad \sigma_\theta = \frac{1}{N - a - 2}\sqrt{\frac{2(a - c)(N - c - 2)}{N - a - 4}} \qquad (34).$$

* *Tracts for Computers*, No. xv.

† The standard errors are for Mean k and σ_k calculated from 200 samples. The first is $\sigma_k/\sqrt{N}$, and in the second case the approximation $\frac{1}{2}\sigma_k\sqrt{(\beta_2 - 1)/N}$ has been used, where here $N = 200$ and β_2 refers to the theoretical distribution of k which for a χ^2 distribution has a value of $3 + 12/(n' - 1)$. Similar expressions are used for q and θ.

Using these values with $N = 20$, $a = 3$, $c = 2$, it was found that

Mean θ; Theory ·0667, Observation ·0727, Standard Error ·0074.
σ_θ; „ ·1046, „ ·1074.

The distribution of θ is a J-curve, and the expression used above for the standard error of a standard deviation will hardly be satisfactory. Using the transformation to a Type I curve, and comparing theory and observation for 11 groups, the Goodness of Fit Test gave $P = \cdot 409$.

Correlation between k and q.

As we should expect, there is no evidence for such a correlation. The observed values for the 200 samples are

$$r_{kq} = -\cdot 0342, \quad \eta_{kq}^2 = \cdot 1227.$$

The standard error for r_{kq} on "normal theory" is $1/\sqrt{200-1} = \cdot 0709$, while if we may consider the arrays of q in the k, q-correlation table sufficiently nearly normal to apply the test we are now discussing and as described in section (6) below, then equations (44) give Mean $\eta^2 = \cdot 1156$ and $\sigma_{\eta^2} = \cdot 0319$, so that the observed value of ·1227 is not significant.

Taken collectively these results show an admirable agreement between observation and theory.

Experiment II.

The population contained five arrays ($a = 5$) with proportions and array standard deviations as follows:

Array	1	2	3	4	5
p_x	·1667	·2666	·2167	·1833	·1667
σ_x	5·7471	5·3191	5·0000	4·7619	4·5872

The standard deviations are in terms of the grouping unit employed for the sampling. The regression was linear and the coefficient of correlation was $\rho = + \cdot 4626$. The distribution in each array followed a Type III curve with $\beta_1 = 0{\cdot}20$, $\beta_2 = 3{\cdot}30$. If x is taken to be increasing as we pass from Array 1 to Array 5, and ρ is taken as positive, then these curves were negatively skew, the steeper tail pointing in the direction of increasing y. 300 random samples of 30 were now drawn, again using Tippett's Random Numbers. A sloping straight line

$$Y_x = \alpha_1 + \alpha_2 x \quad \text{.............................(29 } bis\text{)}$$

was fitted to each sample, so that $N = 30$, $a = 5$, $c = 2$.

Distribution of k.

The population array standard deviations vary, but the weighted mean of the variances, or $\bar{\sigma}^2 = 26{\cdot}1306$, has been substituted for σ^2 in the expression for k, (21), and also later in that for q, (23). Equation (22) becomes

$$f(k)\,dk = \text{constant} \times k^{\frac{1}{2}}\,e^{-\frac{1}{2}k}\,dk \quad \text{........................(35).}$$

The following results were obtained:

Mean k; Theory 3·000, Observation 2·842, Standard Error* 0·141.
σ_k; „ 2·449, „ 2·457, „ 0·173.

Theoretical frequencies were obtained from the *Tables of the Incomplete Gamma Function*, taking $p=0\cdot5$ and $u=k/\sqrt{6}$; testing for goodness of fit with 14 groups it was found that $P=\cdot329$. A comparison of cumulative frequencies is given in Table I.

Distribution of q.
Equation (24) becomes

$$f(q)\,dq = \text{constant} \times q^{\frac{23}{2}} e^{-\frac{1}{2}q}\,dq \quad \ldots\ldots\ldots\ldots\ldots\ldots(36).$$

The following results were obtained:

Mean q; Theory 25·000, Observation 25·127, Standard Error 0·408.
σ_q; „ 7·071, „ 8·052, „ 0·321.

Theoretical frequencies were again obtained from the *Incomplete Gamma Function Tables* taking $p=11\cdot5$, $u=q/\sqrt{50}$, and on testing for goodness of fit with 13 groups it was found that $P=\cdot474$.

TABLE I.

Frequency Distributions from Experiment II.

Distribution of k			Distribution of q			Distribution of 25θ		
k greater than:	Observation	Normal Theory	q greater than:	Observation	Normal Theory	25θ greater than:	Observation	Normal Theory
0·0	300	300·0	8	300	299·8	0·0	300	300·0
0·5	272	275·7	10	297	299·0	0·4	281	281·4
1·0	237	240·4	12	293	296·0	0·8	245	254·2
1·5	192	204·7	14	283	288·5	1·2	219	225·8
2·0	158	171·7	16	269	274·4	1·6	194	198·6
2·5	128	142·6	18	244	252·7	2·0	171	173·6
3·0	111	117·5	20	216	224·0	2·4	141	151·2
3·5	87	96·2	22	183	190·7	2·8	124	131·3
4·0	66	78·4	24	154	155·8	3·2	97	113·8
4·5	53	63·7	26	122	122·3	3·6	79	98·6
5·0	42	51·5	28	96	92·4	4·0	73	85·4
5·5	37	41·6	30	68	67·3	4·4	63	73·9
6·0	32	33·5	32	54	47·4	4·8	57	64·0
7·0	26	21·6	34	39	32·4	5·2	47	55·4
8·0	13	13·8	36	29	21·5	5·6	42	48·0
9·0	6	8·8	38	22	13·9	6·0	37	41·6
10·0	5	5·6	40	17	8·8	6·4	31	36·1
11·0	4	3·5	42	12	5·4	7·2	21	27·2
			44	10	3·3	8·0	17	20·6
			46	7	2·0	8·8	15	15·6
			48	2	1·2	9·6	11	11·9
						10·4	8	9·1
						11·2	6	7·0
						12·0	4	5·4

* The standard errors were calculated as for Experiment I, using $N=300$ (see footnote to p. 345).

Distribution of $\theta = k/q$.

Equation (25) becomes

$$f(\theta)\,d\theta = \text{constant} \times \theta^{\frac{1}{2}}(1+\theta)^{-14}\,d\theta \quad\text{.....................(37).}$$

Using equations (34) we obtain the following comparison:

Mean θ; Theory ·1304, Observation ·1195, Standard Error ·0068.
σ_θ; „ ·1185, „ ·1052.
σ_θ^2; „ ·01404, „ ·01107, „ ·00238.

The distribution of θ is so skew that the approximation to the standard error of a standard deviation used above is of doubtful value. The variances have therefore been compared, and differ by 1·25 times the standard error*. A comparison of goodness of fit was obtained by calculating the mid-ordinates of the Type VI curve for θ, (37), and correcting to obtain the group frequencies. Using 17 groups, a value of $P = {}$·270 was obtained. The cumulative frequencies are compared in Table I.

FIG. I. CORRELATION OF q AND k.

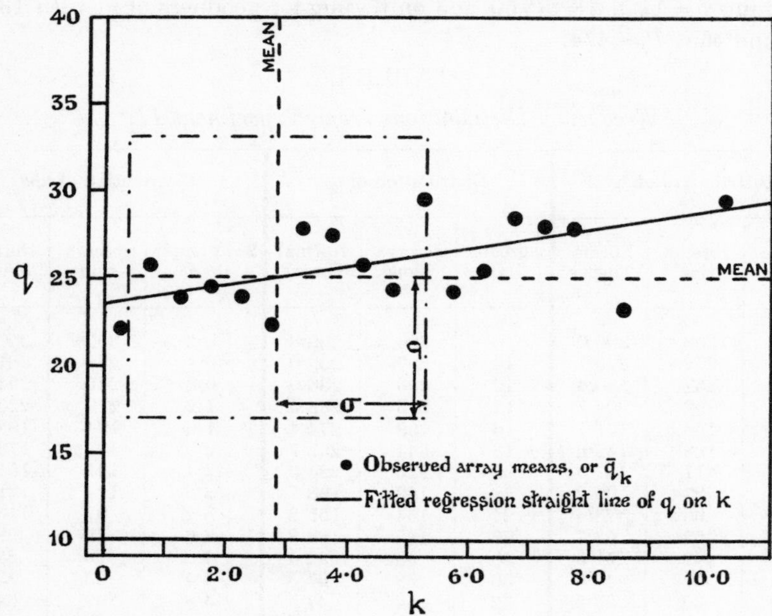

Correlation between k and q.

It was found that $r_{kq} = +{}$·1604; the standard error for zero theoretical correlation, were k and q normally distributed, is ·0578, so that r_{kq} differs from zero by about 2·8 times this standard error. The means of q for constant k are plotted in Fig. 1, where the observed regression straight line of q or k, or

$$\bar{q}_k = 23{\cdot}6669 + {\cdot}5278k \quad\text{.............................(38),}$$

has also been drawn.

* For 300 samples the standard error of the variance is very nearly $\sigma_\theta^2\sqrt{(\beta_2 - 1)/N}$, where the β_2 for distribution (37) is approximately 9·67.

If these results are taken as a whole it will be seen that there is nowhere any marked difference between the observed distributions and those of "normal theory." Owing to the changing array standard deviations the position is not as simple as that considered in section (4) above, but there seems to be evidence that the changes there contemplated are beginning to occur. We may note:

(*a*) The distribution of k is in good agreement with theory.

(*b*) The mean q differs from the expected value by only about one-third its standard error, but the observed σ_q is significantly greater than the "normal theory" value. This is as we should expect from (28), the array β_2 being 3·3; the slight excess of large values of q can be seen in Table I.

(*c*) The observed mean θ and σ_θ are a little low, but hardly significantly so, and a comparison of the cumulative frequencies of 25θ in Table I does not suggest that any serious error would be introduced by making use of the θ distribution (25).

(*d*) Finally a positive correlation between k and q has appeared which is probably significant.

There are, of course, so many directions in which the population form may be modified and so many changes to be rung in the values of N, a, c and ρ that it would be dangerous to draw too sweeping conclusions from a single experiment. Yet, as far as it goes, this appears to be a satisfactory result, and it suggests that in cases where we believe that the deviations from normal homoscedasticity in the y-arrays are of about the order existing in this experimental population, Fisher's test may be used with confidence.

(6) THE PRACTICAL DETERMINATION OF THE PROBABILITY INTEGRAL OF $f(\theta)$.

Let us first restate the problem; it is that of testing the hypothesis that a given sample comes from a population in which the regression of y on x follows a curve

$$Y_x = f(x;\, \alpha_1, \alpha_2, \ldots \alpha_c) \quad \text{.........................(9 } bis\text{)}.$$

We either know that the population y-arrays are normal homoscedastic curves, or are prepared to take the risk of assuming that the deviation from this form is not sufficient to invalidate the test. We fit the regression curve to the sample by least squares and calculate

$$\theta = \frac{\eta_{yx}^2 - R^2}{1 - \eta_{yx}^2} = \frac{\overset{a}{\underset{x=1}{S}} \{n_x (\bar{y}_x - Y_x)^2\}}{\overset{a}{\underset{x=1}{S}} (n_x s_x^2)} \quad \text{.................(20 } bis\text{)}.$$

Since it is when θ is large that the hypothesis is unlikely to be true, we refer this quantity to the distribution it would follow in repeated samples were the hypothesis true, namely,

$$f(\theta)\, d\theta = \text{constant} \times \theta^{\frac{a-c-2}{2}} (1+\theta)^{-\frac{N-c}{2}} d\theta \quad \text{........(25 } bis\text{)},$$

find $P_\theta = \int_\theta^\infty f(\theta)\, d\theta$, and on the basis of these odds judge whether or no so great a value of θ is likely to have arisen through chance fluctuations. The two simplest cases that arise are when:

(*a*) $c = 1$, and we wish to test the hypothesis that the population array means are constant. In this case the fitted regression line $Y_x = \alpha_1$ becomes $Y_x = \bar{y}$, the mean of the N individuals in the sample, while from the definition of (18) $R = 0$ and $\theta = \eta^2/1 - \eta^2$.

(*b*) $c = 2$, and we wish to test the hypothesis that the regression curve is linear but not necessarily parallel to the axis of x. Here $Y_x = \alpha_1 + \alpha_2 x$ is the ordinary regression straight line of y on x, and $R = r_{xy}$, the coefficient of correlation in the sample. Then $\theta = (\eta^2 - r^2)/(1 - \eta^2)$.

We shall now discuss several methods of calculating P_θ, the chance of obtaining in random sampling a more divergent result than that observed.

1. *R. A. Fisher's Method.*

(25) is a special case of Fisher's general distribution referred to in section (1), which he takes as

$$f(\theta)\, d\theta = \text{constant} \times \theta^{\frac{n_1 - 2}{2}} (1 + \theta)^{-\frac{n_1 + n_2}{2}} d\theta \quad \text{...............(39).}$$

Writing $z = \frac{1}{2} \log_e \left(\frac{n_2}{n_1} \theta\right)$, it follows that the distribution of z* is

$$f(z)\, dz = \text{constant} \times \frac{e^{n_1 z} dz}{(n_1 e^{2z} + n_2)^{\frac{1}{2}(n_1 + n_2)}} \quad \text{.................(40).}$$

Tables VI of his *Statistical Methods for Research Workers* give for different values of n_1 and n_2 the values of z corresponding to the ·05 and ·01 proportionate tail areas of the z curve. In the present problem $n_1 = a - c$, $n_2 = N - a$, and

$$z = \frac{1}{2} \log_e \left\{\frac{\eta^2 - R^2}{1 - \eta^2} \cdot \frac{N - a}{a - c}\right\} \quad \text{..........................(41).}$$

The Tables can be entered with integral values of n_1 from 1 to 6, then for 8, 12, 24 and ∞; and of n_2 from 1 to 30, then for 60 and ∞. For many purposes this is adequate, but greater refinement is sometimes required.

2. *T. L. Woo's Tables.*

These have been published in the present volume of this Journal. They were primarily intended for testing the significance of a value of η^2, i.e. for the case $c = 1$. If we use the transformation $\zeta = \theta/(1 + \theta)$, equation (25) becomes of the form of (8) or

$$f(\zeta)\, d\zeta = \text{constant} \times \zeta^{\frac{a - c - 2}{2}} (1 - \zeta)^{\frac{N - a - 2}{2}} d\zeta \quad \text{..............(42),}$$

where

$$\zeta = \frac{\eta^2 - R^2}{1 - R^2} \quad \text{...................................(43).}$$

Then if $c = 1$, $\zeta = \eta^2$, and if $c = 2$, $\zeta = (\eta^2 - r^2)/(1 - r^2)$.

* This z must be distinguished from "Student's" z.

Mr Woo has taken $c=1$, and his tables are entered with N and n, which is a of the present paper. They may, however, be used for any value of c by equating his N to our $N-c+1$ and his n to our $a-c+1$. The tables give for a wide range of values of N and n*, (1) Mean ζ, (2) σ_ζ, and (3) the ratio $(\zeta - \text{Mean } \zeta)/\sigma_\zeta$ corresponding to tail areas of about ·02 and ·01.

3. *Other Methods of Approximation.*

The *Tables of the Incomplete Beta Function*, which are nearing completion in the Biometric Laboratory, will give the probability integral of (42) for a certain range of values of N, a and c, but it seems of interest to describe a form of approximation adequate for moderately large samples based on the Type III curve and the Incomplete Gamma Function. For the Type I curve written in the form

$$y = y_0 \zeta^{p-1}(1-\zeta)^{q-1}$$

we have the following moment constants:

$$\left.\begin{aligned} \text{Mean} &= \frac{p}{p+q} = \frac{a-c}{N-c} \text{ if } p=\tfrac{1}{2}(a-c),\ q=\tfrac{1}{2}(N-a) \\ \text{Variance} &= \frac{pq}{(p+q)^2(p+q+1)} = \frac{2(a-c)(N-a)}{(N-c)^2(N-c+2)} \\ \beta_1 &= \frac{4(p-q)^2(p+q+1)}{pq(p+q+2)^2} = \frac{8(N-2a+c)^2(N-c+2)}{(N-a)(a-c)(N-c+4)^2} \end{aligned}\right\} \quad \text{.........(44).}$$

Further, we know that

$$6(\beta_2-\beta_1-1)/(2\beta_2-3\beta_1-6) = -(p+q),$$

and consequently

$$2\beta_2 - 3\beta_1 - 6 = -12(\beta_2-\beta_1-1)/(N-c) \quad \text{...............(45).}$$

The relation (45) suggests that if N be not too small the (β_1, β_2) point of the curve of ζ, (42), will lie close to the Type III line. The extent to which this is so is illustrated in Fig. 2, which shows for $c=2$ how for a constant number of arrays, a, the point converges on the Type III line as N increases. We shall therefore examine the adequacy of the following approximation · to represent the Type I curve (42) by a Type III curve with its mean, variance and β_1 having the values of (44), or approximations to these values.

The equation to the curve, whose integral $I(u, p)$ is given in the *Tables of the Incomplete Gamma Function*†, is

$$y = \text{constant} \times u^p e^{-\sqrt{p+1}\,u} \quad \text{...........................(46),}$$

where
$$\left\{\begin{aligned} u &= (\text{deviation from start})/(\text{standard deviation}), \\ \sqrt{p+1} &\times \text{standard deviation} = \text{distance from start to mean}, \\ p &= 4/\beta_1 - 1. \end{aligned}\right.$$

* $N=51$ to 1000 and $n=3$ to 20.

† His Majesty's Stationery Office, 1922.

Hence we must take

$$p = \frac{a-c}{2}\,\frac{(N-c-(a-c))\,(N-c+4)^2}{(N-c-2\,(a-c))^2\,(N-c+2)} - 1$$

$$= \frac{a-c}{2}\left(1-\frac{a-c}{N-c}\right)\left(1+\frac{8}{N-c}+\dots\right)\left(1+\frac{4\,(a-c)}{N-c}+\dots\right)\left(1-\frac{2}{N-c}+\dots\right)-1$$

$$= \frac{a-c}{2}\left\{1+\frac{3\,(a-c+2)}{N-c}+\dots\right\}-1 \quad\dots\dots(47),$$

where we have expanded in inverse powers of $N-c$.

FIG. II. SHOWING THE β_1, β_2 POINTS FOR THE DISTRIBUTION OF ζ IN THE CASE $c=2$.

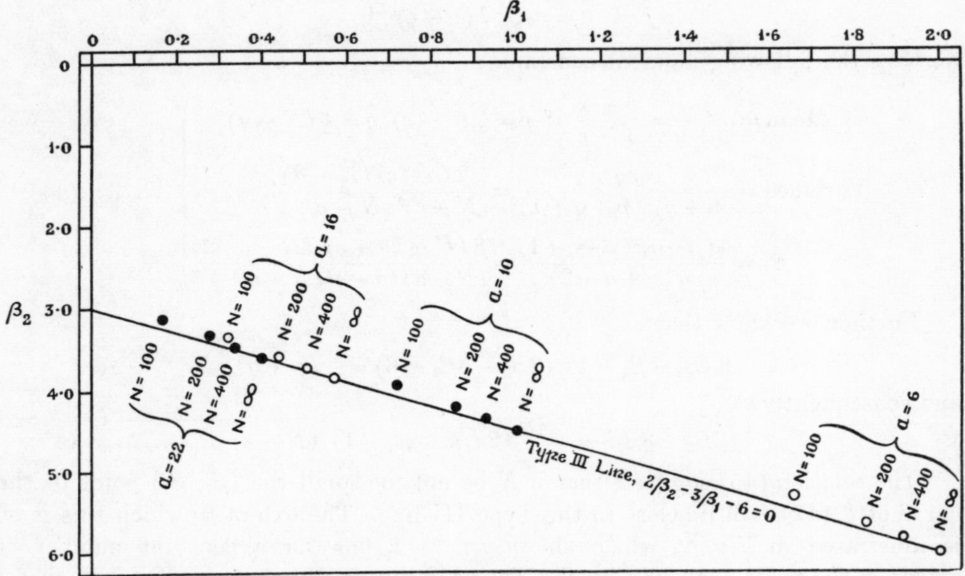

In the same way we may obtain an expansion for the expression for σ_ζ given in (44), namely,

$$\sigma_\zeta = \frac{\sqrt{2\,(a-c)}}{N-c}\left(1-\frac{a-c}{N-c}\right)^{\frac{1}{2}}\left(1+\frac{2}{N-c}\right)^{-\frac{1}{2}}$$

$$= \frac{\sqrt{2\,(a-c)}}{N-c}\left\{1-\frac{1}{2}\,\frac{a-c+2}{N-c}+\dots\right\} \quad\dots\dots(48).$$

Hence combining (47) and (48) we have

$$\text{Distance from start to mean} = \sqrt{p+1}\,\sigma_\zeta$$

$$= \frac{a-c}{N-c}\left\{1+\frac{a-c+2}{N-c}+\dots\right\} \quad\dots\dots(49).$$

The fitted Type III curve does not start exactly at $\zeta=0$; the position is represented in Fig. 3. The Type III curve starts at A, the true curve at O, the means coincide at M, and it is desired to approximate to the tail area under the true curve beyond P by taking the corresponding area under the Type III curve,

$$\begin{aligned} AP = OP + AO &= OP + AM - OM \\ &= \zeta + \frac{a-c}{N-c}\left\{1+\frac{a-c+2}{N-c}\ldots\right\} - \frac{a-c}{N-c} \\ &= \zeta + \frac{(a-c)(a-c+2)}{(N-c)^2} + \ldots, \end{aligned}$$

using equations (44) and (49). The *Tables of the Incomplete Gamma Function* are now to be entered with the p of (47) and $u = AP/\sigma_\zeta$ or

$$u = \frac{(N-c)\left\{\zeta + \dfrac{(a-c)(a-c+2)}{(N-c)^2} + \ldots\right\}}{\sqrt{2(a-c)}\left\{1 - \dfrac{1}{2}\dfrac{a-c+2}{N-c} + \ldots\right\}} \quad \ldots\ldots\ldots\ldots\ldots(50).$$

FIG. III

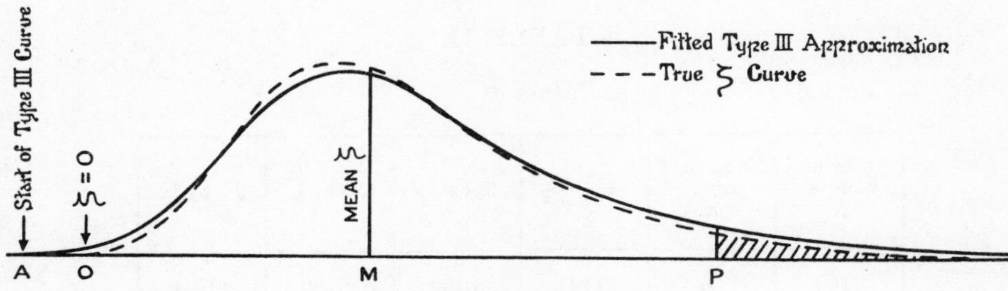

There are now possible two degrees of approximation.

Method I.

Take the p of (47) and the u of (50) as far as the terms given; this will involve interpolating for both p and u.

Method II.

Take $p = \frac{1}{2}(a-c)$, $u = N\zeta/\sqrt{2(a-c)}$, that is to say assume that a and c may be neglected compared with N. In this case it may only be necessary to interpolate for u*.

If the *Tables of the Incomplete Gamma Function* are not available, use can be made in certain cases of Elderton's χ^2 Tables in *Tables for Statisticians and Biometricians*. The χ^2 distribution is

$$y = \text{constant} \times (\chi^2)^{\frac{n'-3}{2}} e^{-\frac{1}{2}\chi^2} \quad \ldots\ldots\ldots\ldots\ldots\ldots\ldots\ldots(51).$$

* In the *Incomplete Gamma Function Tables* (1922) the argument interval for p is 0·1 up to 5·0, but beyond this it is 0·2, e.g. there is a column for $p=4{\cdot}5$, but for 5·5 we must interpolate between $p=5{\cdot}4$ and 5·6.

This corresponds to (46) if we write

$$\chi^2 = 2u\sqrt{p+1}, \quad n' = 2p+3,$$

and consequently we have two approximations corresponding to Methods I and II.

Method III.

Enter Elderton's Tables with

$$\begin{cases} \chi^2 = (N-c)\left(1+\dfrac{2(a-c+2)}{N-c}\right)\left(\zeta+\dfrac{(a-c)(a-c+2)}{(N-c)^2}\right), \\ n' = a-c+1+\dfrac{3(a-c)(a-c+2)}{N-c}. \end{cases}$$

It is here necessary to interpolate between the columns of n', which is not easy to do accurately.

Method IV.

To a rougher approximation use

$$\chi^2 = N\zeta, \quad n' = a-c+1.$$

Here n' will have an integral value and it is only necessary to interpolate for χ^2.

TABLE II.

Values of P_ζ.

Size of sample N	Number of arrays a	$\zeta=\dfrac{\eta^2-r^2}{1-r^2}$	True P_ζ	P_ζ by I	P_ζ by II
100	6	·1141	·0193	·0190	·0284
200	6	·0618	·0136	·0136	·0145
	14	·1120	·0285	·0277	·0322
	14	·1191	·0176	·0173	·0208
	22	·1657	·0248	·0236	·0314
500	14	·0453	·0292	·0291	·0307
	14	·0482	·0184	·0183	·0196
	22	·0672	·0260	·0257	·0285
1000	22	·0338	·0264	·0263	·0277

By taking certain values from Mr Woo's tables, it has been possible to examine the closeness of approximation of Methods I and II; except for the difficulty in accurate interpolation III and IV would give the same results as I and II respectively. Suppose that we take the case $c=2$, or are testing whether the regression of y or x is linear, and that we found in the nine samples with values for N and a shown in Table II, the values of $\zeta=(\eta^2-r^2)/(1-r^2)$ given in the 3rd column. Then the true values of P_ζ* found by Mr Woo from the appropriate Type I distributions are set out in the 4th column, while those found by using the approximate

* That is to say the chance of ζ exceeding the observed value in random sampling were the hypothesis tested true.

Methods I and II are in the 5th and 6th columns. While not attempting to be mathematically exact, there can be little doubt that Method I gives values for P_ζ accurate enough for most practical statistical work. As we should expect for a given N the error increases as the number of arrays is increased. For N below 100 and a large number of arrays the approximation will no doubt become less satisfactory, but this field will be covered by the *Tables of the Incomplete Beta Function.* For large samples the gain in speed by using Method II may well be felt to compensate for the loss in accuracy.

These results only provide a comparison at the level of significance $P_\zeta = {\cdot}03$ to ·01. It seemed desirable to examine the degree of approximation throughout the whole range of the curve, and this has been done in three cases, namely, $N=102$, $c=2$, $a=8$; $N=202$, $c=2$, $a=14$; $N=502$, $c=2$, $a=22$. The true probability integrals were found by quadrature of the curves

$$y = y_0 \zeta^2 (1-\zeta)^{46}; \quad y = y_0 \zeta^5 (1-\zeta)^{93}; \quad y = y_0 \zeta^9 (1-\zeta)^{239},$$

TABLE III.

Showing the Chance of Exceeding Certain Values of ζ.

$N=102$, $c=2$, $a=8$				$N=202$, $c=2$, $a=14$				$N=502$, $c=2$, $a=22$			
	P_ζ, or chance of exceeding ζ				P_ζ, or chance of exceeding ζ				P_ζ, or chance of exceeding ζ		
ζ	True value	Method I	Method II	ζ	True value	Method I	Method II	ζ	True value	Method I	Method II
·000	1·0000	·9996	1·0000	·000	1·0000	1·0000	1·0000	·000	1·0000	1·0000	1·0000
·012	·9789	·9731	·9940	·024	·9676	·9642	·9636	·016	·9926	·9919	·9918
·036	·7414	·7362	·8348	·050	·6250	·6170	·6116	·030	·7825	·7791	·7747
·060	·4301	·4233	·5295	·076	·2280	·2215	·2269	·038	·5256	·5212	·5193
·084	·2089	·2026	·2726	·102	·0540	·0522	·0582	·050	·1985	·1953	·1995
·108	·0893	·0859	·1219	·128	·0093	·0093	·0118	·064	·0399	·0391	·0427
·132	·0346	·0334	·0493	·154	·0012	·0013	·0020	·076	·0074	·0073	·0087
·156	·0123	·0122	·0186	·180	·0001	·0002	·0003	·090	·0008	·0008	·0011
·180	·0041	·0043	·0066					·102	·0001	·0001	·0002
·204	·0012	·0014	·0023								
·228	·0003	·0005	·0008								
·252	·0001	·0001	·0002								

ordinates being computed at intervals for ζ of ·003 in the first case and of ·002 in the other two cases. The results are shown in Table III. The adequacy of Method I for the common purposes of this test can hardly be questioned; Method II is less satisfactory, particularly for the sample of 102, but in all cases the agreement will be better as the number of arrays is decreased compared with the size of the sample.

(7) The Distribution of the Correlation Coefficient in the Experiments.

The sampling distribution of r first obtained by R. A. Fisher in 1915* is for two normally correlated and continuous variables. The population distributions of Experiments I and II are neither of them of this form. In the first case the y-arrays are normally distributed and contain five groups to the standard deviation, but there are only three alternative values of x, -1, 0 and $+1$; further, the proportions in these three x-marginal totals are $p_1 = \cdot 40$, $p_2 = \cdot 35$, $p_3 = \cdot 25$. That is to say, the x-distribution makes no approach either to normality or continuity. For Experiment II the y-arrays are skew curves with varying standard deviations, while there are five values for x, with proportional frequencies in the x-margin of $p_1 = \cdot 1667$, $p_2 = \cdot 2666$, $p_3 = \cdot 2167$, $p_4 = \cdot 1833$, $p_5 = \cdot 1667$. Here again there is no approach to a continuous normal distribution. Let us examine how closely the observed distributions of r conform to the sampling distributions of "normal theory."

TABLE IV.

Distribution of the Correlation Coefficient.

Experiment I			Experiment II		
r (Central Values)	Observed Frequency	Normal Theory Frequency	r (Central Values)	Observed Frequency	Normal Theory Frequency
−·05	1	0·8 (−·05 & below)	+·02	2	2·2 (+·02 & below)
·00	—	0·7	+·06	1	1·6
+·05	—	1·1	+·10	3	2·7
+·10	1	1·8	+·14	1	4·1
+·15	3	2·7	+·18	6	6·1
+·20	5	4·0	+·22	8	8·8
+·25	8	5·8	+·26	17	12·1
+·30	6	8·2	+·30	15	16·0
+·35	15	11·1	+·34	20	20·4
+·40	24	14·4	+·38	18	24·8
+·45	19	18·0	+·42	31	28·7
+·50	15	21·4	+·46	30	31·5
+·55	21	23·8	+·50	37	32·4
+·60	19	24·5	+·54	33	31·0
+·65	26	22·8	+·58	28	27·2
+·70	21	18·5	+·62	19	21·4
+·75	13	12·3	+·66	15	14·8
+·80	1	6·0	+·70	5	8·6
+·85	2	2·1 (+·85 & above)	+·74	5	4·0
			+·78	5	1·3
			+·82	1	0·3 (+·82 & above)
Total	200	200·0	Total	300	300·0

* *Biometrika*, Vol. x. pp. 507 *et seq.*

Experiment I.

Here $N = 20$, $\rho = \cdot 5346$ (population coefficient of correlation), and the theoretical distribution can be obtained by interpolating between the columns of ordinates for $\rho = \cdot 5$ and $\cdot 6$ given in Table A, p. 396, of the Cooperative Study on the distribution of r*. Second difference interpolation was used and a correction made to obtain group frequencies from mid-ordinates. The observed and theoretical results are compared in Table IV; the Goodness of Fit test with 11 groups gives $P = \cdot 223$. The following comparison was also made:

Mean r: Theory ·5244, Observation ·5160, Standard Error† ·0120.
σ_r: „ ·1704, „ ·1614, „ ·0097.

These two quantities are somewhat less than the "normal theory" values, but the differences are less than the standard errors. The frequencies show some irregularity in the centre, but the numbers are not large enough to prove any significance in this.

Experiment II.

Here $N = 30$, $\rho = \cdot 4626$. We are now beyond the range of tables of ordinates contained in the "Cooperative Study." The theoretical frequencies given in Table IV were calculated with the help of Fisher's transformation by a method which will be described below. The agreement between "normal theory" and observation is excellent, the Goodness of Fit test with 14 groups giving $P = \cdot 916$. Further, we have the following comparison:

Mean r: Theory ·4563, Observation ·4631, Standard Error† ·0086;
σ_r: „ ·1488, „ ·1475, „ ·0064;

the differences being again less than the standard errors.

These two series of results are of considerable interest and suggest that the normal bivariate surface can be mutilated and distorted to a remarkable degree without affecting the frequency distribution of r in samples as small as 20. The x-distribution in both cases has been made platykurtic, and it is possible that less satisfactory results would follow if the surface were pulled out into a more leptokurtic form.

(8) R. A. FISHER'S TRANSFORMATION OF THE r-DISTRIBUTION.

This method of transformation, which has been referred to in the preceding section, appears to be of such value in small sample work that it seems worth recording here the following examination of the degree of approximation involved. The equation for the distribution of r in samples of n may be written‡

$$f(r)\,dr = \text{constant} \times (1 - r^2)^{\frac{n-4}{2}} \frac{\partial^{n-2}}{\partial (r\rho)^{n-2}} \left\{ \frac{\cos^{-1}(-r\rho)}{\sqrt{1 - r^2\rho^2}} \right\} dr \quad \text{.........(52).}$$

* *Biometrika*, Vol. XI. p. 396.

† The standard errors are calculated as described in the footnote to p. 345.

‡ *Biometrika*, Vol. X. p. 511.

Then the transformation

$$r = \tanh z, \quad \rho = \tanh \zeta \quad \text{.........................(53)},$$

or

$$\left.\begin{aligned} z &= \tfrac{1}{2}\{\log_e(1+r) - \log_e(1-r)\} \\ \zeta &= \tfrac{1}{2}\{\log_e(1+\rho) - \log_e(1-\rho)\} \end{aligned}\right\} \quad \text{....................(54)},$$

applied to (51) is such as to give for the distribution of z a close approximation to a normal curve with mean at ζ and standard deviation equal to $1/\sqrt{n-3}$. That is to say, the distribution of z is almost invariant in form with a standard deviation depending only on the size of the sample and not on ρ. The moment constants of the distribution of z have been given by Fisher in the form of series in inverse powers of $n-1$*, and it is seen from these that the approximation is likely to be least satisfactory when ρ is large and n is small. The results shown in Table V have been computed for samples of 10 and of 20 from his series. Mean z differs from ζ by a quantity of the order of $\rho/2(n-1)$ and is the most variable of the expressions tabled. $1/\sqrt{n-3}$ is seen to be quite a good approximation to σ_z, at any rate in samples of 20, and if the distributions are slightly leptokurtic they are at any rate symmetrical.

TABLE V.

Moment Constants of Distribution of z.

ρ	$n=10$				$n=20$			
	Mean $z-\zeta$	σ_z	β_1	β_2	Mean $z-\zeta$	σ_z	β_1	β_2
·0	·0000	·375	·000 000	3·272	·0000	·2423	·000 000	3·116
·2	·0113	·375	·000 015	3·273	·0053	·2422	·000 002	3·117
·4	·0226	·374	·000 036	3·277	·0106	·2418	·000 004	3·118
·6	·0340	·372	·000 020	3·281	·0159	·2412	·000 002	3·118
·8	·0455	·369	·000 005	3·281	·0213	·2403	·000 001	3·116
·9	·0513	·367	·000 068	3·277	·0240	·2398	·000 007	3·114

$$\frac{1}{\sqrt{n-3}} = \cdot 378 \qquad\qquad \frac{1}{\sqrt{n-3}} = \cdot 2425$$

These results do not of course show whether sufficient terms are given in Fisher's series to insure convergence with n as low as 10, but it is possible to test the adequacy of the assumption that z is distributed normally in another way. Two tests were carried out.

Test (a). The moment coefficients of the true theoretical distribution of r are given as series in the Cooperative Study†. Taking a sample of 30 and $\rho = \cdot 462\,579$ (as for Experiment II above), the following values were obtained:

$$\text{Mean } r = \cdot 456\,265\,; \ \sigma_r = \cdot 148\,818\,; \ \beta_1 = \cdot 244\,; \ \beta_2 = 3\cdot 252 \text{.........(55)}.$$

* *Metron*, Vol. I. Part iv. pp. 13 and 14.

† *Biometrika*, Vol. XI. equations (xx), (xxi), (xxv), (xxvi).

Using Fisher's series from *Metron* we find

Mean $z = \cdot 508\,60$; $\sigma_z = \cdot 192\,04$ (N.B. $1/\sqrt{n-3} = \cdot 1925$); $\beta_1 = \cdot 000\,001$; $\beta_2 = 3\cdot 0742$ ....(56).

Next values of r at intervals of ·02 were taken between − ·24 and + ·86, and the corresponding values of z found from (54)*. The chance of a value of r lying in any of these subranges is the same as that of z lying in the corresponding subrange. We assume that z is normally distributed about ·508 60 with standard deviation ·192 04, obtain the proportional group frequencies from Sheppard's Tables of the Normal Curve, and hence have the grouped frequency distribution of r. The "normal theory" frequencies in the final column of Table IV above were obtained in this way. The moment constants of this distribution, were the process completely accurate, should be those of the series (55). Actually they were found to be

$$\text{Mean } r = \cdot 4560;\ \sigma_r = \cdot 1489;\ \beta_1 = \cdot 229;\ \beta_2 = 3\cdot 175 \quad \text{............(57).}$$

The agreement in the betas is not exact, but the z transformation seems to provide a quite adequate representation of the distribution of r.

TABLE VI.

Distributions of r.

r	Chance of r lying below values shown in 1st column	
	From quadrature with true ordinates	From the z transformation
− ·6	·000 008	·000 0003
− ·4	·000 067	·000 011
− ·2	·000 36	·000 13
·0	·0016	·0010
+ ·2	·0062	·0054
+ ·4	·0249	·0255
+ ·6	·1037	·1109
+ ·8	·4431	·4509
+ ·85	·6165†	·6193
+ ·90	·8133†	·8130
+ ·95	·9677†	·9688

Test (*b*). Suppose a sample of 10 taken from a normal population with $\rho = \cdot 8$. In this case the distribution of r is included in the Table A of the Cooperative Study (*loc. cit.* p. 386). It is seen to be a very skew curve with a modal ordinate at about $r = \cdot 85$, and $\beta_1 = 3\cdot 1377$, $\beta_2 = 8\cdot 0534$. Clearly it is not an easy distribution to handle, and but for these tables of ordinates we should be in difficulties when wanting to find the chance of r exceeding a certain value. The second column in

* A table of this function is given at the end of the *Metron* paper. Only about 1 sample in 10,000 lies outside the range $r = -\cdot 24$ to $+\cdot 86$.

† These values cannot be quite accurate as the r curve is too abrupt for a satisfactory quadrature from the tabled ordinates.

Table VI has been formed by applying quadrature to these ordinates. The z transformation leads to a distribution whose moment constants were calculated in forming Table V; they are

$$\text{Mean } z = \zeta + \cdot 0455 = 1 \cdot 1441 ; \; \sigma_z = \cdot 3691 ; \; \beta_1 = \cdot 000\,005 ; \; \beta_2 = 3 \cdot 2808.$$

Now make the simplifying assumption that z is normally distributed about 1·1441 with a standard deviation of ·3691, and it is easy to find from Sheppard's Tables the chance of $z = \tanh^{-1} r$ exceeding any given value. Is the approximation adequate? The figures in Table VI suggest that for most purposes it is. It must also be remembered that in taking $n = 10$ and $\rho = \cdot 8$ we have chosen a most unfavourable case.

The author is very much indebted to Miss M. Page for the sampling and computing work for Experiment I; to Mr A. E. Stone for the sampling and Mrs L. J. Comrie for the computing for Experiment II; to Mr Ernest Martin for the computing required for the comparison of Table III; and to Miss Ida McLearn for the three diagrams.

THE ANALYSIS OF VARIANCE IN CASES OF NON-NORMAL VARIATION

THE ANALYSIS OF VARIANCE IN CASES OF NON-NORMAL VARIATION.

By EGON S. PEARSON, D.Sc.

(1) *The Problem.*

In its simplest form, the problem to be discussed may be illustrated on the following example, the data for which are taken from a paper by Dr W. A. Shewhart of the Bell Telephone Laboratories, New York*. Table I contains records of 200 tests for insulation resistance made upon a certain material which was under examination in those Laboratories. In order to determine whether the construction and testing of the material were remaining uniformly under control, or were varying from day to day more than would be expected through chance, the observations have been broken up into subsets. I have chosen subsets of 10; thus the first column of 10 represents the results of the first group of 10 experiments, the second column, of the second group of 10, and so on up to the twentieth. At the bottom of each column is given the mean of the 10 values. The practical problem is to ascertain whether or not it is likely that these differences in means are significant; that is to say, we wish to test the hypothesis that the variation among the means of the 20 groups is no more than might be expected through chance, having regard to the observed variation among the individual values.

If x represent the group number and y the resistance, the problem reduces to that of testing the significance of the correlation ratio, η_{y_x}. Suppose that the total of N observations is divided into k groups of size, $n_1, n_2 \dots n_k$, and that $\bar{y}_x$ and s_x represent the observed mean and standard deviation† in the xth group ($x = 1, 2 \dots k$); further that $\bar{y}$ is the mean of the whole N values. In the present example

$$N = 200, \qquad k = 20, \qquad n_x = 10 \ (x = 1, 2 \dots k).$$

Then upon the assumption that the observations in the groups or arrays have been drawn from normally distributed universes with a common (but unknown) standard deviation σ, the problem has been solved. We may either calculate

$$\eta^2 = \underset{x}{S}\{n_x(\bar{y}_x - \bar{y})^2\}/S\{(y-\bar{y})^2\}\ddagger \quad \dots\dots\dots\dots\dots\dots\dots(1)$$

and judge its significance by reference to the sampling distribution,

$$df = \text{constant} \times (\eta^2)^{\frac{1}{2}(k-1)-1}(1-\eta^2)^{\frac{1}{2}(N-k)-1}\, d\eta^2 \quad \dots\dots\dots\dots(2).$$

* *The American Mathematical Monthly*, Vol. XXXVIII. p. 252, May 1931. I have used the first 200 of the 204 observations there given.

† Here and throughout the paper the sample variance, s_x^2, is taken as the sum of the squares of the deviations from the sample mean divided by the sample size, n_x.

‡ In this expression $\underset{x}{S}$ indicates summation for each of the k groups, and S the sum for each of the N observations.

TABLE I.

Tests for Control of Insulation Resistance in Manufacture.

Groups of 10 Observations

Resistance in Megohms (Central Values)	1	2	3	4	5	6	7	8	9	10	11	12	13	14	15	16	17	18	19	20	Totals
2875	—	—	—	—	—	1	1	—	—	—	—	—	—	—	—	—	—	—	—	—	2
3025	—	—	—	—	—	—	—	—	—	—	—	—	1	—	—	—	—	—	—	—	1
3175	—	—	—	—	—	—	—	—	—	—	—	—	—	—	—	—	—	—	—	—	—
3325	—	1	—	—	—	—	—	—	—	—	—	—	—	—	—	—	—	—	—	—	1
3475	—	1	—	—	—	—	—	—	—	—	—	—	—	—	—	—	—	—	—	—	1
3625	—	2	—	—	—	—	—	—	2	—	—	—	—	—	4	—	—	—	—	—	8
3775	—	1	—	—	1	—	—	—	—	—	—	—	—	—	1	—	—	—	—	—	3
3925	3	—	—	—	—	—	—	—	1	—	—	1	1	—	1	—	—	—	—	1	8
4075	—	—	1	1	—	—	1	—	3	—	2	2	2	1	—	—	—	—	—	2	15
4225	2	—	—	1	2	4	—	4	—	—	1	1	1	1	—	—	—	1	—	1	19
4375	3	—	1	1	1	3	5	—	1	3	2	1	3	3	2	—	—	—	1	1	31
4525	1	—	2	1	—	1	—	—	—	2	2	2	—	2	—	2	2	1	3	—	21
4675	—	1	4	2	1	1	1	4	3	2	—	3	—	1	—	1	1	—	3	3	31
4825	—	—	1	4	3	—	—	—	—	1	3	—	2	2	1	4	3	—	2	1	27
4975	1	—	—	—	1	—	2	2	—	2	—	—	—	—	1	2	3	3	1	—	18
5125	—	2	1	—	—	—	—	—	—	—	—	—	—	—	—	1	1	3	—	1	9
5275	—	1	—	—	—	—	—	—	—	—	—	—	—	—	—	—	—	1	—	—	2
5425	—	1	—	—	—	—	—	—	—	—	—	—	—	—	—	—	—	—	—	—	1
5575	—	—	—	—	—	—	—	—	—	—	—	—	—	—	—	—	—	1	—	—	1
5725	—	—	—	—	1	—	—	—	—	—	—	—	—	—	—	—	—	—	—	—	1
Means	4300	4340	4640	4600	4660	4200	4340	4580	4200	4660	4470	4380	4140	4510	4090	4790	4820	4960	4640	4440	4488

Methods of dealing with this Type I distribution have been discussed elsewhere*. Alternatively we may follow R. A. Fisher's procedure of "analysis of variance," and make the following table,

	Sum of squares	Degrees of freedom
From variation of means	$\underset{x}{S}\{n_x(\bar{y}_x-\bar{y})^2\}$	$k-1$
From variation about means	$\underset{x}{S}\{n_x s_x^2\}$	$N-k$
Total	$S\{(y-\bar{y})^2\}$	$N-1$

Then if the hypothesis that the means only differ through chance fluctuations be true, $\underset{x}{S}\{n_x(\bar{y}_x-\bar{y})^2\}/(k-1)$ and $\underset{x}{S}\{n_x s_x^2\}/(N-k)$ will be two independent estimates of the unknown group variance σ^2. The hypothesis is tested by examining the significance of z, the natural logarithm of the ratio of these two estimates of variance†.

For the example of Table I, I find $\eta^2=\cdot 2532$, while for the sampling distribution (2)

$$\text{Mean } \eta^2=\frac{k-1}{N-1},\quad \sigma_{\eta^2}=\frac{1}{N-1}\sqrt{\frac{2(k-1)(N-k)}{N+1}}\quad\text{.........(3)},$$

giving in the present instance: Mean $\eta^2=\cdot 0955$, $\sigma_{\eta^2}=\cdot 0293$‡. Hence

$$(\text{Observed } \eta^2-\text{Mean } \eta^2)/(\text{Standard Error})=(\cdot 2532-\cdot 0955)/\cdot 0293=5\cdot 4,$$

and is clearly significant.

Using Fisher's method it is found that $z=\cdot 577$; entering the tables of z with $n_1=k-1=19$ and $n_2=N-k=180$, it may be estimated that in only 1% of random samples z would exceed the value of about ·38, if the hypothesis tested were true. The observed value is therefore clearly significant.

The two tests must of course lead to identical results, since z is a single valued function of η^2, in fact

$$z=\tfrac{1}{2}\log_e\{(N-k)\,\eta^2/(k-1)(1-\eta^2)\}\quad\text{.....................(4)}.$$

There is no doubt therefore that the manufacture of the insulating material or the method of testing were undergoing changes during the period of experimentation. In fact it is interesting to note that a statistical analysis along these lines actually enabled Dr Shewhart to identify and remove certain causes of variation.

Let us now consider the assumptions involved in applying the test.

(*a*) That the k groups or samples have been drawn from universes with a common variance. This is a hypothesis that may or may not be true; a method of testing it has been developed elsewhere by Dr J. Neyman and the present writer§. If it be not true, it is probable that the test for the difference in means will not be seriously invalidated, unless the difference in group variances be very considerable||.

* *Biometrika*, Vol. XXI. pp. 350—355.

† Tables of the 5 % and 1 % points for z are given in R. A. Fisher's *Statistical Methods for Research Workers*.

‡ These values can be obtained from T. L. Woo's Tables, *Biometrika*, Vol. XXI. pp. 10—66; also *Tables for Statisticians*, Part II, Table IV.

§ In a paper in course of publication in the *Bulletin of the Polish Academy of Science and Letters*.

|| A single experiment on this point was carried out by the writer, *Biometrika*, Vol. XXI. pp. 346—349.

(*b*) That the samples have been drawn from normally distributed material. It is the object of the present paper to examine the effect of non-normality. In the example of Table I it is found that on combining the 200 observations

$$\sqrt{\beta_1} = -\cdot 760, \quad \beta_1 = \cdot 578, \quad \beta_2 = 4\cdot 317.$$

The divergence from normality is clearly significant*. Now it is true that this divergence may be due to the heterogeneity of the material. But the fact that the group means differ significantly could not be established until the η^2 or z-test had been applied, and logically if any value is to be placed on the result of this test, the user must have confidence that it remains valid for homogeneous material which is not normally distributed.

In section (3) below the results of experimental sampling from a variety of non-normal distributions following Pearson-type curves are discussed, and it will be

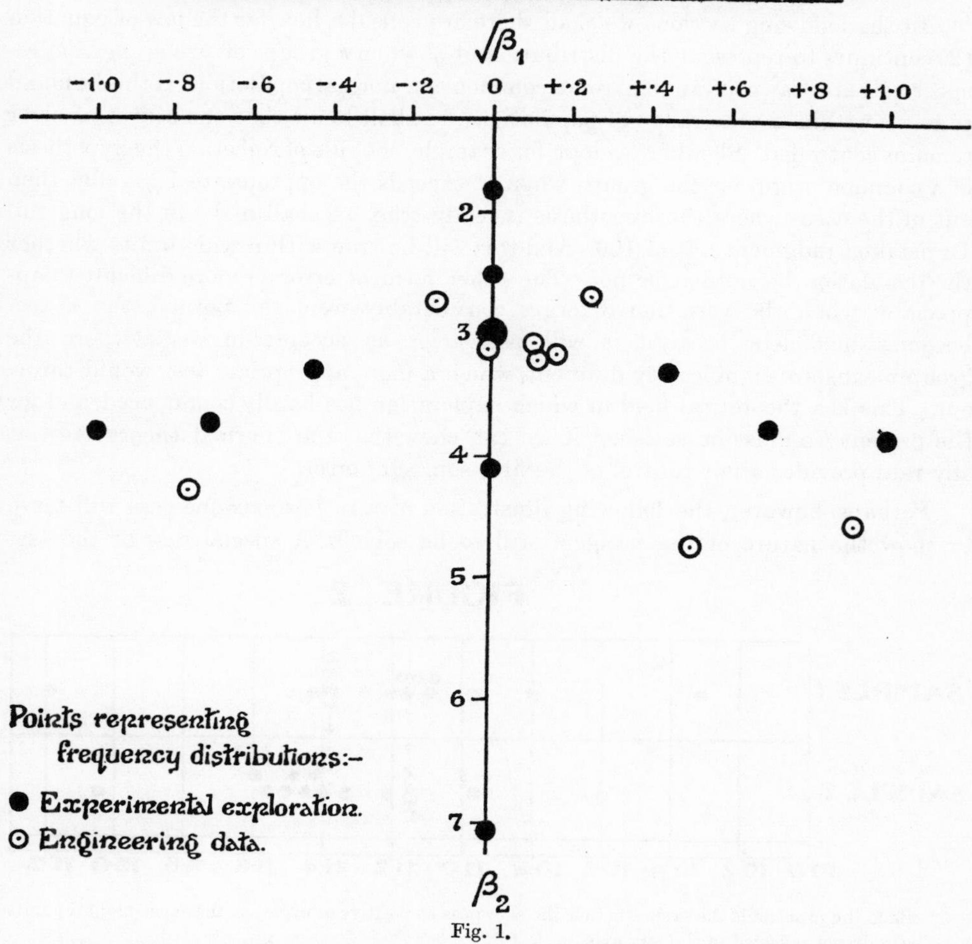

Fig. 1.

* See for example Table XXXVII*bis*, *Tables for Statisticians and Biometricians*, Part II.

shown that the sampling distribution of η^2 is remarkably insensitive to changes in population form. The field covered by this experimental work is shown in Figure 1, in which the solid black circles indicate the values of $\sqrt{\beta_1}$ and β_2 of the curves used to represent the population distributions*. I have also shown on this diagram the $(\sqrt{\beta_1}, \beta_2)$ points of a variety of frequency distributions each based on several hundred observations collected by the Bell Telephone Laboratories in the course of their work and kindly placed at my disposal by Dr W. A. Shewhart. Except for the point at $\sqrt{\beta_1} = -\cdot 760$, $\beta_2 = 4\cdot 317$ representing the example discussed above, Dr Shewhart informs me that the material was believed to be homogeneous, that is to say the underlying cause systems were constant. It will be seen that the experimental field represents a very fair sounding of that met on this practical experience. If some of the leptokurtic distributions found by "Student"† in problems of chemical analysis were added, the purpose of the trial point at $\sqrt{\beta_1} = 0$, $\beta_2 = 7\cdot 1$ would be realised.

In the following sections we shall therefore consider how far the law of equation (2) continues to represent the distribution of η^2 when k groups of size $n_1, n_2 \ldots n_k$ respectively are drawn at random from a common non-normal population. If this be found to be so within a wide range of populations we shall know that one source of error remains controlled. Should we adopt, for example, the rule of rejecting the hypothesis of a common origin for the groups when η^2 exceeds the appropriate 1 % value, then out of the cases where the hypothesis is really true, we shall make in the long run 1 mistaken judgment out of 100. And this will be true within wide limits whether the population be normal or not. The other form of error is more difficult to appreciate; when the variation diverges considerably from the normal, the η^2-test becomes inefficient because it will pass over as acceptable cases where the group means are significantly different, which a more appropriate test would throw out. This is a theoretical field in which exploration has hardly commenced, and for the present we must be satisfied if we can show that the "normal theory" test at any rate provides a fair control of the first source of error.

Perhaps, however, the following illustration of a rather extreme case will serve to show the nature of the problem still to be solved. A special case of the test

FIGURE 2.

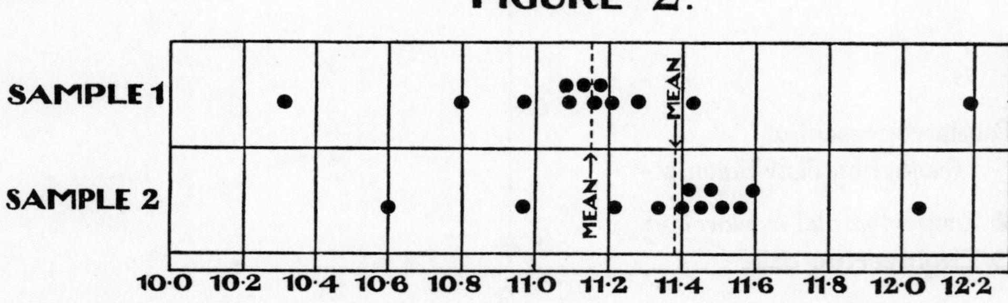

* Since the problem is the same whether the skewness be positive or negative, the experimental points have been drawn reflected in the $\sqrt{\beta_1}$ axis.

† See for example "Student's" paper on Routine Analysis, *Biometrika*, Vol. XIX. pp. 151—164.

occurs when $k=2$, and Fig. 2 represents diagrammatically two samples of 12 scaled observations, drawn it may be supposed from symmetrical, but very leptokurtic distributions. In this case

$$n_1 = n_2 = 12; \quad \text{Mean} \quad \bar{x}_1 = 11{\cdot}1517, \quad \bar{x}_2 = 11{\cdot}3825.$$
$$\text{Variances } s_1^2 = {\cdot}1709, \quad s_2^2 = {\cdot}1136.$$

We may ask whether the means differ significantly, assuming that the variances do not. The experimental results discussed below suggest that if the population value of β_2 is at any rate not greater than about 7, the distribution of the criterion t of equation (21) below will still follow approximately "Student's" law (22) below, if the samples have come from a common parent population.

It is found that $t = -1{\cdot}44$ and the tables* show that in as many as about 16 pairs of samples out of 100 a value of t outside the limits $\pm 1{\cdot}44$ would be reached through chance. Yet a glance at the diagram suggests that the hypothesis of a common origin for the samples is almost certainly untrue. In each sample there are two central blocks of points clustering about differently placed means; the two or three extreme points have however given high values to the standard deviations, leading to a relatively low value of t. In such a case in fact t is no longer an efficient criterion for the purpose of discrimination, because the standard deviation is not a satisfactory measure of variation when samples are drawn from very leptokurtic distributions.

(2) *A brief mathematical Analysis of the Position.*

In an earlier paper†, after giving a summary of R. A. Fisher's deduction of the distribution law of equation (2) above, I discussed briefly the possible effect of non-normality. It seems well to give here a brief summary of a somewhat more extensive analysis of the problem.

The "normal theory" proof depends upon the fact that

$$\theta = \eta^2 (1 - \eta^2) = h/q$$

is the ratio of two independent quantities,

$$h = \underset{x}{S} \{n_x (\bar{y}_x - \bar{y})^2\}/\sigma^2 \quad \text{.............................(5)},$$

$$q = \underset{x}{S} (n_x s_x^2)/\sigma^2 \quad \text{..................................(6)},$$

both of whose sampling distributions are Type III curves. To investigate the position more fully the values of Mean $(h) = h$, Mean $(q) = \bar{q}$, σ_h^2, σ_q^2 and $r_{hq}\sigma_h\sigma_q$ have been obtained, on the hypothesis that sets of k samples of size $n_1, n_2 \dots n_k$ are drawn randomly from a population distribution which is not normal‡. The results are as

* Student's Tables given in *Metron* v. 1925, pp. 113—128.

† *Biometrika*, Vol. XXI. pp. 338—344.

‡ This point should be remembered, namely, that we are considering the variation in θ or η^2 when repeated sets of samples are drawn in which the n_x's retain the same values from set to set. This is the situation contemplated when discussing a problem of group differentiation such as that illustrated in Table I. If the problem is one in which the n_x's should be thought of as varying from sample to sample, the position is not so simple, for in this case it is only when the variation is normal that the distributions of h and q are independent of n_x.

follows and they have been obtained by extending the method employed in section (4) of the paper referred to above. Equations (8) and (10) are in fact taken directly from pp. 343—44 of that paper.

$$\text{Mean }(h) = \bar{h} = k - 1 \quad \text{.........................(7)},$$

$$\text{Mean }(q) = \bar{q} = N - k \quad \text{.........................(8)}.$$

$$\sigma_h^2 = 2(k-1) + (\beta_2 - 3)\left\{\underset{x}{S}\left(\frac{1}{n_x}\right) + \frac{1-2k}{N}\right\} \quad \text{.................(9)},$$

$$\sigma_q^2 = 2(N-k) + (\beta_2 - 3)\left\{\underset{x}{S}\left(\frac{1}{n_x}\right) + N - 2k\right\} \quad \text{..............(10)},$$

$$r_{hq}\sigma_h\sigma_q = (\beta_2 - 3)\left\{k - 1 + \frac{k}{N} - \underset{x}{S}\left(\frac{1}{n_x}\right)\right\} \quad \text{.................(11)}.$$

In the simple but important case in which all the groups contain the same frequency, $k \times n_x = N$, $(x = 1, 2 \ldots k)$ or

$$\underset{x}{S}\{1/n_x\} = k^2/N \quad \text{..............................(12)},$$

and it follows that

$$\sigma_h^2 = 2(k-1)\{1 + \tfrac{1}{2}(\beta_2 - 3)(k-1)/N\} \quad \text{.................(13)},$$

$$\sigma_q^2 = 2(N-k)\{1 + \tfrac{1}{2}(\beta_2 - 3)(N-k)/N\} \quad \text{..............(14)},$$

$$r_{hq}\sigma_h\sigma_q = (\beta_2 - 3)(k-1)(N-k)/N \quad \text{.....................(15)}.$$

If $\beta_2 = 3$ it will be seen that $r_{hq} = 0$, and σ_h and σ_q assume the "normal theory" values of $\sqrt{2(k-1)}$ and $\sqrt{2(N-k)}$.

We are concerned with the sampling distribution of $\theta = \eta^2/(1 - \eta^2) = h/q$. Some appreciation of its change in form with β_2 can be obtained from approximations to its mean value and standard deviation. If we write $h = \bar{h} + \delta h$ and $q = \bar{q} + \delta q$, then

$$\theta = \frac{\bar{h}}{\bar{q}}\left\{1 + \frac{\delta h}{\bar{h}} - \frac{\delta q}{\bar{q}} + \frac{\delta q^2}{\bar{q}^2} - \frac{\delta h\,\delta q}{\bar{h}\bar{q}} \ldots\right\} \quad \text{.................(16)}.$$

Hence it follows that

$$\text{Mean }(\theta) = \frac{\bar{h}}{\bar{q}}\left\{1 + \frac{\sigma_q^2}{\bar{q}^2} - \frac{r_{hq}\sigma_h\sigma_q}{\bar{h}\bar{q}} + \ldots\right\} \quad \text{.......................(17)},$$

$$\text{Mean }(\theta^2) = \left(\frac{\bar{h}}{\bar{q}}\right)^2\left\{1 + \frac{\sigma_h^2}{\bar{h}^2} - \frac{4r_{hq}\sigma_h\sigma_q}{\bar{h}\bar{q}} + \frac{3\sigma_q^2}{\bar{q}^2} + \ldots\right\} \quad \text{...........(18)}.$$

If we may use (12), which will be a fairly good approximation even though the group frequencies are not exactly equal, it is found on inserting (7), (8), (13), (14) and (15) into (17) and (18) that *the coefficients of the terms in* $(\beta_2 - 3)$ *vanish*. In fact we obtain

$$\text{Mean }\theta = \frac{k-1}{N-k}\left\{1 + \frac{2}{N-k} + \ldots\right\}; \qquad \sigma_\theta^2 = \frac{2(k-1)(N-1)}{(N-k)^3} + \ldots \quad \text{...(19)}.$$

It follows that in so far as the relation (12) and the expansion (16) up to the second order terms only are adequate, the values of Mean θ and σ_θ are independent of the distribution of y. Consequently we should expect that the sampling distribution of θ—and therefore of η^2—will not be very sensitive to changes in population form, and this is confirmed by the experimental results considered below.

It is also of interest to note that the existence of a correlation between h and q when β_2 differs from 3 contributes to this result. In the different problem where we are comparing two essentially different estimates of variance, such as the variances s_1^2 and s_2^2 found in two independent samples, the distribution of the ratio is considerably more sensitive to changes in population form because of the absence of this correlation. This point will be illustrated in section (4) below.

(3) *Results of Experimental Sampling.*

The forms of the six population distributions used in sampling have been described elsewhere*. Fig. 3 shows the shapes of the four most extreme curves, while the $(\sqrt{\beta_1}, \beta_2)$ points are plotted in Fig. 1. They will be referred to as on p. 122 by their (β_1, β_2) values.

The distributions (0·0, 7·1) and (1·0, 3·8) are undoubtedly of rather extreme form, and in dealing with samples from these the standard deviation ceases to be a very efficient measure of variation. It appears, however, of interest to ascertain, even in such extreme cases, how far the sampling distributions of the various criteria used in statistical tests are still approximated to by the "normal theory" law.

The distribution of η^2 depends upon the number of groups or arrays, k, and the total size of the sample, N. I have chosen a series of values for k and N which is of course by no means exhaustive, and in the case where N is large, my material was not sufficient to provide many sets of samples. But a fairly wide field has been surveyed; and it has been the small sample field, simply because this is the most critical region in which divergences from "normal theory" may be expected to be greatest.

(*a*) *The Case* $k = 2$.

If there are only two groups, the problem reduces to that of testing the significance of the difference between the means of two samples. It is easy to show that the η^2 of (1) reduces so that

$$\theta = \eta^2/(1-\eta^2) = t^2/(n_1+n_2-2) \quad \text{.....................(20)},$$

where

$$t = \frac{\bar{y}_1 - \bar{y}_2}{\sqrt{\dfrac{n_1 s_1^2 + n_2 s_2^2}{n_1+n_2-2}\left(\dfrac{1}{n_1}+\dfrac{1}{n_2}\right)}} \quad \text{.........................(21)},$$

or is the ratio of the difference in means to a sample estimate of the standard error of this difference. Consequently η^2 will be distributed according to equation (2), if the distribution of $|t|$ (the positive value of t) between 0 and $+\infty$ follows the half of the appropriate "Student" Type VII curve (22). This point was examined in a previous paper† for certain of the experimental populations, in the cases

(i) $n_1 = 5$, $n_2 = 10$, (ii) $n_1 = 5$, $n_2 = 20$, and (iii) $n_1 = 10$, $n_2 = 20$.

* Five of them were described in *Biometrika*, Vol. XXI. p. 263. A sixth has been since added, namely, a very skew Type I distribution for which $\beta_1 = 0{\cdot}99$, $\beta_2 = 3{\cdot}83$ and with a standard deviation equal to 12·37 of the grouping units. Most of the sampling and a portion of the computing work on this population were undertaken by Prof. T. Kondo who kindly placed his results at my disposal. The detailed frequency distributions for the six cases have since been tabled by Dr J. M. le Roux, *Biometrika*, Vol. XXIII. p. 160.

† *Biometrika*, Vol. XXI. pp. 274—276. In that paper "Student's" original notation of z was used. The use of $t = z\sqrt{n_1+n_2-2}$, seems however more satisfactory.

Symmetrical Curves	(0·0, 2·5),	(0·0, 4·1),	(0·0, 7·1).
Type III Curves	(0·2, 3·3),	(0·5, 3·7).	
Type I Curve	(1·0, 3·8).		

DISTRIBUTION CURVES OF POPULATIONS SAMPLED.

MEAN = 100·0
STANDARD DEVIATION = 10·0

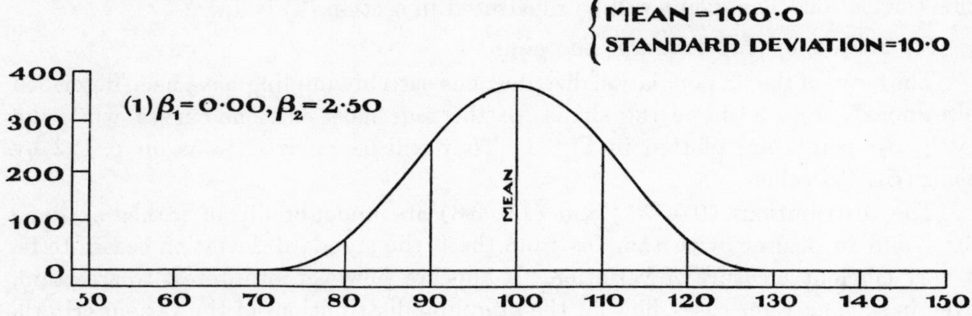

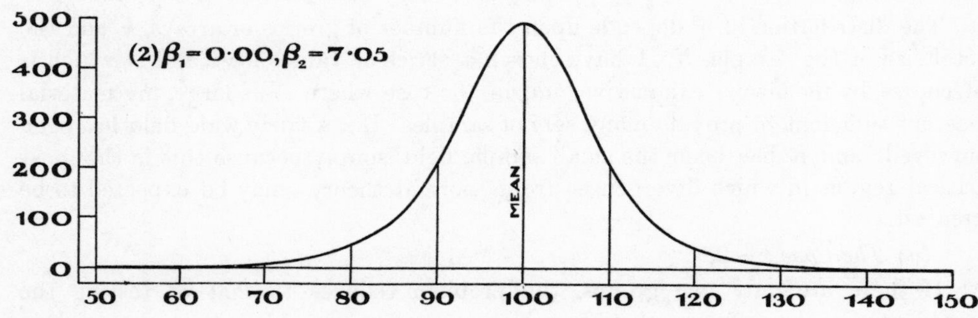

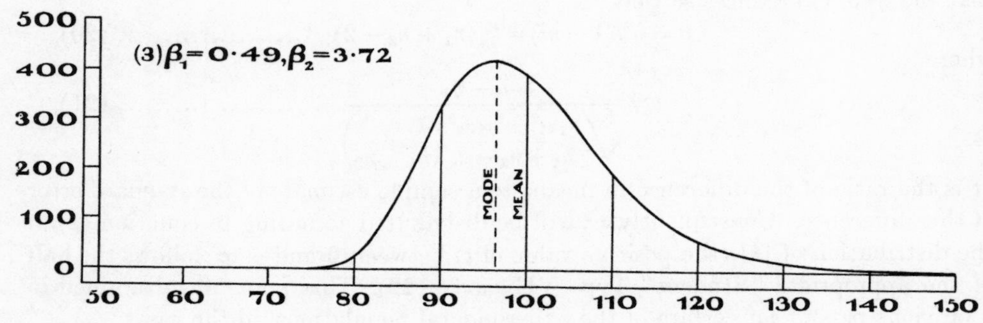

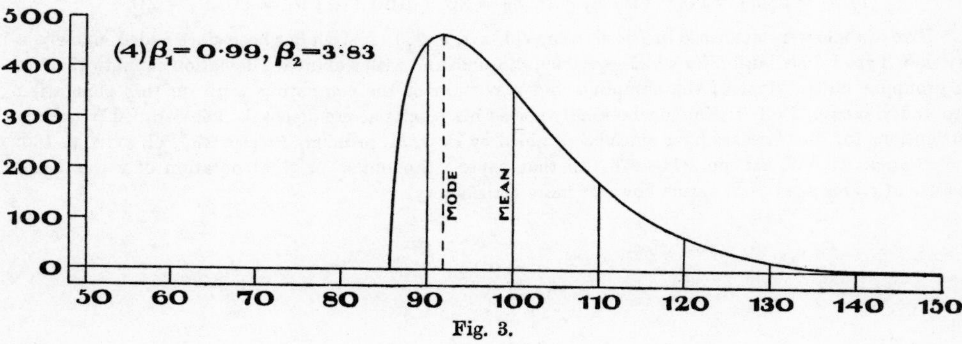

Fig. 3.

The results have since been somewhat extended and a summary of the most relevant information is given in Tables II and III below.

The observed sampling frequencies have been compared with three theoretical sets of values.

(1) Those obtained from "Student's" curve, namely

$$df = \text{constant}\,\{1 + t^2/(n_1 + n_2 - 2)\}^{-\frac{1}{2}(n_1+n_2-1)}\,dt \quad \text{..............(22).}$$

(2) Those obtained by assuming that t is adequately represented by a normal curve with standard deviation equal to the σ_t of equation (22), namely

$$\sigma_t = \sqrt{(n_1 + n_2 - 2)/(n_1 + n_2 - 4)}.$$

This is called "normal curve (a)" in Tables II and III.

(3) Those obtained by using $s_0^2 = (n_1 s_1^2 + n_2 s_2^2)/(n_1 + n_2)$, instead of

$$(n_1 s_1^2 + n_2 s_2^2)/(n_1 + n_2 - 2),$$

as an estimate of the unknown population σ^2, and consequently assuming that $\bar{y}_1 - \bar{y}_2$ is distributed in random samples with a standard error of $s_0 \sqrt{(n_1 + n_2)/n_1 n_2}$. This would lead to the supposition that the sampling distribution of t could be represented by a normal curve with standard deviation $\sqrt{(n_1 + n_2 - 2)/(n_1 + n_2)}$, and this curve gives the frequencies headed "normal curve (b)" in the tables.

TABLE II.

The Case of 2 *Groups.*

Frequencies in 500 Pairs of Samples.

e of Samples		$\lvert t\rvert$ greater than	Expected			Observed in Experimental Sampling from Populations						Average of Experimental Values
n_1	n_2		Student's curve	Normal curve (a)	Normal curve (b)	(0·0, 2·5)	(0·0, 4·1)	(0·0, 7·1)	(0·2, 3·3)	(0·5, 3·7)	(1·0, 3·8)	
5	5	2·400 3·400	21·6 4·7	18·8 1·6	3·6 0·07	30 8	21 2	21 5	17 4	16 6	12 2	19·5 4·5
5	10	2·208 2·944	22·9 5·7	21·1 3·4	8·9 0·78	15 7	21 3	35 7	22 5	23 6	24·5* 8*	23·4 6·0
5	20	2·145 2·788	21·4 5·2	20·2 3·9	12·7 1·8	23 6	21 3	23 4	23 6	18* 1·5*	20 3	21·3 3·9
0	10	2·100 2·850	25·0 5·3	23·9 3·6	13·4 1·3	— —	— —	— —	— —	— —	25 5	— —
0	20	2·160 2·808	19·7 4·4	18·7 3·4	12·7 1·8	25 8	17 5	19 5	25 6	19 3	20 7	20·8 5·7
0	20	1·962 2·615	28·6 6·4	28·1 5·4	22·1 3·6	— —	— —	— —	— —	24 7	— —	— —

* Figures reduced from 1000 observations.

TABLE III‡.

The Case of 2 Groups.

n_1, n_2		σ_t, Normal Theory	Observed in Experimental Sampling from Populations (0·0, 2·5)	(0·0, 4·1)	(0·0, 7·1)	(0·2, 3·3)	(0·5, 3·7)	(1·0, 3·8)
5, 5	σ_t	1·155	1·217	1·153	1·164	1·140	1·099	1·099
	(Obs. − Theo.)/S.E.		+1·29	−0·04	+0·19	−0·31	−1·17	−1·17
	Student's Curve χ^2		14·93	6·47	25·46	13·21	8·68	35·12
	Student's Curve P		·312	·925	·020	·432	·796	·002
	Normal Curve (*a*) χ^2		38·67	13·73	21·36	7·81	19·44	30·82
	Normal Curve (*a*) P		$<$·001	·394	·067	·855	·111	·004
5, 10	σ_t	1·087	1·089	1·086	1·196	1·090	1·090	1·107*
	(Obs. − Theo.)/S.E.		+0·05	−0·02	+2·72	+0·07	+0·07	+0·71
	Student's Curve χ^2		19·1†	13·33	31·0†	16·8†	12·9†	15·70
	Student's Curve P		·264	·649	·013	·401	·677	·614
	Normal Curve (*a*) χ^2		18·51	9·87	40·52	—	15·01	20·40
	Normal Curve (*a*) P		·296	·873	$<$·001	—	·524	·311
5, 20	σ_t	1·047	1·043	1·022	1·093	1·057	1·001*	1·042
	(Obs. − Theo.)/S.E.		−0·11	−0·69	+1·28	+0·28	−1·84	−0·14
	Student's Curve χ^2		9·0†	11·99	10·7†	11·5†	19·2†	10·99
	Student's Curve P		·620	·363	·465	·393	·085	·444
	Normal Curve (*a*) χ^2		10·06	14·36	9·71	—	18·06	9·35
	Normal Curve (*a*) P		·525	·215	·557	—	·114	·590
10, 20	σ_t	1·038	1·030	1·031	1·043	1·049	1·057	1·095
	(Obs. − Theo.)/S.E.		−0·23	−0·20	+0·14	+0·31	+0·54	+1·62
	Student's Curve χ^2		17·3†	7·07	4·7†	14·3†	16·4	11·42
	Student's Curve P		·099	·793	·943	·217	·128	·409
	Normal Curve (*a*) χ^2		21·49	7·38	5·01	—	13·83	10·52
	Normal Curve (*a*) P		·029	·766	·931	—	·243	·485

Additional Results		$n_1 = 10 = n_2$ Population (1·0, 3·8)	$n_1 = 20 = n_2$ Population (0·5, 3·7)
	σ_t Observed ...	1·076	1·019
	σ_t Normal Theory ...	1·061	1·027
	σ_t (Obs. − Theo.)/S.E.	+0·41	−0·24
	Student's Curve χ^2 ...	7·90	8·92
	Student's Curve P ...	·927	·629
	Normal Curve (*a*) χ^2 ...	7·68	7·57
	Normal Curve (*a*) P ...	·935	·750

* In these two cases the results have been based on 1000 pairs of samples; in all the remaining cases there were 500 pairs.

† The values of P only were available in these cases at the time of writing up the paper; values of χ^2 were obtained from these roughly by interpolating backwards in to Elderton's Tables.

‡ The data were regrouped since the forming of Tables IV (*a*), (*b*) and (*c*) in *Biometrika*, Vol. XXI. pp. 275—277, and consequently the values of (P, χ^2) differ somewhat.

The comparison is of importance, as it will suggest an answer to the question "*If the sampled population be not normal, is it an unwarranted refinement to use the probability integral of 'Student's' curve when dealing with small samples?*"

Limits for t were chosen as near as possible to the 5 °/。 and 1 °/。 points of "Student's" curve*, and Table II shows the frequency among 500 samples with which $|t|$ was both "expected" on the different hypotheses and observed in the experiments to exceed the limits indicated in the 3rd column. In Table III I have first compared the observed values of σ_t (i.e. the standard deviations of the complete distribution of t, not of $|t|$) with the "normal theory" value of

$$\sqrt{(n_1+n_2-2)/(n_1+n_2-4)}.$$

The quantity (Obs. − Theo.)/S.E. is the difference of these values divided by the standard error. For the latter the approximation $\frac{1}{2}\sigma_t\sqrt{({}_t\beta_2-3)/M}$ has been used, where M is the number of pairs of samples (500 in all cases but two), and ${}_t\beta_2$ is the appropriate constant for the curve (22), namely $3+6/(n_1+n_2-6)$. Afterwards are given the results of the (P, χ^2) test obtained on fitting half of "Student's" curve and half the normal curve (a) to the observed distributions of $|t|$†.

The conclusions which it appears possible to draw from a study of these Tables may be summarised as follows:

(1) The observed values of σ_t agree on the whole very closely with the "normal theory" values, and there is no clearly marked systematic discrepancy. Possibly in the case of very small samples there is a tendency for σ_t to be too great when the population is leptokurtic, and too small when it is skew, but the evidence is somewhat conflicting.

(2) An analysis of the results of the χ^2 tests, using "Student's" curve, again does not appear to bring out any systematic rule of divergence. Taken as a whole the values of χ^2 are higher than we should expect if the variation from theory was solely due to chance. Also the fits are on the whole better for the larger sized samples.

(3) Such differences as can be picked out between the fits with "Student's" curve and those with normal curve (a), are slightly in favour of the former in the case of the smallest samples. By the time n_1 and n_2 are both as great as 10, there is practically no difference between the two.

(4) The relative values of the different curves is brought out well in Table II. It will be seen that for the smallest samples, normal curve (a) allows for considerably too few extreme variations. Owing to the necessity of grouping up at the tails, this point is not shown in the results of the goodness of fit tests. For example, for the case $n_1=5=n_2$, "Student's" curve predicts that in 4·7 samples out of 500, $|t|>3·400$, while the normal curve (a) allows only 1·6. The observed six values were 8, 2, 5, 4,

* The ratio computed from the samples was not t, but a convenient multiple of this quantity. To obtain the frequency beyond the exact 5 °/。 and 1 °/。 points would have involved considerable extra labour, and is not essential to the argument.

† The number of groups used in the fitting were as follows:

$n_1=5=n_2$, 14 groups; $n_1=5$, $n_2=10$, 17 groups except in the case of Population—(1·0, 3·8) where 1000 pairs of samples were available and 19 groups were used; $n_1=5$, $n_2=20$, 12 groups (except for case (0·5, 3·7) where 13 were used); $n_1=10$, $n_2=20$, 12 groups; $n_1=10=n_2$, 16 groups; $n_1=20=n_2$, 12 groups.

6 and 2, giving an average of 4·5. The same situation will be observed for $n_1 = 5$, $n_2 = 10$. Taken as a whole the results suggest clearly that in dealing with very small samples, (say if $n_1 + n_2 < 20$), the use of the t-probability scale rather than the normal probability scale is justified, even if the population varies very considerably from the normal.

(5) The importance of adjusting the estimated standard error of the difference in means for the size of samples, is shown very clearly by the total inadequacy of prediction obtained in using normal curve (*b*) when the samples are small.

(*b*) *Cases with* $k > 2$.

In the following table crosses indicate the range of cases examined.

TABLE IV.

Populations sampled	20 groups of 2 ($N=40$, $k=2$)	10 groups of 4 ($N=40$, $k=4$)	5 groups of 5 ($N=25$, $k=5$)	10 groups of 5 ($N=50$, $k=5$)	10 groups of 10 ($N=100$, $k=10$)
Rectangular (0·0, 1·8)	—	×	—	—	—
(0·0, 2·5)	×	—	—	×	—
(0·0, 4·1)	×	—	—	×	—
(0·0, 7·1)	×	—	×	×	—
(0·5, 3·7)	×	—	×	—	×
(1·0, 3·8)	—	—	×	×	—

TABLE V (*a*).

20 *Groups of* 2.

Limits of η^2	Normal Theory Frequencies	Frequencies in Samples from Experimental Populations			
		(0·0, 2·5)	(0·0, 4·1)	(0·0, 7·1)	(0·5, 3·7)
Less than ·*30*	2·2	3	5	2	—
·*30*—·*34*	2·5	3	4	2	2
·*34*—·*38*	3·9	2	5	3	6
·*38*—·*42*	5·3	3	6	5	1
·*42*—·*46*	6·5	7	5	8	8
·*46*—·*50*	6·9	12	7	8	7
·*50*—·*54*	6·7	7	4	4	7
·*54*—·*58*	5·7	6	7	3	8
·*58*—·*62*	4·4	4	2	4	4
·*62*—·*66*	2·9	—	2	5	3
·*66*—·*70*	1·7	2	1	4	4
Greater than ·*70*	1·3	1	3	2	—
Totals	50·0	50	50	50	50
Mean η^2	·4872	·4816	·4628	·5036	·5048
σ_{η^2}	·1104	·1002	·1275	·1150	·0979
χ^2	—	4·62	5·00	4·01	1·64
P	—	·33	·29	·41	·80

Standard Errors for 50 Series: of Mean η^2, ·0156; of σ_{η^2}, ·0103.

The observed distributions of η^2 are compared with expected values calculated from equation (2) in Tables V (*a*), (*b*), (*c*), (*d*) and (*e*). The number of sets of samples used range only from 50 to 200; consequently no very critical analysis of the difference between observation and theory is possible, but there is enough evidence to show that even in the extreme cases the "normal theory" distribution of η^2 will give a very good practical approximation to the actual distribution found in sampling.

The following points are suggested by an examination of the tables.

(1) The deviations in Mean η^2 are not significant and do not appear to be systematic. For the leptokurtic populations, σ_{η^2} is probably significantly too large, and for the skew populations significantly too small*.

TABLE V (*b*).

5 *Groups of* 5.

Limits of η^2	Normal Theory Frequencies	Frequencies in Samples from Experimental Populations		
		(0·0, 7·1)	(0·5, 3·7)	(1·0, 3·8)
·00—·02	3·9 } 13·8	2 } 17	3 } 16	3 } 18
·02—·04	9·9 }	15 }	13 }	15 }
·04—·06	13·8	18	9	8
·06—·08	16·0	16	18	13
·08—·10	16·9	16	17	17
·10—·12	16·9	13	18	18
·12—·14	16·3	20	20	20
·14—·16	15·3	9	18	21
·16—·18	14·0	16	15	11
·18—·20	12·5	17	13	11
·20—·22	11·1	7	11	16
·22—·24	9·6	9	11	12
·24—·26	8·3	5	6	5
·26—·28	7·0	4	6	7
·28—·30	5·9 } 10·7	7 } 14	5 } 8	6 } 11
·30—·32	4·8 }	7 }	3 }	5 }
·32—·34	4·0 } 9·7	2 } 9	3 } 9	1 } 8
·34—·36	3·2 }	5 }	3 }	3 }
·36—·38	2·5 }	2 }	3 }	4 }
·38—·40	2·0 } 8·1	4 } 10	2 } 5	1 } 4
·40—·42	1·6 }	1 }	— }	1 }
·42—·44	1·2 }	3 }	1 }	— }
Greater than *·44*	3·3 }	2 }	2 }	2 }
Totals	200·0	200	200	200
Mean η^2	·1667	·1636	·1579	·1608
σ_{η^2}	·1034	·1060	·0932	·0932
χ^2	—	13·98	6·64	14·66
P	—	·53	·97	·48

Standard Errors for 200 Series: of Mean η^2, ·0073; of σ_{η^2}, ·0061.

* The standard error of mean η^2 is $\sigma_{\eta^2}/\sqrt{M}$, where M is the number of sets of samples used. For the standard error of σ_{η^2} the approximation $\frac{1}{2}\sigma_{\eta^2}\sqrt{({}_{\eta^2}\beta_2 - 1)/M}$ has been used, where the ${}_{\eta^2}\beta_2$ for equation (2) is taken from the equations (44) and (45) of *Biometrika*, Vol. XXI. p. 35.

TABLE V (*c*).

10 *Groups of* 5.

Limits of η^2	Normal Theory Frequencies		Frequencies in Samples from Experimental Populations							
			(0·0, 2·5)		(0·0, 4·1)		(0·0, 7·1)		(1·0, 3·8)	
Less than ·*04*	0·5		1		3		3		—	
·*04*—·*06*	1·9		2		2		2		1	
·*06*—·*08*	4·1	13·0	3	15	7	15	4	14	5	11
·*08*—·*10*	6·5		9		3		5		5	
·*10*—·*12*	8·6		10		7		9		10	
·*12*—·*14*	10·0		13		11		9		5	
·*14*—·*16*	10·6		14		6		10		16	
·*16*—·*18*	10·5		8		12		17		19	
·*18*—·*20*	9·7		7		10		5		9	
·*20*—·*22*	8·6	15·8	4	16	9	15	3	9	10	13
·*22*—·*24*	7·2		12		6		6		3	
·*24*—·*26*	5·9	10·5	6	7	4	8	5	14	7	9
·*26*—·*28*	4·6		1		4		9		2	
·*28*—·*30*	3·5		1		5		6		1	
·*30*—·*32*	2·6		2		4		2		2	
·*32*—·*34*	1·8		2		3		1		—	
·*34*—·*36*	1·3	11·3	1	10	1	16	—	13	4	8
·*36*—·*38*	0·8		1		1		2		—	
·*38*—·*40*	0·5		2		2		—		1	
Greater than ·*40*	0·8		1		—		2		—	
Totals	100·0		100		100		100		100	
Mean η^2	·1837		·1774		·1852		·1848		·1772	
σ_{η^2}	·0767		·0851		·0835		·0868		·0682	
χ^2	—		5·20		5·52		10·89		14·39	
P	—		·74		·70		·21		·07	

Standard Errors for 100 Series: of Mean η^2, ·0077; of σ_{η^2}, ·0059.

(2) Too much weight must not be placed on the results of the χ^2 tests. The groupings used at the ends of the distributions are indicated in the tables by brackets, except in the case of the 20 groups of 2, Table V (*a*) and the 10 groups of 4, Table V (*d*)*. The total value of χ^2 from the Tables V is 93·54 contributed by 13 different series containing a total of 115 groups. Were the "normal theory" law truly applicable in all cases, the expected or mean value of χ^2 for such a combined test would be as great as $115 - 13 = 102$. The observed value of 93·54 is therefore no more than might be expected through chance. But the necessity of clubbing together the extreme tail groups when applying the tests has rendered these not very critical.

* In the first case 5 groups were used in the χ^2 test; $\eta^2 < \cdot 40$; ·40—·46; ·46—·52; ·52—·58; $> \cdot 58$. In the second case 6 groups were used; $\eta^2 < \cdot 14$; ·14—·18; ·18—·22; ·22—·26; ·26—·32; $> \cdot 32$.

TABLE V (*d*) AND (*e*).

(*d*) 10 *Groups of* 4.

Rectangular Population (0·0, 1·8).

Limits of η^2	Normal Theory Frequencies	Experimental Frequencies
Less than ·08	1·4	2
·08—·12	4·0	6
·12—·16	6·8	3
·16—·20	8·3	8
·20—·24	8·4	12
·24—·28	7·2	5
·28—·32	5·5	4
·32—·36	3·8	7
·36—·40	2·3	—
·40—·44	1·2	2
Greater than ·44	1·1	1
Totals	50·0	50
Mean η^2	·2308	·2296
σ_{η^2}	·0931	·0928
χ^2	—	1·70
P	—	·88

(*e*) 10 *Groups of* 10.

Population (0·5, 3·7).

Limits of η^2	Normal Theory Frequencies	(grouped)	Experimental Frequencies	(grouped)
·00—·02	0·2		—	
·02—·04	3·4	11·8	2	16
·04—·06	8·2		14	
·06—·08	10·4		8	
·08—·10	9·7		5	
·10—·12	7·3		7	
·12—·14	4·8		6	
·14—·16	2·9		6	
·16—·18	1·6	10·8	1	14
·18—·20	0·8		—	
Greater than ·20	0·7		1	
Totals	50·0		50	
Mean η^2	·0909		·0930	
σ_{η^2}	·0405		·0429	
χ^2	—		5·29	
P	—		·26	

Standard Errors for 50 Series:

(*d*) of Mean η^2, ·0132; of σ_{η^2}, ·0098. (*e*) of Mean η^2, ·0057; of σ_{η^2}, ·0048.

(3) On comparing the detailed frequencies, we may observe the tendency noticed when examining σ_{η^2}, for too many high values of η^2 to occur when the population is leptokurtic and too few when it is skew. There also appear in several cases to be rather too many low values of η^2. This end of the distribution may sometimes be of importance, for in certain problems subnormal variation in the group means may be a feature requiring investigation.

(4) *A Comparative Case in which the Two Estimates of Variance are Essentially Independent.*

It is important to emphasise the fact that while in the problem we have considered the ratio of the two estimates of variance is not at all sensitive to changes in population form, this will not necessarily be the case in other problems. If two random samples of size n_1 and n_2, with variances s_1^2 and s_2^2, are randomly drawn from a parent *normal* population, and it is desired to test the hypothesis that the population variances are the same, we may calculate

$$x = n_1 s_1^2/(n_1 s_1^2 + n_2 s_2^2) \quad \text{..........................(23)}$$

and refer to the sampling distribution of x if the hypothesis be true, namely to the Type I curve*,

$$df = \text{constant}\, x^{\frac{1}{2}(n_1-1)-1}(1-x)^{\frac{1}{2}(n_2-1)-1}\,dx \qquad (24),$$

for which

$$\text{Mean } x = \frac{n_1-1}{n_1+n_2-2}, \qquad \sigma_x = \frac{1}{n_1+n_2-2}\sqrt{\frac{2(n_1-1)(n_2-1)}{n_1+n_2}} \qquad (25).$$

If the variation be normal the situation is exactly similar to that of the η^2 test, equation (24) corresponding to equation (2). But when the variables are no longer normally distributed, the correspondence ceases. In one case the two estimates of variance remain independent, in the other they become correlated. To illustrate this consider the case of 5 groups of 5 observations dealt with experimentally above. Here $\theta(N-k)/(k-1) = 5\theta$ is the ratio of two estimates of σ^2, one based on 4 and the other on 20 degrees of freedom. If the population be normal the distribution of η^2 will correspond exactly to that of the x of (23) if $n_1 = 5$ and $n_2 = 21$. I had not available samples of 5 and 21, but had 500 pairs of samples of 5 and 20 from the six experimental populations, and in Table VI have given a summary comparison of observation and "normal theory." If this table be compared with Table V (*b*), the difference in the position will be seen at once. The theoretical distribution of x fails completely to represent the observed distributions in the case of the populations (0·0, 4·1), (0·0, 7·1) and (1·0, 3·8). This is brought out by a comparison of the

TABLE VI.

Two Independent Samples, $n_1 = 5$, $n_2 = 20$.

Frequencies in 500 pairs of Samples.

Limits for $x = \frac{n_1 s_1^2}{n_1 s_1^2 + n_2 s_2^2}$	Expected on Normal Theory	Observed in Experimental Sampling Populations					
		(0·0, 2·5)	(0·0, 4·1)	(0·0, 7·1)	(0·2, 3·3)	(0·5, 3·7)	(1·0, 3·8)
x less than ·02	8·9	4	15	18	8	13	17
,, ,, ·04	31·8	28	47	60	29	45	50
x greater than ·38	24·3	15	40	51	37	25	41
,, ,, ·48	5·4	2	17	20	10	6	13
,, ,, ·56	1·1	1	7	9	5	2	3
Mean x	·1739	·1734	·1715	·1779	·1823	·1684	·1778
σ_x	·1072	·0973	·1262	·1418	·1185	·1090	·1240
χ^2 (using 21 groups)	—	21·44	51·31	86·91	20·57	13·17	52·21
P	—	·372	·0002	$<$·0001	·423	·869	·0002

Standard Errors for 500 pairs of samples: of Mean x, ·0048; of σ_x, ·0040.

* This is a modified form of R. A. Fisher's test, see *Statistical Methods for Research Workers*, pp. 194—196.

standard deviations; it will be seen that in passing from symmetrical platykurtic to symmetrical leptokurtic forms, σ_x changes from a value 10 °/₀ below "normal theory" to 30 °/₀ above*. Also the value in the case of (1·0, 3·8) differs from the theoretical σ_x by over 4 times the standard error. For the less extreme populations (0·0, 2·5), (0·2, 3·3) and (0·5, 3·7) the fit is more reasonable.

Further investigation is required to ascertain more precisely the limits of sample size and population form within which the test may be safely used; but the illustration should serve to emphasise the fact that certain of the "normal theory" tests can be used with greater confidence than others when dealing with samples from populations whose distribution laws are not certainly known.

(5) *The more Complex Problems in the Analysis of Variance.*

In the test that has been discussed, which was illustrated on the problem of Table I, we allow for the presence of a single factor, A, whose contribution, a_x, to y varies from group to group. That is to say, if $y_{t,x}$ be the tth observation in the xth group we suppose

$$y_{t,x} = a_x + Y_{t,x} \qquad \ldots\ldots\ldots\ldots(26),$$

where $Y_{t,x}$ is a random variation, and a_x is constant for all individuals in the xth group. And the method of investigation has consisted in testing the hypothesis that a_x does not vary with x, i.e. that the group means are not in fact differentiated.

In the more complex problems it is supposed that y is subject to a random term and to the sum of a number of terms due to different factors A, B, C, etc., so that

$$y_{t.\,x,y,z,\,\ldots} = a_x + b_y + c_z + \ldots + Y_{t.\,x,y,z} \qquad \ldots\ldots\ldots\ldots(27).$$

The exact values of a_x, b_y, etc. are not known, but the factors, if present, are to some extent under control so that we can collect a group of $n_{x,y,z,\ldots}$ observations all of which must contain the same value of a_x due to the A factor, the same value of b_y to the B factor, and so on.

There are a variety of problems in which the situation can be pictured as represented approximately in this manner. In addition to those in agricultural plot experimentation in connection with which the technique was first developed by R. A. Fisher, Tippett has for example recently applied the method in problems of textile research†. The essential idea in the process of analysis is to group the observations in such a way that it is possible to test separately for the presence of an A factor, a B factor, etc. This is done by obtaining in each case two estimates of the unknown variance, σ^2, of the residual term Y, which would differ only through chance fluctuations if that particular factor were either without influence or made the same contribution to every group.

It is not possible to enter here into the details of the method, but corresponding to the equations (5) and (6), the estimates may be written as proportional to two

* A similar trend is very clearly apparent in other cases I have examined, viz. $n_1=5=n_2$; $n_1=5$, $n_2=10$; $n_1=10$, $n_2=20$.

† L. H. C. Tippett, "Statistical Methods in Textile Research." *Shirley Institute Memoirs*, Vol. VIII. 1929.

quantities h and q, the first based on f_1 degrees of freedom, the second on f_2*. As long as the variation of the residual terms, Y, is normal and independent of the factors A, B, etc., these two estimates are independent, and each is distributed according to a Type III law, giving a Type VI law for the sampling distribution of their ratio. But such will not be exactly true if the variation in Y be not normal. Taking the case where the analysis is arranged to test for the presence of two factors, A and B, and where $n_{x,y}$ is constant for all combinations of x and y†, it is possible to show by an extension of the methods which lead to equations (7), (8), (13), (14) and (15), that

$$\left.\begin{array}{l} \bar{h}=f_1; \qquad \bar{q}=f_2 \\ \sigma_h^2=2f_1\{1+\tfrac{1}{2}(\beta_2-3)f_1/N\}; \quad \sigma_q^2=2f_2\{1+\tfrac{1}{2}(\beta_2-3)f_2/N\} \\ r_{hq}\sigma_h\sigma_q=(\beta_2-3)f_1f_2/N \end{array}\right\} \qquad \text{......(28)},$$

in which β_2 refers to the distribution of Y. Following the same procedure as in equations (16) to (19), we obtain for $\theta=h/q$,

$$\text{Mean } \theta=\frac{f_1}{f_2}\left\{1+\frac{2}{f_2}+\ldots\right\}; \qquad \sigma_\theta^2=\frac{2f_1(f_1+f_2)}{f_2^3}+\ldots \qquad \text{.........(29)},$$

or to this order of approximation, Mean θ and σ_θ will be independent of β_2. These results could probably be generalised to apply to the analysis employed when more than two factors are present, and they suggest that in all such cases the distribution of θ may not be very sensitive to changes in population form. But how far this approximation will really represent the situation in cases where as often in practice f_2 is a small number, it is not at present possible to say.

(6) *Summary.*

(i) The main problem which has been considered is that encountered in the simplest form of arrangement for the analysis of variance; it is the same problem as that of testing the significance of η^2. In practice the worker may either know that the variation in his populations is not exactly normal, or it may be that he has no means of being certain of the precise form of this variation at all. He therefore needs to feel some confidence that the test which he applies will not be invalid provided that the deviation from normality is not extreme.

(ii) There is no doubt that in such cases the sampling distribution of η^2 if expressed in exact mathematical form would be found to differ from the "normal theory" law. But in practical statistics measures of probability are usually not required on a very fine scale, and the results of this paper suggest that within the range of the experimental populations indicated in Fig. 1, η^2 is adequately represented for very many purposes by this law.

ııi) This will mean that in applying the test we shall not be liable to make unexpected errors by rejecting the hypothesis of a common origin of the groups, when in fact it is true. But in the more extreme cases of non-normal variation,

* In the simple problem discussed $f_1=k-1$, $f_2=N-k$.

† This condition is not in fact very limiting as experiments will generally be arranged in this form.

where the standard deviation becomes an unsatisfactory measure of variability, there will always be a danger of accepting the hypothesis when some more efficient test (yet to be devised!) would enable us to pick out a real difference.

(iv) The case in which the variation changes from one group to another has not been considered here.

(v) The problem of testing the significance of the difference in the variances of two independent samples must be distinguished from that dealt with. The sampling distributions of the criteria are only the same when the variation is normal. This other test has been found in small samples to be considerably more sensitive to changes in population form than is the η^2 test.

(vi) It seems probable that the more elaborate forms of analysis of variance are also of fairly wide application, provided that the number of degrees of freedom apportioned to the residual variation is not too small.

I should like again to thank Mrs L. J. Comrie for her very efficient performance of the greater part of the computing; also for their share in the calculating or sampling, Miss Augusta Jones, Mr Ernest Martin and Mr A. E. Stone; for Fig. 1, Mrs F. Larmor, and for Figs. 2 and 3, Miss E. Irvine.

METHODS OF STATISTICAL ANALYSIS APPROPRIATE FOR k SAMPLES OF TWO VARIABLES.

By E. S. PEARSON, D.Sc. and S. S. WILKS*, Ph.D.

CONTENTS.

I. Introduction.

(1) *The Testing of Statistical Hypotheses.* Statistical theory which is not purely descriptive is largely concerned with the development of tools which will assist in the determination from observed events of the probable nature of the underlying cause system that controls them. The measured characteristics of quality vary from unit to unit, and the statistical technique is required to analyse this variation and covariation to break it into parts with which may be associated assignable causes, to test and compare alternative hypotheses, and to express the resulting conclusions in terms of measures of probability. It will be found that some of the most recent generalisation of theory has resulted from an attempt to provide critical tests of increasingly complex hypotheses. We may trace the development through a chain of questionings: Is it likely, (*a*) that this sample has been drawn from a specified population, P; (*b*) that these two samples have come from a common but unspecified population; (*c*) that these k samples have come from a common but unspecified population? Again the population P may be (*d*) completely specified or, (*e*) only partly specified, e.g. its mean is given but not its standard deviation; or when there are a number of samples we may allow the means in the sampled population to be different and question whether the standard deviations are the same. Another line of advance is from (*f*) problems dealing only with a single variable, to (*g*) those in which there may be a number of correlated variables.

Now we may frankly admit that in so far as the technique is to be used in handling data broken up into small groups, the recent theoretical developments assume normal variation. But to place the procedure for testing statistical hypotheses on a firm logical basis under one set of simplified conditions, is in itself an

* International Research Fellow in Mathematics.

achievement of some value, and perhaps the most practical line of advance is the following:

(*a*) To establish what we may term "normal theory."

(*b*) To study in a more systematic way than has been attempted the extent of departure from normality met with in different fields of application.

(*c*) To examine how rapidly normal theory tests become inefficient as the form of variation and covariation departs from the normal, and to determine the nature of the errors in judgment that will arise if these tests are still used.

(2) *The Analysis of Variance.* R. A. Fisher's methods of Analysis of Variance may be regarded from the following viewpoint:

(*a*) In any given problem it will generally be possible to specify certain factors which may be the cause of part of the variation, while there will be a residual part which, in the state of knowledge at the moment, must be regarded as due to unidentifiable or chance causes.

(*b*) An experiment may be designed to test whether a certain factor is operative or not; for example:

(i) Do differences in manurial treatment affect the yield of some variety of cereal?

(ii) Does modification in the production process alter the quality of output of some manufactured product?

(*c*) At the same time, in addition to these factors whose influence is under investigation, there may be other assignable causes of variation inevitably present, the effect of which would be obscuring were it not eliminated. Thus, for example, in the illustrations given above, there might be

(i) Variation due to changing soil fertility.

(ii) Variation due to differences in the skill of operatives or in the state of wear of machines.

(*d*) It follows that it is often possible to regard the variation in a character x as made up of parts due to different assignable causes A, B, C, ..., and of a residual part which, for the time being, we must attribute to chance causes. This may be expressed as follows:

$$x_{t.u,v,w,...} = a_u + b_v + c_w + \ldots + X_{t.u,v,w,...} \quad \text{..................(1),*}$$

where $x_{t.u,v,w,...}$ is the character of the t-th individual of a group of $n_{u,v,w,...}$, all of which receive the same contribution a_u from the A factor, the same contribution b_v from the B factor and so on. $X_{t.u,v,w,...}$ represents the residual term. In so far as the causes of variation are assignable, this grouping is possible.

* [The reader must bear in mind that for (1) to be true the effect of the causes A, B, C, ... on the character x must be *additive*. For example, the real effect of A and B might lead to a ratio a_u/b_v in the expression for $x_{t.u,v,w,...}$, in which case the assumption of an additive relation would involve the influence of A, B, C, ... appearing in $X_{t.u,v,w,...}$. Ed.]

(*e*) The technique of analysis consists in arranging the data so as to test separately for the presence of an A factor, or a B factor, etc. as desired. This is effected by obtaining in each case two estimates of the unknown variance, σ^2, of the residuals X, which would differ only through chance fluctuations if changes in the particular factor had no influence on variation within the limits covered by the experiment.

This method of analysis is based upon the assumptions that the residuals X, (*a*) are normally distributed, and (*b*) have the same standard deviation, σ, whatever be the values of the terms a, b, c, etc., that is to say, for all combinations of the assignable causes. We may be justified in accepting this to be the true position in very many practical cases, but it should be recognised that the method outlined above does not put these assumptions to the test. There are indeed a number of problems in which (*b*) is not true and where the discovery of significant differences, from group to group, in the variation among the individuals, X, may lead to the identification of further assignable causes of variation. Such has been found to be the case, for example, in the analysis of variation in quality of articles in mass-production industry. Further, we may be concerned not only with a single variable x, but with a number of correlated variables $x, y, z, \ldots$, and we may then need to examine the stability from group to group of the covariation as well as the variation among residuals $X, Y, Z, \ldots$.

(3) *An Illustration of the Problem.* The purpose of this paper is to develop certain methods recently suggested for dealing with these problems*. We shall treat here only the case of two correlated variables x and y, and shall suppose that the observations have been divided into k samples or groups. The problem will be to test whether these groups can be differentiated owing to significant differences either in the average values of x and y, or in the variation and covariation of the residuals within the groups. The choice of suitable criteria, i.e. of the tests to be applied, has been based upon the use of the principle of likelihood as suggested by J. Neyman and E. S. Pearson. More recently† these writers have suggested a more fundamental method of determining the most efficient test of a statistical hypothesis; this method of choice has been shown in many cases to be identical with the method of likelihood, but in the particular problems we are now considering the correspondence has not yet been established.

The following example, which is treated more fully below, will indicate the nature of the problem. In certain cases of manufacture tests of quality are destructive. Such, for example, is a test for breaking strength; it is therefore important to find an alternative correlated measure which may be used in its place in routine testing. In dealing with metal products a measure of hardness, based on a test which is not destructive, is sometimes used as an index of tensile strength. If,

* For the case of a single variable: see J. Neyman and E. S. Pearson: *Bulletin de l'Académie Polonaise des Sciences et des Lettres*, Série A, 1930 and 1931. For the case of many variables, see S. S. Wilks: *Biometrika*, Vol. XXIV (1932), pp. 471—494.

† *Phil. Trans. of the Royal Soc.*, Series A, Vol. 231, pp. 289—337.

however, we are to predict strength from hardness, using the correlation method, it is essential that the degree of relationship between the two qualities should remain stable. It must not change from one plant to another or from one month to the next; in other words a preliminary research investigation should not only be concerned with changes in average strength and hardness which can be attributed to assignable causes, but also with the stability of the covariation among the residuals X and Y. Table I shows a preliminary statistical analysis of 60 pairs of test results made on a certain aluminium die-casting, divided into 5 groups of 12 pairs. Within a group the assignable causes of variation are believed to be constant, but it is necessary to analyze not only the figures in the 2nd and 4th columns, but also those in the 3rd, 5th and 6th.

TABLE I.

Data for Aluminium Die-Castings. (Samples of 12 observations.)*

Sample No.	Tensile Strength (10^3 lb. per sq. in.)		Hardness (Rockwell's E)		Coefficient of Correlation
	Mean	Standard Deviation	Mean	Standard Deviation	
1	33·399	2·565	68·49	10·19	0·683
2	28·216	4·318	68·02	14·49	0·876
3	30·313	2·188	66·57	10·17	0·714
4	33·150	3·954	76·12	11·08	0·715
5	34·269	2·715	69·92	9·88	0·805

II. Derivation of the Criteria.

(4) We shall suppose that each of k samples, $\Sigma_1, \Sigma_2, \ldots \Sigma_k$, of two variables x and y has been drawn from some normal population. Let π_t be the population from which Σ_t has been drawn and let the means of x and y in π_t be a_t and b_t, the standard deviations σ_{xt} and σ_{yt} and the correlation coefficient $\rho_t\,(t=1, 2, \ldots k)$. Thus, the distribution law of π_t will be

$$\frac{1}{2\pi\sigma_{xt}\sigma_{yt}\sqrt{1-\rho_t^2}}\,e^{-\frac{1}{2(1-\rho_t^2)}\left[\frac{(x-a_t)^2}{\sigma_{xt}^2}+\frac{(y-b_t)^2}{\sigma_{yt}^2}-\frac{2\rho_t(x-a_t)(y-b_t)}{\sigma_{xt}\sigma_{yt}}\right]} \quad \ldots\ldots(2).$$

Therefore, the probability of the joint occurrence of the samples Σ_t from their respective populations $\pi_t\,(t=1, 2, \ldots k)$, with values of x and y falling in the intervals $x_{ta} \pm dx_{ta}$, $y_{ta} \pm dy_{ta}$ $(\alpha=1, 2, \ldots n_t,\ t=1, 2, \ldots k)$ will be given, except for infinitesimals of higher order than dx_{ta} and dy_{ta}, by

$$C=\prod_{t=1}^{k}\left(\frac{1}{2\pi\sigma_{xt}\sigma_{yt}\sqrt{1-\rho_t^2}}\right)^{n_t} e^{-\theta}\,dX\,dY \quad \ldots\ldots\ldots\ldots\ldots\ldots(3),$$

* The data are taken from W. A. Shewhart's *Economic Control of Manufactured Product*, Macmillan 1931. Although they would hardly be adequate for a research investigation in practice, they are suggestive and provide a good illustration of method.

in which

$$\theta=\sum_{t=1}^{k} n_t\left[\frac{s_{xt}^2+(\bar{x}_t-a_t)^2}{2\sigma_{xt}^2(1-\rho_t^2)}+\frac{s_{yt}^2+(\bar{y}_t-b_t)^2}{2\sigma_{yt}^2(1-\rho_t^2)}-\frac{2\rho_t\left[s_{xt}s_{yt}r_t+(\bar{x}_t-a_t)(\bar{y}_t-b_t)\right]}{2\sigma_{xt}\sigma_{yt}(1-\rho_t^2)}\right] \quad (4),$$

where $\bar{x}_t$ and $\bar{y}_t$ are the means, s_{xt} and s_{yt} the standard deviations*, r_t the correlation coefficient of x and y, and n_t the number of individuals in the sample Σ_t, and

$$dX\,dY=\prod_{t=1}^{k}\prod_{a=1}^{n_t} dx_{ta}\,dy_{ta} \quad \text{.............................(5).}$$

We shall now consider the derivation of criteria for testing the following three hypotheses concerning the populations π_t:

(i) The hypothesis H that the populations π_t are identical, that is, that

$$\sigma_{xt}=\sigma_x, \quad \sigma_{yt}=\sigma_y, \quad \rho_t=\rho \quad \text{..........................(6),}$$

$$a_t=a, \quad b_t=b \qquad (t=1, 2, \ldots k) \quad \text{...........(7).}$$

(ii) The hypothesis H_1 that the samples have come from populations with the same set of variances and correlations but having means with any differing values whatever, that is, that (6) is true whatever may be the values of the means a_t and b_t.

(iii) The hypothesis H_2 that the samples are from populations in which (7) is true, when it is assumed that (6) is true.

These are generalisations to two variables of the three hypotheses considered by Neyman and Pearson† for the case of k samples of a single variable; or they may be regarded as special cases of the more general problem whose solution has been considered more recently by Wilks‡. Thus, it will only be necessary to indicate briefly the steps involved in applying the method of likelihood to determine criteria appropriate in testing H, H_1 and H_2. In each case we must fix:

(*a*) The class Ω of admissible sets of populations π_t $(t=1, 2, \ldots k)$ from one set of which the set of samples Σ_t is assumed to have been drawn.

(*b*) The subclass ω of Ω to which the set π_t must belong if the hypothesis tested be true.

Then we must find the maximum of C in (3) for variations of the population parameters under the assumption that the set π_t is (i) a member of Ω; call this $C(\Omega \max)$; and (ii) a member of ω; this we call $C(\omega \max)$. Then the expression for the likelihood of the composite hypothesis H has been defined to be

$$\lambda_H=\frac{C(\omega \max)}{C(\Omega \max)} \quad \text{................................(8).}$$

Let us consider this λ-criterion for each of the hypotheses H, H_1 and H_2.

* Here and throughout the paper the standard deviation in a sample of n will be defined by the relation $ns^2=\Sigma(x-\bar{x})^2$.

† *Bulletin de l'Académie Polonaise des Sciences et des Lettres*, Série A, 1931.

‡ *Loc. cit.*

(i) Criterion for H. We find that $C(\Omega \text{ max})$ occurs when

$$a_t = \bar{x}_t, \quad b_t = \bar{y}_t \quad \text{.................................(9)},$$

$$\sigma_{xt} = s_{xt}, \quad \sigma_{yt} = s_{yt}, \quad \rho_t = r_t \qquad (t = 1, 2, \dots k) \quad (10),$$

and $C(\omega \text{ max})$ occurs when

$$a = \bar{x}_0, \quad b = \bar{y}_0 \quad \text{.................................(11)},$$

$$\sigma_x^2 = v_{110} = v_{11a} + v_{11m}, \;. \; \sigma_y^2 = v_{220} + v_{22m}, \quad \sigma_x \sigma_y \rho = v_{120} = v_{12a} + v_{12m} \;\dots(12),$$

where

$$\bar{x}_0 = \frac{1}{N} \sum_{t=1}^{k} n_t \bar{x}_t, \quad \bar{y} = \frac{1}{N} \sum_{t=1}^{k} n_t \bar{y}_t \quad \text{.......................(13)},$$

$$\left.\begin{aligned} N v_{110} &= \sum_{t=1}^{k} \sum_{a=1}^{n_t} (x_{ta} - \bar{x}_0)^2 = N s_{x0}^2 \\ N v_{220} &= \sum_{t=1}^{k} \sum_{a=1}^{n_t} (y_{ta} - \bar{y}_0)^2 = N s_{y0}^2 \\ N v_{120} &= \sum_{t=1}^{k} \sum_{a=1}^{n_t} (x_{ta} - \bar{x}_0)(y_{ta} - \bar{y}_0) = N s_{x0} s_{y0} r_0 \end{aligned}\right\} \quad \text{...............(14)},$$

that is to say $\bar{x}_0$, $\bar{y}_0$, s_{x0}, s_{y0} and r_0 are the means, standard deviations and correlation coefficient obtained on combining the N pairs of observations from the k samples. Further

$$\left.\begin{aligned} N v_{11a} &= \sum_{t=1}^{k} \sum_{a=1}^{n_t} (x_{ta} - \bar{x}_t)^2 = \sum_{t=1}^{k} n_t s_{xt}^2 \\ N v_{22a} &= \sum_{t=1}^{k} \sum_{a=1}^{n_t} (y_{ta} - \bar{y}_t)^2 = \sum_{t=1}^{k} n_t s_{yt}^2 \\ N v_{12a} &= \sum_{t=1}^{k} \sum_{a=1}^{n_t} (x_{ta} - \bar{x}_t)(y_{ta} - \bar{y}_t) = \sum_{t=1}^{k} n_t s_{xt} s_{yt} r_t \end{aligned}\right\} \quad \text{............(15)},$$

$$N v_{11m} = \sum_{t=1}^{k} n_t (\bar{x}_t - \bar{x}_0)^2, \quad N v_{22m} = \sum_{t=1}^{k} n_t (\bar{y}_t - \bar{y}_0)^2, \quad N v_{12m} = \sum_{t=1}^{k} n_t (\bar{x}_t - \bar{x}_0)(\bar{y}_t - \bar{y}_0) \quad \text{......(16)}.$$

We shall write for each sample $(t = 1, 2, \dots k)$

$$\left.\begin{aligned} n_t v_{11t} &= \sum_{a=1}^{n_t} (x_{ta} - \bar{x}_t)^2 = n_t s_{xt}^2, \quad n_t v_{22t} = \sum_{a=1}^{n_t} (y_{ta} - \bar{y}_t)^2 = n_t s_{yt}^2 \\ n_t v_{12t} &= \sum_{a=1}^{n_t} (x_{ta} - \bar{x}_t)(y_{ta} - \bar{y}_t) = n_t s_{xt} s_{yt} r_t \end{aligned}\right\} \quad \text{......(17)}.$$

Placing these values in (3) and taking the ratio as defined by (8) we find,

$$\lambda_H = \prod_{t=1}^{k} \left[\frac{|v_{ijt}|}{|v_{ij0}|} \right]^{\frac{n_t}{2}} \quad \text{.............................(18)},$$

where*

$$|v_{ijt}| = \begin{vmatrix} v_{11t} & v_{12t} \\ v_{12t} & v_{22t} \end{vmatrix} = s_{xt}^2 s_{yt}^2 (1 - r_t^2) \quad \text{....................(19)},$$

$$|v_{ij0}| = \begin{vmatrix} v_{110} & v_{120} \\ v_{120} & v_{220} \end{vmatrix} = s_{x0}^2 s_{y0}^2 (1 - r_0^2) \quad \text{....................(20)},$$

* For convenience we shall call $|v_{ijt}|$ the generalised variance of the tth sample with elements having $n_t - 1$ degrees of freedom. Similarly, $|v_{ij0}|$, $|v_{ijm}|$ and $|v_{ija}|$ will be generalised variances derived from the combined samples, with elements having $N-1$, $k-1$ and $N-k$ degrees of freedom respectively.

(ii) Criterion for H_1. We find that $C(\Omega \max)$ occurs for the same values of the parameters as in the case of H, namely, those given by (9) and (10). $C(\omega \max)$ occurs when (9) is true and when

$$\sigma_x^2 = v_{11a}, \quad \sigma_y^2 = v_{22a}, \quad \sigma_x \sigma_y \rho = v_{12a} \quad \text{.....................(21).}$$

Thus it follows that

$$\lambda_{H_1} = \prod_{t=1}^{k} \left[\frac{|v_{ijt}|}{|v_{ija}|} \right]^{\frac{n_t}{2}} \quad \text{..............................(22),}$$

where $|v_{ija}|$ is a determinant analogous to those of (19) and (20).

(iii) Criterion for H_2. $C(\Omega \max)$ occurs when (9) and (21) are satisfied and $C(\omega \max)$ when the parameters have the values (11) and (12). Consequently

$$\lambda_{H_2} = \left[\frac{|v_{ija}|}{|v_{ija} + v_{ijm}|} \right]^{\frac{N}{2}} = \left[\frac{|v_{ija}|}{|v_{ij0}|} \right]^{\frac{N}{2}} \quad \text{.....................(23)}$$

As in the case of the single-variable problem we observe that

$$\lambda_H = \lambda_{H_1} \times \lambda_{H_2} \quad \text{..................................(24).}$$

III. INTERPRETATION OF THE CRITERIA.

(5) *The H_2 test.* We note that the structure of each of the λ's given by (18), (22) and (23) differs from that of the corresponding λ of the single-variable problem only in that determinants of the second order matrices of variances and covariances appear in place of the corresponding sums of squares in the single-variable case. In other words, determinants of the second order now take the place of determinants of the first order.

We shall first examine λ_{H_2}; in testing H_2 we have assumed that (6) is true and logically we should first consider the grounds for this assumption, if necessary by testing H_1. The test of H_2 is, however, related to R. A. Fisher's tests in the analysis of variance, and it will be clearer to consider this first.

A λ-criterion must lie between 0 and 1, and if the principle underlying the selection is valid, as it decreases from unity towards zero we should be more and more inclined to reject the hypothesis tested in favour of some one of the admissible alternative hypotheses. How far do our intuitional requirements appear satisfied by λ_{H_2}? The ratio of determinants

$$\lambda_{H_2}^{2/N} = \frac{|v_{ija}|}{|v_{ija} + v_{ijm}|} \quad \text{..............................(25)}$$

is of the form of the ratio ψ of Theorem I of the Appendix, if we set $v_{ija} = A_{ij}$, and

$$\sqrt{\frac{n_t}{N}}\,(\bar{x}_t - \bar{x}_0) = \eta_{1t}, \qquad \sqrt{\frac{n_t}{N}}\,(\bar{y}_t - \bar{y}_0) = \eta_{2t} \quad \text{..............(26).}$$

It follows that

(a) $0 \leqslant \lambda_{H_2} \leqslant 1$; and when $|v_{ija}| > 0$;

(b) a necessary and sufficient condition for $\lambda_{H_2} = 1$ is that $\bar{x}_t = \bar{x}_0$, $\bar{y}_t = \bar{y}_0$ $(t = 1, 2, \dots k)$, that is, that all the sample means be the same;

(*c*) a necessary and sufficient condition that $\lambda_{H_2}=0$ is that at least one of the differences $\bar{x}_t-\bar{x}_0$, $\bar{y}_t-\bar{y}_0$ $(t=1, 2, \ldots k)$ be infinite.

It can also be shown by the ordinary methods of differentiation that λ_{H_2} cannot have any other maximum but that of unity (occuring when $\bar{x}_t=\bar{x}_0$ and $\bar{y}_t=\bar{y}_0$) for any given values of the v_{ija}. In fact the maximum is the only stationary point. Therefore, if we keep the intra-sample variation the same, and allow the system to vary from one in which all of the sample means are equal to the other extreme in which at least one sample mean differs very greatly from the mean of the whole, λ_{H_2} will at the same time decrease from 1 to 0.

The case where $$|v_{ija}|=0 \quad \text{.................................(27)}$$ needs special consideration. The determinant is essentially of the form

$$\begin{vmatrix} \Sigma\, \xi_{ta}^2 & \Sigma\, \xi_{ta}\,\eta_{ta} \\ \Sigma\, \xi_{ta}\,\eta_{ta} & \Sigma\, \eta_{ta}^2 \end{vmatrix} \quad \text{..............................(28)},$$

where $$\Sigma=\sum_{t=1}^{k}\sum_{a=1}^{n_t},\quad \xi_{ta}=\frac{(x_{ta}-\bar{x}_t)}{\sqrt{N}} \text{ and } \eta_{ta}=\frac{(y_{ta}-\bar{y}_t)}{\sqrt{N}};$$

which can vanish only when $\xi_{ta}=c\eta_{ta}$, i.e. when $x_{ta}-\bar{x}_t=c\,(y_{ta}-\bar{y}_t)$ where c is a constant for all t and a, which may be finite or infinite. In this case the observation points (x_{ta}, y_{ta}) for each sample lie on a straight line, and the lines are all parallel. If $c=0$ the lines will be horizontal as in Fig. 1 (*a*), if $c=\pm\infty$ they will be vertical as in (*b*), otherwise they will be sloping as in (*c*)*. Hypothesis H_2 is exceedingly improbable (and $\lambda_{H_2}=0$) unless these lines coincide, which will occur only when

$$x_{ta}-\bar{x}_0=c\,(y_{ta}-\bar{y}_0),$$

that is when $\bar{x}_t-\bar{x}_0=c\,(\bar{y}_t-\bar{y}_0)$. In this case $\lambda_{H_2}=0/0$, and we are really reduced to a single-variable problem, and could apply the appropriate H_2 test for that case. It appears therefore that the criterion λ_{H_2} does satisfy our intuitional requirements, at any rate as far as the limiting values 1 and 0 are concerned.

(6) *Alternatives to* λ_{H_2}. In the one-variable problem λ_{H_2} is expressible in terms of η^2, the squared correlation ratio, and hence also in terms of $1-\eta^2$†. In fact, using the present notation, and considering the x variable only,

$$\frac{v_{11m}}{v_{11a}+v_{11m}}=\eta^2,\qquad \frac{v_{11a}}{v_{11a}+v_{11m}}=1-\eta^2 \quad \text{..................(29)},$$

and consequently it is immaterial which of the two ratios is regarded as the criterion. In the case of two variables the corresponding ratios will be

$$\frac{|v_{ijm}|}{|v_{ija}+v_{ijm}|}=U_2^2,\qquad \frac{|v_{ija}|}{|v_{ija}+v_{ijm}|}=\lambda_{H_2}^{2/N}=L_2^2 \quad \text{..............(30)},$$

but here U_2 cannot be expressed as a single valued function of L_2. As will be shown below, the sampling distributions of both L_2 and U_2 are very simple functions, and it is natural to ask whether U_2 might be used as an alternative criterion

* In the diagram the spots represent observation points (x, y) and the circles represent means of samples.

† Actually $\lambda_{H_2}^{2/N}=1-\eta^2$.

for testing hypothesis H_2, decreasing from 1 to 0 as the hypothesis becomes more and more likely. It can be readily seen however that U_2 is not a suitable criterion. Suppose that the v_{ija} are finite and not zero, so that there is variation within the samples; then $U_2 \to 0$ when $|v_{ijm}| \to 0$. This may occur,

(*a*) When $\bar{x}_t \to \bar{x}_0$ and $\bar{y}_t \to \bar{y}_0$ for $t = 1, 2, \ldots k$, i.e. when the means of all samples tend to coincide, and hypothesis H_2 is probable.

Diagram representing certain exceptional cases of sample variation

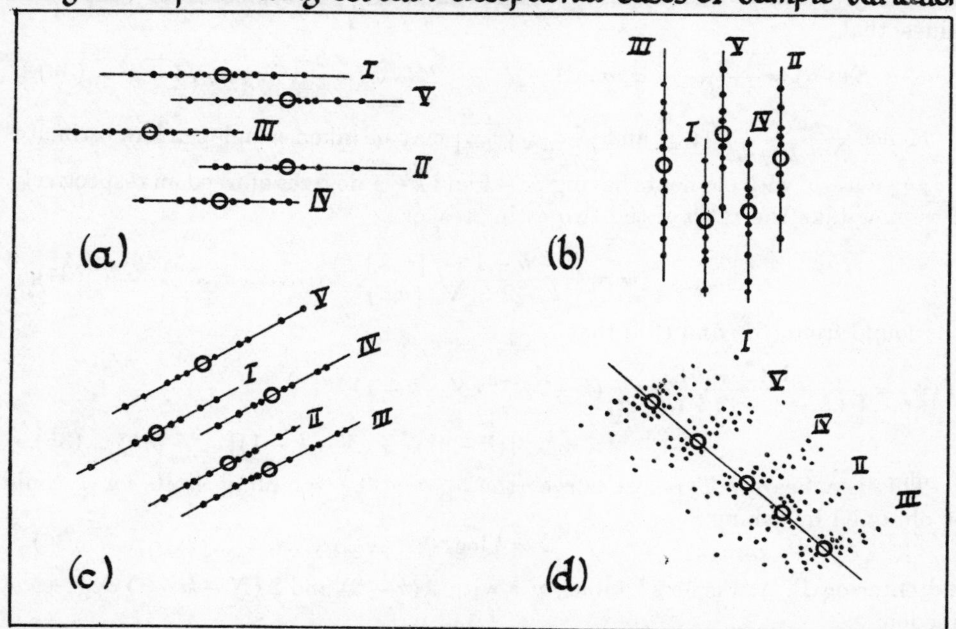

N.B. The numbers are inserted to indicate lines of points corresponding to different samples.

Fig. 1.

(*b*) But since $|v_{ijm}|$ is of the form (28) it follows that it will also tend to zero when $\bar{x}_t - \bar{x}_0 \to c(\bar{y}_t - \bar{y}_0)$, c being the same constant for all t. This would happen when the sample means tend to lie on a straight line, and when, as suggested in Fig. 1 (*d*), hypothesis H_2 may be quite untenable. Clearly therefore U_2 is not an acceptable criterion.

There are two other forms of alternative criteria which it is of interest to refer to here. On the assumption that the samples have been drawn from identical normal populations, it is possible to obtain from the data two independent estimates of both,

$$(a) \quad \sigma_x \sigma_y \sqrt{1-\rho^2},$$

$$(b) \quad \sigma_x \sigma_y \rho.$$

Case (a). If we write $\theta = |v_{ija}|$, $\phi = |v_{ijm}|$, then it is known* that

$$df(\theta) = \frac{2^{N-k-2}\,\Delta^{\frac{1}{2}(N-k-1)}}{\Gamma(N-k-1)}\,\theta^{\frac{1}{2}(N-k-3)}\,e^{-2\sqrt{\Delta\theta}}\,d\theta \quad\text{..............(31)},$$

$$df(\phi) = \frac{2^{k-3}\,\Delta^{\frac{1}{2}(k-2)}}{\Gamma(k-2)}\,\phi^{\frac{1}{2}(k-4)}\,e^{-2\sqrt{\Delta\phi}}\,d\phi \quad\text{..................(32)},$$

where $\Delta = N^2/[4\sigma_x^2\sigma_y^2(1-\rho^2)]$. Furthermore θ and ϕ are independently distributed, and it may be readily shown from (31) and (32), using the symbol E for "expected" values, that

$$E(\sqrt{\theta}) = \frac{N-k-1}{N}\,\sigma_x\sigma_y\sqrt{1-\rho^2}, \qquad E(\sqrt{\phi}) = \frac{k-2}{N}\,\sigma_x\sigma_y\sqrt{1-\rho^2} \quad\text{...(33)}.$$

Hence $\dfrac{N}{N-k-1}\sqrt{|v_{ija}|}$ and $\dfrac{N}{k-2}\sqrt{|v_{ijm}|}$ may be taken as independent estimates of $\sigma_x\sigma_y\sqrt{1-\rho^2}$ with elements having $N-k$ and $k-1$ degrees of freedom respectively. If we now take the ratio of the two estimates, or

$$\psi = \frac{N-k-1}{k-2}\sqrt{\frac{|v_{ijm}|}{|v_{ija}|}} \quad\text{..........................(34)},$$

it is found from (31) and (32) that

$$df(\psi) = \frac{\Gamma(N-3)}{\Gamma(N-k-1)\,\Gamma(k-2)}(k-2)^{k-2}(N-k-1)^{N-k-1}$$
$$\times\,\psi^{k-3}[(k-2)\psi + (N-k-1)]^{(N-3)}\,d\psi \quad\text{...(35)}.$$

This is a Pearson Type VI curve; the 5% and 1% sampling limits for ψ could be obtained by taking

$$z = \tfrac{1}{2}\log_e\psi \quad\text{..................................(36)},$$

and entering R. A. Fisher's† tables of z with $2(k-2)$ and $2(N-k-1)$ degrees of freedom.

The criterion ψ, will not, however, be suitable for testing the hypothesis H_2. We may write

$$|v_{ijm}| = s_{xm}^2\,s_{ym}^2(1-r_m^2) \quad\text{..........................(37)},$$

where s_{xm}, s_{ym} and r_m are the standard deviations and coefficient of correlation of the weighted sample means. Then clearly, it would be possible for ψ to be unity and $|v_{ija}|$ fixed and finite, while $r_m \to 1$ and either s_{xm} or $s_{ym} \to \infty$. In such a situation H_2 would be untenable and yet the two independent estimates of $\sigma_x\sigma_y\sqrt{1-\rho^2}$ would be equal.

Case (b). It can be easily shown that $\dfrac{Nv_{12a}}{N-k}$ and $\dfrac{Nv_{12m}}{k-1}$ are two independent estimates $\sigma_x\sigma_y\rho$, but their ratio, say ψ', would again be unsuitable for testing H_2 for reasons similar to those holding in the case of ψ. It should also be pointed out that the sampling distribution of ψ' is extremely complicated.

* S. S. Wilks: *loc. cit.* p. 477.

† R. A. Fisher: *Statistical Methods for Research Workers*, 4th edition 1932. Edinburgh: Oliver and Boyd.

These illustrations bring out forcibly an important but often neglected consideration. A critical examination of the efficiency of any statistical criterion is necessary before it is applied to testing a hypothesis. The fact that its sampling distribution is known if the hypothesis be true, does not by itself justify its use. In the present case in using U_2, ψ or ψ' we should be in danger of accepting the hypothesis H_2 in certain cases when it is evidently not true. It is only the likelihood criterion, λ_{H_2}, which appears suitable for our purpose.

(7) *The H_1 test.* λ_{H_1} has been defined by (22); clearly $\lambda_{H_1}^{2/N}$ is of the form of the ratio θ discussed in Theorem II of the Appendix, and it satisfies all of the conditions of that theorem. It follows that $\lambda_{H_1}^{2/N}$ and consequently λ_{H_1}

(*a*) must lie between 0 and 1;

(*b*) will be unity when and only when $v_{ijt} = v_{iju}$, $(i, j = 1, 2)$ for all values of t and u, that is, when the variances and covariances of x and y are respectively equal in all the k samples;

(*c*) will be zero when, (i) $x_{t\alpha} - \bar{x}_t = c_t\,(y_{t\alpha} - \bar{y}_t)$ for at least one value of t, where c_t is a constant for all values of α; this means that the sample points in at least one sample will lie on a straight line, and there is perfect correlation in some but not all samples. However, if there be a c such that $x_{t\alpha} - \bar{x}_t = c\,(y_{t\alpha} - \bar{y}_t)$ for all values of α and t, λ_{H_1} has the indeterminant form 0/0, and the points of each of the samples will lie on a straight line and the lines will all be parallel. In this case the problem is reduced to that of a single variable, and the appropriate H_1 test could be applied; (ii) one of the deviations $x_{t\alpha} - \bar{x}_t$ or $y_{t\alpha} - \bar{y}_t$ or both are infinite for at least one value of α and t (but not all values of t, assuming $|v_{ijt}| > 0$ for all t), subject to the condition that the limiting values of the generalised variances remain finite and not zero as these deviations become infinite. Under these conditions it follows by the argument of the proof of (*c*) in Theorem I of the Appendix that $|v_{ijo}|$ becomes infinite while the $|v_{ijt}|$ remain finite and different from zero. The situation is a limiting form of that in which the variation is very much greater in some samples than in others.

(8) *The H test.* Since λ_H is the product of λ_{H_1} and λ_{H_2} it must lie between 0 and 1. It can be unity only when both λ_{H_1} and λ_{H_2} are unity, that is to say, when the means, variances and covariances of x and y in all k samples are respectively identical. It will approach zero when λ_{H_1} or λ_{H_2} or both approach zero.

As in the single-variable problem, the three λ ratios appear therefore to satisfy our intuitive requirements as criteria for testing H, H_1 and H_2, for they are quantities which tend to unity as the corresponding hypothesis becomes intuitively more probable (as far as the information contained in the sample is concerned) and tend to zero as it becomes more likely that the hypothesis is false. Whether the tests based on these criteria satisfy the more fundamental conditions laid down by Neyman and Pearson*, we do not yet know. The problem of testing these hypotheses

* *Phil. Trans. Roy. Soc.*, Ser. A, Vol. 231 (1933).

will be completed by determining the sampling distributions of the λ's on the assumption that the corresponding hypotheses are true, for without these we have no means of testing the significance of an observed value of λ. In the following section we shall first give expressions for the moment coefficients, and then by inverting the moment equations show how the frequency distributions may be obtained. The result is simple only in the case of λ_{H_2}; for λ_H and λ_{H_1} numerical values for the probability integrals can be obtained only by some method of approximation.

IV. The Moment Coefficients and Distributions of the Criteria.

(9) *The Moment Coefficients.* In the single-variable problem it was found to be convenient to study the sampling distributions of some fractional power of the λ's, rather than that of the λ's themselves, owing to the extreme skewness of the latter distributions*. The use of $\lambda^{2/N}$ was suggested largely because in this case

$$\lambda_{H_2}^{2/N} = 1 - \eta^2,$$

(where η^2 is the squared correlation ratio) and had a sampling distribution of Type I form. In the present bivariate case we shall find for similar reasons, which will become apparent as we proceed, that some advantage will be gained by using the $\frac{1}{N}$-th power of the λ's. The moments of the λ's have been given by one of the writers† in a recent paper for the case of an n-variate normal system. If we denote by M_{0h}, M_{1h} and M_{2h} the h-th moment coefficients about zero of $\lambda_H^{1/N}$, $\lambda_{H_1}^{1/N}$, and $\lambda_{H_2}^{1/N}$ respectively, when the corresponding hypotheses H, H_1 and H_2 are true, then we have at once from the paper just cited, for the case of two variables (i.e. $n = 2$),

$$M_{2h} = \frac{\Gamma\left(\frac{N-1}{2}\right)\Gamma\left(\frac{N-2}{2}\right)}{\Gamma\left(\frac{N-k}{2}\right)\Gamma\left(\frac{N-k-1}{2}\right)} \cdot \frac{\Gamma\left(\frac{N-k+h}{2}\right)\Gamma\left(\frac{N-k-1+h}{2}\right)}{\Gamma\left(\frac{N-1+h}{2}\right)\Gamma\left(\frac{N-2+h}{2}\right)} \quad \text{...........(38)},$$

$$M_{1h} = \frac{\Gamma\left(\frac{N-k}{2}\right)\Gamma\left(\frac{N-k-1}{2}\right)}{\Gamma\left(\frac{N-k+h}{2}\right)\Gamma\left(\frac{N-k-1+h}{2}\right)} \times \prod_{t=1}^{k}\left\{\left(\frac{N}{n_t}\right)^{\frac{hn_t}{N}} \frac{\Gamma\left(\frac{n_t-1}{2}+\frac{hn_t}{2N}\right)\Gamma\left(\frac{n_t-2}{2}+\frac{hn_t}{2N}\right)}{\Gamma\left(\frac{n_t-1}{2}\right)\Gamma\left(\frac{n_t-2}{2}\right)}\right\} \quad \text{......(39)},$$

$$M_{0h} = M_{1h} \times M_{2h} \quad \text{.................................(40)}.$$

* Cf. J. Neyman and E. S. Pearson: *Bulletin de l'Académie Polonaise des Sciences et des Lettres*, Série A (1931), pp. 475—476.

† S. S. Wilks: *Biometrika*, Vol. XXIV (1932), pp. 471–494. In this paper the generalisations of λ_H, λ_{H_1} and λ_{H_2} were denoted by $\lambda_{H(n)}$, $\lambda_{H'(n)}$ and λ_H respectively.

These expressions may be considerably simplified by making use of the duplication formula of the Gamma function which can be written

$$\Gamma(a+\tfrac{1}{2})\,\Gamma(a+1)=\frac{\Gamma(\tfrac{1}{2})\,\Gamma(2a+1)}{2^{2a}} \quad\ldots\ldots\ldots\ldots(41).$$

Applying this to (38) and (39) we get

$$M_{2h}=\frac{\Gamma(N-2)\,\Gamma(N-k-1+h)}{\Gamma(N-k-1)\,\Gamma(N-2+h)} \quad\ldots\ldots\ldots\ldots(42)$$

and

$$M_{1h}=\frac{\Gamma(N-k-1)}{\Gamma(N-k-1+h)}\prod_{t=1}^{k}\left[\left(\frac{N}{n_t}\right)^{\frac{nh_t}{N}}\frac{\Gamma\left(n_t-2+\frac{hn_t}{N}\right)}{\Gamma(n_t-2)}\right] \quad\ldots\ldots(43).$$

(10) *The Distributions of L_2 and U_2.* To find the distribution of $\lambda_{H_2}^{1/N}=L_2$, we use the relation

$$\frac{\Gamma(N-k-1+h)}{\Gamma(N-2+h)}=\frac{1}{\Gamma(k-1)}\int_0^1 u^{N-k-2+h}(1-u)^{k-2}\,du \quad\ldots\ldots(44)$$

in (42). Accordingly, we find that the h-th moment of L_2 is identical with that of u, where the distribution of u is

$$\frac{\Gamma(N-2)}{\Gamma(N-k-1)\,\Gamma(k-1)}\,u^{N-k-2}(1-u)^{k-2} \quad\ldots\ldots\ldots\ldots(45).$$

Therefore it follows from the uniqueness of the solution of the moment problem for a finite interval* that the distribution of L_2 must be identical with that of u, and is given by

$$df(L_2)=\frac{\Gamma(N-2)}{\Gamma(N-k-1)\,\Gamma(k-1)}\,L_2^{N-k-2}(1-L_2)^{k-2}\,dL_2 \quad\ldots\ldots(46).$$

In a similar manner, it follows that the distribution of U_2 is given by

$$df(U_2)=\frac{\Gamma(N-2)}{\Gamma(N-k)\,\Gamma(k-2)}\,U_2^{k-3}(1-U_2)^{N-k-1}\,dU_2 \quad\ldots\ldots(47).$$

In both these cases the probability integral is an incomplete B-Function.

(11) *The Distribution of L_1.* Let us consider the sampling distribution of

$$\lambda_{H_1}^{1/N}=L_1,$$

say. The h-th moment of L_1 about zero is given by (43). If we multiply and divide (43) by $\Gamma(N-2k+h)$ and then use the following relations,

$$\frac{\Gamma(N-2k+h)}{\Gamma(N-k-1+h)}=\frac{1}{\Gamma(k-1)}\int_0^1 u^{N-2k-1+h}(1-u)^{k-2}\,du \quad\ldots\ldots(48)$$

and

$$\frac{\prod_{t=1}^{k}\Gamma(n_t-2+hp_t)}{\Gamma(N-2k+h)}=\int_0^1\!\int_0^{l_1}\!\cdots\int_0^{l_{k-2}}(1-v_1-v_2-\ldots-v_{k-1})^{n_k-3+hp_k}\prod_{t=1}^{k-1}(v_t^{n_t-3+hp_t}\,dv_t) \quad\ldots(49),$$

* See W. Stekloff: *Mémoires de l'Académie Impériale des Sciences de St Pétersbourg*, Vol. XXXIII, No. 9 (1915).

where $l_i = 1 - v_1 - v_2 - \ldots - v_i$ $(i = 1, 2, \ldots k-2)$ and $p_t = \frac{n_t}{N}$ $(t = 1, 2, \ldots k)$, we find that the h-th moment $(h = 0, 1, 2, \ldots)$ of L_1 is identical with that of

$$\phi = \frac{1}{p_1^{p_1} p_2^{p_2} \ldots p_k^{p_k}} u v_1^{p_1} v_2^{p_2} \ldots v_{k-1}^{p_{k-1}} (1 - v_1 - v_2 - \ldots - v_{k-1})^{p_k} \quad \ldots\ldots(50),$$

where u and the v's are distributed according to the function

$$Cu^{N-2k-1}(1-u)^{k-2}(1 - v_1 - v_2 - \ldots - v_{k-1})^{n_k - 3} \prod_{t=1}^{k-1} v_t^{n_t - 3} \quad \ldots\ldots\ldots(51),$$

where $0 \leqslant u \leqslant 1$, $v_t \geqslant 0$, and $v_1 + v_2 + \ldots + v \leqslant 1$ and C is a constant depending only on k and the n's. Therefore, it follows from the argument used in establishing the uniqueness of (46) that the distribution of L_1 is identical with that of ϕ*. The problem of finding the distribution of ϕ is equivalent to that of solving (50) for the u or one of the v's and substituting in (51) and integrating with respect to all variables except ϕ. This process is extremely complicated, even when the p's are all equal, that is, when $n_1 = n_2 = \ldots = n_k = n$; in this case we can find an expression for the distribution of the L_1 by considering a transformation of M_{1h}. The new form of M_{1h} is found by applying the transformation†

$$\Gamma(mz) = \frac{m^{mz - \frac{1}{2}}}{(2\pi)^{\frac{1}{2}(m-1)}} \Gamma(z)\, \Gamma\left(z + \frac{1}{m}\right) \ldots \Gamma\left(z + \frac{m-1}{m}\right) \quad \ldots\ldots\ldots(52)$$

to $\Gamma(N - k - 1)$ and $\Gamma(N - k - 1 + h)$ in (43), by writing $m = k$ and $z = n - 1 - 1/k$ in the first and $m = k$ and $z = n - 1 - 1/k + h/k$ in the second. Accordingly, we get

$$M_{1h} = C \frac{\Gamma^k\left(n - 2 + \frac{h}{k}\right)}{\Gamma\left(n - \frac{k+1}{k} + \frac{h}{k}\right) \Gamma\left(n - \frac{k}{k} + \frac{h}{k}\right) \ldots \Gamma\left(n - \frac{2}{k} + \frac{h}{k}\right)} \quad \ldots\ldots(53),$$

where $$C = \frac{\Gamma\left(n - \frac{k+1}{k}\right) \Gamma\left(n - \frac{k}{k}\right) \ldots \Gamma\left(n - \frac{2}{k}\right)}{\Gamma^k(n-2)}.$$

Distribution functions with moments of this type have been considered by one of the authors‡, from which we can write at once as the distribution of L_1

$$df(L_1) = C' L_1^{N-3k} (1 - L_1^k)^{2k - \frac{(k+1)(k+2)-2}{2k} - 1} d(L_1^k)$$
$$\times \int_0^1 \int_0^1 \ldots \int_0^1 \theta_1^{\frac{k-1}{k} - 1} \theta_2^{\frac{k}{k} - 1} \ldots \theta_{k-1}^{\frac{2k-3}{k} - 1}$$

* In this connection we note that a simple alternative proof of (*a*) in Theorem II of the Appendix can be constructed at once for the case where the p's are rational numbers and the a_{ijt} are product moments, by showing that the maximum of ϕ is unity for variations of u and the v's in the region over which (51) is defined. Indeed, for a given value of u we find that the only stationary point with respect to the v's is the true maximum which occurs where $v_t = p_t$ $(t = 1, 2, \ldots k-1)$. Therefore, ϕ, which is necessarily positive, has a maximum of unity, and since the range of ϕ and L_1 must be the same we have $0 \leqslant L_1^2 \leqslant 1$, that is, $0 \leqslant \theta \leqslant 1$.

† See Whittaker and Watson: *Modern Analysis* (4th edition), p. 240.

‡ Wilks, *loc. cit.* pp. 474—475.

$$\times (1-\theta_1)^{2(k-1)-\frac{k(k+1)-2}{2k}-1}(1-\theta_2)^{2(k-2)-\frac{(k-1)k-2}{2k}-1}\ldots$$

$$\ldots (1-\theta_{k-1})^{2-\frac{2\cdot 3-2}{2k}-1}$$

$$\times [1-\theta_1(1-L_1{}^k)]^{-\frac{k}{k}}[1-\{\theta_1+\theta_2(1-\theta_1)\}(1-L_1{}^k)]^{-\frac{k+1}{k}}\ldots$$

$$\times [1-\{\theta_1+\theta_2(1-\theta_1)+\ldots+\theta_{k-1}(1-\theta_1)\ldots$$

$$\ldots(1-\theta_{k-2})\}(1-L_1{}^k)]^{-\frac{2k-2}{k}}\, d\theta_1\ldots d\theta_{k-1}\;\ldots\ldots(54),$$

where (using formula (52))

$$C' = \frac{C}{\Gamma\left(\frac{k-1}{k}\right)\Gamma\left(\frac{k}{k}\right)\ldots\Gamma\left(\frac{2k-2}{k}\right)} = \frac{\Gamma(N-k-1)}{\Gamma^k(n-2)\,\Gamma(k-1)\,k^{N-2k}},$$

a slightly more condensed form of (54) can be obtained by setting

$$\theta_t = 1-\phi_t \quad (t=1, 2, \ldots k-1).$$

Thus $df(L_1) = C' L_1{}^{nk-3k}(1-L_1{}^k)^{2k-\frac{(k+1)(k+2)-2}{2k}-1}\, d(L_1{}^k)$

$$\times \int_0^1\int_0^1\ldots\int_0^1 \phi_1^{\,2(k-1)-\frac{k(k+1)-2}{2k}-1}\,\phi_2^{\,2(k-2)-\frac{(k-1)k-2}{2k}-1}\ldots\phi_{k-1}^{\,2-\frac{2}{k}-1}$$

$$\times [(1-\phi_1)^{\frac{k-1}{k}-1}(1-\phi_2)^{\frac{k}{k}-1}(1-\phi_3)^{\frac{k+1}{k}-1}\ldots(1-\phi_{k-1})^{\frac{2k-3}{k}-1}]$$

$$\times [1-(1-\phi_1)(1-L_1{}^k)]^{-1}[1-(1-\phi_1\phi_2)(1-L_1{}^k)]^{-1-\frac{1}{k}}\ldots$$

$$\ldots[1-(1-\phi_1\phi_2\ldots\phi_{k-1})(1-L_1{}^k)]^{-2+\frac{2}{k}}\, d\phi_1 d\phi_2\ldots d\phi_{k-1}$$

$$\ldots\ldots(55).$$

The distribution of L_1 for two samples ($k=2$) turns out to be

$$df(L_1) = \frac{\Gamma(2n-3)}{\Gamma^2(n-2)\,2^{2n-6}}\, L_1{}^{2n-5}\log\left(\frac{1+\sqrt{1-L_1{}^2}}{L_1}\right) dL_1\;\ldots\ldots\ldots(56),$$

and the significance of an observed value L_1 can be obtained from the probability integral (57), which results from integrating (56) by parts.

$$P(L_1 < l_1) = \int_0^{l_1} df(L_1)$$

$$= \frac{\Gamma(2n-3)}{\Gamma(n-1)\,\Gamma(n-2)\,2^{2n-5}}\left\{(l_1^2)^{n-2}\log\left(\frac{1+\sqrt{1-l_1{}^2}}{l_1}\right)+\tfrac{1}{2}\int_0^{l_1^2} y^{n-3}(1-y)^{-\frac{1}{2}}\,dy\right\}$$

$$\ldots\ldots(57).$$

This expression depends on the Incomplete Beta Function. When $k>2$ we have so far been unable to find any simple expression for $df(L_1)$, and some method of approximation seems necessary. Approximate methods are discussed below.

(12) *The Distribution of* L. In a similar manner, if we let $\lambda_H^{1/N} = L$ then the h-th moment of L when $n_1 = n_2 = \ldots = n_k = n$ is

$$M_{0h} = \frac{\Gamma(nk-2)}{\Gamma(nk-2+h)}\, k^h\, \frac{\Gamma^k\left(n-2+\frac{h}{k}\right)}{\Gamma^k(n-2)}\;\ldots\ldots\ldots\ldots\ldots\ldots(58),$$

and the distribution of L can be expressed as

$$df(L) = \frac{\Gamma(nk-2)}{\Gamma^k(n-2)\,\Gamma(2k-2)\,k^{nk-2k}} L^{(n-3)k} (1-L^k)^{2k+\frac{(k-3)(k-2)-6}{2k}-1}\, d(L^k)$$

$$\times \int_0^1\int_0^1 \ldots \int_0^1 \phi_1^{2(k-1)+\frac{(k-3)(k-2)-2}{2k}-1} \phi_2^{2(k-2)+\frac{(k-3)(k-2)}{2k}-1} \ldots \phi_{k-1}^{2+\frac{k-3}{k}-1}$$

$$\times (1-\phi_1)^{2-\frac{2}{k}-1}(1-\phi_2)^{2-\frac{1}{k}-1}\ldots(1-\phi_{k-1})^{2+\frac{k-4}{k}-1}[1-(1-\phi_1)(1-L^k)]^{-2+\frac{1}{k}}$$

$$\times [1-(1-\phi_1\phi_2)(1-L^k)]^{-2}\ldots[1-(1-\phi_1\phi_2\ldots\phi_{k-1})(1-L^k)]^{-2-\frac{k-3}{k}}$$

$$d\phi_1\ldots d\phi_{k-1} \quad \ldots\ldots(59).$$

For the case $k=2$, (59) becomes

$$df(L) = \frac{\Gamma(2n-2)}{\Gamma^2(n-2)\,2^{2n-6}} L^{2n-5}\left\{\log\left(\frac{1+\sqrt{1-L^2}}{L}\right) - \sqrt{1-L^2}\right\} dL \quad \ldots(60).$$

The probability integral of (60) assumes the form

$$P(L<l) = \int_0^l df(L) = \frac{\Gamma(2n-2)}{\Gamma(n-1)\,\Gamma(n-2)\,2^{2n-5}}\left\{(l^2)^{n-4}\left[\log\left(\frac{1+\sqrt{1-l^2}}{l}\right)\right.\right.$$

$$\left.\left. - (1-l^2)^{\frac{1}{2}}\right] + \tfrac{1}{2}\int_0^{l^2} y^{n-3}(1-y)^{\frac{1}{2}}\, dy\right\} \quad \ldots(61).$$

Again, if $k>2$ some approximate solution appears necessary.

We note from the distributions of L_1 and L that (55) and (59) are actually the distributions of the n-th roots of λ_{H_1} and λ_H respectively.

(13) *Approximate Solution for testing* H_1. When $k>2$ it appears necessary to employ some approximate method to calculate the probability integral of the sampling distribution of λ_{H_1} or of $L_1 = \lambda_{H_1}^{1/N}$. To establish the best and simplest method of procedure fuller investigation is required, but we believe that the relatively simple form of approximation which has been used in the single variable case is also suitable here. This involves the assumption that the sampling distribution of L_1 may be represented by the law

$$f(L_1) = \frac{\Gamma(m_1+m_2)}{\Gamma(m_1)\,\Gamma(m_2)} L_1^{m_1-1}(1-L_1)^{m_2-1} \quad \ldots\ldots\ldots\ldots\ldots\ldots(62),$$

where m_1 and m_2 are determined so that the first and second moment coefficients of $f(L_1)$ about $L_1=0$ have the values given by (43) for $h=1$ and 2 respectively. In other words we represent the distribution of L_1 by a Type I curve having the correct terminals and first two moment coefficients. In many practical applications it is possible to plan for the number of individuals in each sample to be the same, i.e. for $n_t = n\,(t=1, 2, \ldots k)$. This is the situation considered in the illustrations which follow. The equations for determining m_1 and m_2 then become

$$m_1 = \frac{M_{11}(M_{11}-M_{12})}{M_{12}-M_{11}^2}, \qquad m_2 = \frac{(1-M_{11})(M_{11}-M_{12})}{M_{12}-M_{11}^2} \quad \ldots\ldots\ldots(63),$$

from which, since $N = nk$, we obtain from (43)

$$M_{11} = \frac{k}{N-k-1}\left\{\frac{\Gamma\left(n-2+\frac{1}{k}\right)}{\Gamma(n-2)}\right\}^k \quad \text{.....................(64)},$$

$$M_{12} = \frac{k^2}{(N-k-1)(N-k)}\left\{\frac{\Gamma\left(n-2+\frac{2}{k}\right)}{\Gamma(n-2)}\right\}^k \quad \text{..............(65)}.$$

For the probability integral of (62), we have

$$P(L_1 \leqslant l_1) = I_{l_1}(m_1, m_2) \quad \text{...........................(66)},$$

which is the Incomplete Beta Function. This may be obtained from the *Tables of the Incomplete Beta Function** if m_1 and m_2 are $\leqslant 50$ or by means of R. A. Fisher's *z*-transformation as has been suggested elsewhere†. If m_1 and m_2 are both large or nearly equal, (62) will approach the normal form and the ratio

$$\frac{L_1 - \text{Mean } L_1}{\sigma_{L_1}} = \frac{L_1 - M_{11}}{\sqrt{M_{12} - M_{11}^2}} \quad \text{.......................(67)}$$

can be used as an index of significance to be interpreted on the normal probability scale.

The probability integral of $L = \lambda_H^{1/N}$ could be obtained by a similar approximation, but in general it is likely that the hypotheses H_1 and H_2 will be tested separately.

V. Practical Illustrations.

(14) *Example* 1. *Relation between Tensile Strength and Hardness in Aluminium Die-Castings.*

This example has been referred to above in Section (3). We shall proceed first to test H_1, that is, the hypothesis that there is no significant difference between the samples as regards variation and covariation in strength and hardness. A summary of the necessary calculations is shown in Table II; we have $N = 60$, $k = 5$, $n = 12$. The unit for x (strength) is 1000 lb. per square inch, and for y it is Rockwell's E.

From (22) we have

$$L_1 = \lambda_{H_1}^{1/N} = \sqrt{\frac{\prod_{t=1}^{k}(|v_{ijt}|)^{\frac{1}{k}}}{|v_{ija}|}} \quad \text{....................... (68)},$$

and as indicated in the table it is found that $L_1 = \cdot 9065$. From (64) and (65) it is found that if H_1 were true‡, then Mean $L_1 = M_{11} = \cdot 889274$, $M_{12} = \cdot 792592$,

* To be issued shortly as a *Biometrika* publication.

† *Biometrika*, Vol. xxiv. p. 415.

‡ Brownlee's Seven-Figure Tables of the Logarithm of the Gamma Function were used, *Tracts for Computers*, No. ix.

TABLE II.

Strength (x) and Hardness (y) in Aluminium Die-Castings. Test of H_1 (bivariate).

t (Sample No.)	Sums of Squares $nv_{11t} = \sum_{a=1}^{n} (x_{ta} - \bar{x}_t)^2$	Sums of Squares $nv_{22t} = \sum_{a=1}^{n} (y_{ta} - \bar{y})^2$	Sums of Products $nv_{12t} = \sum_{a=1}^{n} (x_{ta} - \bar{x}_t)(y_{ta} - \bar{y})$	Generalised Variances $\lvert v_{ijt} \rvert = v_{11t}v_{22t} - v_{12t}^2$	$\log \lvert v_{ijt} \rvert$
1	78·948	1247·18	214·18	365·204	2·56254
2	223·695	2519·31	657·62	910·401	2·95923
3	57·448	1241·78	190·63	243·029	2·38566
4	187·618	1473·44	375·91	938·451	2·97241
5	88·456	1171·73	259·18	253·281	2·40360
Totals	636·165 $= Nv_{11a}$	7653·44 $= Nv_{22a}$	1697·52 $= Nv_{12a}$		13·28344 $= \sum_{t=1}^{5} \log(\lvert v_{ijt} \rvert)$

$$\lvert v_{ija} \rvert = v_{11a} v_{22a} - v_{12a}^2 = 552{\cdot}018,$$

$$\log L_1 = \tfrac{1}{2} \left\{ \frac{1}{k} \log \prod_{t=1}^{k} (\lvert v_{ijt} \rvert) - \log(\lvert v_{ija} \rvert) \right\} \quad \text{(from definition (68))}$$

$$= \bar{1}{\cdot}957367,$$

$$L_1 = {\cdot}9065.$$

$$\left.\begin{array}{c}\text{Estimate of correlation}\\ \text{within samples}\end{array}\right\} r_a = \frac{Nv_{12a}}{\sqrt{Nv_{11a} \times Nv_{22a}}} = +{\cdot}7693.$$

$\sigma_{L_1} = {\cdot}04223$. The observed value of L_1 is therefore nearer to unity than the mean value expected in repeated samples, and the ratio (67) is only $+0{\cdot}41$. Therefore there is clearly no reason for rejecting H_1. If, however, we were to proceed in more detail we should find from (63) that $m_1 = 48{\cdot}210$, and $m_2 = 6{\cdot}003$, and by interpolating in the Tables of the Incomplete Beta Function that $P(L_1 < {\cdot}9065) = {\cdot}621$.

We may now proceed to test H_2, the hypothesis that neither mean strength nor mean hardness differs significantly from sample to sample. Table III contains a summary of the calculations in the form of an analysis of variance table. It is seen that $L_2 = {\cdot}6896$, while if H_2 were true, the probability law for L_2 is obtained from (46) as

$$P(L_2) = \frac{\Gamma(58)}{\Gamma(54)\,\Gamma(4)} L_2^{53} (1 - L_2)^3 \quad \text{..................... (69).}$$

The mean of (69) is ·9310 and the standard error* is ·0330, so that the observed value differs from the mean by more than seven times the standard error. By actually integrating (69) it is found that $P(L_2 < {\cdot}6896) = {\cdot}0000019$. H_2 must clearly be rejected. To discover whether this is due to significant differences in mean strength or in mean hardness or in both, we must consider the two single-variable problems

* For (46): Mean $L_2 = \frac{N-k-1}{N-2}$, $\sigma_{L_2} = \frac{1}{N-2} \sqrt{\frac{(N-k-1)(k-1)}{N-1}}$.

TABLE III.

Strength (x) and Hardness (y) in Aluminium Die-Castings. Tests of H_2.

	Degrees of Freedom	Sums of Squares (x)	Sums of Squares (y)	Sums of Products (x, y)	Generalised Variances
Between Samples	$k-1=4$	$Nv_{11m}=306{\cdot}089$	$Nv_{22m}=662{\cdot}77$	$Nv_{12m}=214{\cdot}86$	$\lvert v_{ijm}\rvert=43{\cdot}528$
Within Samples	$N-k=55$	$Nv_{11a}=636{\cdot}165$	$Nv_{22a}=7653{\cdot}42$	$Nv_{12a}=1697{\cdot}52$	$\lvert v_{ija}\rvert=552{\cdot}018$
Totals	$N-1=59$	$Nv_{11o}=942{\cdot}254$	$Nv_{22o}=8316{\cdot}19$	$Nv_{12o}=1912{\cdot}38$	$\lvert v_{ijo}\rvert=1160{\cdot}77$

$$L_2=\lambda_2^{1/N}=\sqrt{\lvert v_{ija}\rvert/\lvert v_{ijo}\rvert}={\cdot}6896,$$

$$\eta_{xt}^2=v_{11m}/v_{11o}={\cdot}3248, \qquad \eta_{yt}^2=v_{22m}/v_{22o}={\cdot}0797.$$

	Estimates of Variance	$\log_{10}$ (est.)	Estimates of Variance	$\log_{10}$ (est.)
Between Samples	$\frac{Nv_{11m}}{k-1}=76{\cdot}522$	1·883786	$\frac{Nv_{22m}}{k-1}=165{\cdot}69$	2·219296
Within Samples	$\frac{Nv_{11a}}{N-k}=11{\cdot}566$	1·063183	$\frac{Nv_{22a}}{N-k}=139{\cdot}15$	2·143483
Difference		·820603	Difference	·075813
$z=1{\cdot}15129\times$ Difference		·9448	z	·0873

separately. Tests may be applied to the squared correlation ratios η_{xt}^2 and η_{yt}^2, or R. A. Fisher's z-transformation can be used. The necessary calculations are shown in Table III.

Using Woo's tables*, it is found that η_{xt}^2 is clearly significant while η_{yt}^2 is not. Alternatively, referring to Fisher's z-tables† with $n_1=k-1=4$, $n_2=N-k=55$, it is seen that the 5 % point lies at about ·47 and the 1 % at about ·65, showing, as before, that mean strength differs significantly from sample to sample but not mean hardness.

The limited amount of test records available would therefore suggest the following tentative conclusions:

(*a*) Within the samples the relationship between the two qualities is stable, and represented by $\sigma_x=3{\cdot}401\times10^3$ lb. per sq. in., $\sigma_y=11{\cdot}80$ in Rockwell's E,

* *Tables for Statisticians and Biometricians*, Part II, Table IV.

† *Statistical Methods for Research Workers*, Table VI.

$r_{xy} = +\cdot 769$. (The first two values are the square roots of $Nv_{11a}/(N-k)$ and $Nv_{22a}/(N-k)$ respectively, and the last is the value of v_a given in Table II.)

(*b*) While the variation in mean strength from sample to sample is imperfectly controlled, the variation in hardness appears no more than might be expected through chance.

From the practical point of view this is not an altogether satisfactory result and further investigation into the anomaly (*b*) would be necessary before hardness could be used with confidence as an index of strength.

(15) *Example 2. Relation between Length and Breadth of Human Skulls.*

The data consist of standard measurements of length and breadth of skull in millimetres obtained for 20 adult males from each of 30 different races or groups*, i.e. $N = 600$, $n = 20$, and $k = 30$. That there would be considerable inter-racial variation for mean length and breadth was obvious, but it seemed to be of interest to examine the hypothesis H_1, that is to say, to test the extent of inter-racial uniformity in the relationship of length to breadth. These characters appear sufficiently nearly normally distributed within a race for the normal-theory tests to be applicable. Length will be denoted by x and breadth by y; a summary of the calculations is shown in Table IV. We find from these that

$$|v_{ija}| = 656{\cdot}369 \qquad \frac{1}{k}\sum_{t=1}^{k} \log\{|v_{ija}|\} = 2{\cdot}644429$$

$$\log |v_{ija}| = 2{\cdot}817148$$

$$\text{Difference} \quad \bar{1}{\cdot}827281$$

$$\log L_1 = \tfrac{1}{2} \times \text{difference} = \bar{1}{\cdot}913640, \; L_1 = {\cdot}8197.$$

From (64) and (65) we obtain Mean $L_1 = M_{11} = {\cdot}923678$, $M_{12} = {\cdot}853317$, $\sigma_{L_1} = {\cdot}0117$. The observed L_1 is below the expected mean value, and the ratio (67) is $-8{\cdot}9$. This is so clearly significant that, without further refinement in calculation, we can say that H_1 is untenable. We must now examine whether this lack of uniformity is present both in the group standard deviations s_{xt} and s_{yt}, and in the correlations r_{xyt}.

For the first problem Neyman and Pearson's single variate test for H_1 may be applied†. This involves the calculation of the sums of the logarithms of the quantities nv_{11t} and of v_{22t} given in Table IV, since in this case

$$L_1 = \lambda_{H_1}^{2/N} = \prod_{t=1}^{k} (v_{iit})^{1/k}/(v_{iia}) \qquad \text{.......................(70)},$$

where $i = 1$ for length and $i = 2$ for breadth. The calculations are shown in Table V, v_{11a} and v_{22a} being obtained from Table IV. It is found that were H_1 true, then:

$$\text{Mean } L_1 = {\cdot}9496, \quad \sigma_{L_1} = {\cdot}0129.$$

* We are indebted to Dr G. M. Morant for providing us with the necessary sources of information.

† For an illustration of the use of this test, see *Biometrika*, Vol. XXIV. p. 415.

TABLE IV.

Length (x) and Breadth (y) of Skulls. Tests of H_1; data for separate samples.

t	Race	nv_{11t}	nv_{22t}	nv_{12t}	$\lvert v_{ijt}\rvert$	$\bar{x}_t$	$\bar{y}_t$	s_{xt}	s_{yt}	r_t
1	Aëtas	612·00	300·14	41·50	454·91	172·00	143·92	5·532	3·874	+·097
2	Aleuts	218·20	391·20	57·80	205·05	183·30	149·20	3·303	4·423	+·198
3	Andamanese	216·45	311·25	149·50	112·55	167·95	136·25	3·290	3·945	+·576
4	Anglo-Saxons	975·44	777·45	−12·88	1895·47	191·62	142·45	6·984	6·235	−·015
5	Armenians	551·20	320·20	72·80	427·99	176·80	145·70	5·250	4·001	+·173
6	Australians. (South Australia)	1114·20	280·95	427·30	326·12	195·70	127·05	7·464	3·748	+·764
7	Australians. (Victoria)	1131·20	472·95	−27·20	1335·65	182·80	132·45	7·521	4·863	−·037
8	Copts	722·20	558·55	423·90	559·23	174·30	135·85	6·009	5·285	+·667
9	Dayake. (Borneo)	431·50	881·24	8·50	950·46	174·50	138·97	4·645	6·638	+·014
10	Easter Islanders	834·74	331·64	−59·16	683·33	191·72	133·42	6·460	4·072	−·112
11	Egyptians, 1st Dynasty. (Abydos) ...	518·71	319·07	89·03	393·95	185·62	136·50	5·093	3·994	+·219
12	Egyptians, Modern. (Cairo)	1115·45	382·30	−99·28	1041·45	186·86	133·90	7·468	4·372	−·152
13	Egyptians, Predynastic. (Badari) ...	542·05	356·64	140·23	434·13	184·65	131·42	5·206	4·223	+·319
14	English, Mediaeval. (Hythe)	714·95	748·14	227·08	1208·29	179·45	148·07	5·979	6·116	+·310
15	English, Roman? (Spitalfields)	1021·80	550·75	14·25	1406·38	181·10	143·75	7·148	5·248	+·019
16	English, 17th century. (Farringdon St)	697·80	312·24	207·80	436·75	192·10	145·97	5·907	3·951	+·445
17	Eskimos. (Greenland)	325·75	278·95	123·75	188·88	192·75	133·55	4·036	3·735	+·410
18	Gaunche. (Canary Islands)	327·75	158·55	215·75	13·54	189·25	141·65	4·048	2·816	+·946
19	Hindus. (Bengal)	650·55	700·55	11·95	1139·00	176·85	131·65	5·703	5·918	+·018
20	Indonesians. (Ceram)	887·75	1033·80	153·50	2235·48	177·25	134·90	6·662	7·190	+·160
21	Javanese	1018·14	392·14	112·61	966·43	171·57	141·42	7·135	4·428	+·178
22	Mongols. (Urga)	488·95	212·20	245·70	108·47	189·05	145·30	4·944	3·257	+·763
23	Moriori. (Chatham Islands)	232·45	488·24	33·97	280·84	186·05	142·27	3·409	4·941	+·101
24	Negroes, Teita. (Kenya Colony) ...	562·74	368·50	204·50	413·87	187·72	130·00	5·304	4·292	+·449
25	Papuans. (New Guinea)	404·80	448·95	104·60	426·98	188·40	132·05	4·499	4·738	+·245
26	Tagals. (Philippine Islands)	454·64	303·20	133·70	299·93	178·92	138·80	4·768	3·894	+·360
27	Tasmanians	698·00	237·75	241·00	269·67	190·00	139·25	5·908	3·448	+·592
28	Turks	381·80	393·20	−199·60	275·71	168·10	141·80	4·369	4·434	−·515
29	Swiss. (Münster)	405·75	587·20	11·00	595·34	177·75	151·20	4·504	5·418	+·023
30	Venezuelians	480·00	239·20	86·00	268·55	178·00	140·80	4·899	3·458	+·254
	Totals	18736·96 $= Nv_{11a}$	13137·14 $= Nv_{22a}$	+3139·60 $= Nv_{12a}$						

Consequently we have

	Length (x)	Breadth (y)
Observed L_1	·9000	·9074.
$(L_1 - \text{Mean } L_1)/\sigma_{L_1}$	$-3·84$	$-3·27$

TABLE V.

Length and Breadth of Skulls. Tests of H_1 (Single-variate).

	Length (x) $i=1$	Breadth (y) $i=2$
$\frac{1}{30}\sum_{t=1}^{30} \log(20v_{iit})$	2·749829	2·599191
$\log 20$	1·301030	1·301030
$\frac{1}{30}\sum_{t=1}^{30} \log(v_{iit})$	1·448799	1·298161
$\log(v_{iia})$	1·494548	1·340349
$\log L_1$	$\bar{1}$·954251	$\bar{1}$·957812
L_1	·9000	·9074

The divergence shown by the ratios is significant, and it does not seem necessary to enter here into the approximate calculation of the probabilities $P(L_1 < ·9000)$ and $P(L_1 < ·9074)$, (which are both under ·01), since examples have been discussed elsewhere and it is hoped to publish shortly convenient tables for use with the test.

We must now examine the variation among the 30 correlation coefficients r_{xyt} $(t = 1, 2, \ldots 30)$; the best method of procedure is probably as follows:

If x and y are normally correlated it is known that in repeated samples of n that

$$z' = \tfrac{1}{2}\{\log_e(1+r) - \log_e(1-r)\} \quad \text{.......................(71)}$$

is approximately normally distributed with a standard error of $1/\sqrt{n-3}$*. Consequently, we may test whether k independent values of r differ only through chance fluctuations from some unknown population value of ρ, by calculating

$$\chi^2 = \sum_{t=1}^{k} \{(n_t - 3)(z_t' - \bar{z}')^2\} \quad \text{..........................(72)},$$

where $\bar{z}' = \sum_{t=1}^{k} (z_t'/k)$, and entering the (χ^2, P) tables with $k-1$ degrees of freedom (i.e. $n' = k$ in the notation of Elderton's Table). In the present instance it is found that $\chi^2 = 96·01$, while $n' = 30$, which is evidently significant. χ, in fact, deviates from the expected value by about 6·3 times the standard error†.

We have found therefore that the covariation in length and breadth of skull within a race cannot be considered as uniform from race to race; further, that while

* R. A. Fisher: *Metron*, Vol. I. No. IV. p. 13. An illustration of using this test with k values of r has been given by L. H. C. Tippett: *The Methods of Statistics* (1931), p. 143.

† This result is obtained by using the rule that when $f = n' - 1$ is large, $\sqrt{2\chi^2} - \sqrt{2f-1}$ is approximately normally distributed about zero with unit standard error.

the standard deviations certainly differ significantly, the lack of uniformity is due in much greater degree to the instability of the correlation coefficient. Having regard to the great variety in the data, these results were to be expected since a "race" is a loosely defined term, and the coefficient of correlation between two measures of size within a group will depend upon the homogeneity of that group. The more similar the skulls are in shape the higher is r likely to be. In considering the possible value of the criterion L_1 in anthropometric work, it should be remembered that, although the present paper is concerned only with the case of two correlated variables, the general theory developed by one of us* is applicable in the case of any number of variables.

Although the difference in mean length and breadth for the different races is so obvious that a statistical test is hardly required, it may be useful to summarise what would be the formal method of approach:

(1) Considering the two variables together it is found that $H_1(x \text{ and } y)$ is quite untenable; therefore we should not proceed to test H_2 (x and y).

(2) $H_1(x)$ and $H_1(y)$ are also improbable, but the differences in the standard deviations s_x and s_y are hardly sufficient to invalidate the tests $H_2(x)$ and $H_2(y)$.

(3) From two tables for analysis of variance similar to those contained in Table III, it is found that $\eta_{xt}^2 = \cdot6489$ and $\eta_{yt}^2 = \cdot6294$. If H_2 were true for the case of a single variable, then Mean $\eta^2 = \cdot0484$, and $\sigma_{\eta^2} = \cdot0124$. Clearly, therefore, $H_2(x)$ and $H_2(y)$ are untenable, that is, the 30 samples of 20 provide convincing evidence that the racial mean characters differ significantly.

VI. CONCLUSION.

Certain general methods of analysis of multivariate data have been developed by one of us elsewhere. In the present paper the special case of two correlated variables has been taken, in order to illustrate (*a*) the process of reasoning underlying the methods, (*b*) the practical application of the resulting tests, (*c*) their relation to other tests in use. The following points may be emphasised:

(1) It is necessary to recognise that in many problems, hypotheses of the H_1 type need to be tested, as well as those of the H_2 type. The technique of Analysis of Variance does not appear suited to deal with the former when more than two samples are concerned.

(2) In the multivariate problem it would be possible to deal with the variation of each character and the correlation of each pair of characters separately, but the application in the first instance of a single comprehensive test has several advantages. If, for example, on the evidence available H can be accepted, it is unnecessary to proceed to test H_1 and H_2. Similarly, if H_1 (using p variates) can be accepted there should be no need to proceed to the p single-variate H_1 tests and the $\frac{1}{2}p(p-1)$

* Wilks, *loc. cit.*

correlation tests. The same situation arises in dealing with H_2. Even when the comprehensive test is not satisfied, and it is necessary to apply the separate tests in order to locate the source of disturbance, relatively little labour will have been wasted in applying the comprehensive test first. For example, in the case of two variables which has been illustrated, the calculation of $\log|v_{ijt}|$ needed to test H_1 (two variables) involves little extra work when once nv_{11t}, nv_{22t} and nv_{12t} have been computed. But the latter quantities are in any case required if the sample variances and correlations are to be considered separately.

(3) The methods suggested for calculating the significance of a given value of the λ or L criteria are admittedly not in final form. For convenience in practical working, tables to be entered with n and k are needed, which would show certain levels of significance of these criteria. The possibility of forming such tables is under consideration.

(4) It has been assumed throughout that the variables are normally distributed. Some investigations on the stringency of this assumption are in progress.

VII. Appendix.

To assist in the interpretation of λ_H, λ_{H_1} and λ_{H_2} as criteria for testing the corresponding hypotheses H, H_1 and H_2 we shall find it convenient to prove the following theorems.

Theorem I. *Let η_{ik} ($i=1, 2$; $k=1, 2, \ldots m$) be any set of real numbers, and let the matrix*

$$\begin{Vmatrix} A_{11} & A_{12} \\ A_{21} & A_{22} \end{Vmatrix}$$

be real and positive definite with $A_{12}=A_{21}$ and

$$\psi=\frac{\begin{vmatrix} A_{11} & A_{12} \\ A_{21} & A_{22} \end{vmatrix}}{\begin{vmatrix} A_{11}+\Sigma\eta_{1k}^2 & A_{12}+\Sigma\eta_{1k}\eta_{2k} \\ A_{21}+\Sigma\eta_{1k}\eta_{2k} & A_{22}+\Sigma\eta_{2k}^2 \end{vmatrix}},$$

where the moment products of η's are summed for k from 1 to m; then

(*a*) $0\leqslant\psi\leqslant 1$,

(*b*) *a necessary and sufficient condition that $\psi=1$, when*

$$|A_{ij}|>0, \text{ is that } \eta_{ik}=0 \qquad (i=1, 2;\ k=1, 2, \ldots m),$$

(*c*) *a necessary and sufficient condition that $\psi=0$ when $|A_{ij}|>0$, is that at least one of the η's be infinite.*

Proof: Let the determinants in the numerator and denominator of ψ be called A and B respectively. Then (*a*) can be shown at once by induction, for suppose $B\geqslant A$ for $k=t$, then for $k=t+1$, B can be written as B_t+q_{t+1}, where B_t is the value of B for $k=t$ and q_{t+1} is a positive definite quadratic form in $\eta_{1,t+1}$ and $\eta_{2,t+1}$. Therefore, setting $t=0, 1, 2, \ldots m$, we get

$$B\geqslant\ldots\geqslant B_{t+1}\geqslant B_t\geqslant\ldots\geqslant B_0\equiv A>0,$$

which is equivalent to the proof of (*a*).

The sufficient conditions in (*b*) and (*c*) are obvious. To prove the necessary condition of (*b*) we observe that for $B_{t+1}=B_t$ it is necessary that $\eta_{1,t+1}=\eta_{2,t+1}=0$ since q_{t+1} is positive definite in these two variables. Setting $t=0, 1, 2, \ldots m$, we see that a necessary condition for

$$B=\ldots=B_{t+1}=B_t=\ldots=B_0\equiv A,$$

or $\psi=1$ is that $\eta_{ik}=0$ $(i=1, 2;\ k=1, 2, \ldots m)$.

To prove the necessary condition in (*c*), we note that at least one member of the non-decreasing set $B \ldots B_{t+1}, B_t \ldots B_1$ must become infinite. Let B_{i+1} be the first B which is infinite, then clearly, $B, \ldots B_{i+3}, B_{i+2}$ will also be infinite. But $B_{i+1}=B_i+q_{i+1}$, where B_i is finite. Therefore q_{i+1} must be positively infinite which can occur only when at least one of the numbers $\eta_{1,i+1}$ and $\eta_{2,i+1}$ is numerically infinite.

The proof of this theorem for the case when A and B are determinants of the n-th order can be carried out in essentially the same way as the one just given for two variables.

THEOREM II. *Let* a_{ijt} $(i, j=1, 2;\ t=1, 2, \ldots k)$ *be any set of real numbers in which* $a_{ijt}=a_{jit}$ *for* $i\neq j$, *and such that the matrix* $||a_{ijt}||$ *is positive definite, and let* $A=|A_{ij}|$, *where*

$$A_{ij}=\sum_{t=1}^{k} p_t a_{ijt} \qquad \text{(i)},$$

and the p's are positive such that $\Sigma p_t=1$. *Then, if*

$$\theta=\frac{\prod_{t=1}^{k}|a_{ijt}|^{p_t}}{A} \qquad \text{(ii)},$$

we have

(*a*) $0\leqslant\theta\leqslant 1$,

(*b*) *a necessary and sufficient condition that* $\theta=1$ *when* $|a_{ijt}|>0$ $(t=1, 2, \ldots k)$ *is that* $a_{ijt}=a_{ijt'}$ $(i, j=1, 2;\ t, t'=1, 2, \ldots k)$; *that is, that the matrices* $||a_{ijt}||$ *be identical.*

PROOF: For the one-variable case, that is, when $i=j=1$, the theorem simply states that the weighted geometric mean of a set of positive numbers cannot exceed the weighted arithmetic mean of the set, and that the means can be equal only when all of the numbers are equal. The proof for this case can be found in a number of advanced algebra text-books and will be assumed.

The sufficient condition in (*b*) is obvious. Thus, let us consider the necessary condition. For convenience let

$$\phi=A-G \qquad \text{(iii)},$$

where

$$G=\prod_{t=1}^{k} d_t^{p_t} \quad \text{and} \quad d_t=|a_{ijt}|.$$

Then the theorem reduces to the problem of showing that $\phi\geqslant 0$, where the equality will hold only when the matrices $||a_{ijt}||$ are identical. Consider the minimum of ϕ for variations of the a's. If it exists, it will be given by the equations $(t=1, 2, \ldots k)$,

$$\frac{\partial\phi}{\partial a_{11t}}=p_t A_{22}-p_t\frac{a_{22t}}{d_t}G=0 \qquad \text{(iv)},$$

$$\frac{\partial\phi}{\partial a_{22t}}=p_t A_{11}-p_t\frac{a_{11t}}{d_t}G=0 \qquad \text{(v)},$$

$$\frac{\partial\phi}{\partial a_{12t}}=-2p_t A_{12}+2p_t\frac{a_{12t}}{d_t}G=0 \qquad \text{(vi)}.$$

By a straightforward combination of the first equation for all values of t,

$$A_{22}=\prod_{t=1}^{k} a_{22t}^{p_t} \qquad \text{(vii)}.$$

Similarly, with respect to (v),

$$A_{11}=\prod_{t=1}^{k} a_{11t}{}^{p_t} \quad\text{.......................................(viii).}$$

From (vi)

$$a_{12t}d_{t'}=a_{12t'}d_t \qquad (t,\ t'=1,\ 2,\ \ldots\ k) \quad\text{..................(ix).}$$

But from the case of a single variable (vii) and (viii) can hold only when

$$a_{11t}=a_{11t'},\quad a_{22t}=a_{22t'} \qquad (t,\ t'=1,\ 2,\ \ldots\ k) \quad\text{..............(x).}$$

Call their common values a_{11} and a_{22} respectively.

Placing these values in (ix) which must hold for all values of a_{11} and a_{22}, we get at once that

$$a_{12t}=a_{12t'} \qquad (t,\ t'=1,\ 2,\ \ldots\ k) \quad\text{......................(xi).}$$

Let the common value be a_{12}. Therefore (iv), (v) and (vi) are satisfied only when the matrices $||a_{ijt}||$ are identical. The matrix of second order derivatives of ϕ with respect to the a_{ijt} can be shown to be positive definite when (iv), (v) and (vi) are satisfied, provided $||a_{ij}||$ is positive definite. Thus, ϕ has a true minimum, and since the minimum is zero, and G is positive (a) follows at once. The generalisation of this theorem to the case where $i, j=1,\ 2,\ \ldots\ n$ is straightforward.

THE USE OF CONFIDENCE OR FIDUCIAL LIMITS ILLUSTRATED IN THE CASE OF THE BINOMIAL.

By C. J. CLOPPER, B.Sc., and E. S. PEARSON, D.Sc.

(1) *General Discussion.*

In facing the problem of statistical estimation it may often be desirable to obtain from a random sample a single estimate, say a, of the value of an unknown parameter, α, in the population sampled. It has always, however, been realised that this single value is of little use unless associated with a measure of its reliability, and the traditional practice has been to give with a its probable error (or more recently its standard error), in the form

$$a \pm p.e(a) \quad \text{.....................................(1).}$$

From this information it was possible, if the sample was not too small, to draw the conclusion that the unknown value of α lay within the limits

$$\alpha_1 = a - 3 \times p.e(a) \quad \text{and} \quad \alpha_2 = a + 3 \times p.e(a) \quad \text{..............(2)}$$

with a high degree of probability. But it was neither easy to give any precise definition of this measure of probability nor to assess the extent of error involved in estimating the value of $p.e(a)$ from the sample.

The recent work of R. A. Fisher introducing the conception of the fiducial interval has made it possible under certain conditions to treat this problem of estimation in a simple yet powerful manner*. It is proposed in the present paper to illustrate on the following problem the ideas involved in this method of approach.

A sample of n units is randomly drawn from a very large population in which the proportion of units bearing a certain character, A, is p. In the sample x individuals bear the character A and $n-x$ do not. p is unknown and the problem is to obtain limits p_1 and p_2 such that we may feel with a given degree of confidence that

$$p_1 < p < p_2 \quad \text{.....................................(3).}$$

In the first place, how is this degree of confidence to be defined? The underlying conception involved in all problems of this type is extremely simple. In our statistical experience it is likely that we shall meet many values of n and of x; a rule must be laid down for determining p_1 and p_2 given n and x. Our confidence that p lies within the interval (p_1, p_2) will depend upon the proportion of times that this prediction is correct in the long run of statistical experience, and this

* R. A. Fisher, *Proc. Camb. Phil. Soc.* 26 (1930), p. 528; *Proc. Roy. Soc.* A 139 (1933), p. 343. References to the discussion of these concepts in lectures may also be found in papers published by students of J. Neyman. See for instance pp. 28—29 of a paper by W. Pytkowski written in 1929—30 and published at Warsaw in 1932, entitled, "The dependence of the income in small farms upon their area, the outlay and the capital invested in cows."

may be termed the *confidence coefficient.* Thus subject to certain approximations discussed below, arising from the fact that x can assume only discrete integral values in this particular problem, it is possible to choose the fiducial or confidence limits p_1 and p_2 in such a manner that, for example, the prediction

(1) will be correct in 95 °/。 of cases met with in the long run of experience, and wrong in 5 °/。, in 2·5 °/。 because $p \leqslant p_1$, and 2·5 °/。 because $p \geqslant p_2$.

Or again,

(2) will be correct in 99 °/。 of cases and wrong in 1 °/。, in 0·5 °/。 because $p \leqslant p_1$, and in 0·5 °/。 because $p \geqslant p_2$.

These intervals (p_1, p_2) may be termed either the central* confidence or

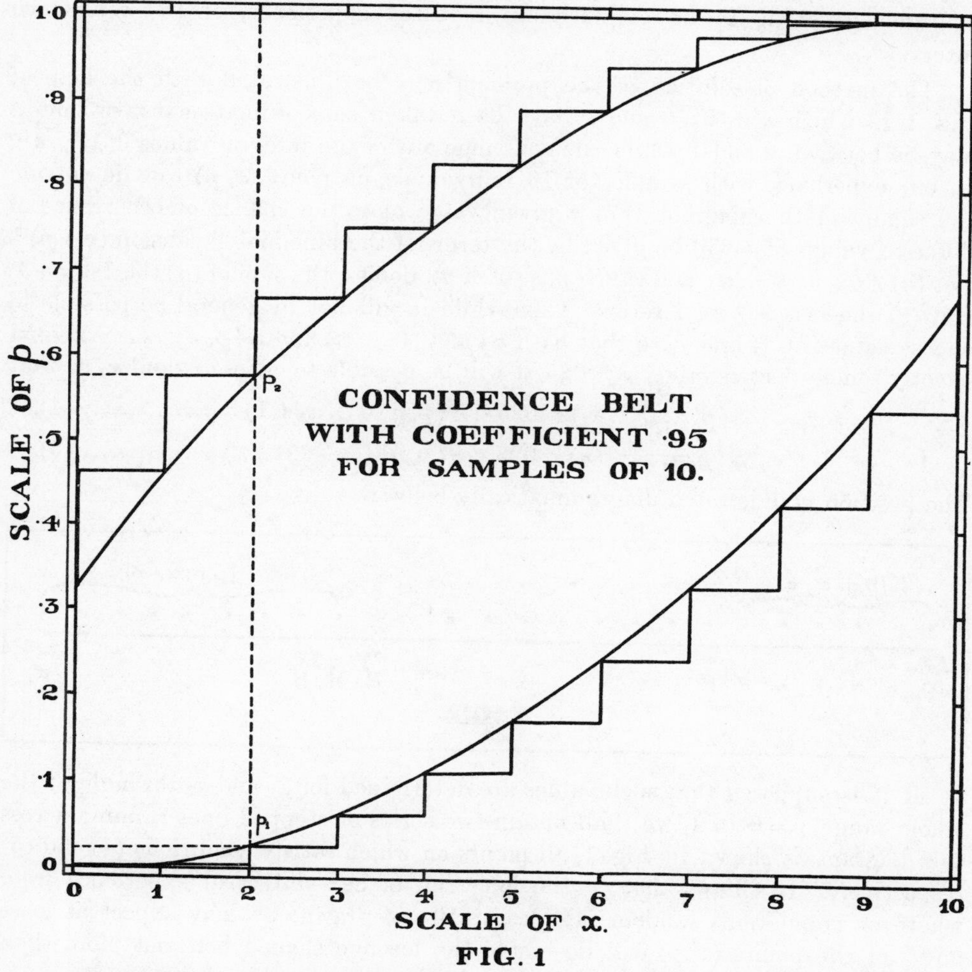

FIG. 1

* In the charts described below the coefficients ·95 and ·99 were chosen as giving two useful pairs of limits. It is not essential that the intervals chosen should be "central," but for many purposes this appears to be the most convenient arrangement.

central fiducial intervals and are associated with confidence coefficients of ·95 and ·99 respectively. In his development of the subject, R. A. Fisher has used the term "fiducial probability" to describe the chance that in the long run a correct prediction will be made of the limits within which the unknown parameter falls. The concept of fiducial probability cannot, it appears, be distinguished from that of ordinary probability, and it seems possible that the use of this term may lead to some misunderstanding, especially when associated with a "fiducial distribution." We are inclined therefore to adopt the terminology suggested by J. Neyman, and to convey what is fundamentally the same notion by specifying the confidence coefficient associated with an interval. Thus the confidence coefficient may be regarded as a particular value of the fiducial probability selected to form the basis of the calculation, to be employed in repeated experience, of the confidence interval*.

The method of solution of the problem may be illustrated with the help of Fig. 1, in which $n = 10$; p and x have been taken as coordinate axes, so that p may lie between 0 and 1, while x may assume any of the integral values 0, 1, ... 10. In our experience with samples of 10 individuals, no point (x, p) can lie outside the square of the diagram. For a given value of p, the chance of occurrence of different values of x will be given by the terms of the binomial expansion $(q+p)^{10}$. Let (*a*) $S(p, n;\ 0 \ldots x)$, and (*b*) $S(p, n;\ x \ldots n)$, denote the sum of (*a*) the 1st $x+1$, and (*b*) the last $n-x+1$ terms. Then while it will not in general be possible to choose values of x_1 and x_2 so that both $S(p, n;\ 0 \ldots x_1)$ and $S(p, n;\ x_2 \ldots n)$ equal exactly some selected value, say ·025, it will be possible to choose x_1 and x_2 so that

$$S(p, n; 0 \ldots x_1) \leqslant \cdot 025 < S(p, n; 0 \ldots x_1+1) \quad \ldots\ldots\ldots\ldots\ldots\ldots (4),$$

$$S(p, n; x_2 \ldots n) \leqslant \cdot 025 < S(p, n; (x_2-1) \ldots n) \quad \ldots\ldots\ldots\ldots\ldots (5).$$

The position is illustrated diagrammatically below:

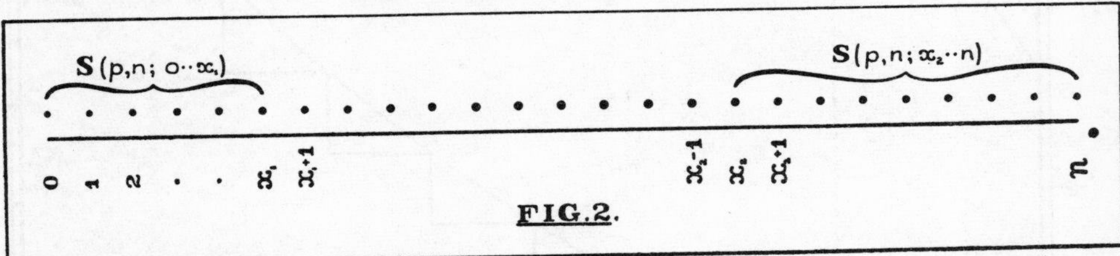

FIG. 2.

If it is supposed that such values are determined for x_1 and x_2 throughout the whole range, $p = 0$ to 1, we shall obtain two series of stepped lines running across the diagram as shown in Fig. 1, all points on which satisfy conditions (4) and (5) respectively. It follows that in the long run of our statistical experience from whatever populations random samples of 10 are drawn, we may expect at least 95 °/。 of the points (x, p) will lie inside the lozenge shaped belt, not more than

* J. Neyman, "On the two different aspects of the representative method: the method of stratified sampling and the method of purposive selection," *Journal of Royal Statistical Society*, xcvii. pp. 558—606, 1934.

$2\frac{1}{2}$ °/. on or above the upper boundary and not more than $2\frac{1}{2}$ °/. on or below the lower boundary. If then as a general rule, when x alone is known these boundaries are used to determine points (x, p_1) and (x, p_2), we may have confidence that we shall be correct in the estimate $p_1 < p < p_2$ in about 95 °/. of cases. If greater confidence is desired, we may determine wider limits leading to a higher value of the expected percentage accuracy, e.g. 99 °/.. In the diagram, values of p_1 and p_2 corresponding to $x = 2$ are shown.

This plan has been carried out below with the following modifications adopted for practical convenience:

(1) The charts prepared are entered with p and $\theta = x/n$, so that $0 \leqslant \theta \leqslant 1$, and boundaries for a number of values of n can be drawn on the same chart.

(2) Instead of the stepped boundaries, curves have been drawn as in Fig. 1 passing through the inner "corner" points, i.e. the points $(x_1 p)$ and $(x_2 p)$ for which p is such that $S(p, n; 0 \ldots x_1)$ and $S(p, n; x_2 \ldots n)$ are exactly equal to the desired chance (in the cases chosen, these chances are ·025 and ·005). These curves are more convenient than the stepped lines for interpolation for intermediate values of n. Since no possible point (x, p) can fall inside the area between a curve and the steps, no error is involved in using the curves.

(3) While the "corner" points could have been calculated precisely and the curves drawn through them, it was considered sufficiently accurate for the purpose to obtain the curves by an approximate method of interpolation described below.

Before describing the charts and illustrating their use, it may be well to make clear the sense in which this method of estimation in terms of a confidence or fiducial interval does not depend on any *a priori* knowledge regarding possible values of p. Consider the following situation. Suppose that in the course of our experience samples of 30 are continually drawn, and that although we are not aware of the fact, these are taken from populations in which p has three different values only, namely $\frac{1}{3}$, $\frac{1}{2}$ and $\frac{2}{3}$. Further that the proportions of times these three cases are met with are as $\frac{8}{10} : \frac{1}{10} : \frac{1}{10}$ respectively.

The expectation, on a basis of 10,000 draws, is shown in Fig. 3, in which the axes of p and x have been reversed for convenience. For example, for $p = \frac{1}{3}$, $x = 12$, the expectation is 881, while for $p = \frac{2}{3}$, $x = 28$, it is 1. The chart of Fig. 4 described below will provide for each of the 31 possible values of x the limits for the confidence interval, with coefficient ·95, for p. Thus when $x = 15$, we find $p_1 = ·31$, $p_2 = ·69$. Taken over the whole experience, these intervals include the true population value of p in 9676 out of the 10,000 cases, and in the remaining 324 do not, that is to say we are wrong in less than 5 % of cases. This is the risk of error that we have accepted, and it is quite independent of the particular set of three values of p introduced, or the relative frequency with which they are encountered in our experience.

It will be noticed, however, from the figures in the margin, that the percentage of wrong judgments differs according to the value of x, from 100 to 0. We cannot

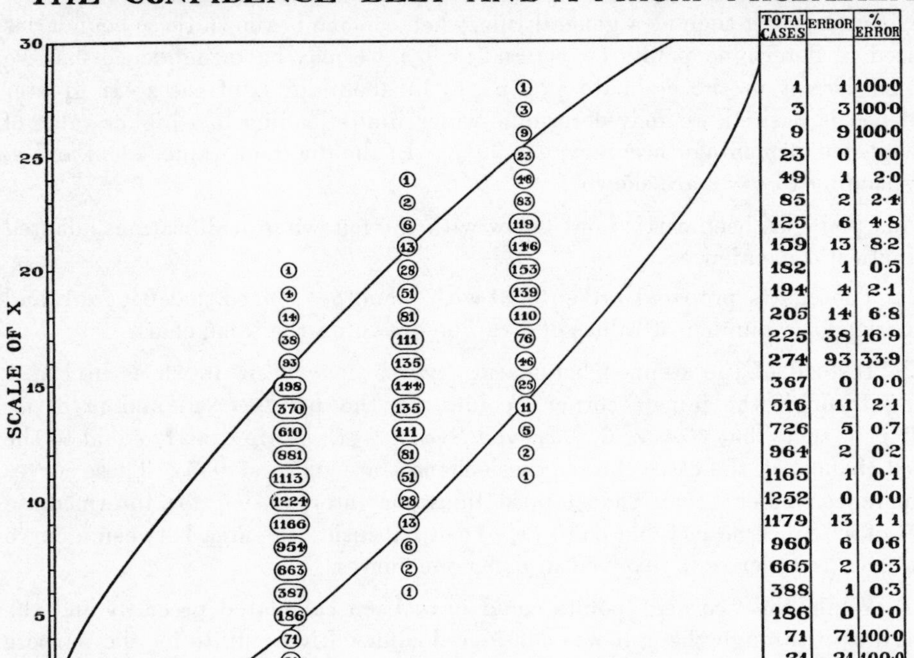

TOTAL CASES	ERROR	% ERROR
1	1	100·0
3	3	100·0
9	9	100·0
23	0	0·0
49	1	2·0
85	2	2·4
125	6	4·8
159	13	8·2
182	1	0·5
194	4	2·1
205	14	6·8
225	38	16·9
274	93	33·9
367	0	0·0
516	11	2·1
726	5	0·7
964	2	0·2
1165	1	0·1
1252	0	0·0
1179	13	1 1
960	6	0·6
665	2	0·3
388	1	0·3
186	0	0·0
71	71	100·0
21	21	100·0
5	5	100·0
1	1	100·0

FIG. 3.

therefore say that for any specified value of x the probability that the confidence interval will include p is ·95 or more. The probability must be associated with the whole belt, that is to say with the result of the continued application of a method of procedure to all values of x met with in our statistical experience.

Indeed it will be clear that *if* we had information *a priori* regarding the values of p likely to be met in our experience, and if this information could be expressed in precise numerical form, it would be possible to shift the confidence belt and so narrow the limits of uncertainty while retaining the same risk of error. For instance, if we knew that $\frac{1}{3} \leqslant p \leqslant \frac{2}{3}$, we should certainly cut off the two points of the lozenge by lines at $p = \frac{1}{3}$ and $p = \frac{2}{3}$.

In practice, however, it is rare

(1) for the *a priori* information to be expressed in exact form,

(2) even when it appears so expressible, for the working statistician to have time to calculate suitable modification for the limits.

Under general conditions, therefore, the statistician will usually be satisfied with limits which are "safe" in the sense that they give an expectation of long run accuracy which is precisely known*, and thus avoid the uncertain risk of error involved in an attempt to introduce *a priori* information.

(2) *Calculation and use of the charts.*

The following method was employed in obtaining points from which to draw the curves in Figs. 4 and 5.

Samples with $n = 10, 15, 20, 30$.

Use was made of the tables giving the continued sum of the binomial terms, published in one of the Medical Research Council's Reports†. From these tables it is possible to find the sum of any number of binomial terms for $p = {\cdot}025, {\cdot}05, {\cdot}075, {\cdot}10, {\cdot}15, {\cdot}20, \ldots, {\cdot}85, {\cdot}90, {\cdot}925, {\cdot}95, {\cdot}975$. It will happen only rarely that for these values of p, $S(p, n; 0 \ldots x_1)$ or $S(p, n; x_2 \ldots n)$ approach the desired values of ·025 or ·005, i.e. that we can obtain directly the inside "corners" of the steps of Fig. 1. For the purpose of the charts, however, it was considered that sufficient accuracy would be obtained by interpolation for x in the tables. Take for example the case of $n = 20$ and consider the sums of the binomial terms for $p = 0{\cdot}45$ given below. At what points should the two curves associated with $n = 20$ cut the lines

x	$S({\cdot}45, 20; 0 \ldots x)$	x	$S({\cdot}45, 20; 0 \ldots x)$
0	·0000	8	·4143
1	·0001	9	·5914
2	·0009	10	·7507
3	·0049	11	·8692
4	·0189	12	·9420
5	·0553	13	·9786
6	·1299	14	·9936
7	·2520	15	·9985

$p = {\cdot}45$ in the charts? The point $x = 3$ $(x/n = {\cdot}150)$ is approximately a "corner" point, since the sum of the first 4 terms equals almost exactly ·005, but the other points must be obtained by interpolation. Thus we argue:

(*a*) *The lower* ·025 *point.* The sum of the terms $0 \ldots 4$ is ·0189 $(< {\cdot}025)$, and the sum of the terms $0 \ldots 5$ is ·0553 $(> {\cdot}025)$; a linear interpolation‡ gives for x, 4·17 $(x/n = {\cdot}208)$.

(*b*) *The upper* ·025 *point.* The sum of the terms $13 \ldots 20$ is $1 - {\cdot}9420 = {\cdot}0580$, and the sum $14 \ldots 20$ is $1 - {\cdot}9786 = {\cdot}0214$. Take $x = 13{\cdot}90$ $(x/n = {\cdot}695)$.

(*c*) *The upper* ·005 *point.* The sum of the terms $15 \ldots 20$ is $1 - {\cdot}9936 = {\cdot}0064$, and the sum $16 \ldots 20$ is $1 - {\cdot}9985 = {\cdot}0015$. Take $x = 15{\cdot}29$ $(x/n = {\cdot}764)$.

* This is not strictly true of course, since only an upper limit to the error is known, owing to the fact that x can assume discrete values only. As n increases, however, the true risk will rapidly approach the limiting value. In cases where the coefficient, x, is a continuous variable such as a sample mean or standard deviation, this difficulty does not arise.

† *Reports on Biological Standards*, "II. Toxicity Tests for Novarsenobenzene," by Durham, Gaddum and Marchal.

‡ This form of interpolation, if crude, appeared adequate for the curve drawing.

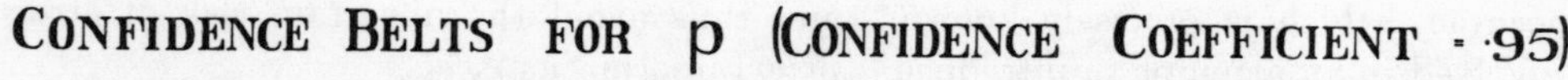
CONFIDENCE BELTS FOR p (CONFIDENCE COEFFICIENT ·95)

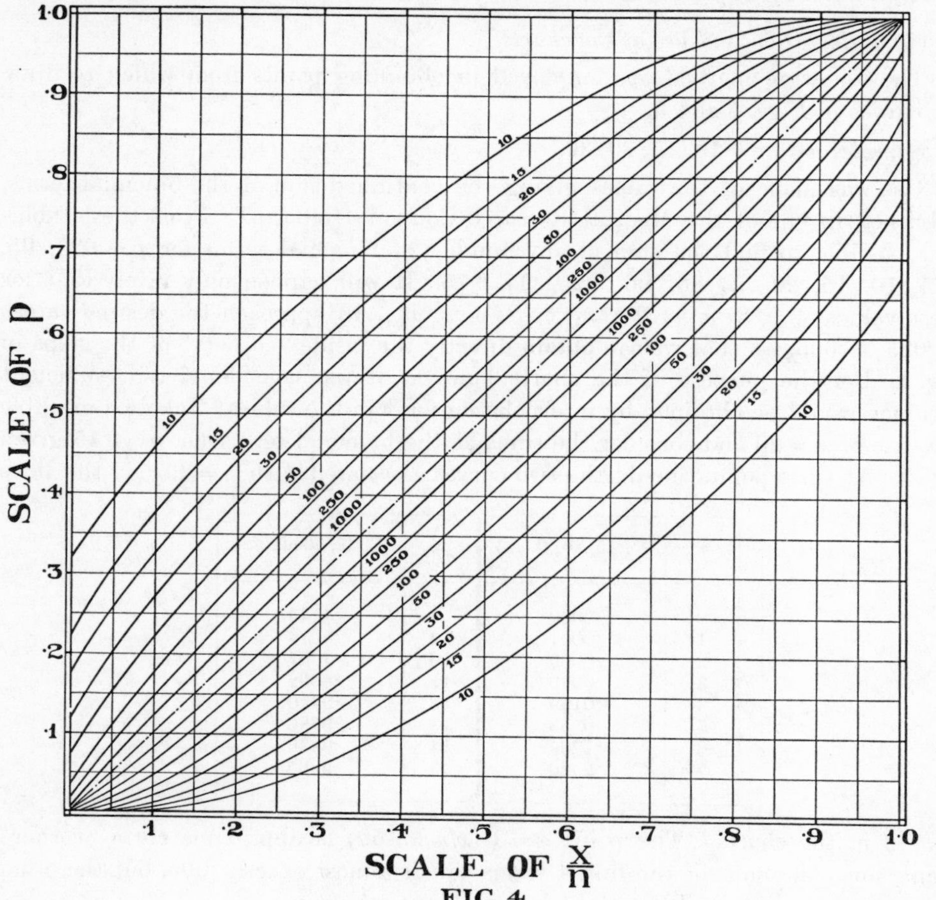

FIG. 4.

Consequently in Fig. 4 the curves marked $n = 20$ cut the line $p = {\cdot}45$ at $x/n = {\cdot}208$ and ·695, and in Fig. 5 at $x/n = {\cdot}150$ and ·764.

Fresh calculations of binomial terms were made for $n = 50$, 100 and 250, while the limits were obtained from the normal curve in the case $n = 1000$.

It will be noted that the curves cut the axis $x/n = 0$ at points at some distance from $p = 0$ when n is small. The points of intersection correspond in the two diagrams to those values of p for which the first term of the binomial $q^n = (1-p)^n$ equals ·025 and ·005 respectively. On the other side, the end points on the axis $x/n = 1$ correspond to values of p for which the last term, p^n, equals ·025 and ·005.

The charts have been prepared to give rapid answers in problems such as the following:

(1) A sample has been drawn (n and x known), to obtain the confidence or fiducial interval for p.

CONFIDENCE BELTS FOR p (CONFIDENCE COEFFICIENT -·99)

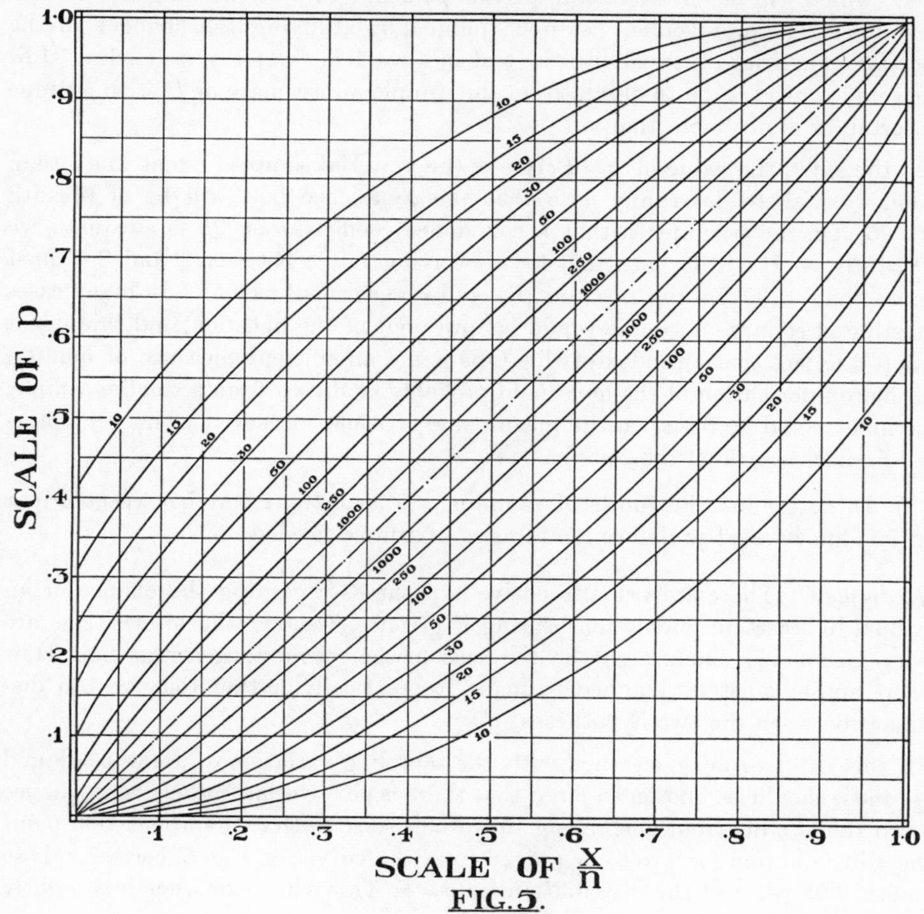

FIG. 5.

Example A. The toxicity of a drug may be measured by the proportion, p, of mice in a standard laboratory population that will die after injection with a dose of given strength. Out of a sample of 30 mice randomly selected from the population, 8 die after injection; within what limits may we expect that p lies? Turning to Fig. 4, and taking $n = 30$, $x/n = 8/30 = {\cdot}267$, it will be seen that we may say that ${\cdot}12 < p < {\cdot}46$, if we are prepared to accept a risk of error of not more than 1 in 20. To obtain greater confidence in prediction (risk of error 1 in 100) we must turn to Fig. 5 and obtain ${\cdot}09 < p < {\cdot}52$.

(2) To plan in advance the size of sample necessary to provide a desired degree of accuracy in estimation.

Example B. In a manufacturing process a crude index of quality, P, has been the percentage of articles which pass a certain test. This index has fluctuated in the past round $P = 60$, but it is proposed to make an intensive effort to improve quality (which will mean the raising of this percentage) by tightening the control of manufacture. Improvement is to be judged by studying the changes in the proportion of articles (x/n) passing the test in a random sample of n articles. How large would n need to be to obtain from the sample an estimate of P, with a range of uncertainty of not more than 5 ?

At the start, the value of $p = P/100$ in the material sampled is not more than ·60, and we wish to determine n so that the confidence belt will be of breadth about ·05. On the assumption that a confidence coefficient of ·95 is adequate, we may use Fig. 4. It will be seen that for x/n having values between ·6 and ·8, n must be more than 1000 for the interval $p_2 - p_1$ to be as small as ·05*. In many cases the testing of so large a sample would be quite out of the question, and this result points to the fact that an index of this type is not an efficient measure of quality. Much more information of changes could probably be drawn from a smaller sample, if the index could be based on the mean value of some measured character determined for each article of the sample.

(3) To determine the limits of sampling variation that may be expected in x when p is known, and so determine the size of sample needed.

Example C. There are two alternative hypotheses regarding the chance of an individual in a certain population bearing a given character; the alternatives are that $p = \frac{1}{4}$ or $p = \frac{1}{2}$. Such might be the case in some genetic investigation. How large a sample must be planned to make it practically certain that we can discriminate between the two hypotheses ?

In this case we are concerned with the sampling variation of x for $p = \frac{1}{4}$ and $p = \frac{1}{2}$, and n should be chosen so large that there is no "overlap" of any consequence between the two distributions. Suppose we choose n so that the upper ·005 point of the x distribution for $p = \frac{1}{4}$, as judged from the curves of Fig. 5, corresponds to the lower ·005 point of the distribution for $p = \frac{1}{2}$. This will occur when n is slightly over 100, say 110†.

* Since for large values of n the upper and lower bounds of the confidence belt are very nearly parallel lines making an angle of 45° with the axes, and the binomial may be represented by a normal curve, the breadth of the belt is approximately $4\sqrt{p(1-p)/n}$, which if equated to ·05 gives $n = 1600$ for $p = {\cdot}60$ and $n = 1000$ for $p = {\cdot}80$.

† [It is interesting to consider what the solution would be, if the two binomials, $(p_1 + q_1)^n$ and $(p_2 + q_2)^n$, were replaced by normal curves. The means of these curves will be np_1 and np_2 $(p_2 > p_1)$ while their standard deviations will be $\sigma_1 = \sqrt{np_1 q_1}$ and $\sigma_2 = \sqrt{np_2 q_2}$. Let l represent the overlap and x_1 represent the distance from mean to overlap in first curve and x_2 represent distance from overlap to mean in second curve. Accordingly

$$n(p_2 - p_1) = x_1 + x_2 \quad \text{...(i).}$$

If l be the overlap, and $\frac{1}{2}(1 - \alpha_1)$ be the area cut off from the first curve and $\frac{1}{2}(1 - \alpha_2)$ from the second curve, it will be reasonable to take

$$\tfrac{1}{2}(1 - \alpha_1) = \tfrac{1}{2}(1 - \alpha_2) = \tfrac{1}{2}l.$$

Thus x_1/σ_1 and x_2/σ_2 must be obtained from the tables of the normal probability integral with $\frac{1}{2}(1 + \alpha) = 1 - \frac{1}{2}l$, or say they have the value ξ.

If we were prepared to accept a greater risk of an inconclusive result, which we might well be prepared to do if the sample could be readily increased in size in a doubtful case, then we might choose n so that the upper and lower ·025 points of the x distributions correspond. Turning to Fig. 4, it is found that this occurs when n is about 65.

It follows from (i) that

$$n(p_2 - p_1) = \xi(\sqrt{np_1q_1} + \sqrt{np_2q_2})$$

or

$$\sqrt{n} = \frac{\xi(\sqrt{p_1q_1} + \sqrt{p_2q_2})}{p_2 - p_1} \qquad \text{(ii).}$$

In the case in the text $p_1 = \frac{1}{4}$, $p_2 = \frac{1}{2}$ and $l = \cdot 005$, $1 - \frac{1}{2}l = \cdot 9975$, which corresponds to $\xi = 2\cdot 81$ nearly. Thus $\sqrt{n} = 2\cdot 81(\sqrt{3} + 2) = 2\cdot 81 \times 3\cdot 7205 = 10\cdot 455$ and $n = 109\cdot 3$, according well with the value in the text. If we desire to alter the overlap, the first factor ξ only is changed in (ii). If $l = \cdot 025$, then $\frac{1}{2}(1 + a) = \cdot 9875$ and $\xi = 2\cdot 2416$ $\sqrt{n} = 2\cdot 2416 \times 3\cdot 7205 = 8\cdot 34$ and $n = 69\cdot 6$, or 70 as against 65 of text above. Ed.]

THE EFFICIENCY OF STATISTICAL TOOLS AND A CRITERION FOR THE REJECTION OF OUTLYING OBSERVATIONS.

By E. S. PEARSON, assisted by C. CHANDRA SEKAR.

1. *Thompson's criterion.*

In an interesting paper recently published in the *Annals of Mathematical Statistics**, Dr William R. Thompson has suggested a new criterion for the rejection of outlying observations. If $x_1, x_2, \ldots x_N$ represent a series of observed values of a variable x, and

$$\bar{x} = \sum_{i=1}^{N} (x_i)/N, \quad s^2 = \sum_{i=1}^{N} (x_i - \bar{x})^2/N \quad \ldots\ldots\ldots\ldots\ldots\ldots\ldots(1),$$

then Thompson writes

$$\tau_i = (x_i - \bar{x})/s \quad \ldots\ldots\ldots\ldots\ldots\ldots\ldots\ldots\ldots\ldots\ldots\ldots(2).$$

He then shows that if x_i is an observation arbitrarily selected from a random sample of N drawn from an infinite normal population, then the elementary probability distribution of τ is

$$p(\tau) = \frac{\Gamma\left(\frac{N-1}{2}\right)}{\sqrt{(N-1)\pi}\,\Gamma\left(\frac{N-2}{2}\right)}\left(1 - \frac{\tau^2}{N-1}\right)^{\frac{N-4}{2}} \quad \ldots\ldots\ldots\ldots(3).$$

This is a symmetrical limited range distribution of Pearson's Type II; the probability integral of the τ-distribution may be found directly from appropriate tables†, or by noticing that if we write

$$\tau = t\sqrt{\frac{N-1}{N-2+t^2}} \quad \ldots\ldots\ldots\ldots\ldots\ldots\ldots\ldots\ldots\ldots\ldots(4),$$

then t follows Student's distribution having $N-2$ degrees of freedom, for which tables of probability levels are available‡. It will also be noted that τ is distributed as $r\sqrt{N-1}$, where r is the coefficient of correlation between N pairs of observations randomly drawn from two completely independent normal distributions.

It is clear—and consequences following from this will be discussed later—that the N values of τ given by the observations of a single sample are not independent. It is however true to say that if for any randomly chosen x_i we denote the probability that the absolute value of τ_i is greater than a specified value, say τ_0, by

$$P = P\{|\tau_i| > \tau_0\} = 2\int_{\tau_0}^{\sqrt{N-1}} p(\tau)\,d\tau \quad \ldots\ldots\ldots\ldots\ldots\ldots\ldots(5),$$

* Vol. VI. (1935), pp. 214—219.

† *Tables for Statisticians and Biometricians*, Part II, Table XXV.

‡ See Student, *Metron*, Vol. V. (1925), pp. 105—120, R. A. Fisher, *Statistical Methods for Research Workers* (1935), Table IV.

and write $\phi = NP$, then ϕ is the expectation of the number of observations per sample of N drawn from a single normal population for which

$$|x_i - \bar{x}| > \tau_0 s \quad\text{.................................}(6).$$

In other words, if we decide to reject all observations for which the inequality (6) is true, then in the long run we shall reject one observation, on the average, in every $1/\phi$ samples unnecessarily, i.e. when all the observations have in fact been drawn from a common normal population.

Thompson has given a Table of the limits, τ_0, for three values of ϕ, namely 0·2, 0·1 and 0·05, and for the following values of N,

3, 4, ... 21, 22, 32, 42, 102, 202, 502, 1002.

Thus using the second value of ϕ, (0·1), and the rule of rejection denoted by the inequality (6), we shall on the average reject unnecessarily one observation per 10 samples; this figure will be the same whatever the value of N.

An alternative form of Table would be one in which limits, τ_0, were given for fixed values of $P = \phi/N$; thus ϕ would increase and $1/\phi$ decrease with the sample size. If for example $P = {}$·01, the observer would be likely, on the average, to discard unnecessarily one observation in every 10 samples when each of these contained 10 observations, one in every sample when it contained 100, and 10 in every sample when it contained 1000 observations. The fixing of ϕ or of P is, however, a matter of choice, the basis of Thompson's criterion being simply the equation (3) giving the probability distribution of τ.

It will be found that the great majority of criteria that have been invented for rejecting outlying observations contain as an initial condition the assumption that σ, the standard deviation in the hypothetical common population, is known*. Under certain circumstances this may be true, as for example when dealing with errors of observation where the value of σ may be estimated with great precision from past experience. Generally, however, in practice it is necessary to substitute into the formulae obtained the standard deviation calculated from the sample of observations under consideration, and this limitation, sometimes frankly recognised by the inventor of the test, sometimes apparently overlooked, renders inaccurate the probability basis upon which the criterion rests.

Dr Thompson's criterion is free from this defect; it provides, by a process which has sometimes been termed "studentizing," a true measure of the risk of rejecting an observation when in fact the whole sample has been drawn from a single normal distribution. In other words, if we describe the application of the criterion as that of testing the hypothesis, say H_0, that the sample has been drawn from a single normal population, then Thompson's method gives precise control of the risk of rejecting H_0 when it is true. This is what J. Neyman and E. S. Pearson† in their

* For an extensive survey of such tests see P. R. Rider, *Washington University Studies, Science and Technology*, No. 8 (1933).

† See, for example, *Biometrika*, Vol. xx^A. (1928), pp. 175—240, *Phil. Trans. Roy. Soc.* Vol. CCXXXI. A (1933), pp. 289—337 and *Statistical Research Memoirs* (issued by the Department of Statistics, University College, London), Vol. I. (1936), pp. 1—37.

general treatment of the theory of testing statistical hypotheses have termed the control of the first kind of error. It is, however, necessary to point out that by satisfying this condition alone it does not follow that an efficient tool has been placed in the hands of the experimenter.

This consideration has so important a bearing on the choice of statistical tests in general that it has seemed to us worth while discussing in some detail the conditions under which it appears that Thompson's method provides an efficient criterion for the rejection of outlying observations.

2. *The efficiency of statistical tools.*

What requirements should the theoretical statistician bear in mind in constructing efficient working tools for the experimenter? We think he may usefully remember two considerations which are of general application in the construction of any scientific exploratory tool:

(*a*) A tool is devised for use under certain limited conditions and will only be fully efficient as long as these conditions are satisfied.

(*b*) To test whether these conditions hold good other tools are generally needed.

An illustration of the meaning of these points from a non-statistical field may be useful. The lead-line is used at sea to measure the depth of the ocean bottom. Soundings at fixed but discrete intervals of time may be taken from a moving ship either by the hydrographer who is engaged on a survey of the ocean bottom, or by the navigator who in a fog, using the hydrographer's chart, wishes to test the hypothesis that his ship is just entering a certain channel. In both cases an assumption is made that changes in the sea bottom are gradual; if there might exist unknown pinnacled rocks of great height, sudden changes in contour or sunken ships, the lead, cast at discrete intervals of time, would be an inefficient, and even dangerous, tool to rely upon. Further, some form of dragging operation, rather than sounding, would be required to test whether it was justifiable to assume the bottom to be free from sudden changes.

The same considerations will be found to apply in the case of nearly all the tools of physical and biological science, although in many cases the conditions are so universally satisfied that the worker hardly stops to remember that limitations to the efficiency of the tool exist.

Keeping these points in mind, we may turn to the problem of the theoretical statistician who is concerned with the design of statistical tools. In the first place it must be noted that, as in other branches of applied mathematics, it is necessary for him to construct a precise but probably a simplified model which he believes will represent the phenomena of observation with sufficient accuracy to provide useful results. In so far as there is a practical problem to solve, this model will contain certain unknowns, and what is required is to devise the most effective method of obtaining information from the data concerning these unknowns. The tool will only be efficient provided that the model is appropriate, or, in other words, provided certain conditions are satisfied. To determine whether this is the case, a different set of tools will generally be required.

Some of the chief procedures of statistical analysis may usefully be classified under two heads:

(1) *The estimation of characteristics of a population*, that is to say the estimation of the values of unknowns in our model. The old procedure was to record a single-valued estimate of the unknown parameter and attach to it a probable error. More recently the conception of the confidence or fiducial interval has been introduced*. In either case the procedures employed have only a precise meaning in so far as it is possible to specify in mathematical terms the alternative forms of population distribution that are considered possible. For example, the standard error of a sample correlation coefficient, r, as ordinarily calculated, or the confidence interval, (ρ_1, ρ_2)†, have no exact meaning unless we can assume that the population distribution is of the normal form. Further, to test the validity of this assumption a different form of test is required.

(2) *The testing of statistical hypotheses.* Here the problem is to determine whether it is likely that certain unknowns in the model have specified values. In Dr Thompson's case, the problem is to test whether the sample has been drawn from a single normal population, but it is not possible to devise an efficient test if we only bring into the picture this single normal probability distribution with its two unknown parameters. We must also ask how sensitive the test is in detecting failure of the data to comply with the hypothesis tested, and to deal with this question effectively we must be able to specify the directions in which the hypothesis may fail. In other words, an efficient test of a statistical hypothesis, H_0, must be associated with a set of admissible alternative hypotheses and not solely with H_0. This set provides the model on which the statistical tool-maker can set to work.

Even when the alternatives cannot be specified in such precise form as to allow mathematical methods to be applied to full advantage, we feel sure that much is gained by a review of the types of alternatives between which it is wished to discriminate.

3. *Limitations of the τ criterion.*

Approaching from this point of view the problem of testing the hypothesis, H_0, that a sample of N observations has been drawn from a single normal population, we must ask what are the possible alternatives. Unless it is possible to conceive some alternative to H_0 there would be no justification in rejecting outlying observations. In the first place we are presumably making the assumption that the majority of observations come from some single normal population‡; we believe

* R. A. Fisher, *Proc. Camb. Phil. Soc.* Vol. xxvi. (1930), p. 528; J. Neyman, *Journ. Roy. Stat. Soc.* Vol. xcvii. (1934), p. 589; E. S. Pearson and J. C. Clopper, *Biometrika*, Vol. xxvi. (1934), pp. 404—413.

† Tables which will facilitate the calculation of these intervals prepared by Miss F. N. David will be issued shortly as a *Biometrika* Publication.

‡ If an admissible alternative to H_0 were that the observations came from a single non-normal population, then what would be required would be a test of normality, not a test for the rejection of outlying observations

however that it is possible that one or two of them do not belong to this set. We may therefore perhaps adequately represent the situation by using the following model: alternative to H_0 are hypotheses that k of the observations ($k \geqslant 1$) come from s normal populations ($s \leqslant k$) having different means or standard deviations (or both) from the single population from which the majority ($N-k$) of the observations have been drawn. The assumption of normality in the other populations is not necessary, but as far as the present discussion goes nothing is lost by making it.

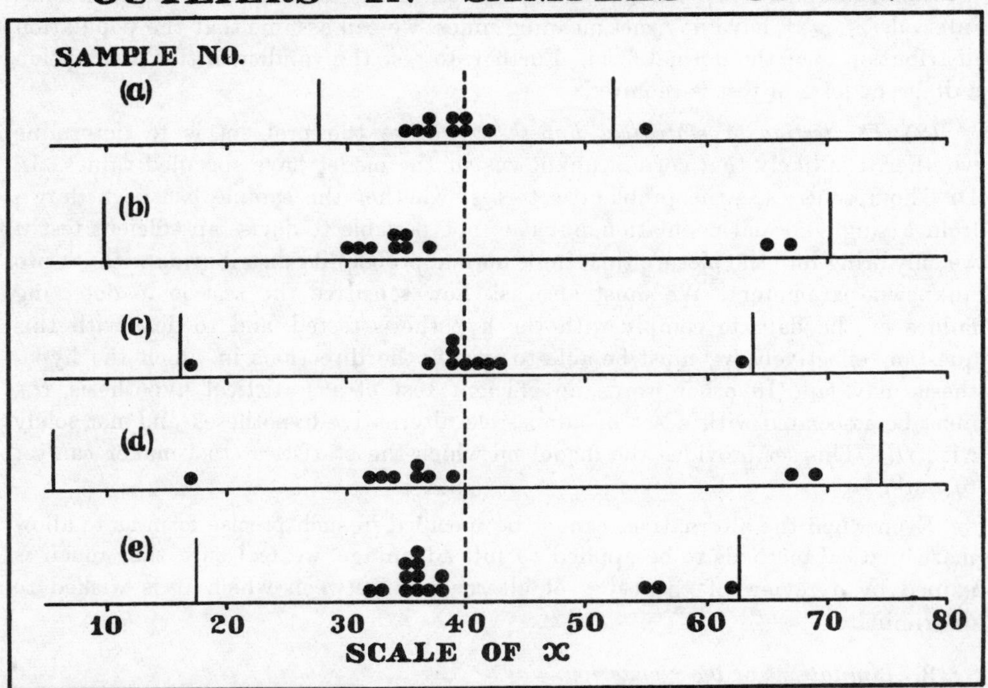

N.B. STROKES SHOW REJECTION LEVEL FOR $\varphi = 0{\cdot}1$

Fig. 1.

The point that we wish now to make is that if $k > 1$, Thompson's criterion is not very suitable for the purpose in view, at any rate for relatively small samples. In other words, it would appear that the criterion is only really efficient in the presence of a *single* outlying observation. To appreciate the reason for this criticism consider the data shown in Figure 1. They represent 4 different samples of 10 observations and 1 sample of 15, each having a mean of 40 on the scale shown. On intuitive grounds we should be inclined to say that in every case H_0 should be rejected, i.e. that there exist outlying observations not belonging to the main set. Yet if we apply Thompson's criterion, taking the level of significance $\phi = 0{\cdot}1$ (i.e.

running the risk of rejecting 1 observation in every 10 samples when H_0 is true), we find that it is only in the case of sample (*a*) that an outlier is picked out. In the remaining four cases none of the values of $|x_i - \bar{x}|$ exceed $\tau(\phi = 0{\cdot}1) \times s$. The limits $\bar{x} \pm \tau(\phi = 0{\cdot}1) \times s$ are marked by vertical strokes on the diagram.

We may next consider the data in Figure 2, which are based on 50 samples of 5 drawn randomly from a normal distribution with the help of Tippett's Random Sampling Numbers*.

We shall use the following notation:

(*a*) for the N values of τ in a sample arranged in descending order of absolute magnitude, write $\tau_1, \tau_2, \ldots \tau_N$; thus

$$|\tau_1| \geqslant |\tau_2| \geqslant \ldots \geqslant |\tau_N| \quad \ldots\ldots(7);$$

(*b*) for the N values arranged in magnitude taking account of sign, write $\tau^{(1)}, \tau^{(2)}, \ldots \tau^{(N)}$; thus

$$\tau^{(1)} \geqslant \tau^{(2)} \geqslant \ldots \geqslant \tau^{(N)} \quad \ldots\ldots(8).$$

Since the probability distribution for any τ taken at random follows the law of equation (3), it follows that, although the 5 values of τ obtained from the same sample are not independent, the total distribution of the $50 \times 5 = 250$ values of τ obtained in the experiment may be graduated by the curve obtained by writing $N = 5$ in the equation. This is shown in the upper portion of Figure 2. Below are shown distributions of (*A*) τ_1, (*B*) τ_2 and (*C*) τ_3, τ_4 and τ_5, and again of (*A*) $\tau^{(1)}$, (*B*) $\tau^{(2)}$, (*C*) $\tau^{(3)}$, (*D*) $\tau^{(4)}$ and (*E*) $\tau^{(5)}$.

The outer limits for τ_1 are $\pm\sqrt{N-1} = 2$; there are also outer limits for τ_2 and τ_3 which are shown by vertical strokes. Again limits exist for $\tau^{(i)}$. An explanation is at once suggested of the failure of the criterion to pick out the outlying observations in Figure 1; for certain sizes of sample the upper limit of $|\tau_i|$ $(i \geqslant 2)$ lies within the significance level given by the test. When this is so, only 1 observation can possibly be rejected however heterogeneous the data, and if the two extreme observations are close together none can be rejected at all.

To investigate this point more fully we must take the general case of a sample of N, and consider what limits there are to the value of the τ's. The problem may be put in this form:

If $\tau_1, \tau_2, \ldots \tau_N$ are any real numbers satisfying the equalities

$$\tau_1 + \tau_2 + \ldots + \tau_N = 0 \quad \ldots\ldots(9),$$

$$\tau_1^2 + \tau_2^2 + \ldots + \tau_N^2 = N \quad \ldots\ldots(10),$$

and the inequalities

$$\tau_1^2 \geqslant \tau_2^2 \geqslant \ldots \geqslant \tau_N^2 \quad \ldots\ldots(11),$$

it is required to determine the maximum value of τ_i^2 $(i = 1, 2, \ldots N)$.

* *Tracts for Computers*, XV.

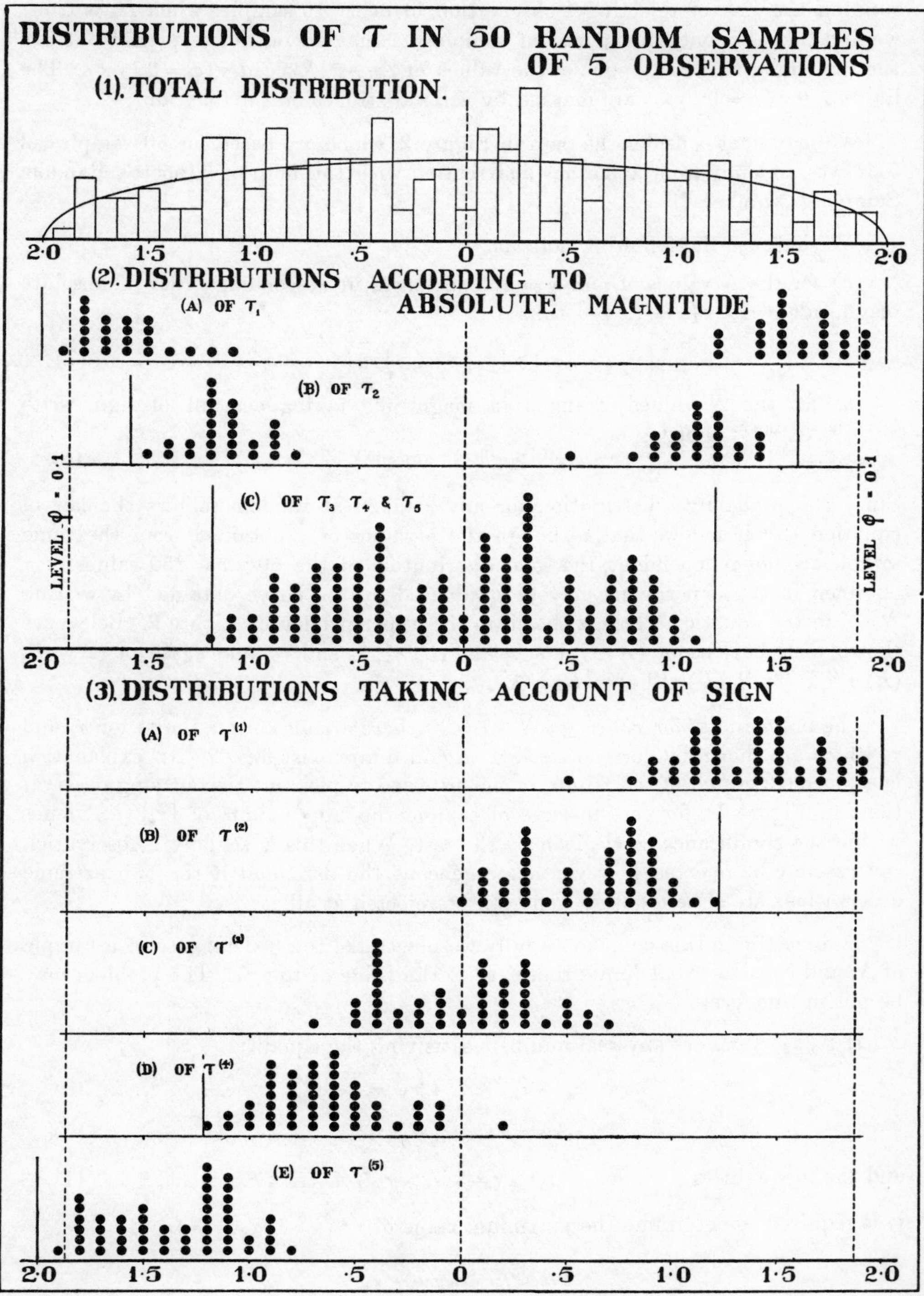
DISTRIBUTIONS OF τ IN 50 RANDOM SAMPLES OF 5 OBSERVATIONS
(1). TOTAL DISTRIBUTION.
2·0
1·5
1·0
·5
0
·5
1·0
1·5
2·0
(2). DISTRIBUTIONS ACCORDING TO ABSOLUTE MAGNITUDE
(A) OF τ1
(B) OF τ2
(C) OF τ3 τ4 & τ5
LEVEL φ = 0·1
LEVEL φ = 0·1
(3). DISTRIBUTIONS TAKING ACCOUNT OF SIGN
(A) OF τ(1)
(B) OF τ(2)
(C) OF τ(3)
(D) OF τ(4)
(E) OF τ(5)

Fig. 2.

A detailed solution given by Mr J. M. C. Scott is set out in an Appendix to this paper. Here we shall only quote the results.

(1) If i is odd, but $< N$,

$$\text{Maximum } |\tau_i| = \sqrt{\frac{N}{i + \dfrac{1}{N-i}}} \qquad \text{(12)},$$

e.g.
$$\begin{cases} i = 1, \text{ maximum } |\tau_1| = \sqrt{N-1}, \\ i = 3, \text{ maximum } |\tau_3| = \sqrt{N(N-3)/(3N-8)}, \\ i = 5, \text{ maximum } |\tau_5| = \sqrt{N(N-5)/(5N-24)}. \end{cases}$$

(2) If $i = N$ and is odd,

$$\text{Maximum } |\tau_N| = \sqrt{\frac{N-1}{N+1}} \qquad \text{(13)}.$$

(3) If i is even, $$\text{Maximum } |\tau_i| = \sqrt{\frac{N}{i}} \qquad \text{(14)},$$

e.g.
$$\begin{cases} i = 2, \text{ maximum } |\tau_2| = \sqrt{\tfrac{1}{2}N}, \\ i = 4, \text{ maximum } |\tau_4| = \sqrt{\tfrac{1}{4}N}. \end{cases}$$

(4) A further result will be useful. If we do not consider the absolute magnitude, but the maximum value of the second largest value of τ or of $\tau^{(2)}$, we find

$$\left.\begin{aligned} \text{Maximum } \tau^{(2)} &= \sqrt{\tfrac{1}{2}(N-2)} \\ \text{Similarly} \qquad \text{Minimum } \tau^{(N-1)} &= -\sqrt{\tfrac{1}{2}(N-2)} \end{aligned}\right\} \text{(15)}.$$

Putting $N = 5$, we obtain the limits shown in Figure 2.

As shown in the Appendix, the maximum value of $|\tau_1|$ occurs when $N-1$ observations have identical values, and the remaining observation any other different value; the situation in Figure 1 (a) is approaching this. The maximum $\tau^{(2)}$ occurs when $N-2$ observations have identical values and the other two have a different common value, i.e. $\tau^{(1)} = \tau^{(2)}$ (see Figure 1 (b)). The maximum $|\tau_2|$ occurs when $N-2$ observations have identical values, the other 2 differ and $\tau_1 = -\tau_2$ (see Figure 1 (c)). The maximum $|\tau_3|$ occurs when $N-3$ observations have identical values, the other 3 differ and $\tau_1 = \tau_2 = -\tau_3$ (see Figure 1 (d)).

In Figure 3 we have plotted for different values of N:

(a) the maximum values of $|\tau_i|$ ($i = 2$, 3 and 4) from equations (12) and (14);

(b) the levels of significance for τ from Thompson's tables with $\phi = 0{\cdot}20$, $0{\cdot}10$ and $0{\cdot}05$ with an additional limit $\phi = 0{\cdot}02$;

(c) the maximum value of $\tau^{(2)}$ from equation (15).

Thus if we use the significance level for ϕ of 0·10, involving the risk of rejection of 1 observation in every 10 samples when H_0 is true, we see that under no circumstances can we reject more than 1 observation until we reach a sample of 11; we cannot reject more than 2 observations until $N = 22$; and we cannot reject more than 3 observations until $N = 32$. This result corresponds to the extreme

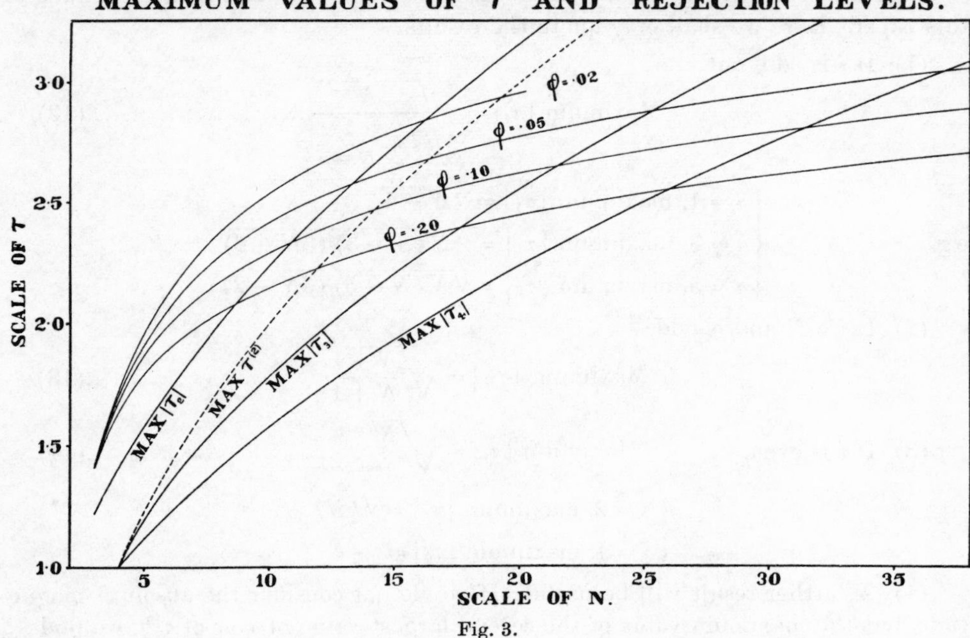

Fig. 3.

cases in which the $N-i$ observations are identical; for cases more likely to occur, such as those shown in Figure 1, the sample sizes must of course be larger.

It seems to follow, therefore, that if the situation we are faced with can be represented by a model in which the alternative to H_0 is that *one* observation has been drawn from a population with divergent mean (and possibly different standard deviation) to the remaining $N-1$ observations, Thompson's criterion will be very useful. If however the alternatives are that $k>1$ observations come from another or other systems, then the test may be quite ineffective, particularly if the sample contains not more than 30 or 40 observations.

No doubt suitable criteria could be devised for each type of alternative; thus if it were possible that 2 observations had come from a population with different mean to the remainder (Figure 1 (*b*)), the criterion might involve the calculation of the ratio of, (i) the deviation of the mean of two extreme observations from the mean of the whole to, (ii) the standard deviation. But this test would be quite unsuitable if the divergent observations had come from two populations with means diverging in opposite directions from the mean of the remainder, as in Figure 1 (*c*).

The statistician who does not know in advance with which type of alternative to H_0 he may be faced, is in the position of a carpenter who is summoned to a house to undertake a job of an unknown kind and is only able to take one tool with him! Which shall it be? Even if there is an "omnibus" tool, it is likely to be far less sensitive at any particular job than a specialised one; but the specialised tool will be quite useless under the wrong conditions.

Following the lines that Student has suggested when using "range" as a criterion*, it might be thought that a suitable "omnibus" tool for rejecting outlying observations could be obtained as follows: (1) apply Thompson's criterion to the N observations; (2) if it rejects $k \geqslant 1$ outliers, apply the criterion again to the remaining $N-k$ observations, calculating $\bar{x}$ and s afresh for the reduced sample; (3) repeat this process until a stage is reached when no further observations are rejected. Two points must however be remembered:

(*a*) Even when there are obvious outliers, the process may never get started at all for reasons already discussed. This is the case with the samples shown in Figure 1 (*b*)—(*e*).

(*b*) In order to control the first kind of error (in Neyman and Pearson's sense), i.e. the risk of rejecting H_0 when it is true, considerable development of theory would be required involving the determination of the simultaneous distribution of τ_1, τ_2, τ_3, etc.

In conclusion, since it is sometimes held that the appropriate test can be chosen *after* examining the data in the sample, a final word of caution is necessary. To base the choice of the test of a statistical hypothesis upon an inspection of the observations is a dangerous practice; a study of the configuration of a sample is almost certain to reveal some feature, or features, which are exceptional if the hypothesis is true. In the present instance it might appear, for example, that the 1st and 2nd observations (in order of magnitude) were unusually far apart, or a gap might occur between the 2nd and 3rd or between the 5th and 6th; again, the standard deviation might be large compared to the range, or there might appear to be too few observations near the mean.

By choosing the feature most unfavourable to H_0 out of a very large number of features examined, it will usually be possible to find some reason for rejecting the hypothesis. It must be remembered, however, that the point now at issue will not be whether it is exceptional to find a given criterion with so unfavourable a value. We shall need to find an answer to the more difficult question. Is it exceptional that the most unfavourable criterion of the n, say, examined should have as unfavourable a value as this?

4. *The percentage limits of the extremes,* $\tau^{(1)}$ *and* $\tau^{(N)}$.

An examination of Figure 2 for the case $N=5$ shows how the form of the total τ-distribution at its extreme depends only on the distributions of $\tau^{(1)}$ and $\tau^{(5)}$. This is because the upper limit of $\tau^{(2)}$ lies at $+1{\cdot}225$ and the lower limit of $\tau^{(4)}$ at $-1{\cdot}225$. In general for $\tau^{(1)} > \sqrt{\tfrac{1}{2}(N-2)}$ we have for the probability law of $\tau^{(1)}$,

$$p(\tau^{(1)}) = Np(\tau) \qquad\qquad (16),$$

where $p(\tau)$ is given in equation (3). A similar form holds for the lowest τ if $\tau^{(N)} < -\sqrt{\tfrac{1}{2}(N-2)}$. Since $\phi = NP$, where P is defined in equation (5), it follows that the limits of τ which Thompson has tabled for $\phi = 0{\cdot}20$, $0{\cdot}10$ and $0{\cdot}05$ will

* *Biometrika*, Vol. xix. (1927), pp. 161—162.

correspond to the upper 10 %, 5 % and 2·5 % probability levels of $\tau^{(1)}$ (and the corresponding lower levels for $\tau^{(N)}$), as long as these levels fall beyond

$$\text{Max. } \tau^{(2)} = \sqrt{\tfrac{1}{2}(N-2)}.$$

In Figure 3 a dotted line has been drawn showing the changing value of this latter function and, by observing where it crosses the successful levels of ϕ, we can tell up to what size of sample the general distribution of τ of equation (3) may be used to give the percentage limits of the τ's calculated from the two extreme observations in a sample. Besides Thompson's levels at $\phi = 0{\cdot}20$, 0·10 and 0·05 an additional level at $\phi = 0{\cdot}02$ has been calculated*. From these we obtain the following table, in which columns 2, 3 and 4 repeat Thompson's results. While it would be useful to find the percentage limits of the extreme τ for values of N beyond those shown in the table, these cannot be obtained from the probability integral of the general τ-distribution, owing to the overlap of the distributions of $\tau^{(2)}$ and $\tau^{(1)}$ for larger values of N.

Upper probability limits for $\tau = \dfrac{x - \bar{x}}{s}$, *for the highest observation in a sample of* N, *i.e. for* $\tau^{(1)}$.

N	10 %	5 %	2·5 %	1 %
3	1·4065	1·4123	1·4137	1·4142
4	1·6454	1·6887	1·7103	1·7234
5	1·791	1·869	1·917	1·955
6	1·895	1·997	2·067	2·130
7	1·973	2·093	2·182	2·265
8	2·041	2·170	2·274	2·374
9	2·099	2·237	2·348	2·464
10	2·144	2·295	2·413	2·540
11	2·190	2·343	2·472	2·606
12	—	2·388	2·521	2·663
13	—	2·425	2·567	2·713
14	—	2·463	2·598	2·759
15	—	—	2·636	2·800
16	—	—	2·670	2·837
17	—	—	—	2·871
18	—	—	—	2·903
19	—	—	—	2·932

N.B. The same limits, with negative sign, will apply to the τ calculated from the lowest observation, i.e. to $\tau^{(N)}$.

In concluding this paper we should like it to be clear that we consider Dr W. R. Thompson has suggested a useful, practical criterion which the experi-

* This was done by backward interpolation in Table XXV of *Tables for Statisticians and Biometricians*, Part II, for $N=5$ to 19. For the case $N=4$ the law of equation (3) gives a rectangular distribution and for $N=3$ a simple result follows on noting that if we write $\tau = \sqrt{2}\cos\theta$, θ is distributed uniformly between 0 and π.

menter may employ provided that he recognises that it may be inefficient in the presence of more than one outlying observation. The criterion possesses a great advantage which so many criteria that have been invented before lack, in that it provides complete control over the risk of rejecting the hypothesis tested when it is true. Our purpose has been to show that even when this control is assured, other difficulties exist which appear to be inevitably inherent in the problem of the rejection of outlying observations.

APPENDIX.

BY J. M. C. SCOTT.

THE object of this note is to find the values of $\tau_1, \ldots \tau_N$ which satisfy the following relations:

$$\begin{cases} |\tau_1| \geqslant |\tau_2| \geqslant \ldots \geqslant |\tau_i| \ldots \geqslant |\tau_N| \quad \ldots\ldots(17), \\ \tau_1+\tau_2+\ldots+\tau_N=0 \quad \ldots\ldots(18), \\ \tau_1^2+\tau_2^2+\ldots+\tau_N^2=N \quad \ldots\ldots(19), \\ |\tau_i| \text{ to be as great as possible} \quad \ldots\ldots(20). \end{cases}$$

Line (20) may be replaced by the requirement

$$\frac{\tau_1^2+\tau_2^2+\ldots+\tau_N^2}{\tau_i^2} \text{ to be as small as possible} \quad \ldots\ldots(21).$$

Now (17), (18) and (21) are homogeneous, and their solutions are the solutions of (17), (18), (19) and (21)—i.e. of (17), (18), (19) and (20)—multiplied by an arbitrary factor. If this arbitrary factor is determined by

$$\tau_i=1 \quad \ldots\ldots(22),$$

instead of by (19), we are led to consider the following problem which is equivalent to the original one:

$$\begin{cases} |\alpha_1| \geqslant |\alpha_2| \geqslant \ldots \geqslant |\alpha_i| \ldots \geqslant |\alpha_N| \quad \ldots\ldots(23), \\ \alpha_1+\alpha_2+\ldots+\alpha_N=0 \quad \ldots\ldots(24), \\ \alpha_i=1 \quad \ldots\ldots(25), \\ \alpha_1^2+\alpha_2^2+\ldots+\alpha_N^2 \text{ to be as small as possible} \quad \ldots\ldots(26). \end{cases}$$

We have to find i numbers (α_1 to α_i) numerically $\geqslant 1$, and $N-i$ numbers (α_{i+1} to α_N) numerically $\leqslant 1$, satisfying (24), (25) and (26). The order within these sets can be settled afterwards by (23), and is irrelevant at present.

Lemma 1. *The numbers* α_{i+1} to α_N *are equal; the positive numbers among* α_1 *to* α_i *are equal; and the negative numbers among* α_1 *to* α_i *are equal.*

Proof. If in one of these sets there are two unequal numbers, replace them by their mean. This gives a permissible set of α's but diminishes $\Sigma(\alpha^2)$, contradicting (26).

Further, the positive numbers among α_1 to α_i must be $=1$, since $\alpha_i=1$. Thus we have

$$\begin{cases} r \quad \text{numbers equal to } A \leqslant -1, \text{ say,} \\ i-r \quad \text{,,} \quad \text{,,} \quad \text{,,} \ +1, \\ N-i \quad \text{,,} \quad \text{,,} \quad \text{,,} \ C, \text{ where } |C| \leqslant 1. \end{cases}$$

Henceforward we will suppose $i<N$.

Lemma 2. $A=-1$, *if* $r>0$.

Proof. Suppose the lemma is not true; then there is an $\alpha_k<-1$. Change α_k from A to $A+\epsilon$ where $\epsilon>0$, and change α_N from C to $C-\epsilon$. This is possible if $C>-1$. It decreases $\Sigma(\alpha^2)$ by

$$A^2+C^2-(A+\epsilon)^2-(C-\epsilon)^2=2\epsilon(C-A-\epsilon)>0 \text{ for small enough } \epsilon,$$

which contradicts (26). This argument fails if $C=-1$. In this case, change the signs of α_1 to

α_{i-1}, and change α_{i+1} to α_N from -1 to $1-\dfrac{2}{N-i}$. This gives a permissible set of α's. If now $i<N-1$, $\Sigma(\alpha^2)$ is reduced, contrary to (26); if $i=N-1$, $\Sigma(\alpha^2)$ is left unchanged and some of the α's are equal to $-A>1$, which is contrary to Lemma 1. Thus Lemma 2 is established.

It follows that either $A=-1$ or $r=0$. In each case

$$C=\frac{2r-i}{N-i} \qquad \text{.....(27)},$$

leading to

$$\Sigma(\alpha^2)=i+\frac{(2r-i)^2}{N-i} \qquad \text{.....(28)}.$$

We have now to determine r so that this expression is a minimum, and to remember that

$$\tau_s^2=\alpha_s^2\frac{\Sigma(\tau^2)}{\Sigma(\alpha^2)}=\frac{\alpha_s^2 N}{\Sigma(\alpha^2)} \qquad \text{.....(29)}.$$

Case 1. If i is even, $r=\frac{1}{2}i$, $C=0$ and therefore

$$\Sigma(\alpha^2)=i.$$

It follows that

$$\text{Maximum } |\tau_i|=\sqrt{\frac{N}{i}} \qquad \text{.....(30)},$$

and that of $\tau_1, \dots \tau_i$ half are equal to $\sqrt{N/i}$ and half equal to $-\sqrt{N/i}$, while the remaining $N-i$ values are zero. This result is otherwise obvious, for if $\tau_i^2>N/i$, then

$$\sum_{s=1}^{N}(\tau_s^2)\geqslant\sum_{s=1}^{i}(\tau_s^2)>N.$$

Case 2. If i is odd, then $r=\frac{1}{2}(i\pm 1)$, $C=\pm 1/(N-i)$ and

$$\Sigma(\alpha^2)=i+\frac{1}{N-i}.$$

It follows that

$$\text{Maximum } |\tau_i|=\sqrt{\frac{N}{i+\dfrac{1}{N-i}}} \qquad \text{.....(31)}.$$

Of $\tau_1, \dots \tau_i$,

$$\begin{cases} \frac{1}{2}(i\pm 1) \text{ values}=-\sqrt{\dfrac{N}{i+\dfrac{1}{N-i}}}, \\ \frac{1}{2}(i\mp 1) \text{ values}=+\sqrt{\dfrac{N}{i+\dfrac{1}{N-i}}}, \end{cases}$$

while

$$\tau_{i+1}=\dots=\tau_N=\pm\sqrt{\frac{N}{(N-i)(Ni-i^2+1)}}.$$

It finally remains to consider the position where $i=N$. If N is even, the result is clearly the same as for case 1 above. If N is odd, $\frac{1}{2}(N-1)$ of the α's will equal $-(N+1)/(N-1)$ and $\frac{1}{2}(N+1)$ will equal $+1$. Therefore

$$\Sigma(\alpha^2)=\frac{N(N+1)}{N-1}.$$

Hence

$\frac{1}{2}(N-1)$ of the τ's will equal $\pm\sqrt{(N+1)/(N-1)}$ and $\frac{1}{2}(N+1)$ will equal $\mp\sqrt{(N-1)/(N+1)}$;

thus

$$\text{Maximum } |\tau_i|=\sqrt{\frac{N-1}{N+1}} \qquad \text{.....(32)}.$$

A further result used in the main paper is that of the maximum value of $\tau^{(2)}$, the second τ in order of magnitude. Following a similar line of proof, it can be readily shown that this occurs when

$$\left.\begin{aligned} \tau^{(1)}=\tau^{(2)}&=\sqrt{\tfrac{1}{2}(N-2)} \\ \tau^{(3)}=\dots=\tau^{(N)}&=-\sqrt{2/(N-2)} \end{aligned}\right\} \qquad \text{.....(33)}.$$

SOME ASPECTS OF THE PROBLEM OF RANDOMIZATION

By E. S. PEARSON

1. Introductory

The practical problem of mathematical statistics is to provide a conceptual model which will be of value to the man who needs to draw conclusions from the data of observation. In handling statistical data one of the commonest problems to be faced is that of drawing inferences from a part to the whole, from a sample to the population; such inferences are uncertain inferences, and it follows not only that in such cases the conceptual model must be constructed with the aid of the theory of probability but that its value to the practical man will be to some extent psychological. An historical study of the development of mathematical statistics shows an ever-increasing complexity in the structure of the abstract model and also an evolution of ideas as to how that model is to be of most use in practical application. In this course of evolution it is inevitable that many different suggestions should have been thrown out by mathematical statisticians as to the best way of linking the world of concepts with the world of experience. Ultimately, it is likely that the practical scientist, who may know relatively little mathematics but has to apply the methods of statistics in his research work, will play the decisive part in determining the form in which the theory of probability may be applied most usefully in different situations as a guide to judgment. But in the meantime it is necessary that amid the growing complication of the mathematical background statisticians should attempt to keep clear the simple principles which in their view have the greatest claim for acceptance.

An example of the gradual evolution of ideas is found in the changing attitude with which tests of goodness of fit and tests to determine whether differences are "significant" have been regarded. Perhaps one may say that 20 or 30 years ago the question posed by the statistician in applying such tests was often somewhat as follows:

"If my sample had come (*a*) from the population represented by my fitted curve, or (*b*) from a population whose parameters had the values given by the sample (and these estimates obtained from the sample cannot be very different from the unknown population values), what is the probability that a difference as great or greater than that observed would have occurred?"

It will be seen that the situation posed was to some extent hypothetical, since in fact the population sampled was not represented by the sample values. Nevertheless, the probability measure, P, obtained as an answer to this question seemed to give the measure of assurance needed to make a decision. In so far as each problem was considered in isolation from other similar problems, the basis for any decision taken was to a large extent psychological.

In recent years we can follow the gradual introduction of a somewhat different conception. Its origin may be traced partly to the application of statistical methods in new fields where decisions had to be taken on evidence supplied by small samples, so that the differences between population values and sample estimates became so large that the hypothetical situation referred to above was seen to be noticeably unreal; and partly to the fact that in agricultural research investigations precisely similar tests were being applied again and again to the same type of experiment. Thus the relation was emphasized between (*a*) the probability measure, P, leading to a decision in an individual experiment, and (*b*) the expected proportion of times that a hypothesis of "no difference" would be wrongly rejected in the routine work of a research station. In terms of the older approach there might be little difference in an isolated problem between the psychological reaction to a P of ·05 and a P of ·02. But where experimental procedures were being repeated continually, the difference between a risk of mistake of 1 in 20 and of 1 in 50 might be of some consequence.*

Emphasis was therefore given in statistical literature to a new idea; that of planning a sampling procedure and the subsequent analysis of the data collected, in such a way as to control at any desired level the risk of making a wrong decision—that risk which can never be entirely eliminated in any form of work involving sampling. This change in attitude is illustrated by the form which many recently constructed probability tables have taken, following R. A. Fisher's suggestion. Instead of providing the statistician with the precise value of a probability measure, P, which he needed when regarding each problem in isolation, these tables are arranged so as to enable him to discover whether his test criterion falls below a certain "probability level", e.g. a 10, 5, 2, or 1 per cent. level. If then, for example, as a usual practice he rejects the hypothesis he is testing when the criterion falls below the 1 per cent. level (but not otherwise), he knows that in the long run of his experience this action will lead to one wrong decision in every hundred, a frequency of error which he may be quite prepared to accept.

This form of introduction of abstract theory into the world of experience has an obvious appeal to the practical man. If you tell him that theory enables him to assess the probability of a certain event in an individual trial or even to assess the frequency with which it would occur under somewhat hypothetical conditions, he may be unconvinced of the value of this theory to him. But if you can illustrate the statistician's objective by two examples of the following type, you are much more likely to convince him of the value of statistical tools.

* This has been brought out very clearly in questions of routine sampling in industry.

Example 1. A frequent problem is one in which, having a sample of n values of a variable x, it is wished to determine limits between which the unknown population mean, ξ, almost certainly lies. Under certain conditions the statistician can here provide a rule for determining from the sample data two limits ξ_a and ξ_b, such that the statement

$$\xi_a \leqslant \xi \leqslant \xi_b$$

may be made with a specified measure of confidence. The details of the procedure advocated depend on the application of the twofold principle that in making such a statement we are concerned, (*a*) to know the percentage of times it will be correct in long-run application under appropriate conditions, (*b*) to make the interval in some way as narrow as possible. To reduce the risk of error and to reduce the breadth of interval are, beyond a certain point, conflicting objectives and a balance must be struck between them; the statistical method shows how this may be done.

Example 2. Another common problem is one in which two samples are available and it is wished to test the hypothesis that they have been drawn from populations having the same means, $\xi_1 = \xi_2$. Again, the statistician can under certain conditions give a rule of procedure suggesting when the hypothesis should be rejected, and he may base this on another twofold principle: arrange so that in the long run application of the rule, (*a*) the hypothesis of "no difference" in means will only be rejected when it is true on a small and known percentage of occasions; (*b*) the hypothesis will be rejected as often as possible when there is a true difference in means, i.e. when $\xi_1 - \xi_2 \neq 0$.

These conceptions have no doubt always been present in the minds of mathematical statisticians but they have only been given precise formulation in recent years. The principle illustrated in Example 1 forms the basis of J. Neyman's work on confidence intervals and the confidence coefficient (1), and although presented in somewhat different form, I think, underlies R. A. Fisher's conception of fiducial probability (2). The principle mentioned in Example 2 forms the basis of J. Neyman and the present writer's work on the testing of statistical hypothesis (3), (4), but in the application of the conception (*b*) we are at variance with R. A. Fisher. In our view, just as in the simple problem of "interval estimation" mentioned in Example 1, it is necessary to specify the form of population distribution before the interval ξ_a, ξ_b can be calculated, so it is only possible to determine in any precise manner which is the most efficient test of a hypothesis if we can specify the class of alternative hypotheses. Thus, following quite simple principles, we may construct in the conceptual workshop the tests most appropriate in different precisely defined situations. It is then for the practical man to decide which of these situations corresponds most closely to that with which he is faced.

In Fisher's view the experimenter cannot and need not define the alternatives to the hypothesis he is testing. Indeed, Fisher would seem to consider it to be important to a test of significance that it should be free from the necessity of introducing any elaborate type of background or alternatives which might be true. While I agree that the experimenter cannot specify all conceivable alternatives to the hypothesis tested, I think that a study of the situations met with in practice suggests that he does in fact usually have a fairly clear idea of the alternatives most likely to be true, and that if the mathematical statistician enables him to use this knowledge in picking out the most efficient statistical tool, he will be grateful. If it can be shown that in the situation most likely to exist (e.g. normal variation) one test will detect the falsity of the hypothesis of "no difference" more often than any other test, the appeal in favour of its adoption will surely be very strong.

2. Randomization

I have referred to the idea of arranging a sampling procedure so that conclusions drawn upon application of an appropriate statistical technique will be subject to a known and controlled risk of error. The principle of randomization, whose introduction is largely due to R. A. Fisher, provides a device to aid in the achievement of this objective. Most of the statistical tests used in the more complex sampling problems have been developed on the assumption that the variables are normally distributed, and while it is often clear that considerable departure from normality will not seriously effect their validity, it may be asked how far can tests be constructed which are completely independent of any assumption of normality?

Fisher has given an interesting illustration of such a test based on randomization in section 21 of his book, *The Design of Experiments* (5). The example is suggested by an investigation of Darwin's into the growth-rate of crossed and self-fertilized plants.

In the arrangement of the experiment fifteen seeds resulting from each type of fertilization were used; denote these by A-type and B-type seeds. Fifteen pairs of plots, say p_{si} ($s=1, 2, \dots 15$, $i=1, 2$), were chosen and prepared in such a way that the environmental conditions within each pair were as alike as possible. Following the principle of randomization it would then be necessary to determine at random, and for each pair independently, which site should be occupied by A and which by B-type seed.* After the experiment was completed, the grown plants were measured; suppose the character considered (height at given age) had values of a_s and b_s respectively, for the sth pair of plots. Darwin's problem was to determine whether there was any evidence that the type of fertilization affected the vigour of the plant. Statistically, this can be examined by testing the hypothesis, say H_0, that as far as the character measured on the grown plants is concerned, the two samples of seeds have been drawn from identical populations.

* This process of random assignment was not, of course, actually performed by Darwin.

The character in the grown plant depends on (i) the environmental conditions which may be slightly different between plots p_{s1} and p_{s2}, (ii) some quality inherent in the individual seed. We may now imagine in the conceptual field a continued repetition of the experiment, fifteen seeds of each type being randomly selected, fifteen pairs of plots being prepared and a random assignment of the seeds. If then the method of fertilization is unconnected with subsequent growth, a given quality of seed will be as likely to be associated with an A as a B-type seed, and owing to the randomization will be as likely to be associated with the environmental condition of plot p_{s1} as plot p_{s2}. Hence a difference

$$x_s = a_s - b_s$$

of given numerical magnitude will be as likely to be positive as negative. This will be true independently for all fifteen plots.

It follows that the conceptual population of possible experimental results $x_1, x_2, \ldots, x_{15}$ may be divided into an infinite number of subpopulations each defined by a given set of fifteen values of $| x_s |$, and each containing the 2^{15} elements that will be generated by assigning to these numerical values all possible combinations of positive and negative signs. If the hypothesis, H_0, of no differentiation between the A-type and B-type seed populations is true, each of these 2^{15} elements is equally likely to arise.

To construct a test it is now necessary to find a rule, *applicable to every one of these subpopulations*, which will divide the 2^{15} elements into two classes:

(1) a class I containing a proportion P of the elements,

(2) a class II containing a proportion $1-P$ of the elements.

If then we reject the hypothesis, H_0, of no differentiation when the element represented by the fifteen differences $x_1^0, x_2^0, \ldots, x_{15}^0$, actually observed falls into class I, but not otherwise, we may be sure that the risk of rejecting H_0 when it is true is controlled at a value of P: e.g. if $P = \cdot 05$ we should be using what is ordinarily termed a 5 per cent. significance level. The practical question is, of course, how to determine classes I and II. Clearly they should be so determined that if one type of seed in fact produces larger plants than the other, the element represented by the observed differences $x_1^0, \ldots, x_{15}^0$ would be likely to fall into class I, and thus H_0 would, correctly, be rejected. It is seen at once that some consideration of the alternatives to the hypothesis tested is entering into the construction of the test; it has already entered into the design of the experiment since the care taken to make the environmental conditions associated with the pair of plots p_{s1} and p_{s2} similar, was aimed at increasing the chance of detecting a true difference in seed type if one exists.

Fisher's suggestion is to put into class I the $100P$ per cent. of the 2^{15} elements or a number as near that figure as possible for which the fifteen x's have the largest numerical mean value. Thus, for the data of Darwin's experiment, the values of $x_1^0, x_2^0, \ldots, x_{15}^0$ were: 49, −67, 8, 16, 6, 23, 28, 41, 14, 29, 56, 24, 75, 60, −48, giving a mean of $314/15 = 20{\cdot}9\dot{3}$.

Taking the subpopulation of $2^{15} = 32{,}768$ elements generated by all possible assignments of positive and negative signs to the fifteen values of $|x_s^0|$, Fisher finds that in 1722, or 5·26 per cent., the numerical value of the mean, $\bar{x}$, is greater than the observed value, $20{\cdot}9\dot{3}$. Consequently, the observed result falls just outside the class I associated with a 5 per cent. significance level and we should probably not be prepared to risk rejecting the hypothesis H_0.

The test proposed by Fisher depends upon a particular definition of the class I. It is important to note that this definition is in no sense unique. For example, we could have put into class I the $100P$ per cent. of the 2^{15} elements for which the geometric mean of the fifteen values $(100 + x_s)$ differed most from 100. I do not suggest that this would be a rational classification, but it is worth while reflecting whether, if we choose to use the arithmetic mean as criterion, we are not being influenced, perhaps unconsciously, by

(*a*) the knowledge that if variation is normal, a criterion based on the observed mean difference in samples will be most efficient in detecting a real population difference in seed types;

(*b*) the belief that the characters measured, a_s and b_s, are likely to be approximately normally distributed.

If this is the case, it would seem that the usefulness of the test is in fact dependent on the form of the alternative hypotheses.

Another illustration of the application of this principle of randomization has been recently given by Fisher elsewhere (6). He supposes we have available measures of the stature of a random sample of, say, n Frenchmen and n Englishmen, and wish to test the hypothesis that the mean height of the sampled populations of Frenchmen and Englishmen are identical. Let the observations be written as follows:

$$\begin{cases} \text{Frenchmen } x_1, x_2, \ldots, x_n, \text{ Mean } \bar{x}; \\ \text{Englishmen } y_1, y_2, \ldots, y_n, \text{ Mean } \bar{y}. \end{cases}$$

If the $2n$ observations were written on cards and shuffled without regard to nationality, it would be possible to divide them into a group A and a group B, each containing n cards, in $(2n)!/(n!)^2$ ways. For each way of division we shall have a mean $\bar{a}$ for group A and a mean $\bar{b}$ for group B, giving a difference

$$d = \bar{a} - \bar{b}.$$

Just as in the last example, divide these $(2n)!/(n!)^2$ possible differences into

(1) class I containing the $P\,(2n)!/(n!)^2$ (or a number as near below this as possible) giving largest values of $|\,d\,|$,

(2) class II containing the remaining cases.

Suppose P is chosen to be ·05. Then if the difference $\bar{x} - \bar{y}$ for the observed

French-English subdivision falls into class I, we may reject the hypothesis tested, knowing that the risk we run of rejecting it when it is in fact true is ·05 or less.

This ingenious suggestion of Fisher's leads to the following result: if we adopt the rule wherever a problem of this type arises in our statistical experience, we shall have precise control of the risk of wrong rejection no matter what was the type of variation in the populations sampled.

Of course the procedure needed to determine whether the observed sample falls into class I or class II is very lengthy, unless the samples are very small. I am concerned, however, not with this point, but with the question of whether there is something fundamental about the form of the test suggested, so that it can be used as a standard against which to compare other more expeditious tests, such as Student's. It seems to me that Fisher is overstating the claim of an extremely ingenious device when he writes ((6), p. 59): "Actually, the statistician does not carry out this very simple and very tedious process, but his conclusions have no justification beyond the fact that they agree with those which could have been arrived at by this elementary method." The following example should at any rate help to bring out some points which appear to need careful consideration.

The figures given below represent two samples of seven observations from two populations; they form Experiment I of Table I.

Sample 1. 45, 21, 69, 82, 79, 93, 34. Mean $= \bar{x}_1 = 60{\cdot}43$. Midpoint between extreme values $= m_1 = 57$.

Sample 2. 120, 122, 107, 127, 124, 41, 37. Mean $= \bar{x}_2 = 96{\cdot}86$. Midpoint between extreme values $= m_2 = 82$.

After pooling these fourteen numbers, they can be redivided into two groups A and B, of seven each, in $(14!)/(7!)^2 = 3432$ ways. We may now ask in how many of these ways:

(1) the difference in means of the two groups has an equal or greater negative value than the observed

$$\bar{x}_1 - \bar{x}_2 = 60{\cdot}43 - 96{\cdot}86 = -36{\cdot}43;$$

(2) the difference in midpoints has an equal or greater negative value than the observed

$$m_1 - m_2 = 57 - 82 = -25?$$

After a rather troublesome investigation into the possible arrangements I find the answer to question (1) is 126 out of 3432 or 3·67 per cent., and to question (2) is 45 out of 3432 or 1·31 per cent. It may be said therefore that random assignments of the fourteen numbers into two groups of seven would give (1) as large or a larger numerical value than that observed to the difference in *means* on 7·3 per cent. of occasions, and (2) as large or a larger numerical value to the difference in *midpoints* on 2·6 per cent. of occasions. It follows that in applying this form of test to the midpoints, we should be more likely to suspect a difference in populations sampled than in applying the test to the means.

Now of course it is quite possible that in individual cases an inferior test may detect a real difference when a better test does not. I give below therefore four further pairs of random samples from the same two populations, as well as the

TABLE I

Experimental Sampling Data

Experiment	I		II		III		IV		V	
Sample	1	2	1	2	1	2	1	2	1	2
	45	120	29	50	14	60	47	60	67	47
	21	122	41	125	70	104	4	90	18	71
	69	107	27	112	32	81	49	84	41	43
	82	127	5	86	79	41	49	100	41	115
	79	124	27	40	87	69	23	93	65	66
	93	41	58	98	25	40	52	32	8	124
	34	37	92	50	2	48	67	98	52	56
Mean	60·43	96·86	39·86	80·14	44·14	63·29	41·57	79·57	41·71	74·57
Midpoint	57·0	82·0	48·5	82·5	44·5	72·0	35·5	66·0	37·5	83·5

TABLE II

Number of pairs of samples, under randomization, having negative values for $\bar{x}_1 - \bar{x}_2$ and $m_1 - m_2$ as great as or greater than the observed pairs

	Mean			Midpoint		
	Greater difference	Equal difference*	Total	Greater difference	Equal difference*	Total
Experiment I	121	5	126	40	5	45
II	56	1	57	44	10	54
III	Over 250	$\geqslant 3$	> 253	100	41	141
IV	17	3	20	17	14	31
V	82	2	84	28	25	53

* Including the observed difference itself.

results of applying the two tests. It will be seen that in only one case out of the five does the mean supply stronger evidence of difference than the midpoint. Both these tests are equally valid in the sense that, using either, we can control the error of rejecting the hypothesis that the populations are the same when it is in fact true. In the case taken the population means were at 49·5 and 79·5 respectively and their two standard deviations were the same (= 28·86)

Yet as far as the very limited experimental evidence goes, the midpoint test has been the more effective in detecting the presence of the real difference of 30 units in population means. The reason for this is explained at once when we know that the population distributions were rectangular, e.g.

for population 1 any value of x between 00 and 99 was equally likely to occur;
for population 2 any value of x between 30 and 129 was equally likely to occur.*

Since the standard error of the midpoint in samples of n from a rectangular population of standard deviation σ is

$$\sigma_m = \sigma\sqrt{\frac{6}{(n+1)(n+2)}},$$

which for $n=7$ is $\cdot 289\sigma$; while for the mean

$$\sigma_{\bar{x}} = \frac{\sigma}{\sqrt{n}},$$

which for $n=7$ is $\cdot 378\sigma$; we should expect on theoretical grounds that the difference in sample midpoints, rather than in sample means, would be more efficient in detecting real differences in population means. Such a property would certainly appeal to the practical experimenter, were not both tests for other reasons too lengthy to carry out as a common practice.

Now of course in practice it is extremely unlikely that we should deal with variables whose probability distribution is rectangular, but I have introduced these examples because it seems to me to suggest that in problems of this kind it is impossible to make a rational choice between alternative tests unless we introduce some information beyond that contained in the sample data, i.e. some information as to the kind of alternatives with which we are likely to be faced.

If the variation is approximately normal and the standard deviations in the two populations are the same, the advantages of Student's t-test can be expressed in simple terms which appeal to the practical statistician. Its use gives control of the risk of rejecting the hypothesis of "no difference" when it is true, and at the same time makes more probable than does any other test the detection of a real difference in means.† It is certainly possible to claim that these reasons justify its use rather than the relation it bears to the test of Fisher's which I have outlined. It is true that when variation departs from the normal the t-test will not give quite accurate control of the risk of wrong rejection of H_0 (although the error will usually be small), while the test based on randomization will continue to do so. It is in this that the value of the randomization test lies; but as I have pointed out, in so far as this latter test is applied to *means*, it cannot be regarded as unique, and for wide departures from normality it could probably be improved on by use of other central estimates.

* Tippett's Random Sampling Numbers were used; *Tracts for Computers*, No. XV.

† For discussion of this conception see (3) and (4).

3. Randomization applied to the Latin Square

The conceptual model which lies behind the design of the Latin Square experiment leads to the following expression for the yield on the plot in the ith row and jth column receiving the kth treatment:

$$y_{ij(k)} = A + R_i + C_j + T_k + \eta_{ijk}.$$

Here, for a given experiment with an $s \times s$ Latin Square, A, R_i, C_j and T_k ($i = 1, \ldots, s; j = 1, \ldots, s;\ k = 1, \ldots, s$) may be regarded as constants and the η's as normally and independently distributed about zero with standard deviation, σ_η. The hypothesis, H_0, which it is generally wished to test is that $T_k = 0$ ($k = 1, \ldots, s$), i.e. that there are no treatment differences.

It has always been recognized, however, that the additive row and column contributions, R_i and C_j, given in this equation cannot provide sufficient elasticity to fit all forms of fertility gradient found in practice. Consequently there is bound to be some correlation among the η's from neighbouring plots, and further the η's may not be normally distributed. In a single experiment it is of course quite impossible to decide whether the s^2 values of η can be reasonably regarded as independent normal deviates. Two lines of procedure seem therefore to have been followed.

In the first place emphasis has been laid on the importance of randomization; in assigning the s treatments to their plots, the particular Latin Square pattern used is chosen at random from the very many possible patterns, say N_s in number. The infinite population of results which can be conceived as obtainable from the experiment, if H_0 is true, may then be divided into an infinite set of subpopulations, each containing a finite number of elements, N_s. Each subpopulation is defined by a set of s^2 yields, y_{ij}, and an element corresponds to a partition of these yields into s treatment groups in accordance with a particular one of the N_s Latin Square patterns. The observed result following from the Latin Square pattern chosen for the experiment represents a single one of these elements.

If now, as far as yield is concerned, the s treatments are identical, it will follow that each of these N_s elements is equally likely to occur owing to the random choice of patterns, even if the η's are not normal or independent. Consequently, as in the previous illustrations, it is only necessary to find a rule, applicable to all sets of s^2 yields, which will enable us to separate from the N_s elements a suitable class I containing a proportion P of them. If this can be done, and the hypothesis of no treatment differences is rejected when the experiment performed gives a result falling into this class, we shall run a risk equal to P of rejecting the hypothesis H_0 when it is true.

Exactly as in the simpler examples, many ways might be found of classifying N_s partitions of the yields, y_{ij}; the choice between them may be influenced by expediency or by the efficiency of the resulting test in detecting the presence of real treatment differences when they exist. From both points of view it seems reasonable to employ the usual z-criterion, although as soon as we must depart from the original model of the equation above, the fundamental association between sums of squares and normal variation is blurred. Accepting this criterion, class I will consist of the PN_s partitions leading to the largest values of z.

In his paper (7) published on pp. 21–52 above, B. L. Welch has suggested a method of determining approximately the lower limit of z bounding this class and he finds that, if for example $P = \cdot 05$ or $\cdot 01$, this limit does not necessarily correspond exactly to the 5 and 1 per cent. significance levels found from the usual tables of the z probability integral. Where it falls will in fact depend upon the particular set of s^2 yields, y_{ij}. Thus, in one example taken, as few as 2·8 per cent. and in another as few as 2·9 per cent. of the N_s partitions obtained by randomization of yields from a uniformity trial gave values of z above the normal theory 5 per cent. level. This line of approach suggests, therefore, that if we are to obtain a correct probability level for z from the classification of the N_s partitions, it might be necessary to apply a somewhat lengthy procedure to each set of s^2 yields obtained from an experiment.

The second method of attack is one which, while recognizing that the η's may not be exactly independent or normal, asks how far an analysis of uniformity trial data (for which the T_k in the equation are zero) suggests that the distribution of z differs at all seriously from the normal theory form. In this case only a single z is obtained from each experiment, and we are concerned with the distribution of z resulting from experiments which have actually been carried out, rather than that generated hypothetically under randomization when all possible N_s partitions are obtained from the s^2 yields of a single experiment. The investigation carried out by O. Tedin (8) showed that for certain types of Latin Square pattern the distribution of z found in 91 uniformity trials was definitely biased, but for other patterns selected at random this bias was not evident.

It should be noted that even if the assumptions underlying the Latin Square equation were perfectly satisfied, there can be little doubt as a result of B. L. Welch's work that certain sets of plot yields will occur in practice from time to time which, under randomization, will lead to distributions of z differing from normal theory. Some of these distributions, however, would be biased in one way, some in another, so that when they are all combined together the resulting z-distribution should approach that of normal theory. From each randomization set the experimenter is concerned in fact with only one value of z, and this has been selected at random if he has chosen his Latin Square pattern randomly; consequently from the point of view of his long-run experience, the appropriate probability distribution for him to use would appear to be that of normal theory.*

* Possibly we have here another instance of the difference referred to above between regarding a test as giving essentially a rule to be applied and justified by long-run experience, rather than a probability measure associated with an isolated experiment.

On the other hand if the equation fails to represent the situation commonly met with in the field in such a way that there is a general bias in one direction, the resulting under (or over) estimate of significance could be avoided by the lengthy process of referring the observed z in each case to its appropriate randomization distribution.

To throw further light on these points it would certainly seem to be of interest to extend Welch's investigation by applying his results to further uniformity trial data.

The conception of randomization illustrated in the examples given above is both exceedingly suggestive and often practically useful, but perhaps it should be described as a valuable device rather than a fundamental principle. Its adoption, when it can be followed by the calculation necessary to determine what I have described as the class I elements, ensures accuracy in the determination of the probability level of a test criterion, but without the aid of some further principle it cannot help us to decide which of a number of alternative tests to choose. It seems hardly possible to build the methods of statistics into a consistent whole without facing squarely the why of that choice.

REFERENCES

(1) J. Neyman (1934). *J. R. statist. Soc.* xcvii, Appendix, p. 589, and (1937) *Phil. Trans. Roy. Soc.* (at press).

(2) R. A. Fisher (1930). *Proc. Camb. phil. Soc.* xxvi, 528.

(3) J. Neyman and E. S. Pearson (1933). *Philos. Trans.* A, ccxxxi, 289.

(4) —— —— (1936). *Statistical Research Memoirs* (Dept. of Statistics, University College, London), i, 1.

(5) R. A. Fisher (1935). *The Design of Experiments.* Oliver and Boyd.

(6) —— (1936). *J. R. anthrop. Inst.* lxvi, 57.

(7) B. L. Welch (1937). *Biometrika*, xxix, 21.

(8) O. Tedin (1931). *J. agric. Sci.* xxi, 191.

THE PROBABILITY INTEGRAL TRANSFORMATION FOR TESTING GOODNESS OF FIT AND COMBINING INDEPENDENT TESTS OF SIGNIFICANCE

THE PROBABILITY INTEGRAL TRANSFORMATION FOR TESTING GOODNESS OF FIT AND COMBINING INDEPENDENT TESTS OF SIGNIFICANCE

By E. S. PEARSON

1. Introductory

If $p(x)$ is the elementary probability law of a continuous random variable x in the interval $a \leqslant x \leqslant b$, so that $p(x) = 0$ for $x < a$ or $> b$ and

$$\int_a^b p(x)\,dx = 1, \qquad \text{......(1)}$$

then we may write

$$y = \int_a^x p(x)\,dx. \qquad \text{......(2)}$$

y is a non-decreasing function of x, having values confined to the interval (0, 1). Further

$$p(y) = p(x) \Big/ \frac{dy}{dx} = 1 \quad \text{for} \quad 0 \leqslant y \leqslant 1. \qquad \text{......(3)}$$

In other words the probability law for the integral, y, is rectangular, all values of y between 0 and 1 being equally likely to occur. It follows that if we wish to use a set of n independent observations $x_1, x_2, \ldots, x_n$ to test the hypothesis H_0 that a probability law is of specified form, say $p(x \mid H_0)$, it may be possible to carry out this by testing the equivalent hypothesis, h_0, that the corresponding values $y_1, y_2, \ldots, y_n$, obtained by means of the transformation (2), have been randomly drawn from the rectangular distribution (3). The relation between x_i and y_i is illustrated in Fig. 1; corresponding to the abscissae x_i, $(i = 1, 2, \ldots, 10)$, of the ten ordinates drawn above, are ten values of y shown below on the scale 0 to 1. The hypothesis H_0 that the ten x's are a random sample from a population distribution represented by the frequency curve is therefore equivalent to the hypothesis h_0 that the ten y's form a random sample from a rectangular distribution, range 0 to 1.

If the probability laws $p(x)$ are not the same for all the x's, so that

$$y_i = \int_{a_i}^{x_i} p_i(x)\,dx \quad (i = 1, 2, \ldots, n), \qquad \text{......(4)}$$

the n values of y_i will still be distributed independently as in (3). It follows that the transformation is applicable not only to problems generally classed under the heading of tests of goodness of fit, where $p_i(x)$ is the same for all i, but also in another important type of problem where x_i are a number of independent test criteria, e.g. a number of values of "Student's" t or Fisher's z associated with differing degrees of freedom, and it is wished to obtain a single test of a comprehensive hypothesis. Thus for example we may either:

(*a*) Test whether it is likely that a sample of ten values of a variable x has been drawn from a Normal distribution with specified mean and standard deviation, ξ_0 and σ_0.

(*b*) Test the hypothesis that there is no difference between the gain in weight of children fed on (i) raw, (ii) pasteurized milk, using ten values of t obtained from a comparison in ten age groups of the mean difference in weight increase of children fed for six months on the two diets.

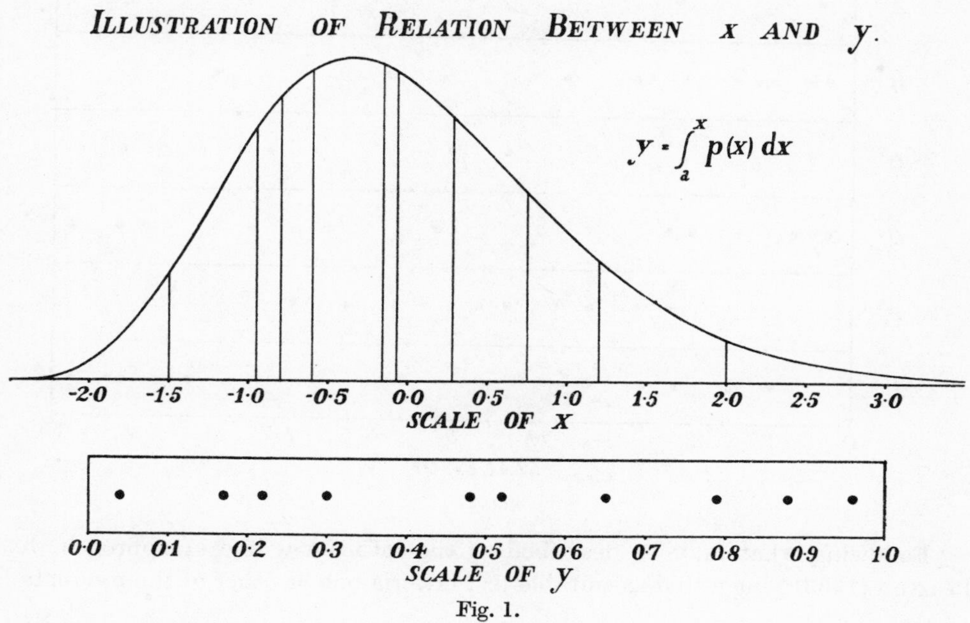

Fig. 1.

Results following from this idea of using the probability integral transformation, which seems likely to be one of the most fruitful conceptions introduced into statistical theory during the last few years, have been developed by R. A. Fisher (1932), Karl Pearson (1933, 1934) and J. Neyman (1937). It is my purpose in this article to review and link together some of the suggestions that have been put forward.

2. Choice of the appropriate test criterion

The probability that in a random sample of size n from the rectangular distribution (3), the y's will fall within the elementary intervals $y_i \pm \frac{1}{2}dy_i$ $(i = 1, 2, \ldots, n)$ is $dy_1 dy_2 \ldots dy_n$, i.e. is independent of the particular values of y. Thus any set of values of y is as likely to occur as another. What criterion are we therefore to use in testing the hypothesis, h_0, that the sample has been drawn from the rectangular population? Established custom in analogous problems might suggest that we should compare the moments of the sample with those of the rectangle. But which moments and how many? Fig. 2 shows six possible y-samples of size $n = 10$; of these sample (a) is likely to have moments agreeing most closely with those of the rectangle. Nevertheless each of the spot patterns illustrated is equally likely to occur in sampling if h_0 is true, and to assume that the test must be based on moments would appear to prejudice the issue.

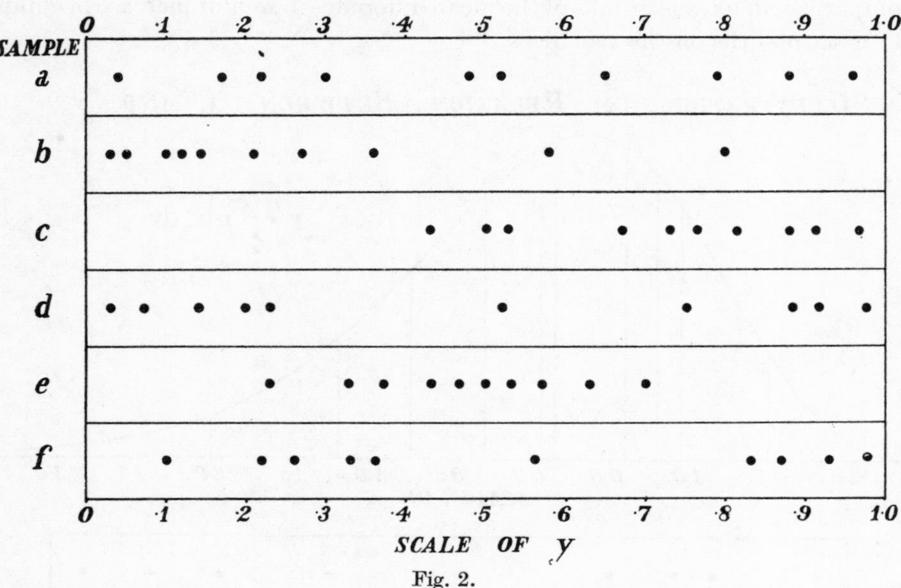

Fig. 2.

Following what may be described as the intuitional line of approach, K. Pearson (1933)* suggested as suitable test criteria one or other of the products

$$Q_1 = y_1 y_2 \dots y_n, \qquad \dots\dots(5)$$

or

$$Q_1' = (1-y_1)(1-y_2)\dots(1-y_n).\dagger \qquad \dots\dots(6)$$

Here Q_1 is the joint probability that in random sampling from $p_i(x)$ the n values of x will be as small or smaller than the corresponding observed values; Q_1' is the probability that they will be as great or greater than their observed values. In Fig. 2, sample (b) will give a relatively low value to Q_1, and a relatively high value to Q_1'; for sample (c) the position is reversed. To form a complete statistical test it is clearly necessary to know how these Q criteria are distributed in random sampling if the hypothesis h_0 regarding the y's, and therefore the hypothesis H_0 regarding the x's, were true.

* R. A. Fisher (1932) was primarily concerned with a combination of tests of significance, where the distinction between Q_1 and Q_1' did not arise in the same way.

† K. Pearson denoted these products by λ_n.

By means of a simple transformation to new variables

$$v_i = -2\log_e y_i \quad (i = 1, 2, \ldots, n), \qquad \ldots\ldots(7)$$

it is easy to show that $-2\log_e Q$ is distributed as χ^2 with degrees of freedom $f = 2n$, i.e.

$$p(\chi^2) = \frac{1}{\Gamma(\frac{1}{2}f)\, 2^{\frac{1}{2}f}} (\chi^2)^{\frac{1}{2}f-1} e^{-\frac{1}{2}\chi^2}. \qquad \ldots\ldots(8)$$

Exceptionally small values of Q_1 or Q_1' correspond to large values of χ^2. Thus a straightforward test is available which, on choice of the appropriate probability level from the χ^2 tables, gives a precise control of the risk of rejecting the hypothesis tested regarding the $p_i(x)$ when it is true.

In discussing the application of this test K. Pearson was aware of the difficulty of choice between Q_1 and Q_1'. From which tail of the distributions should the probability integral be calculated? He suggested that the smaller of the two should be used as giving the "more stringent test". It may be noted that as an alternative to Q_1 and Q_1' a third criterion may be used, namely

$$Q_2 = \prod_{i=1}^{n} (y_i'), \qquad \ldots\ldots(9)$$

where

$$\left.\begin{aligned} y_i' &= 2\int_a^{x_i} p_i(x)\,dx = 2y_i \text{ if } x_i \text{ is below median } x, \\ &= 2\int_{x_i}^{b} p_i(x)\,dx = 2(1-y_i) \text{ if } x_i \text{ is above median } x. \end{aligned}\right\} \qquad \ldots\ldots(10)$$

It is seen that y_i' follows the rectangular distribution (3) if H_0 is true, and therefore $-2\log_e Q_2$ is also distributed as χ^2 with $f = 2n$. The criterion Q_2 will be exceptionally small if the x's lie towards either tail of their probability distributions,* e.g. in sample (*d*) of Fig. 2; it will be exceptionally large for sample (*e*).

Provided that the test based on one of the products Q is being used to combine together a number of independent tests of significance, the intuition which lead to its choice appears on the whole to be sound, though it cannot be claimed that it is necessarily the best test. In such a problem the separate test criteria x_i (whether t, z, r, χ^2, etc.) have been chosen so that small values of y_i or of $1-y_i$ suggest that the individual hypotheses are improbable. Consequently a small value of Q is essentially associated with improbability of the combined result. Nor will it generally be difficult to decide on *a priori* grounds which of the three forms of Q is appropriate.† In the case of tests of goodness of fit, however, when it is wished to test whether a sample $x_1, x_2, \ldots, x_n$ can have been randomly drawn from a population with probability law $p(x) = p(x \mid H_0)$, there appear to be no *a priori* reasons for choosing the Q type of criterion based on the *product* of the

* This form of the criterion appears first to have been defined precisely in print by P. V. Sukhatme (1935, p. 587).

† It is of course important not to make the decision as to which end of the x-distribution to start from in taking the integral depend on the observed values of the x's.

probability integrals. When all the forms of pattern of the y's, as shown in Fig. 2, are equally likely to occur if h_0 be true, how, it must be asked, are we to settle when the hypothesis should be rejected? It seems only possible to proceed further by specifying what other forms of probability law are to be regarded as possible alternatives to $p(x \mid H_0)$.

Denote by $p(x \mid H_1)$ some alternative law. If now this is the true probability law, but the y's have been calculated from equations (2) on the assumption that $p(x) = p(x \mid H_0)$, then, as Neyman has pointed out,

$$p(y \mid h_1) = \frac{p(x \mid H_1)}{\dfrac{dy}{dx}} = \left.\frac{p(x \mid H_1)}{p(x \mid H_0)}\right|_{x=f(y)} \quad \text{for } 0 \leqslant y \leqslant 1, \qquad \text{......(11)}$$

where $f(y)$ means the solution of

$$y = \int_a^x p(x \mid H_0)\,dx \qquad \text{......(12)}$$

with regard to x. Thus the probability distribution of y, when H_1 is true, is obtained by calculating at points $x = f(y)$ the ratio of the ordinates of the true and hypothetical probability functions. As an example, suppose that we are using n values of x to test the hypothesis that the sampled population is represented by a normal curve with mean at zero and unit standard deviation. Then

$$p(x \mid H_0) = \frac{1}{\sqrt{(2\pi)}}\,e^{-\frac{1}{2}x^2}. \qquad \text{......(13)}$$

Consider what would be the equation of $p(y \mid h_1)$ if the following had been the true forms of the population sampled:

(I) $$p(x \mid H_1) = \frac{1}{\sqrt{(2\pi)}}\,e^{-\frac{1}{2}(x-\frac{1}{2})^2}, \qquad \text{......(14)}$$

a normal curve with mean at $+0{\cdot}5$ and unit standard deviation.

(II) $$p(x \mid H_1) = \frac{2}{3\sqrt{(2\pi)}}\,e^{-\frac{1}{2}\left(\frac{2x}{3}\right)^2}, \qquad \text{......(15)}$$

(III) $$p(x \mid H_1) = \frac{3}{2\sqrt{(2\pi)}}\,e^{-\frac{1}{2}\left(\frac{3x}{2}\right)^2}, \qquad \text{......(16)}$$

normal curves with means at zero and standard deviations of $\frac{3}{2}$ and $\frac{2}{3}$ respectively.

(IV) $$p(x \mid H_1) = c(1 + \tfrac{1}{2}\,x\sqrt{\beta_1})^{\frac{4}{\beta_1}-1}\,e^{-\frac{2x}{\sqrt{\beta_1}}}$$

where $(a)\ \sqrt{\beta_1} = 0{\cdot}4$, $\quad (b)\ \sqrt{\beta_1} = 0{\cdot}7$, ...(17)

Pearson Type III curves with mean at zero, unit standard deviation and $\beta_1 = 0{\cdot}16$ or $0{\cdot}49$.

Values for $p(y \mid h_1)$ were calculated from (11), corresponding to the points

$y = 0, 0{\cdot}05, 0{\cdot}10, 0{\cdot}20, \ldots, 0{\cdot}80, 0{\cdot}90, 0{\cdot}95, 1{\cdot}00$;* the resulting curves are drawn in Fig. 3. They represent a number of different forms of departure from the rectangular y-distribution, corresponding in $p(x)$ to: (I) a shift in mean; (II) and (III) changes in standard deviation; (IV) a change in shape. Clearly, in Fig. 2,

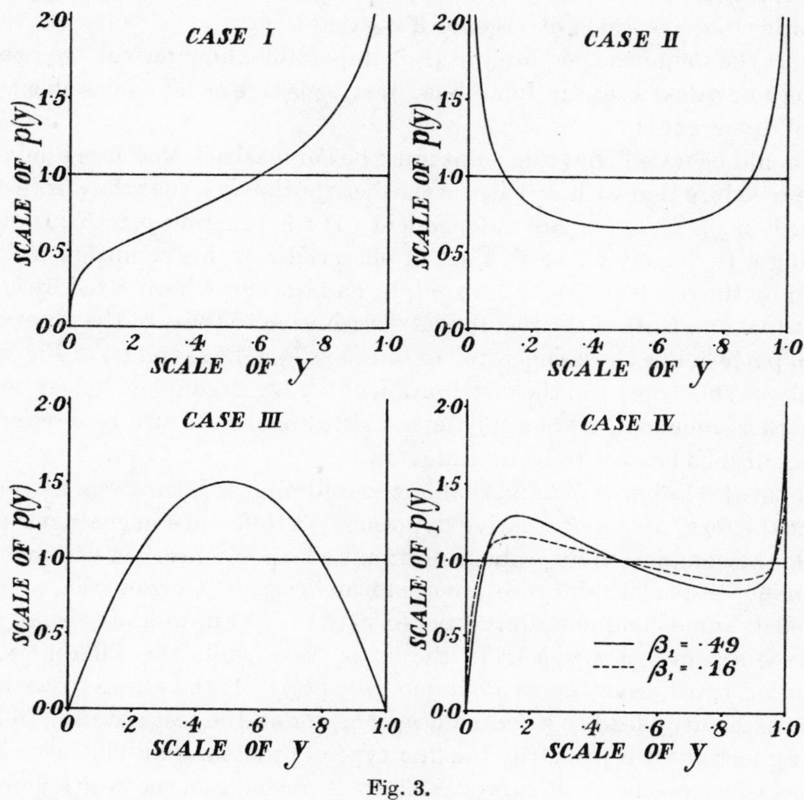

Fig. 3.

Alternatives to $p(x\,|\,H_0) = \dfrac{1}{\sqrt{(2\pi)}}\, e^{-\frac{1}{2}x^2}$.

I. $p(x\,|\,H_1) = \dfrac{1}{\sqrt{(2\pi)}}\, e^{-\frac{1}{2}(x-\frac{1}{2})^2}$.

II. $p(x\,|\,H_1) = \dfrac{2}{3\sqrt{(2\pi)}}\, e^{-\frac{1}{2}\left(\frac{2x}{3}\right)^2}$.

III. $p(x\,|\,H_1) = \dfrac{3}{2\sqrt{(2\pi)}}\, e^{-\frac{1}{2}\left(\frac{3x}{2}\right)^2}$.

IV. $p(x\,|\,H_1) = c(1 + \frac{1}{2}x\sqrt{\beta_1})^{\frac{4}{\beta_1}-1}\, e^{-\frac{2x}{\sqrt{\beta_1}}}$.

samples (c), (d), (e) and (f) are of patterns we might expect to find when testing H_0, if the populations sampled differed from (13) in the directions of (14), (15), (16) and (17) respectively.

The questions, therefore, that need consideration appear to be the following.

* For the Type III curve, the tables of ordinates entered against a standardized abscissa, published by L. R. Salvosa (1930), were found very useful.

In testing, on observed sample values, whether $p(x \mid H_0)$ represents the population probability law,

(i) Can we define in what way the true probability law may diverge from that specified by H_0 (e.g. in location, scaling, shape, etc., one or all)?

(ii) If this is possible, can we determine the most efficient test to apply to the y's in order to detect such divergence if it exists?

(iii) If the definition required in (i) is impossible, how far can we determine what may be called a useful "omnibus" test, sensitive as far as possible to many forms of divergence?

It should be noted, and this point must be emphasized, that it is fundamental to any procedure that we may base on the distribution of y that the n transformed observations $y_1, y_2, \ldots, y_n$ are independent. If the function $p(x \mid H_0)$ is obtained by fitting a frequency curve to a set of observed x's, this condition will not be satisfied by the resulting y's. For example, had the curve been fitted by equating the first two moments of the theoretical distribution to those of the observations, types of pattern like those suggested in samples (*b*), (*c*), (*d*) and (*e*) of Fig. 2 would probably be ruled out, and the distribution of $-2\log_e Q$ could no longer be that of χ^2. Whether some method of applying a test to the y's can still be devised under these conditions has yet to be investigated.

It must also be borne in mind that once we admit it to be necessary to take into account the form of the alternative hypotheses, a difference in character appears between the goodness of fit problem and that which is concerned with combining independent tests of significance. In the former case, if H_0 is not true, we suppose there exists some common alternative form $p(x \mid H_1)$ appropriate for all the x's, and hence a common $p(y \mid h_1)$. In the latter case, while the different $p_i(x \mid H_0)$ will lead on transformation to a common $p(y \mid h_0) = 1$, the alternatives $p_i(x \mid H_1)$ will not necessarily lead to a common $p(y \mid h_1)$ for all the test criteria. In the two following sections it is primarily the first type of problem that will be considered; the conclusions reached will, however, throw some light on the position obtaining in the second case.

3. A partial solution based on the product criteria, Q

The curves corresponding to cases I, II and III in Fig. 3 could all be graduated roughly by Pearson Type I curves of the form

$$p(y) = p(y \mid h_1) = \frac{\Gamma(m_1+m_2+2)}{\Gamma(m_1+1)\,\Gamma(m_2+1)}\,y^{m_1}(1-y)^{m_2}. \qquad \ldots\ldots(18)$$

In the case when the hypothesis tested is true, i.e. $h_1 = h_0$, the rectangular distribution results from setting $m_1 = m_2 = 0$. The curve

$$p(y \mid h_1) = (m+1)(1-y)^m, \quad -1 < m \leqslant 0, \qquad \ldots\ldots(19)$$

while it has an ordinate of value $(m+1) < 1$ at $y = 0$, provides an approximation to the form of the curve in Case I. Again the curve

$$p(y \mid h_1) = \frac{\Gamma(2m+2)}{\{\Gamma(m+1)\}^2} y^m (1-y)^m, \qquad \text{......(20)}$$

can be made to represent the y-distributions of Case II $(m < 0)$ and Case III $(m > 0)$. No Type I curve can represent the y-distributions in Case IV.

Starting from (18), or its special forms (19) and (20) as representing the possible alternatives, it is of interest to see what criterion, for testing the hypothesis h_0 (that $p(y)$ is rectangular), flows from the application of the likelihood method which J. Neyman and the present writer have made frequent use of in other problems.

This method consists of the following procedure:

(1) Given a sample of n independent observations $y_1, y_2, \ldots, y_n$, their joint elementary probability law if h_0 be true, is,

$$p(y_1, y_2, \ldots, y_n \mid h_0) = 1, \qquad \text{......(21)}$$

while if any other member of the admissible set of alternatives is true, it is

$$p(y_1, y_2, \ldots, y_n \mid h_1) = \left\{\frac{\Gamma(m_1+m_2+2)}{\Gamma(m_1+1)\,\Gamma(m_2+1)}\right\}^n \prod_{i=1}^{n} y_i^{m_1}(1-y_i)^{m_2}. \qquad \text{......(22)}$$

(2) Determine the values of m_1 and m_2 which make (22) a maximum, and call the corresponding maximized function $p(y_1, y_2, \ldots, y_n \mid h \max)$.

(3) Then the likelihood ratio criterion for testing h_0 will be λ, where

$$\lambda = \frac{p(y_1, y_2, \ldots, y_n \mid h_0)}{p(y_1, y_2, \ldots, y_n \mid h \max)}. \qquad \text{......(23)}$$

Taking the form (19) to represent $p(y \mid h_1)$, we have only one parameter, m, to determine

$$\log p(y_1, y_2, \ldots, y_n \mid h_1) = n \log (m+1) + m \log \left\{\prod_{i=1}^{n} (1-y_i)\right\}. \qquad \text{......(24)}$$

Whence
$$\frac{\partial \log p}{\partial m} = \frac{n}{m+1} + \log Q_1',$$

where Q_1' is defined in (6) above. Equating this expression to zero, it is seen that a maximum solution is given by

$$m+1 = \left\{-\frac{1}{n} \log Q_1'\right\}^{-1} = \frac{2n}{\chi^2}, \qquad \text{......(25)}$$

where
$$\chi^2 = -2 \log Q_1' \qquad \text{......(26)}$$

provided that $\chi^2 \geqslant 2n$. If $\chi^2 < 2n$, since $m \leqslant 0$, the maximum solution is given by $m = 0$.

Consequently we find that

$$\lambda = \left(\frac{\chi^2}{2n}\right)^n (e^{-\frac{1}{2}\chi^2})^{1-\frac{2n}{\chi^2}}$$

$$= (2n)^{-n}(\chi^2)^n e^{-\frac{1}{2}\chi^2+n}, \qquad \text{......(27)}$$

provided that $\chi^2 \geqslant 2n$; if $\chi^2 < 2n$ then $\lambda = 1$.*

Thus $\lambda \to 0$ and the hypothesis tested becomes less and less likely when $\chi^2 \to \infty$ and $Q_1' \to 0$. If the hypothesis is true, then we know from the discussion on p. 137 above that $-2\log Q_1'$ is distributed in the standard χ^2 form with $2n$ degrees of freedom.

But not only is the test based on Q_1' that derived from the λ-criterion; it may be easily shown that it is the uniformly most powerful test† of the hypothesis h_0 with regard to the set of alternatives defined by (19). In other words if the admissible alternatives to H_0 lead to forms $p(y \mid h_1)$ following the J-curve (19), then the test based on Q_1' or, if the integrals are more appropriately calculated from the lower terminal, on Q_1 has the following unique property: *it is impossible to find any other test which gives a larger chance of detecting departure of the probability law from the specified form* $p(x \mid H_0)$. A fresh light seems therefore to be thrown on the product criteria Q_1 and Q_1'. While the form (19) will not be exactly followed in practice, a little reflection on the matter suggests that it will represent the general characteristics of the departure of $p(y)$ from the rectangle if the possible changes in $p(x)$ correspond to a translation of the whole $p(x)$ distribution to right (or left). It is of interest to note that apart from its application in goodness of fit tests, this is also the kind of change we may often expect when the x's are the criteria used in a number of independent tests of significance. Thus, if some general hypothesis is not true, a number of independent values of "Student's" t may be distributed approximately about some common mean value other than zero; while the shape and standard deviations of these modified t-distributions will also be altered, the changes involved would relatively be much less than in the mean.

If now we start from the form (20), which as has been pointed out will represent approximately the curves of Cases II and III in Fig. 3, we may proceed to calculate the λ-criterion in a similar manner. The equation to solve for m, to obtain $p(y_1, y_2, \ldots, y_n \mid h\max)$, is

$$\frac{\partial \log \Gamma(2m+2)}{\partial m} - \frac{2\partial \log \Gamma(m+1)}{\partial m} = -\frac{1}{n}\log(Q_1 Q_1'), \qquad \text{......(28)}$$

* Since the admissible alternatives have been restricted to those defined by (19), i.e. with $-1 < m \leqslant 0$, we cannot reject H_0 when high values of Q_1' or low values of χ^2 are obtained from the data. Thus in such cases the value of the λ-criterion is unity, suggesting no reason for rejecting H_0. If however we take $-1 < m < \infty$, equation (19) will now represent J-curves with maxima either at $y=1$ or $y=0$. We are then aiming at a test which is sensitive to translation of $p(x \mid H_1)$ both to right and to left of $p(x \mid H_0)$, and $\lambda \to 0$ either when $Q_1' \to 0$ or when $Q_1' \to 1$.

† See Neyman and Pearson (1933*a*, *b*). The proof that the test possesses this property follows from the results given on pp. 298–302 of the earlier paper.

where $$Q_1 Q_1' = \prod_{i=1}^{n} y_i(1-y_i). \qquad \text{......(29)}$$

Thus it appears that λ, if determined, would be a function of $Q_1 Q_1'$. Without attempting to go further into the problem it may be noted that a test criterion depending on $Q_1 Q_1'$ is likely to be rather closely correlated with the criterion Q_2, defined in equations (9) and (10). It will be seen that

$$Q_2 = \prod_{i=1}^{n} \{1-2\,|\,y_i - \tfrac{1}{2}\,|\}, \qquad \text{......(30)}$$

and the functions (*a*) $1-2\,|\,y_i-\frac{1}{2}\,|$, and (*b*) $4y_i(1-y_i)$ both equal zero when $y_i = 0$, increase monotonically to 1 when $y_i = \frac{1}{2}$ and then decrease to 0 as y_i increases to 1. In so far as this correspondence exists, it points to Q_2 being an appropriate criterion when the alternatives to $p(x \mid H_0)$ are likely to have the same mean but either larger or smaller standard deviations.

Using the more general Type I form of equation (18), it is found that λ will be a function of both Q_1 and Q_1', but not of $Q_1 Q_1'$.

Finally it must again be noted that (18) cannot represent the curves shown as Case IV in Fig. 3, which arose when the probability distribution $p(x \mid H_1)$ had the same mean and standard deviation as $p(x \mid H_0)$ but was a skew rather than a normal curve. It is noted however that for both alternatives represented, i.e. Type III curves with $\beta_1 = 0{\cdot}16$ and $0{\cdot}49$ respectively, the gradient of $p(y \mid h_1)$ increases approximately from $y = 0$ to $0{\cdot}2$, decreases from $y = 0{\cdot}2$ to $0{\cdot}8$, and increases again from $y = 0{\cdot}8$ to $1{\cdot}0$. Bearing in mind that a criterion of the type $Q_1' = \prod_{i=1}^{n} (1-y_i)$ appears to be efficient in detecting the existence of an increasing gradient as in Case I, the following criterion is tentatively suggested as suitable to detect the presence of skewness:

$$Q_3 = \prod_{i=1}^{n} (y_i'), \qquad \text{......(31)}$$

where
$$\left.\begin{aligned} y_i' &= 5(0{\cdot}2-y_i) && \text{for} \quad 0 \leqslant y_i \leqslant 0{\cdot}2, \\ y_i' &= \tfrac{5}{3}(y_i - 0{\cdot}2) && \text{for} \quad 0{\cdot}2 < y_i \leqslant 0{\cdot}8, \\ y_i' &= 5(1-y_i) && \text{for} \quad 0{\cdot}8 < y_i \leqslant 1. \end{aligned}\right\} \qquad \text{......(32)}$$

It will be found that if y_i follows the rectangular distribution, so also does y_i'. Thus $-2\log_e Q_3$ will again be distributed as χ^2 with $f = 2n$, if H_0 is true.

The difference in the character of the critical regions of the tests associated with Q_1, Q_2 and Q_3 may be illustrated diagrammatically for the case $n = 2$, where for clearness a 20 % significance level (rather than, say, 0·05 or 0·01) has been taken. In each case the hypothesis H_0 (or h_0) would be rejected if the sample point (y_1, y_2) falls within the shaded regions; if H_0 be true the sample point is equally likely to fall anywhere within the unit square, so that the area of the shaded portions must be 20 % of the whole. The boundaries of these regions were obtained from the χ^2-transformation. Thus for $f = 4$, the upper and lower 20 %

levels for χ^2 are 1·649 and 5·989 respectively, giving corresponding levels for Q of 0·0501 and 0·4385. To determine the boundaries it is then necessary to find the co-ordinates of y_1 and y_2 satisfying, (i) equation (5) for Q_1; (ii) equations (9) and (10) for Q_2; (iii) equations (31) and (32) for Q_3. A sample such as (*b*) of Fig. 2 will give a y-point in the n-dimensioned cube which is likely to fall into the critical

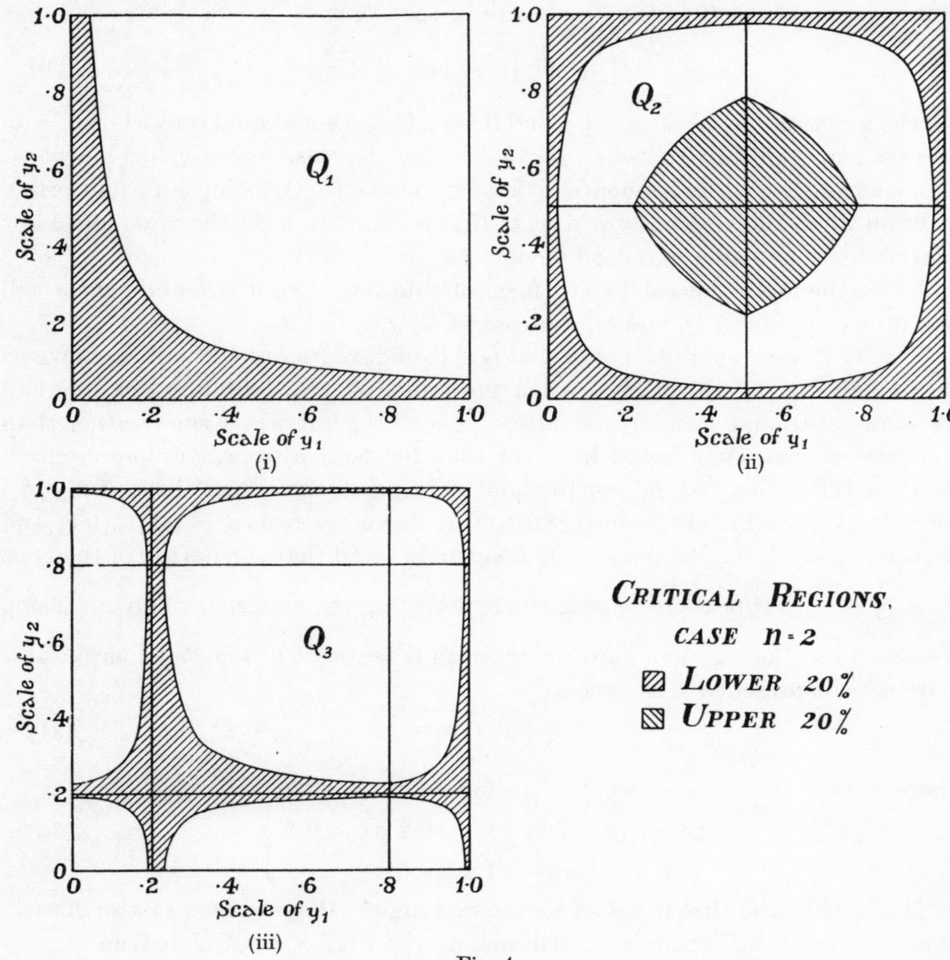

Fig. 4.

region of the type shown in Fig. 4 (i); a sample as (*d*) is likely to give a point falling into a region of the outer ring type of Fig. 4 (ii), while a sample like (*e*) will give a point falling in the central lozenge-shaped type of region of the same diagram. On the other hand samples like (*f*), which seem likely to arise when $p(x \mid H_1)$ has the same mean and standard deviation but greater positive skewness than $p(x \mid H_0)$, will tend to give points in the more complicated region of the type of Fig. 4 (iii), i.e. points with y values between 0·1 and 0·4 or above 0·9.

The suggestion regarding Q_3 is only put forward tentatively. But it appears that in so far as we know the kind of departure from $p(x \mid H_0)$ to be expected, and therefore know the points within the n-dimensioned y-hypercube round which the sample points are likely to cluster, it should be possible to construct appropriate tests of the Q-type on the lines suggested in the case of Q_3. The sampling distribution of such criteria will be always exactly known if H_0 is true,* through the transformation $-2\log_e Q = \chi^2$, while their efficiency in detecting that H_0 is false can be secured on a basis which, if crude, has a definite guiding principle behind it. For a more precise handling of the problem Dr Neyman's work on "smooth tests" must be considered.

4. Dr J. Neyman's method of choosing appropriate test criteria

Neyman (1937) deals with the goodness of fit type of problem, that is to say, he supposes that if $p(y)$ is not a rectangle, then some single alternative $p(y \mid h_1)$ is appropriate for all observations. The system of curves which he has taken to represent the possible alternatives is

$$p(y \mid h_1) = p(y \mid \Theta_1, \Theta_2, \ldots, \Theta_k) = ce^{\sum_{t=1}^{k} \Theta_t \pi_t(y)} \quad \text{for } 0 \leqslant y \leqslant 1. \qquad \ldots\ldots(33)$$

These curves depend on k parameters Θ_t which are at our choice; if all the Θ_t's are zero, $p(y \mid h_1) = p(y \mid h_0)$. c is a function of the Θ_t's. Further $\pi_1, \pi_2, \ldots, \pi_k$ are a system of polynomials in y, orthogonal and standardized in the interval (0, 1) of which the first few are as follows:

$$\left.\begin{aligned} \pi_1(y) &= \sqrt{12}(y-\tfrac{1}{2}), \\ \pi_2(y) &= \sqrt{5}\{6(y-\tfrac{1}{2})^2-\tfrac{1}{2}\}, \\ \pi_3(y) &= \sqrt{7}\{20(y-\tfrac{1}{2})^3-3(y-\tfrac{1}{2})\}, \\ \pi_4(y) &= 210(y-\tfrac{1}{2})^4-45(y-\tfrac{1}{2})^2+\tfrac{9}{8}. \end{aligned}\right\} \qquad \ldots\ldots(34)$$

This form for $p(y \mid h_1)$ was chosen by Neyman partly for simplicity in the development of the appropriate tests and partly on the grounds that any function having the characteristics of $\log p(y)$ can be represented by a series of such orthogonal polynomials $\pi_t(y)$. How many and which terms of such a series are needed to represent curves of such varied form as those shown in Fig. 3 has still to be explored. It will be noted that using only $\pi_1(y)$, (33) gives an exponential which will correspond roughly to Case I, Fig. 3. Again $\pi_2(y)$ will lead to a curve that will approximate to Cases II and III, according as Θ_2 is positive or negative, while $\pi_3(y)$ will introduce a point of inflexion of the kind shown for Case IV. Nevertheless it will be seen that the form (33) may need a considerable number of terms before it will make $p(y \mid h_1)$ approach the values of 0 or ∞ at $y = 0$ and 1.

* In this property the tests are more exact than Neyman's tests discussed in the next section, since the sampling distribution of his criteria are only approximate for small values of n.

In some cases therefore the Pearson Type I curve of (18) may be more suitable than (33). It must be remembered, however, that the curves drawn in Fig. 3 are somewhat exceptional, since the differences between the $p(x \mid H_0)$ of (13) on the one hand and the alternatives (14)–(17) on the other are relatively large. In any practical case where n is not too small, one would hope to be able to detect much smaller differences, i.e. to be dealing with alternative distributions $p(y \mid h_1)$ differing less drastically from the rectangular $p(y \mid h_0) = 1$.

Starting from the basis of equation (33), and assuming that n is not too small, Neyman has developed a series of tests, relatively simple to apply, which he calls "smooth tests" that have the following properties.

(*a*) The particular test which is most appropriate will depend upon the number of polynomials needed in (33) to represent the type of departure from the rectangular form likely to be met with in $p(y \mid h_1)$. This is a point at which practical experience must be introduced. Let it be supposed that in a given problem the first k polynomials are regarded as adequate.

(*b*) The test is so adjusted that when H_0 (or h_0) is true, i.e. when $\Theta_1 = \Theta_2 \dots \Theta_k = 0$, the significance level may be fixed at any desired magnitude, e.g. at 0·05 or 0·01.

(*c*) If H_0 be not true, the test is unbiassed in the sense of Neyman and Pearson (1936, 1938), and is more likely than any other unbiassed test to detect departures from zero in the k parameters Θ_t, i.e. to detect that in the place of $p(x \mid H_0)$ some alternative form of law $p(x \mid H_1)$ holds good.

(*d*) The chance of detection, or the power of the test in Neyman and Pearson's terminology, in the neighbourhood of $\Theta_1 = \Theta_2 \dots \Theta_k = 0$ is approximately a function of

$$\phi^2 = \Theta_1^2 + \Theta_2^2 + \dots + \Theta_k^2. \qquad \dots\dots(35)$$

(*e*) For alternatives to $p(x \mid H_0)$ which lead to a function $p(y \mid h_1)$ needing for its representation *more* than the first k-polynomials, the test will not be sensitive. This means that for an "omnibus" test capable of detecting all manner of departures from the rectangle, we may require to introduce a considerable number of polynomial terms. Such a test will however be less efficient in detecting those forms of departure which one or two polynomial terms would be adequate to represent.

If we write

$$z_i = y_i - \tfrac{1}{2} \qquad \dots\dots(36)$$

and

$$\left.\begin{aligned} u_1^2 &= n^{-1}\left\{\sum_{i=1}^{n} \pi_1(y_i)\right\}^2 = 12n^{-1}\left\{\sum_{i=1}^{n} (z_i)\right\}^2, \\ u_2^2 &= n^{-1}\left\{\sum_{i=1}^{n} \pi_2(y_i)\right\}^2 = 180n^{-1}\left\{\sum_{i=1}^{n} (z_i^2) - \tfrac{1}{12}n\right\}^2, \\ u_3^2 &= n^{-1}\left\{\sum_{i=1}^{n} \pi_3(y_i)\right\}^2 = 7n^{-1}\left\{20\sum_{i=1}^{n} (z_i^3) - 3\sum_{i=1}^{n} (z_i)\right\}^2, \\ &\text{etc.,} \end{aligned}\right\} \qquad \dots\dots(37)$$

then Neyman's criterion for the kth order test is

$$\psi_k^2 = \sum_{t=1}^{k} (u_t^2), \qquad \text{......(38)}$$

which is approximately distributed as χ^2 with k degrees of freedom. The approximation is due to the fact that while, if h_0 is true, the u's have each an expectation of zero, a unit standard deviation and are *uncorrelated* (i.e. the correlation coefficient between any two of them is zero), they are not independent nor exactly normally distributed. As the sample size, n, increases the accuracy will rapidly improve.

It may be shown that when n is large, and the constant c in (33) assumes its limiting form, $\exp[-\frac{1}{2}\Sigma\Theta_i^2]$, then Neyman's test criterion (38) is exactly that which follows from applying to formula (33) the likelihood method of approach used in the preceding section. In fact it is found that

$$\lambda = e^{-\frac{1}{2}n \sum_{t=1}^{k} (u^2)} \qquad \text{......(39)}$$

an expression decreasing from 1 to 0 as the ψ_k^2 of (38) increases from 0 to ∞.

It will be noticed that Neyman's criterion is a sum of polynomial terms in the y_i's, or more simply, using (36), in the z_i's. The product criteria Q_1 and Q_2 of equations (5) and (9) may also be expressed in this form. Thus

$$\begin{aligned} -\log Q_1 &= -\sum_i^n \{\log y_i\} \\ &= -\sum_i^n \{\log(1 + z_i - \tfrac{1}{2})\} \\ &= -\sum_i (z_i - \tfrac{1}{2}) + \tfrac{1}{2}\sum_i (z_i - \tfrac{1}{2})^2 - \tfrac{1}{3}\sum_i (z_i - \tfrac{1}{2})^3 + \dots, \qquad \text{......(40)} \\ -\log Q_2 &= -\sum_i \{\log(1 - 2\,|\,z_i\,|)\} \\ &= 2\sum_i |\,z_i\,| + 2\sum_i (z_i^2) + \tfrac{8}{3}\sum |\,z_i^3\,| + \dots. \qquad \text{......(41)} \end{aligned}$$

These series do not of course bear any immediate relation to Dr Neyman's polynomial expansions (37).

5. Summary

This paper has drawn attention to the somewhat novel character of the problem to be faced in dealing with tests based on the probability integral transformation. The intuitional notions that have often served to determine the most appropriate test when dealing with normal variation are hardly applicable when we are concerned with a variable following the rectangular distribution. The tests proposed by R. A. Fisher and K. Pearson have been discussed, and emphasis has been laid on the need for consideration of the possible alternatives to the hypothesis tested. The situation will differ according to whether the problem is one of testing goodness of fit or of combining the results of a number of independent tests of significance. Some illustration of these ideas has been given in the case where the hypothesis regarding the form of a probability law $p(x)$ is incorrect (*a*) in the position of the mean, (*b*) in the magnitude of the standard deviation, (*c*) in the shape of the probability curve. A method has been suggested of adopting the product criteria, Q, to meet these different cases.

Finally, a summary has been given of J. Neyman's suggestions for dealing with the problem. From the theoretical point of view these suggestions appear to be fundamental in character; it is hoped however that it will be possible before long to carry out further numerical investigations (*a*) to determine how large the number of variables, x, must be to make his results accurate for practical purposes; (*b*) to throw more light on the relation between his polynomial form for $p(y \mid h_1)$, the tests based on Q_1, Q_2, Q_3, ..., discussed in preceding sections and the classes of alternatives met with in different types of statistical problem.

REFERENCES

FISHER, R. A. (1932). *Statistical Methods for Research Workers*, 4th ed. § 21·1.
NEYMAN, J. (1937). *Skand. AktuarTidskr.* pp. 149–99.
NEYMAN, J. and PEARSON, E. S. (1933*a*). *Philos. Trans.* A, **231**, 289–337.
—— —— (1933*b*). *Proc. Camb. Phil. Soc.* **29**, 492–510.
—— —— (1936). *Statist. Res. Mem.* **1**, 1–37.
—— —— (1938). *Statist. Res. Mem.* **2** (in the Press).
PEARSON, K. (1933). *Biometrika*, **25**, 379–410.
—— (1934). *Biometrika*, **26**, 425–42.
SALVOSA, L. R. (1930). *Ann. Math. Statist.* **1**, 191–8.
SUKHATME, P. V. (1935). *Proc. Ind. Acad. Sci.* **2**, 584–604.

Note by J. Neyman. I am grateful to the author of the present paper for giving me the opportunity of expressing my regret for having overlooked the two papers by Karl Pearson quoted above. When writing the paper on the "Smooth test for goodness of fit" and discussing previous work in this direction, I quoted only the results of H. Cramér and R. v. Mises, omitting mention of the papers by K. Pearson. The omission is the more to be regretted since my paper was dedicated to the memory of Karl Pearson.

A NOTE ON FURTHER PROPERTIES OF STATISTICAL TESTS

By E. S. PEARSON

Dr P. L. Hsu has suggested that I should write a short introductory note on the origin of the idea involved in his paper and in that of Dr Simaika's which follows.* In searching some twelve years ago for a systematic method of choosing the best test of a statistical hypothesis H_0, Prof. Neyman and I came to the conclusion that an essential preliminary to any mathematical formulation of the problem was the definition of a set of admissible alternative hypotheses, $C(H)$. Starting from this viewpoint, our first method of selecting a test involved the use of the likelihood ratio, but, however useful as a practical method of attack, the principle underlying this approach was somewhat arbitrary. A more fundamental procedure, later developed, was to choose a test paying regard to its power function, that is to say, to the chance that its use would lead to the rejection of H_0 if an alternative $H \neq H_0$ of $C(H)$ were true. It then appeared that a number of statistical tests in common use had the remarkable property that they maximized this chance for every alternative to H_0 in $C(H)$. Such tests were termed uniformly most powerful tests of H_0 with regard to $C(H)$.

That there were limitations to the situations in which a uniformly most powerful test could exist soon, however, became clear. These limitations were gradually explored, and the following papers are further contributions to the subject. It was found that these tests generally, though not always, concerned the value of a single parameter. Such are tests of the hypothesis that a mean or a standard deviation has a specified value, or that the difference between two means or two standard deviations is zero. Further, in these cases the class of alternatives must be restricted; thus the two-sample t-test of the hypothesis that two population means ξ_1 and ξ_2 are equal, is only uniformly most powerful for the situation in which the alternatives considered are defined by $\xi_1 - \xi_2 \geqslant 0$ or by $\xi_1 - \xi_2 \leqslant 0$ but not for both at the same time.

In this connexion, in 1935, Kołodziejczyk was able to prove that for tests of a linear hypothesis, no uniformly most powerful test could exist if the number of parameters involved was greater than unity. This result was important, since the majority of tests used in the analysis of variance can be reduced to tests of a linear hypothesis.

This limitation of tests regarding the value of two or more parameters can be illustrated by a geometric presentation. Since the most important features of the problem can be illustrated when H_0 is a simple hypothesis concerning the value of two parameters, I shall take this case, using notation already adopted in this connexion.

* See pp. 62–69 and pp. 70–80 below.

Suppose that the elementary probability law of random variables $x_1, \ldots, x_n$, whose particular values are given by observation, is of form

$$p(x_1, \ldots, x_n \mid \theta_1, \theta_2) = p(E \mid \theta_1, \theta_2), \tag{1}$$

θ_1, θ_2 being the two population parameters. For a critical region w of size α associated with a given test, we may write

$$P\{E \epsilon w \mid \theta_1, \theta_2\} = \int \ldots \int_w p(E \mid \theta_1, \theta_2)\, dx_1 \ldots dx_n = \beta(\theta_1, \theta_2 \mid w). \tag{2}$$

If the hypothesis H_0 which w has been selected to test assumes that

$$\theta_1 = \theta_1^0, \quad \theta_2 = \theta_2^0, \tag{3}$$

then $$\beta(\theta_1^0, \theta_2^0 \mid w) = \alpha, \tag{4}$$

where α is the significance level chosen.

A power surface may be obtained by taking rectangular axes for θ_1 and θ_2 in a horizontal plane and plotting $\beta(\theta_1, \theta_2 \mid w)$ as a vertical ordinate. If w_0 were a critical region associated with a uniformly most powerful test of H_0, then its power surface would fall nowhere below the surfaces derived from other critical regions satisfying (4). No unique surface with this property will, however, in general exist. If, for instance, we choose w_0 so that the surface will rise quickly in the direction parallel to the axis of θ_1, we shall reduce the rate of increase in the direction of θ_2, and vice versa. Power surfaces of alternative critical regions may, in fact, cross one another in a complicated way, but no single surface can everywhere lie above all others. If we confine attention to tests for which the power surface has a minimum ordinate of α at the point θ_1^0, θ_2^0, i.e. to unbiased tests of H_0, we shall still be unable to find a uniformly most powerful test in this restricted field.

The difficulty in choice between alternative tests can, indeed, only be solved by a further formulation of the requirements of a satisfactory test. Several lines of attack are open:

(i) To lay down conditions for the form of the power surface in the neighbourhood of the point θ_1^0, θ_2^0. Here we may describe the objective as to make as large as possible the chance of detecting small departures in θ_1 and θ_2 from the values specified by H_0. A method of approaching the problem from this point of view leads to the development of the unbiased test of Type C (Neyman & Pearson, 1938).

(ii) To regard it as of more importance to control the form of the power surface at some distance from its minimum point; for example, to try to select a critical region for which the power surface reaches the level

$$\beta(\theta_1, \theta_2 \mid w) = 0{\cdot}95, \tag{5}$$

along a contour lying inside the corresponding contour associated with any other test. This method of approach has been examined by Dr B. L. Welch, but his results are not yet published. It is possible that methods (i) and (ii) will lead to the same result.

(iii) To consider whether from the practical point of view, if H_0 is not true, the importance of the departure of the unknown parameters from θ_1^0, θ_2^0 can be measured by a single parameter,

$$\lambda = f(\theta_1, \theta_2). \tag{6}$$

If this is so, we are in fact defining a system of contours on the θ_1, θ_2 plane along any one of which we should like the ordinates of the power surface to be constant. Such a system would be defined, for instance, by

$$\lambda^2 = (\theta_1 - \theta_1^0)^2 + (\theta_2 - \theta_2^0)^2, \tag{7}$$

and if $\beta(\theta_1, \theta_2 \mid w)$ is to be constant for values of θ_1, θ_2 satisfying (7), the contours of the power surface will be circles of radius λ. Alternative tests would then be confined to those whose power surfaces had circular contours, H_0 would be the hypothesis that $\lambda = 0$ and the uniformly most powerful test, if it exists, would be that for which

$$\beta(\lambda \mid w_0) \geqslant \beta(\lambda \mid w) \tag{8}$$

for $\lambda > 0$ and all alternative critical regions w satisfying the conditions stipulated.

The problem thus presented in the case of a simple hypothesis concerning two parameters will arise in similar form when H_0 is composite and concerns the value of many parameters $\theta_1, \theta_2, \ldots, \theta_c$. In a number of multivariate problems we have reached a position in which:

(*a*) tests of statistical hypotheses concerning the values of several population parameters have been derived, as well as their power functions;

(*b*) these power functions have been shown to depend on the value of a single function

$$\lambda = f(\theta_1, \theta_2, \ldots, \theta_c)$$

of the parameters considered.

In the following contributions Dr Hsu and Dr Simaika have examined three of these tests, that concerned with the general linear hypothesis, with Hotelling's generalized T^2 and with the multiple correlation coefficient. They have shown that of tests whose power function depends only on a certain function λ of the population parameters, the existing tests are the uniformly most powerful. It is of course true that in the problems in question no alternative tests are at present available or indeed likely to become so. Nevertheless, I believe that the discovery, resulting from Dr Hsu's initiative, of the relationship between the test function and a corresponding comprehensive collective character in the population, has taken us a step farther in our understanding of the properties of statistical tests. Further, this relationship between E^2 and λ, T^2 and ψ^2, D^2 and Δ^2, R^2 and ρ^2 seems to lead us round by another route to the problem of statistical estimation.

REFERENCES

KOŁODZIEJCZYK, ST (1935). *Biometrika*, **27**, 161.
NEYMAN, J. & PEARSON, E. S. (1938). *Statist. Res. Mem.* **2**, 25.

NOTES ON TESTING STATISTICAL HYPOTHESES

By E. S. PEARSON

1. In July 1939, a few weeks before the opening of the present war, a Conference on the Application of the Calculus of Probabilities was held at Geneva under the auspices of the International Institute of Intellectual Co-operation (League of Nations). At the public session at which a paper by Prof. J. Neyman was presented and also subsequently in some informal discussions, a number of questions were raised:

(*a*) In choosing a test for a statistical hypothesis, is it possible or even necessary to specify the hypotheses alternative to that tested? Why should not a test be made to depend only on the form of law associated with the hypothesis tested? For example, Newton's hypothesis of gravitation was formulated and tested without any need to define alternative laws.

(*b*) Is the method of approach to these problems advocated by Prof. Neyman and myself applicable to testing the appropriateness of probability *laws* or only to testing hypotheses regarding the numerical values of *constants* contained in these laws?

After the conclusion of the conference, I set down some Notes for a few of the statisticians who had taken part in the discussions, hoping that at leisure they might feel stimulated to define their views on the subject more precisely. But almost before the Notes were despatched, war in Europe had intervened. The only reply which I received was from Prof. Gumbel, and this, after some unavoidable delay, has now taken shape in the contribution printed on pp. 317–33 below. In publishing this, it seems useful to add my own Notes, which are given with only minor verbal alterations in the following pages. They are in part a restatement with rather different emphasis of views expressed in a paper published four years ago (Pearson, 1938).

2. With regard to one of the points raised under (*a*) above, it should be remembered that a statistical hypothesis as defined by Neyman and myself is a hypothesis concerning the probability law of random variables. The gravitational hypothesis of Newton is not a statistical hypothesis in the sense defined; statistical methods may be introduced to test the Newtonian hypothesis, however, and they will involve tests of statistical hypotheses or 'significance tests' because it will be assumed that errors of observation exist which may be regarded as random variables, probably taken to follow the normal distribution law.

For example, on the Newtonian hypothesis, the angular co-ordinates of a planet measured from the earth as origin may at certain moments be given as $\xi = \xi_t$, $\eta = \eta_t$ $(t = 1, 2, \ldots)$. If we have a number of observations of position x_t, y_t, subject to observational error, the statistical problem will be to test whether these are consistent with the hypothetical position values ξ_t, η_t, or whether they suggest that ξ, η have some other different values at the moments of observation. Thus the 'alternatives' that we have immediately in mind will be alternative values for ξ, η, not alternative gravitational hypotheses. If, however, some alternative law of motion were proposed, so that we could specify definite values ξ'_t, η'_t alternative to the values ξ_t, η_t of the Newtonian law, then undoubtedly we could choose a statistical test which would be particularly efficient in discriminating between the two alternatives. Such a course became possible when the Einstein hypothesis was formulated and the orbit of Mercury considered. But the absence of an alternative gravitational law does not prevent us selecting a statistical test which will be (*a*) sensitive to departures in ξ, η from ξ_t, η_t, but (*b*) relatively insensitive to departures from normality in the distribution of errors. We should make this selection because, if the Newtonian law were incorrect, we believe that this would result in a change in ξ_t, η_t but not in a departure of the distribution of observational errors from the normal law.

This example, of course, concerns a statistical hypothesis regarding the values of two parameters ξ, η, not regarding the form of a probability law of random variables. The following general approach shows, however, that the principles discussed may be applied to testing hypotheses regarding probability laws.

3. Suppose that x is a continuous random variable and that H_0 is a statistical hypothesis which assumes that the elementary probability law for x is $p(x \mid H_0)$ in the interval $-\infty$ to $+\infty$. Thus

$$\int_{-\infty}^{+\infty} p(x \mid H_0)\, dx = 1. \tag{1}$$

Now write

$$y = \int_{-\infty}^{x} p(x \mid H_0)\, dx. \tag{2}$$

y will be a non-decreasing function of x having values confined to the interval $(0, 1)$. Further, the elementary probability law of y will be

$$p(y) = p(x) \Big/ \frac{dy}{dx} = 1 \quad \text{for} \quad 0 \leqslant y \leqslant 1, \tag{3}$$

or all values of y between 0 and 1 are 'equally probable'.

Suppose now that we wish to use a set of n independent values $x_1, x_2, \ldots, x_n$ to test that the probability law is of the assumed form $p(x \mid H_0)$. It is clear that the hypothesis H_0 is exactly equivalent to the hypothesis, say h_0, that the n values $y_1, y_2, \ldots, y_n$ (obtained from the x's by the transformation (2)) have been sampled subject to the probability law (3). Just as the point $(x_1, x_2, \ldots, x_n)$ may be represented in an unlimited n-dimensioned space having probability density

$$p(x_1, x_2, \ldots, x_n \mid H_0) = \prod_{i=1}^{n} \{p(x_i \mid H_0)\}, \tag{4}$$

if H_0 is true, so the point $(y_0, y_1, \ldots, y_n)$ may be placed in an n-dimensioned hypercube with sides of unit length and with uniform probability density, if H_0 and therefore h_0 is true. It follows that if H_0 is what has been termed a 'simple hypothesis', i.e. specifies the form of $p(x \mid H_0)$ completely,* then the test of H_0 may always be transformed to the test of h_0. If then it were correct to say that the test of a statistical hypothesis *depends only on the form of the law specified by* H_0, it follows that for the type of situation considered the testing of a statistical hypothesis could always be reduced to the following simple problem:

To test whether a sample of n independent random variables $y_1, y_2, \ldots, y_n$ $(0 \leqslant y_i \leqslant 1)$ has been selected from the so-called rectangular distribution, i.e. the distribution for which $p(y) = 1$, $(0 \leqslant y \leqslant 1)$.

4. We are at once faced, therefore, with the question of how to test this simple but apparently fundamental hypothesis. If h_0 is true, the sample point is equally likely to fall at any point within the n-dimensioned hypercube. Thus in picking out the critical (or rejection) region in this space we can get no assistance whatsoever from the changes in probability density, as we might do in the x-space. If we wish to use a level of significance of α (say $\alpha = 0{\cdot}01$) for rejecting h_0, it is clear that an infinite number of critical regions satisfying this condition are available; it is only necessary to select a region whose content is α.

If we consider the n values of y and plot them in the interval (0, 1) as follows,

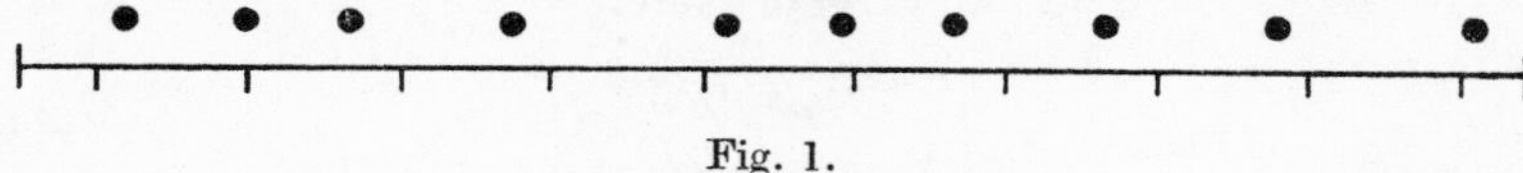

Fig. 1.

the great majority of samples, from a rectangular distribution, at any rate if n is not too small, will be spread out fairly uniformly throughout the interval. Perhaps an 'ideal' sample against which to measure irregularities might be described as one for which the values of y fell at

$$\frac{1}{2n}, \quad \frac{3}{2n}, \quad \frac{5}{2n}, \quad \ldots, \quad \frac{2n-1}{2n}.$$

But what form of departure from this ideal of uniformity are we to pick out as suggesting that the hypothesis h_0 is disproved? Should we judge significance by paying attention to the value of the mean y, of the variance, of the range of variation or of higher moments? Or should we use the χ^2 or ω^2 tests? It seems difficult to find any basis for choice which could be regarded in any sense as the 'best'. For any set of values $y_1, y_2, \ldots, y_n$ *some* critical region of size α can always be found which will contain the sample point and therefore lead to the rejection of h_0. Indeed, the task of selecting a unique region on any rational basis would seem to be insoluble.

* This condition is important. If the values of certain constants contained in the probability law need to be estimated from the observations, then the n values of y will not form a true random sample from a rectangular distribution. They will be subject to certain limitations to their degrees of freedom, though these may be relatively unimportant if n is large.

5. Directly it is recognized, however, that the choice of a test of a statistical hypothesis depends on something more than the form of the law associated with that hypothesis, it can be seen how a solution may be obtained. If we can specify a single alternative H_1 to H_0 or a class of alternatives $C(H)$, then we shall have also an alternative h, or a class $C(h)$ to h_0. Thus, if $p(x \mid H_1)$ denotes a probability law alternative to $p(x \mid H_0)$, then for y the alternative is

$$p(y \mid h_1) = p(x \mid H_1) \Big/ \frac{dy}{dx} = \frac{p(x \mid H_1)}{p(x \mid H_0)}\Bigg|_{x=f(y)} \quad \text{for} \quad 0 \leqslant y \leqslant 1, \tag{5}$$

where $f(y)$ means the solution of

$$y = \int_{-\infty}^{x} p(x \mid H_0)\, dx \tag{6}$$

with regard to x. For example, Fig. 2 shows three typical forms of alternative $p(y \mid h_1)$, $p(y \mid h_2)$ and $p(y \mid h_3)$ associated with alternatives $p(x \mid H_1)$, ..., etc., to $p(x \mid H_0)$.

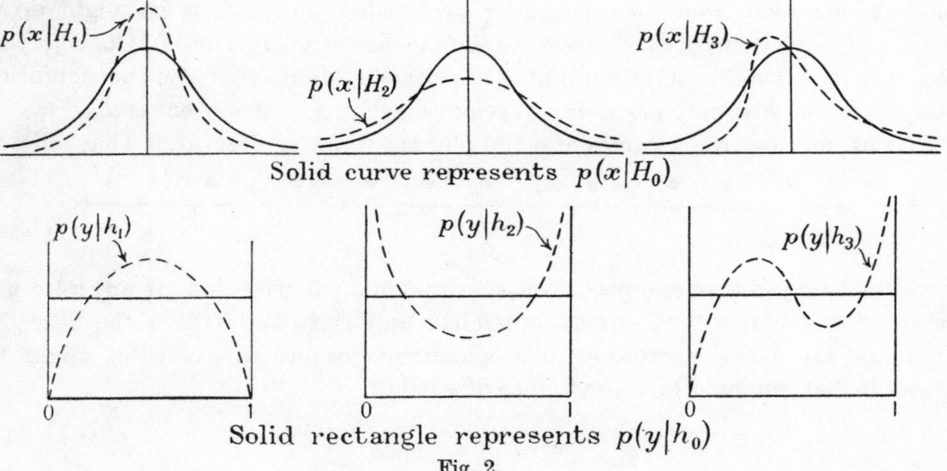

Fig. 2.

We can now see the kind of test which will be most efficient for testing H_0 with regard to possible classes of alternatives. If the alternative laws are of smaller dispersion (as $p(x \mid H_1)$), we must be on the look-out for too many values of y near $\frac{1}{2}$ and too few near 0 and 1. For alternatives with greater dispersion (as $p(x \mid H_2)$), we must reject H_0 when there are too many y's near 0 or 1 and too few near $\frac{1}{2}$. While if the alternatives are likely to be asymmetrical curves (as $p(x \mid H_3)$), then a different rule will be needed, as suggested by the $p(y \mid h_3)$ curve.

6. It follows that in so far as it is possible to formulate the class of admissible probability laws $p(x \mid H)$, the problem of selecting the most efficient test of H_0 reduces to that of choosing a critical region in the n-dimensioned hypercube which is most effective in detecting, from a sample of n values of y, differences between the rectangle $p(y \mid h_0)$ and the appropriate alternative forms $p(y \mid h)$

If H_1 is a single admissible alternative, then it has been shown (Neyman & Pearson, 1933, p. 298) that the region w_0 of content α in the hypercube, within which

$$\frac{\prod_{i=1}^{n} p(y_i \mid h_0)}{\prod_{i=1}^{n} p(y_i \mid h_1)} < k, \tag{7}$$

or, in view of equation (3),

$$\prod_{i=1}^{n} p(y_i \mid h_1) > \frac{1}{k}, \tag{8}$$

where k is chosen so that

$$P\{(y_1, y_2, \ldots, y_n) \epsilon w_0 \mid h_0\} = \alpha \tag{9}$$

has the following property.

Of all regions of content α, w_0 is more likely than any other to include the sample point when h_1, and not h_0, is true. The region has been termed the best critical region for testing h_0 with regard to the alternative h_1.

As soon as H_0 and H_1 are specified, clearly $p(y \mid h_1)$ and therefore the region w_0 can be found, although mathematically it may be rather difficult to determine the appropriate boundary $\prod_{i=1}^{n} p(y_i \mid h_1) = \text{constant}$, so as to satisfy (8). Since this product is the probability density in the hypercube given by h_1, it will be seen that what we set out to do is to include in the critical region those parts of the sample space where the density for h_1 is highest. It is here, on repeated sampling, that sample points would tend to be concentrated if h_1 is true, instead of being uniformly distributed as under h_0.

7. If instead of a single alternative h_1, there is a class of admissible alternatives $C(h)$, there may or may not be common points of concentration that can be included in the critical region. This will depend on whether the inequality (8) above defines a region independent of the particular hypothesis h of the class $C(h)$. Even if there is no single region of content α which is exactly a 'best critical region' for h_0 with regard to all members of $C(h)$, the general principle may still be used as a guide. We build up a critical region out of those parts of the hypercube where the probability density tends to be concentrated when the probability law departs from $p(x \mid H_0)$ in the direction of the alternatives included in $C(H)$.

For example, in my earlier paper (Pearson, 1938) I suggested as appropriate in the following situation a test which, while not based on a common best critical region, was selected so as to include regions of greatest density associated with alternatives of $C(h)$. For the hypothesis tested,

$$p(x \mid H_0) = \frac{1}{\sqrt{(2\pi)}} e^{-\frac{1}{2}x^2}. \tag{10}$$

The alternatives are asymmetrical curves with the same mean and standard deviation as (10). A typical alternative would be the Type III curve

$$p(x \mid H) = c(1 + \tfrac{1}{2}x\sqrt{\beta_1})^{\frac{4}{\beta_1}-1} e^{-\frac{2x}{\sqrt{\beta_1}}}, \tag{11}$$

whose form departs more and more from (10) as $\sqrt{\beta_1}$ increases from zero, but the class need not be defined as precisely as this. In this problem it appears that if n independent observations $x_1, x_2, \ldots, x_n$ are available, the following is a good test of H_0. Take as test function

$$Q = \prod_{i=1}^{n} (y_i'), \tag{12}$$

where

$$\left.\begin{aligned} y_i' &= 5(0{\cdot}2-y_i) \quad \text{for} \quad 0 \leqslant y_i \leqslant 0{\cdot}2, \\ y_i' &= \tfrac{5}{3}(y_i-0{\cdot}2) \quad \text{for} \quad 0{\cdot}2 < y_i \leqslant 0{\cdot}8, \\ y_i' &= 5(1-y_i) \quad \text{for} \quad 0{\cdot}8 < y_i \leqslant 1, \end{aligned}\right\} \tag{13}$$

and

$$y_i = \int_{-\infty}^{x} \frac{1}{\sqrt{(2\pi)}} e^{-\frac{1}{2}x^2} dx. \tag{14}$$

If H_0 is true it may be shown that $-2\log_e Q$ is distributed as χ^2 with $2n$ degrees of freedom. Hence any desired significance level α, for Q, may be found. We should then reject H_0 when Q is significantly small.

A more systematic method of dealing with such problems has been considered by Neyman (1937) in his paper on 'smooth tests'.

8. To sum up, the position seems to be this. It has often been argued that a statistical test need only depend on the form of the probability law associated with the hypothesis tested. In the case where H_0 concerns the probability law of a single random variable and where $p(x \mid H_0)$ is precisely specified, by the transformation from x to y it has been shown that the problem of testing H_0 on the basis of n independent values of x can always be reduced to another problem, which involves this question. Can we regard a sample $y_1, y_2, \ldots, y_n$ as having been drawn from the rectangular distribution $p(y \mid h_0) = 1$, where $0 \leqslant y \leqslant 1$? We are faced with a single fundamental question and we have to consider whether it can be answered in a rational manner, unless we are prepared to take into account the kind of departures from the rectangular law that we either believe possible or at any rate consider it most important to be on the look out for.

The transformation from x to y seems to have the advantage that it concentrates attention on the main point at issue. That is my reason for emphasizing it in these Notes. Most of us have many preconceived ideas about appropriate tests if the probability law is taken in the form of $p(x \mid H_0)$; we are accustomed to use the mean, the standard deviation, certain functions of moments, the χ^2 test, ... But we are not so accustomed to test whether a sample comes from a rectangular distribution and we are therefore forced or, indeed, more willing to reconsider from first principles what course we should follow and why.

REFERENCES

Neyman, J. (1937). *Skand. Actuar. Tidskr.* 149.
Neyman, J. & Pearson, E. S. (1933). *Philos. Trans.* A, **231**, 289.
Pearson, E. S. (1938). *Biometrika*, **30**, 134.

THE CHOICE OF STATISTICAL TESTS ILLUSTRATED ON THE INTERPRETATION OF DATA CLASSED IN A 2×2 TABLE

By E. S. PEARSON

CONTENTS

(i) Introductory

1. The problem of testing the significance of a difference between two proportions is one which receives early attention in text-books on mathematical statistics, and it might be thought to be one of the questions whose final solution lies behind us. It is a problem whose simplicity makes it easy to examine the logical cogency of the methods put forward for its solution, but, on examination, it is evident that they have not yet been rounded off satisfactorily. The origin of the present paper lies partly in an investigation commenced in 1938 and discussed at the time in College lectures, and partly in recent correspondence in *Nature* in which G. A. Barnard (1945*a*, *b*) and R. A. Fisher (1945*a*) have taken part.* This correspondence has suggested that in a problem of such apparent simplicity, starting from different premises, it is possible to reach what may sometimes be very different numerical probability figures by which to judge significance.

2. Such a difference in levels of significance in the solution of an everyday problem is obviously puzzling to the users of statistical methods who are accustomed to accept the technique as an established procedure and have not the opportunity for a critical examination of the conditions under which probability theory is brought to bear as a guide to action. For the question here at issue is a fundamental one of why and how our judgement is influenced by the calculation of a probability, and the dilemma raised by the Barnard-Fisher correspondence can only be answered in terms of our views on the practical function of the theory. We may all agree that in practice we use probability figures derived from an analysis of numerical data to help us to make up our minds on the next step, whether in experimental research or executive action. But what form of presentation of the probability set-up is likely to result in the greater number of sound decisions is likely to be always a matter for differences of opinion.

3. All that I can do is to approach the problem of the 2×2 table from the viewpoint which appears most helpful to me. In the preceding paper Mr Barnard has elaborated the

* There was also an earlier discussion on the same subject between E. B. Wilson (1941, 1942) and R. A. Fisher (1941).

views expressed in his letters to *Nature*. Such discussion is, I believe, desirable, even though controversial issues are raised. For the value of the whole elaborate structure of the modern theory of mathematical statistics depends at least in part on the sense in which the individual statistician appreciates the meaning of the probability model he is using when drawing the practical conclusions from his analysis of data. I have used the words 'in part', for it is true that the analytical process of applying the statistical technique to experimental data may in itself be enormously illuminating even without paying any close regard to a final probability figure. Such is the case, for example, with the technique of analysis of variance, where the mere process of breaking up a total sum of squares into parts with which different sources of variability can be associated, brings with it a reward in clear thinking even without the application of a probability test.

4. There is a very wide variety in the types of situation in which probability theory is introduced to help in reaching a decision as to further action.

(A) At one extreme we have the case where repeated decisions must be made on results obtained from some routine procedure carried out under controlled conditions.

(B) At the other is the situation where statistical tools are applied to an isolated investigation of considerable importance in which many of the issues involved in the conclusion can hardly be assessed in numerical terms.

5. Two situations of this kind, in which the statistical technique involved is that of testing the significance of a difference between two proportions, may be illustrated from problems arising in the 'proof' of armour-piercing shot or shell.

6. *Example of type A*. In the proof of small anti-tank, armour-piercing shot it might be decided to set aside, as a standard, a batch of shot whose quality has been established by special trials; against this standard, later batches can be compared. The variable measured is the proportion of shot which fail to perforate a plate of specified thickness when fired with a given striking velocity. The use of standard shot is necessary for calibration purposes, because there are inevitable changes in toughness from one proof plate to another and only a limited number of shot can be fired at a single plate. Then the situation might be summed up as follows:*

Aim of proof. To ensure that as few batches as possible are passed into service which are less effective than the standard.

Method of proof. Twelve rounds of the standard and twelve of the batch under test to be fired, round for round, against a single test plate and a record kept of the number of failures in each group, say a and b.

Routine sentencing rule. This should lay down a ready means of determining, from a knowledge of a and b, whether to class the new batch as inferior to the standard or not.

Assumptions accepted in using rule. That the two samples of twelve shot have each been randomly selected from the much larger batches. That against the particular plate used, a proportion p_1 of the standard and p_2 of the new batch would fail to give satisfactory perforation at the specified striking velocity. That while p_1 and p_2 would be different for other plates, if $p_2 > p_1$ for one plate, it will be so for all other plates. The objective is to segregate batches of shot for which $p_2 > p_1$.

* It has been somewhat simplified for illustrative purposes, e.g. complete control of the striking velocity is not in practice possible.

7. *Example of type B.* Two types of heavy armour-piercing naval shell of the same calibre are under consideration; they may be of different design or made by different firms. Since the cost of producing and testing a single round of this kind runs into many hundreds of pounds, the investigation is a costly one, yet the issues involved are far reaching. Twelve shells of one kind and eight of the other have been fired; two of the former and five of the latter failed to perforate the plate. In what way can a statistical test contribute to the decision which must be taken on further action?

8. In dealing with Example A the guiding principle followed in seeking help from the theory of probability can be very simple. We can set as our object a rule which:

(i) will result in an increasing chance of detecting that $p_2 > p_1$, the larger the difference;

(ii) will leave only a small chance of segregating the new batch wrongly when, in fact, $p_2 \leqslant p_1$.

Diagrammatically the rule would consist in segregating the new batch when the point (a, b) falls within some such area as that shown shaded in Fig. 1. In this problem involving a routine procedure, it is the long-run frequency of different consequences of the proof sentencing which is of importance, and probability theory is introduced to provide a measure of expected frequency. This method of introducing the theory of probability into this proof problem is not necessarily the only one that could be adopted in fixing a routine procedure, but it is a simple one and, since simplicity has the merit of appealing to the user's understanding, it has great advantages.

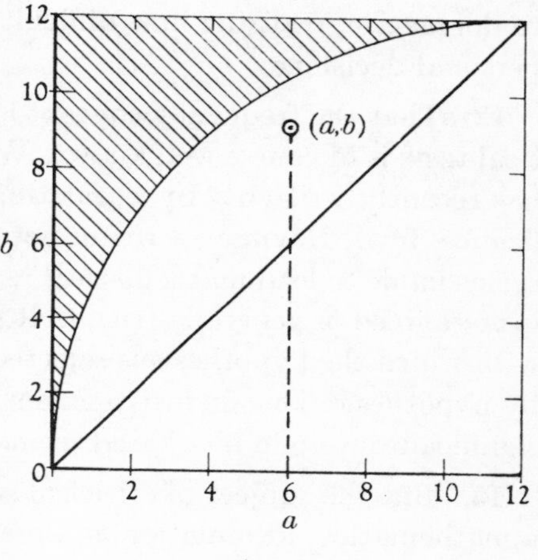

Fig. 1

9. When dealing with Example B a very considerable number of factors must be weighed in the balance, and the result of a statistical test of significance could never be the over-riding one. There will be other information as to the effect of changes in shell design, possibly from shell of different calibre; information as to the uniformity in quality of output of the firm or firms concerned; questions of cost and of general policy. He would be a bold man who would attempt to express these in numerical terms. Whereas when tackling problem A it is easy to convince the practical man of the value of a probability construct related to frequency of occurrence, in problem B the argument that 'if we were to repeatedly do so and so, such and such result would follow in the long run' is at once met by the common-sense answer that we never should carry out a precisely similar trial again.

10. Nevertheless, it is clear that the scientist with a knowledge of statistical method behind him can make his contribution to a round-table discussion, provided he has acquired a grasp of the practical issues. Starting from the basis that individual shell will never be identical in armour-piercing qualities, however good the control of production, he has to consider how much of the difference between (i) two failures out of twelve and (ii) five failures out of eight is likely to be due to this inevitable variability. There may be a number of ways of sizing up the position involving different assumptions or hypothetical constructs; he may follow one or several of these. The value of his advice is dependent almost

entirely on the soundness of his scientific judgement, and very little on whether his back-room calculations have been based on inverse or direct probability or on an appeal to fiducial argument.

11. How far, then, can one go in giving precision to a philosophy of statistical inference? It seems clear that in certain problems probability theory is of value because of its close relation to frequency of occurrence; such seems to be the case for my Example A. Tests can be built up to satisfy the practical requirements in this field. In other and, no doubt, more numerous cases there is no repetition of the same type of trial or experiment, but all the same we can and many of us do use the same test rules to guide our decision, following the analysis of an isolated set of numerical data. Why do we do this? What are the springs of decision? Is it because the formulation of the case in terms of hypothetical repetition helps to that clarity of view needed for sound judgement? Or is it because we are content that the application of a rule, now in this investigation, now in that, should result in a long-run frequency of errors in judgement which we control at a low figure? On this I should not care to dogmatize, realizing how difficult it is to analyse the reasons governing even one's own personal decisions.

12. That the frequency concept is not generally accepted in the interpretation of statistical tests is of course well known. With his characteristic forcefulness R. A. Fisher (1945*b*) has recently written: 'In recent times one often repeated exposition of the tests of significance, by J. Neyman, a writer not closely associated with the development of these tests, seems liable to lead mathematical readers astray, through laying down axiomatically, what is not agreed or generally true, that the level of significance must be equal to the frequency with which the hypothesis is rejected in repeated sampling of any fixed population allowed by hypothesis. This intrusive axiom, which is foreign to the reasoning on which the tests of significance were in fact based seems to be a real bar to progress....'

13. But the subject of criticism seems to me less an intrusive mathematical axiom than a mathematical formulation of a practical requirement which statisticians of many schools of thought have deliberately advanced. Prof. Fisher's contributions to the development of tests of significance have been outstanding, but such tests, if under another name, were discovered before his day and are being derived far and wide to meet new needs. To claim what seems to amount to patent rights over their interpretation can hardly be his serious intention. Many of us, as statisticians, fall into the all too easy habit of making authoritative statements as to how probability theory should be used as a guide to judgement, but ultimately it is likely that the method of application which finds greatest favour will be that which through its simplicity and directness appeals most to the common scientific user's understanding. Hitherto the user has been accustomed to accept the function of probability theory laid down by the mathematicians; but it would be good if he could take a larger share in formulating himself what are the practical requirements that the theory should satisfy in application.

(ii) The choice of statistical tests

14. One approach to follow in determining tests to be applied to the 2×2 class of problem follows the lines that Neyman and I have adopted since 1928 in dealing with tests of statistical hypotheses. Let me first recapitulate in broad terms the steps in that approach when applied to a problem where the universe of possible observations can be represented by a

finite set of discrete points. A test of significance may be described as a method of analysis of statistical data which helps us to discriminate between alternative theories or hypotheses. In order to make use of the theory of probability in the sense here understood, a random process must either have been purposely introduced or be assumed to have been present in the collection of data; then the hypothesis very often concerns the values of parameters contained in the probability laws which, in the conceptual sphere, form the mathematical counterpart of the sampling distributions of experience.

15. We proceed by setting up a specific hypothesis to test, H_0 in Neyman's and my terminology, the null hypothesis in R. A. Fisher's. At the same time, in choosing the test, we take into account alternatives to H_0 which we believe possible or at any rate consider it most important to be on the look out for. Thus we wish the test to have maximum discriminating power within a certain class of hypotheses. Three steps in constructing the test may be defined:

Step 1. We must first specify the set of results which could follow on repeated application of the random process used in the collection of the data; this may be termed the experimental probability set.

Step 2. We then divide this set by a system of ordered boundaries or contours such that as we pass across one boundary and proceed to the next, we come to a class of results which makes us more and more inclined, on the information available, to reject the hypothesis tested in favour of alternatives which differ from it by increasing amounts.

Step 3. We then, if possible, associate with each contour level the chance that, if H_0 is true, a result will occur in random sampling lying beyond that level.

This rather crude statement of procedure will be developed in more detail in discussing the problems that arise in connexion with the 2×2 table.

16. *Notes on these points.* (*a*) *Step* 1. This involves the definition of what Neyman and I have termed the sample space, W. The application in three forms of the 2×2 problem is discussed in paragraphs 19, 27 and 46 below.

(*b*) *Step* 2. For a given hypothesis under test there may be a number of ways of deriving a system of contours, and only in certain cases can there be said to be complete agreement on which is the 'best'. Practical expediency will often carry weight in the choice. It is widely accepted that the choice cannot be made without paying regard to the admissible hypotheses alternative to H_0, whether this process is given formal precision or taken as a broad guide. In our first papers (Neyman & Pearson, 1928*a*, *b*) we suggested that the likelihood ratio criterion, λ, was a very useful one to employ in determining a family of contours which would be ordered in relation to our confidence in the hypothesis tested when set against the background of admissible alternatives. Thus Step 2 preceded Step 3. In later papers (Neyman & Pearson, 1933, 1936 and 1938) we started with a fixed value for the chance, ϵ, of Step 3 and determined the associated contour, taking account of what we termed the power of a test with regard to the alternative hypotheses. The family of Step 2 followed on giving decreasing values to ϵ. However, although the mathematical procedure may put Step 3 before 2, we cannot put this into operation before we have decided, under Step 2, on the guiding principle to be used in choosing the contour system. That is why I have numbered the steps in this order.

(*c*) *Step* 3. If this can be accomplished, we have what Neyman and I called control of the '1st kind of error'. In problems where, as below, we are concerned with discrete rather than continuous probability distributions (e.g. for the binomial, the Poisson, the multinomial and the hypergeometric distributions), this objective cannot always be achieved, and it may be necessary to be satisfied with a knowledge of an upper limit of the chance of rejecting the hypothesis tested when it is true.

(iii) Application of this approach to the analysis of data classed in a 2×2 table

17. The frequencies of the data in the table may be defined in the following notation:

Table 1

	Col. 1	Col. 2	Total
Row 1	a	c	m
Row 2	b	d	n
Total	r	s	N

If we follow in turn the steps defined above to determine the method of interpretation of such data, the requirements of the appropriate tests are seen to follow very simply, although mathematical or computational difficulties arise in implementing them. On taking Step 1 we can separate out at once the three types of problem which Barnard has differentiated;* these I shall call Problems I, II and III. They are distinguished by the sample space having 1, 2 and 3 dimensions respectively. From the mathematical point of view it might seem more logical to take them in the reverse order, adding first one and then a second restriction to the 3-dimensioned case of Problem III. For a simple exposition, I think the reverse procedure of building up from I to III is preferable and this has been adopted in the following sections.

(iv) Problem I

18. This may be described as the test of the significance of the difference between two treatments after these have been randomly assigned to a group of $N = m+n$ individuals (Barnard terms it the 2×2 independence trial). To use the terminology of a particular application, we may say that we are observing the presence or absence of 'reaction X'. The first treatment is applied to m and the second to n of the N individuals; as a result a/m and b/n show reaction X.

19. In this case the random process has been applied within the group of N individuals, and its repetition would simply involve other random reassignments of the two treatments among the N. No assumption is made as to how the N individuals were selected from some larger universe. The repetition may be hypothetical, in the sense that it often could not take place, e.g. if reaction X = death. Indeed, repetition under the same essential conditions is frequently impossible in practice. But this correspondence between the frequency of results upon hypothetical repetition and the probability distribution of the counterpart mathematical model forms an accepted part of the process of reasoning whereby (following

* Statisticians had, of course, all been more or less conscious of these differences, but, at any rate in my own case, it was discussion with Mr Barnard which made it easy to see the problem in its full clarity.

the present approach) we use probability theory as a basis for inference. The hypothesis tested is that while some individuals show reaction X and some do not, the result would be the same whichever treatment were applied *as far as these N individuals are concerned*. Thus, on the null hypothesis, there are $r = a+b$ individuals who will react and $s = c+d$ who will not, whatever the assignment of treatments.

20. The chance that a will react in m and $b = r-a$ in n is, therefore, if the hypothesis be true,

$$P_1\{a \mid N, r, m\} = \frac{m!\,n!\,r!\,s!}{a!\,b!\,c!\,d!\,N!}. \tag{1}$$

This expression is proportional to the coefficient of x^a in the hypergeometric series

$$F(\alpha, \beta, \gamma, x) = F(-r, -m, n-r+1, x). \tag{2}$$

Thus, taking $m \geqslant n$, a can assume values of

$$\begin{aligned} &\text{(i)} \quad 0, 1, \ldots, r \quad \text{if} \quad r \leqslant n,\\ &\text{(ii)} \quad r-n, r-n+1, \ldots, r \quad \text{if} \quad n < r \leqslant m,\\ &\text{(iii)} \quad r-n, r-n+1, \ldots, m \quad \text{if} \quad r > m. \end{aligned}$$

For this probability distribution, it is known (K. Pearson (1899) and Kendall (1943, p. 127))

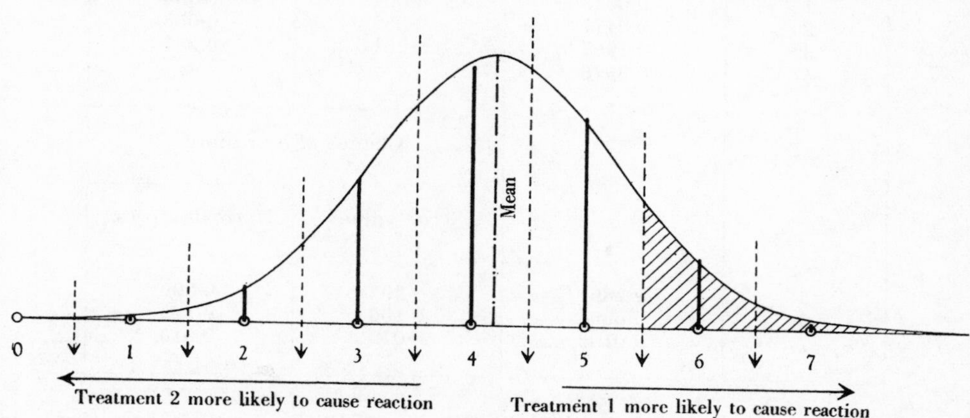

Fig. 2

that

$$\text{Mean}\, a = \frac{rm}{N}, \tag{3}$$

$$\text{Variance of } a = \sigma_a^2 = \frac{mnrs}{N^2(N-1)}. \tag{4}$$

21. For the particular case

$$N = 20, \quad r = 7, \quad m = 12, \quad n = 8,$$

the terms in the distribution of $P_1\{a \mid 20, 7, 12\}$ are shown as ordinates in Fig. 2 and given in the accompanying Table 2. The experimental probability set consists of the eight alternative values for a, viz. $0, 1, \ldots, 7$ with which the probabilities tabled are associated if H_0 is true. Further

$$\text{Mean}\, a = \bar{a} = 4{\cdot}2, \quad \sigma_a = 1{\cdot}0721. \tag{5}$$

22. Next consider step 2. The purpose of the investigation is to test the hypothesis that the difference between $a/12$ and $(r-a)/8$ has resulted simply from a random partition of 20 individuals, of whom r will show reaction X in whichever treatment group they are included. The experiment gives $r=7$. The contour levels fall between the 8 points of the set as shown in Fig. 2; the further a lies towards the right, the more inclined we shall be to accept the alternative hypothesis that $a/12>(r-a)/8$ because treatment 1 is more effective than treatment 2. The further a lies to the left, the more we shall incline towards the reverse alternative. To complete Step 3, we have only to calculate the sums of the tail terms of the hypergeometric series, as shown in Table 2 for the special case.

Table 2. *Problem I. Chances for special case* $N = 20$, $r = 7$, $m = 12$, *if* H_0 *is true*

a	Chance of a	Chance of a or less	
		True value	Normal approx.
0	0·0001	0·000	0·000
1	0·0043	0·004	0·006
2	0·0477	0·052	0·056
3	0·1987	0·251	0·257
4	0·3576	—	—
		Chance of a or more	
		True value	Normal approx.
5	0·2861	0·392	0·390
6	0·0954	0·106	0·113
7	0·0102	0·010	0·016

23. Having set up the machinery of the test, we come to the practical question. Beyond which contour levels must a fall before we infer that there is a treatment difference? Not, I think, in the example, if a were 3, 4 or 5; possibly if $a = 6$, more probably if $a = 2$ and almost certainly if $a = 0$, 1 or 7. Were we to fix as critical levels those between $a = 1$ and 2 on the one hand, and between $a = 6$ and 7 on the other, then we should be guided in our decision by the following knowledge: if there were no treatment difference, so that seven out of the twenty individuals would have shown reaction X whichever treatment were applied, then the chance under random assignment of treatments that $a < 2$ or > 6 is only 0·014 or 1 in 70. Had we taken the critical levels between 2 and 3 and between 6 and 7, the corresponding chance would be 0·062 or 1 in 16. This summing up in terms of probability helps towards the balanced decision on the next practical step to be taken, because it helps us to assess the extent of purely chance fluctuations that are possible. It may be assumed that in a matter of importance we should never be content with a single experiment applied to twenty individuals; but the result of applying the statistical test with its answer in terms of the chance of a mistaken conclusion if a certain rule of inference were followed, will help to determine

the lines of further experimental work and the degree of confidence with which we proceed provisionally to adopt a new technique.

24. An experiment falling under this head has the advantage that the random process introduced is under complete control. The analysis will give an answer in probability terms whether the N individuals have been randomly selected from a larger whole or not. But this answer is limited in the sense that it relates only to the N; if we wish to draw conclusions about a wider population or populations, then a random selection of the N or, separately, of both its parts m and n is needed. Thus we come to Problems II and III.

25. *Approximation to the hypergeometric terms.* When dealing with small numbers, the calculation of the tail terms of the series may not be laborious, but it soon becomes so when r is large. An obvious approximation is that obtained by using an integral under the normal curve with the mean and standard deviation of equations (3) and (4) to represent the sum of the hypergeometric terms. As usual when approximating to the sum of the terms for $x = a, a+1, a+2, \ldots$, etc., of a discrete probability distribution by the integral under a continuous curve, we take this integral from the point $x = a - \frac{1}{2}$. Thus Fig. 3 shows the normal curve

$$p(x) = \frac{1}{\sqrt{(2\pi)}\,\sigma_a} \exp\left[-\tfrac{1}{2}(x-\bar{a})^2/\sigma_a^2\right], \tag{6}$$

with $\bar{a}$ and σ_a as in equations (5), and the approximation to the sum of the hypergeometric terms for $a = 6$ and 7 is

$$\int_{5.5}^{\infty} p(x)\,dx,$$

represented by the area marked with cross-hatching. The approximations for different levels are shown in Table 2, and are seen in this case to be quite adequate for the purpose of the test. Further comparisons are made in the Appendix, and it appears that provided m and n are fairly nearly equal, as they are likely to be in most planned experiments of the Problem I type, the normal approximation is surprisingly good. Yates (1934) has suggested a method of further correction.

26. *The correction for continuity.* In the 2×2 table connexion, the improvement obtained by taking the normal integral (i) from $x = a - \frac{1}{2}$ if $a > \bar{a}$ or (ii) from $x = a + \frac{1}{2}$ if $a < \bar{a}$ (so that we are summing for the lower tail), was pointed out by Yates (1934) and has often been termed 'Yates's correction for continuity'. It is, however, the natural adjustment to make on the basis of the Euler-Maclaurin theorem, when approximating to a sum of ordinates by an integral and without wishing to detract from the value of Yates's suggestion in this particular problem, it should be pointed out that the adjustment was used by statisticians well before 1934, when employing a normal or skew curve to give the sum of terms of a binomial or hypergeometric series.*

(v) PROBLEM II

27. This may be described as the test of whether the proportion of individuals bearing a character A is the same in two different populations, from each of which a random sample has been drawn, i.e. the test of the hypothesis that

$$p_1(A) = p_2(A) = p, \tag{7}$$

* The method was in use in the Department of Applied Statistics when I joined the staff in 1921, and may have been current many years before that.

where p is some common but unspecified proportion. Barnard describes this as the case of the 2×2 comparative trial. Here m individuals have been drawn at random from the first population and n from the second, and it is found that a/m and b/n, respectively, bear the character A. The conditions are assumed to be such that if the random procedure of selection were repeated, the appropriate probability distributions for a and b would be given by the terms of binomial expansions. Table 3 shows the observed results.

Table 3

	No. with character A	No. without A	Total
1st sample	a	c	m
2nd sample	b	d	n
Total	r	s	N

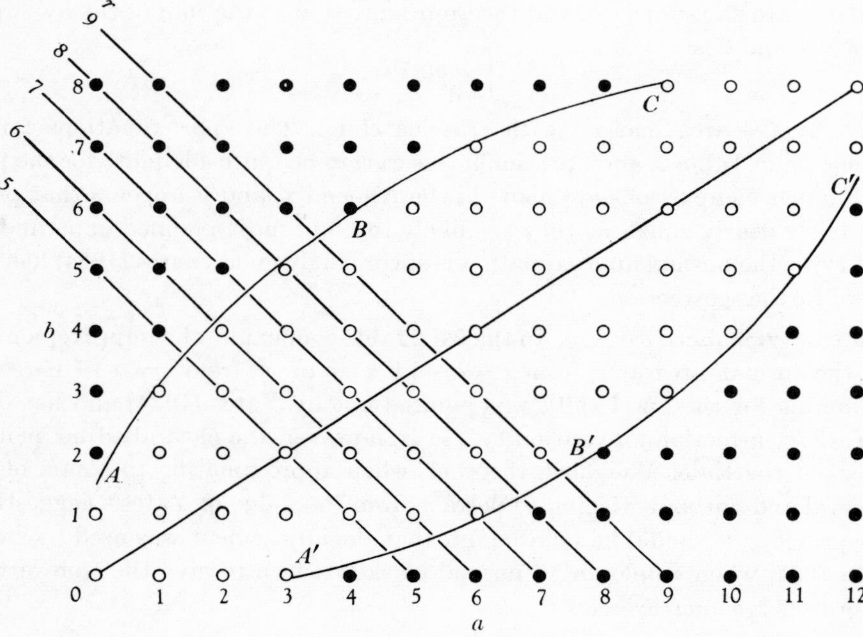

Fig. 3. The curves ABC and $A'B'C'$ represent the significance contours L_ϵ and L'_ϵ, respectively.

In this problem there have been two applications of a random selection process, not one as for Problem I, and the experimental probability set consists of the $(m+1)(n+1)$ alternative values of the doublet (a, b) $(0 \leqslant a \leqslant m, 0 \leqslant b \leqslant n)$ which can be represented in the lattice diagram shown in Fig. 3 for the special case $m = 12$, $n = 8$. It might, of course, be argued that in the hypothetical repetition of the selection process m and n need not remain constant, but this, I think, would introduce an unnecessary complication into the probability set-up.

28. The question before us is whether the result (a, b) is consistent with the hypothesis H_0 defined in equation (7) above, or whether it suggests that either $p_1 > p_2$ or that $p_1 < p_2$. A little reflexion shows that we have no reason to reject H_0 if the point (a, b) lies near the diagonal line on which $a/m = b/n$, but, broadly speaking, are more and more likely to do so the farther the point falls from this line in the direction of the corners $(0, n)$ and $(m, 0)$ of the lattice diagram. This statement requires amplification. In defining the significance contours we may consider the following question: If H_0 is not true, what departures from equality in p_1 and p_2 do we regard it of equal importance to detect? Should the power of the test be roughly the same for constant values, for example, of

$$(a)\quad p_1 - p_2, \qquad (b)\quad p_1/p_2 \qquad \text{or} \qquad (c)\quad \frac{p_1}{1-p_1}\Big/\frac{p_2}{1-p_2}?$$

The procedure which I have adopted in the sections which follow is frankly one of expediency. I have not considered in detail how to choose a family of significance contours satisfying requirements formulated in advance, but have taken those suggested by the customary large-sample procedure which gives contours of the form ABC, $A'B'C'$ drawn in Fig. 3. These will, I believe, make the power of the test to detect a difference more nearly dependent on the ratio of the odds given by (c) than on either of the expressions (a) or (b). E. B. Wilson (1941) chooses the expression (a). This point, however, needs further investigation. It should be noted that a similar problem, in the case where the sampling distributions follow the Poisson law, was discussed very fully by Przyborowski & Wilenski (1939).

29. Besides involving a 2-dimensional instead of a 1-dimensional experimental probability set, Problem II differs from Problem I in that we need an answer which is independent of the unknown common probability p of the null hypothesis. In Problem I the part of p was played by the fraction r/N given by the data. We are concerned now with what Neyman and I (Neyman & Pearson, 1933) have termed a composite hypothesis, and were it possible would like the contour levels to bound regions which are 'similar to the sample space with regard to the parameter p' (loc. cit. p. 313) (i.e. are independent of p). The following considerations show the lines along which a first attack of the problem can proceed.

30. If H_0 is true and equation (7) holds, then the probability of the observed result may be written*

$$P_2\{a \mid p, m\} \times P_2\{b \mid p, n\} = \frac{m!}{a!\,c!}p^a(1-p)^c \times \frac{n!}{b!\,d!}p^b(1-p)^d \tag{8·1}$$

$$= \frac{N!}{r!\,s!}p^r(1-p)^s \times \frac{m!\,n!\,r!\,s!}{a!\,b!\,c!\,d!\,N!} \tag{8·2}$$

$$= P_2\{r \mid p, N\} \times P_1\{a \mid N, r, m\}. \tag{8·3}$$

Thus the probability of obtaining the doublet (a, b) in sampling from two populations with a common p may be regarded as the product of two terms:

(i) The probability that $a + b = r$ or that the point (a, b) in Fig. 3 falls on a diagonal line on which $r =$ constant. This probability, $P_2\{r \mid p, N\}$, is the $(r+1)$th term in the expansion of the binomial

$$((1-p)+p)^N.$$

(ii) The relative probability, given r, of the observed partition into a and $b = r - a$; this is independent of p and is identical with the expression $P_1\{a \mid N, r, m\}$ of equation (1), i.e. is proportional to a term of the hypergeometric series (2).

* It will be seen that $P_1\{\ \}$ has been used to denote a hypergeometric probability and $P_2\{\ \}$ a binomial probability.

31. If, now, it were possible to draw a boundary line L_ϵ such as ABC shown in Fig. 3, cutting off at the end of each diagonal, r = constant, a group of points $(a, r-a)$ such that

$$\sum_a [P_1\{a \mid N, r, m\}] = \epsilon, \tag{9}$$

where ϵ is a fraction between 0 and 1 chosen at will, then the requirement of Step 3 would be satisfied. For in rejecting H_0 when (a, b) fall beyond this boundary,* the chance of doing so if H_0 were true would be

$$\sum_{r=0}^{N} [P_2\{r \mid p, N\} \times \epsilon] = \epsilon \times \sum_{r=0}^{N} [P_2\{r \mid p, N\}] = \epsilon, \tag{10}$$

i.e. would be independent of the unknown common p of the hypothesis tested. The test would then be analogous to 'Student's' test for the significance of the difference between two means, where we have a system of contour levels L_ϵ each associated with a chance ϵ, independent of the values of any unknown parameters which are irrelevant to the composite hypothesis tested.

32. Unfortunately, this objective cannot be achieved because we are not dealing with continuous probability distributions and $P_1\{a \mid N, r, m\}$ exists only at discrete, integral values of a. If we follow the present line of approach, all that is possible is to take contour or significance levels which cut off from an end of each diagonal, r = constant, a group of points for which

$$\sum_a [P_1\{a \mid N, r, m\}] = \beta_r \leqslant \epsilon. \tag{11}$$

Then, in rejecting H_0 when (a, b) falls beyond such a contour, we know that the chance of doing so, if H_0 is true, will be

$$\sum_{r=0}^{N} [P_2\{r \mid p, N\} \times \beta_r] \leqslant \epsilon. \tag{12}$$

It is clear that the amount by which the probability falls below ϵ will be a function of p, and that in taking Step 3 we are only associating with each significance level L_ϵ an upper limit, ϵ, to the probability of rejecting H_0 when it is true.

33. We have still, of course, to determine the most appropriate system of significance levels and to set out a ready means of finding an upper limit, ϵ, associated with the level on which an observed doublet (a, b) falls.† Mr Barnard has broken new ground in

(i) defining for this Problem II one systematic method of determining a family of levels L_ϵ based on certain clearly defined principles;

(ii) determining the true upper bound to the associated probability ϵ which, in the case of small samples at any rate, may be considerably below that which has hitherto been used.

Since, however, much tabling is needed before his theoretical advance can be followed by a practical working rule available for samples of any sizes, m and n, I think it is worth while describing the cruder handling of the lattice diagram which I had discussed in 1938–9

* There would be a similar series of boundaries, L'_ϵ, below the diagonal $a/m = b/n$, such as $A'B'C'$ of Fig. 3.

† The likelihood ratio λ might be used in determining the family of significance contours, as was suggested in connexion with the general χ^2 problem (Neyman & Pearson, 1928*b*, p. 283). In large samples λ would approximately equal $e^{-\frac{1}{2}u^2}$, where u is given by equation (22) below.

lectures. This involves, perhaps, not much more than a restatement of what may be termed the classical approach to Problem II (see paras. 43 and 44 below), but it does bring out the difference between Problems I and II, which I think important.

34. It may be well to emphasize here that this distinction between the handling of Problems I and II is not universally accepted. Fisher has set out his approach as follows in a paper read before the Royal Statistical Society (1935): 'To the many methods of treatment hitherto suggested for the 2×2 table the concept of ancillary information suggests this new one. Let us blot out the contents of the table, leaving only the marginal frequencies. If it be admitted that these marginal frequencies by themselves supply no information on the point at issue, namely, as to the proportionality of the frequencies in the body of the table, we may recognize the information they supply as wholly ancillary; and therefore recognize that we are concerned only with the relative probabilities of occurrence of the different ways in which the table can be filled in, subject to these marginal frequencies.'

This view has also been supported by Yates (1934). As I understand it, Fisher would refer the observation (a, b) to a linear set (as in my Problem I), however the data have been collected; this attitude follows readily if we discard the requirement that the probability distribution used in the test must be related to the frequency distribution that would be generated by repeated application of the random sampling process employed in the experiment. It will be seen that with Fisher's approach there is a gain in simplicity in handling the analysis; it must remain a matter of opinion whether there is a loss in the relevance of the probability construct to the question at issue. It is, of course, only when handling small samples or in cases where (a, b) lies close to one of the corners $(0, 0)$ or (m, n) of the lattice that this need for choice between probability constructs is thrust upon us.

(vi) SOLUTION OF PROBLEM II, USING THE NORMAL APPROXIMATION

35. If the samples are large, the calculation of hypergeometric terms becomes laborious and we turn naturally, as in so many other statistical problems, to the approximation using the normal curve. In fact, except when r or s are very small or m and n very different in magnitude, the normal curve with mean and standard deviation given by equations (3) and (4) provides a surprisingly good approximation to the relative probability distribution of a for fixed r, viz. $P_1\{a \mid N, r, m\}$ (see Appendix). Define u_ϵ as the deviate of the standardized normal curve for which

$$\epsilon = \int_{u_\epsilon}^{\infty} \frac{1}{\sqrt{(2\pi)}} e^{-\frac{1}{2}u^2} du \quad (\epsilon \leqslant \tfrac{1}{2}). \tag{13}$$

Then we can draw across the lattice diagram a significance level L_ϵ above and another L'_ϵ below* the diagonal $a/m = b/n$ such that

(i) all points (a, b) for which

$$\frac{(a + \frac{1}{2}) - \bar{a}}{\sigma_a} \leqslant -u_\epsilon \tag{14}$$

lie beyond, i.e. above, L_ϵ;

(ii) and all points (a, b) for which

$$\frac{(a - \frac{1}{2}) - \bar{a}}{\sigma_a} \geqslant u_\epsilon \tag{15}$$

lie beyond, i.e. below, L'_ϵ.

* The words 'above' and 'below' are used in the sense of Figs. 3 and 4.

If we wish to take special action either when a/m is significantly less than b/n or significantly greater, then we shall use both levels L_ϵ and L'_ϵ; if only, however, when $a/m < b/n$, then we use L_ϵ. The corresponding probability levels would be obtained by making ϵ for the second case twice its value for the first. Fig. 4 shows the 247 relative probabilities $P_1\{a \mid N, r, m\}$ for the case $m = 18$, $n = 12$. The unbroken, stepped lines are two contour levels determined in this way. Purely for convenience in drawing, the level with $\epsilon = 0{\cdot}05$ and $u_{0\cdot05} = 1{\cdot}6445$ has been put above the diagonal and that with $\epsilon = 0{\cdot}01$ and $u_{0\cdot01} = 2{\cdot}3263$ below.

36. If the normal approximation to the hypergeometric series were correct, it would follow that along every diagonal, $r =$ constant, the sum of the relative probabilities for points above L_ϵ would satisfy the inequality (11). Hence the inequality (12) for the complete area of the lattice above L_ϵ would hold, whatever the value of the common p. A similar result would hold for the area below L'_ϵ. Of course, the normal approximation will not hold precisely, particularly when r or s are small, but here we shall generally be on the safe side, in the sense that the hypergeometric distribution is flat-topped with abrupt ends so that the β_r of equation (11) will be considerably less than ϵ, and often zero.

37. It is interesting to examine the results set out in Fig. 4 with the help of the detailed calculations given in Table 4. Columns (2) and (3) give, for constant r, the mean and standard deviation of $P_1\{a \mid 30, r, 18\}$, while columns (4) (for $L_{0\cdot05}$) and (8) (for $L'_{0\cdot01}$) give the cut-off points defined by the normal approximation, i.e.

$$a_1 = \bar{a} - \tfrac{1}{2} - u_{0\cdot05} \times \sigma_a \quad \text{and} \quad a_2 = \bar{a} + \tfrac{1}{2} + u_{0\cdot01} \times \sigma_a. \tag{16}$$

The sums of the relative probabilities $P_1\{a \mid 30, r, 18\}$ for $a \leqslant a_1$ and $a \geqslant a_2$ are given in cols. (5) and (9) respectively. Thus, for example, for $r = 7$

$$a_1 = 4{\cdot}2 - 0{\cdot}5 - 1{\cdot}6449 \times 1{\cdot}1543 = 1{\cdot}80,$$

and the sum of the probabilities for $a = 0$ and 1 is

$$0{\cdot}0004 + 0{\cdot}0082 = 0{\cdot}0086.$$

These are the tail sums, termed β_r in equation (11). It is clear from an examination of cols. (5) and (9) that they are all less, and many of them very much less than 0·05 and 0·01. This is inevitable with a discrete distribution containing few terms. The contour levels have been drawn conventionally in Fig. 4 as steps passing through the half-integer points and not through the cut-off points of cols. (4) and (8). Clearly, whichever way they are drawn, they will separate off the same subset of the $(m+1)(n+1)$ points in the lattice diagram.

38. The next question is this. If we were to use either of these levels, what in fact would be the chance of the sample doublet (a, b) falling beyond, if the null hypothesis were true? This will depend on the common value of p. The product sums

$$\sum_{r=0}^{N} [P_2\{r \mid p, N\} \times \beta_r] = \sum_{r=0}^{N} \left[\frac{N!}{r!\,s!} p^r (1-p)^s \times \beta_r\right] \tag{17}$$

obtained by multiplying the expressions in cols. (5) and (9) of Table 4 by the appropriate binomial terms are shown for a variety of values of p in Table 5, cols. (2) and (3). It is clear at once how far on the safe side we are in saying that these chances are $\leqslant 0{\cdot}05$ and $0{\cdot}01$ respectively. Similar calculations were carried out for a second example, taking $m = n = 10$,

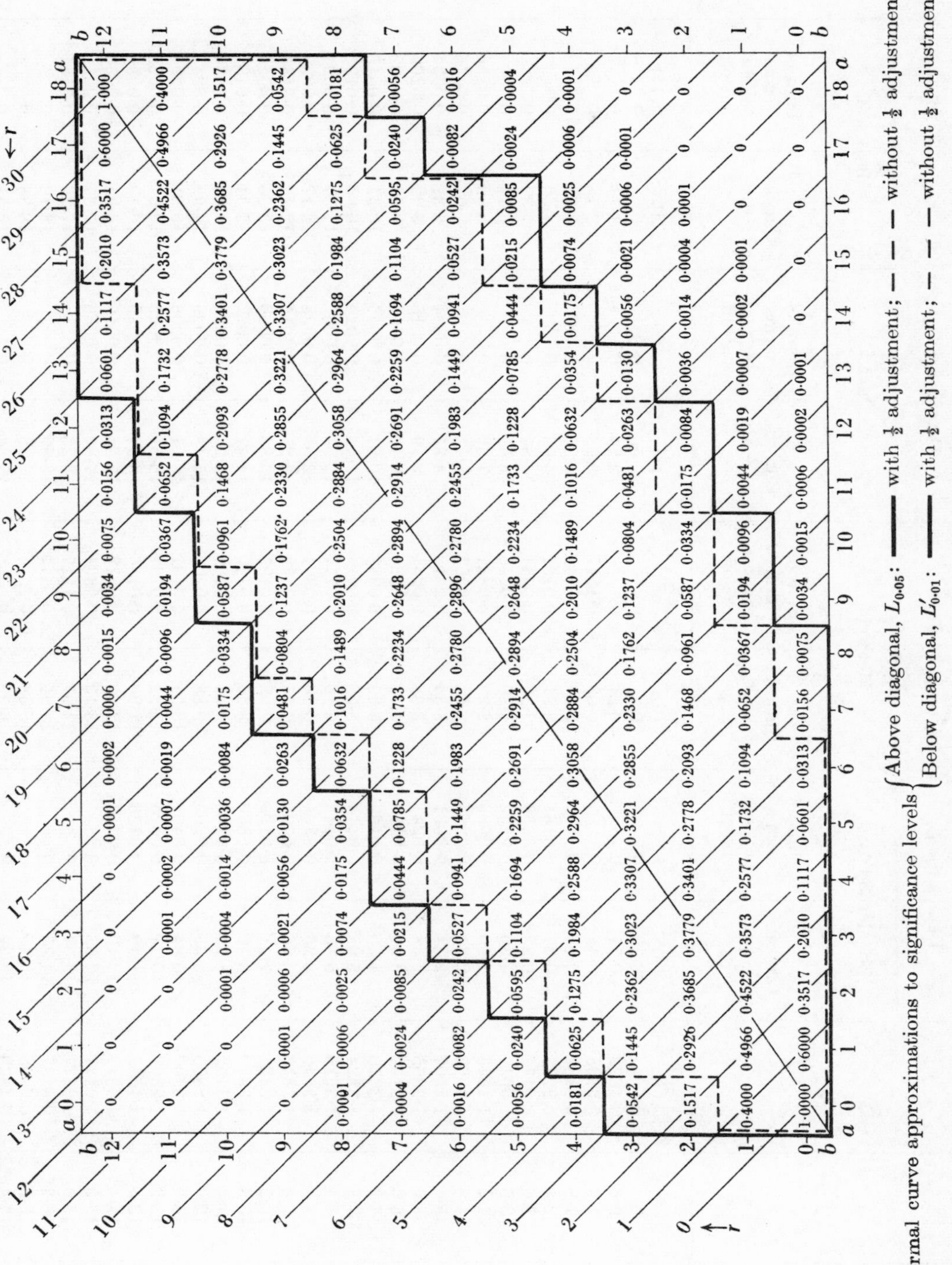

Fig. 4. Hypergeometric probabilities in lattice diagram for $m = 18$, $n = 12$.

Table 4. *Significance levels for case $m = 18$, $n = 12$*

r	$\bar{a}$	σ_a	Details for L_ϵ: $\epsilon = 0{\cdot}05$, $u_{0{\cdot}05} = 1{\cdot}6449$				Details for L'_ϵ: $\epsilon = 0{\cdot}01$, $u_{0{\cdot}01} = 2{\cdot}3263$				r
			Method 1		Method 2		Method 1		Method 2		
			Cut-off $\bar{a}-\frac{1}{2}-u_\epsilon\sigma_a$	Sum of terms beyond cut-off	Cut-off $\bar{a}-u_\epsilon\sigma_a$	Sum of terms beyond cut-off	Cut-off $\bar{a}+\frac{1}{2}+u_\epsilon\sigma_a$	Sum of terms beyond cut-off	Cut-off $\bar{a}+u_\epsilon\sigma_a$	Sum of terms beyond cut-off	
(1)	(2)	(3)	(4)	(5)	(6)	(7)	(8)	(9)	(10)	(11)	(12)
0	0	0	−0·50	0	0	0	0·50	0	0	0	0
1	0·6	0·4899	−0·71	0	−0·21	0	2·24	0	1·74	0	1
2	1·2	0·6808	−0·42	0	0·08	0·1517	3·28	0	2·78	0	2
3	1·8	0·8187	−0·05	0	0·45	0·0542	4·20	0	3·70	0	3
4	2·4	0·9277	0·37	0·0181	0·87	0·0181	5·06	0	4·56	0	4
5	3·0	1·0171	0·83	0·0056	1·33	0·0681	5·87	0	5·37	0	5
6	3·6	1·0917	1·30	0·0256	1·80	0·0256	6·64	0	6·14	0	6
7	4·2	1·1543	1·80	0·0086	2·30	0·0681	7·39	0	6·89	0·0156	7
8	4·8	1·2069	2·31	0·0267	2·81	0·0267	8·11	0	7·61	0·0075	8
9	5·4	1·2507	2·84	0·0091	3·34	0·0618	8·81	0·0034	8·31	0·0034	9
10	6·0	1·2865	3·38	0·0241	3·88	0·0241	9·49	0·0015	8·99	0·0209	10
11	6·6	1·3152	3·94	0·0080	4·44	0·0524	10·16	0·0006	9·66	0·0102	11
12	7·2	1·3370	4·50	0·0197	5·00+	0·0982	10·81	0·0046	10·31	0·0046	12
13	7·8	1·3524	5·08	0·0414	5·58	0·0414	11·45	0·0020	10·95	0·0195	13
14	8·4	1·3615	5·66	0·0145	6·16	0·0777	12·07	0·0007	11·57	0·0091	14
15	9·0	1·3646	6·26	0·0301	6·76	0·0301	12·67	0·0038	12·17	0·0038	15
16	9·6	1·3615	6·86	0·0091	7·36	0·0572	13·27	0·0015	12·77	0·0145	16
17	10·2	1·3524	7·48	0·0195	7·98	0·0195	13·85	0·0060	13·35	0·0060	17
18	10·8	1·3370	8·10	0·0380	8·60	0·0380	14·41	0·0022	13·91	0·0197	18
19	11·4	1·3152	8·74	0·0102	9·24	0·0689	14·96	0·0080	14·46	0·0080	19
20	12·0	1·2865	9·38	0·0209	9·88	0·0209	15·49	0·0026	14·99	0·0241	20
21	12·6	1·2507	10·04	0·0401	10·54	0·0401	16·01	0·0006	15·51	0·0091	21
22	13·2	1·2069	10·71	0·0075	11·21	0·0727	16·51	0·0025	16·01	0·0025	22
23	13·8	1·1543	11·40	0·0156	11·90	0·0156	16·99	0·0086	16·49	0·0086	23
24	14·4	1·0917	12·10	0·0313	12·60	0·0313	17·44	0·0016	16·94	0·0256	24
25	15·0	1·0171	12·63	0	13·13	0·0601	17·87	0·0056	17·37	0·0056	25
26	15·6	0·9277	13·57	0	14·07	0·1117	18·26	0	17·76	0·0181	26
27	16·2	0·8187	14·35	0	14·85	0	18·60	0	18·10	0	27
28	16·8	0·6808	15·18	0	15·68	0	18·88	0	18·38	0	28
29	17·4	0·4899	16·09	0	16·59	0	19·04	0	18·54	0	29
30	18·0	0	17·50	0	18·00	0	18·50	0	18·00	0	30

and the results are shown in Table 5, cols. (6) and (7). In this case, the actual chances of (a, b) falling on or beyond the significance levels are even further below the nominal limits of 0·05 and 0·01. In fact, it becomes clear that in the case of small samples, at any rate, this method of introducing the normal approximation gives such an overestimate of the true chances of falling beyond a contour as to be almost valueless.

Table 5. *Showing the difference between nominal and actual significance levels*

p (if H_0 true)	1st example: $m = 18$, $n = 12$				2nd example: $m = 10 = n$				p (if H_0 true)
	Method 1		Method 2		Method 1		Method 2		
	True chance of falling on or beyond		True chance of falling on or beyond		True chance of falling on or beyond		True chance of falling on or beyond		
	$L_{0\cdot05}$	$L'_{0\cdot01}$	$L_{0\cdot05}$	$L'_{0\cdot01}$	$L_{0\cdot05}$	$L'_{0\cdot01}$	$L_{0\cdot05}$	$L'_{0\cdot01}$	
(1)	(2)	(3)	(4)	(5)	(6)	(7)	(8)	(9)	(10)
0·05	0·0010	0·0000	0·0478	0·0000	0·0000	0·0000	0·0069	0·0000	0·05
0·1	0·0054	0·0000	0·0602	0·0003	0·0005	0·0000	0·0251	0·0005	0·1
0·2	0·0141	0·0003	0·0483	0·0043	0·0037	0·0007	0·0455	0·0037	0·2
0·3	0·0174	0·0012	0·0490	0·0091	0·0058	0·0014	0·0495	0·0058	0·3
0·4	0·0204	0·0023	0·0542	0·0108	0·0062	0·0017	0·0546	0·0062	0·4
0·5	0·0219	0·0028	0·0498	0·0109	0·0062	0·0015	0·0572	0·0062	0·5
0·6	0·0221	0·0035	0·0437	0·0119	Repeat as for $1-p$				0·6
0·7	0·0204	0·0037	0·0431	0·0120					0·7
0·8	0·0126	0·0031	0·0459	0·0113					0·8
0·9	0·0019	0·0009	0·0282	0·0052					0·9
0·95	0·0001	0·0001	0·0058	0·0010					0·95

39. Before considering a second method, it will be useful to recapitulate certain characteristics of what I have termed Method 1. It provides for any nominal value of ϵ one systematic procedure of defining a critical boundary or significance level cutting off a region from the lattice diagram. Neither the subgroup of points cut off, nor the sum of the probabilities associated with them for a given p, will alter continuously with ϵ; they will change by discrete steps as the cut-off point, defined in para. 37, passes through a point (a, b). While we shall sometimes want to know whether the observed (a, b) falls beyond a level L_ϵ specified in advance, more often we shall ask what is the level on which (a, b) falls. This, using Method 1, we find by calculating

$$u = \frac{\bar{a} - (a + \frac{1}{2})}{\sigma_a} \quad \text{if} \quad a < \bar{a} \quad \text{or} \quad u = \frac{a - \frac{1}{2} - \bar{a}}{\sigma_a} \quad \text{if} \quad a > \bar{a}, \tag{18}$$

and finding ϵ from the normal integral of equation (13). In this way the nominal chance ϵ will be a little nearer the true upper limit than the figures in Table 5 suggest,* but not enough to modify the criticism expressed above.

* It will be seen from Table 4 that no point (a, b) gives a β_r in cols. (5) and (9) of exactly 0·05 or 0·01, respectively, so that no points actually lie on $L_{0\cdot05}$ or $L_{0\cdot01}$.

40. *Method* 2. The introduction of the correction of $\frac{1}{2}$ for continuity is certainly appropriate in using the normal approximation to the hypergeometric series in Problem I, but I think it is not helpful in Problem II where we are concerned with a 2-dimensional experimental probability set. If instead of obtaining significance levels L_ϵ and L'_ϵ as in paras. 35–37, we obtain them from inequalities similar to (14) and (15) but with the correction of $\frac{1}{2}$ omitted, then there are several points to be noted:

(*a*) For the significance level L_ϵ, the expression

$$\beta_r = \sum_a [P_1\{a \mid N, r, m\}], \tag{19}$$

where the summation is for values of a on the diagonal, r = constant, for which

$$a \leqslant a_1 = \bar{a} - u_\epsilon \times \sigma_a \tag{20}$$

will be sometimes less and sometimes greater than ϵ. Hence, in the balance, it seems likely that the chance of the point (a, b) lying beyond L_ϵ or

$$\sum_{r=0}^{N} \left[\frac{N!}{r!\,s!} p^r (1-p)^s \times \beta_r\right] \tag{21}$$

will lie closer to ϵ than when the $\frac{1}{2}$ correction is used. The position will be the same for L'_ϵ.

(*b*) In drawing repeated samples of m and n from two populations in which there is a common chance, p, of an individual possessing character A, the ratio

$$u = \frac{a-\bar{a}}{\sigma_a} = \frac{a - rm/N}{\sqrt{\dfrac{mnrs}{N^2(N-1)}}} \tag{22}$$

has, whatever be p, (i) an expectation of zero, (ii) a unit standard deviation.* The shape of the distribution will, of course, depend on p, but, *faut de mieux*, we may not in the long run do too badly by assuming it to be normal. It is, of course, the weighted combination of a number of hypergeometric series whose shape depends on r.

41. Consider the result of applying this Method 2 to the case $m = 18$, $n = 12$ already discussed. The procedure for determining the 0·05 and 0·01 significance levels will be exactly as under Method 1, except that the continuity correction of $\frac{1}{2}$ is omitted. The resulting levels are shown as dashed, stepped lines in Fig. 4.† They fall, on the whole, inside the significance levels obtained by Method 1. Now turn to Table 4, where cols. (6) and (10) show the cut-off points a half unit further in towards the diagonal $a/m = b/n$. Cols. (7) and (11) give the values of β_r; some of these are considerably above the nominal values of $\epsilon = 0{\cdot}05$ and 0·01, others are still well below. But from the approach to Problem II that has been adopted, this is immaterial since the experimental probability set is the 2-dimensioned one of the lattice diagram and is not restricted to the diagonal r = constant on which the observed point (a, b) may happen to lie. What we are concerned with is the summed chance given by expression (21) and the value of this is given for eleven values of p in cols. (4) and (5) of Table 5. It will be seen that this true chance does sometimes exceed the nominal values of 0·05 and 0·01,

* Provided cases where r or s are zero, making the expression (22) indeterminate with $u = 0/0$, are excluded. Mr Barnard has pointed out that one way of avoiding this exclusion would be to lay down that, when $u = 0/0$, we assign to the ratio a value chosen at random from a population (say normal) with zero mean and unit variance.

† Again, for convenience the 5 % level is drawn above and the 1 % level below the diagonal.

but never by very much. Again, for the second example with $m = 10 = n$ (Table 5, cols. (8) and (9)) the true chance, while it sometimes exceeds the nominal value, is always considerably nearer it than using the significance levels of Method 1.

42. It is clear that no final conclusions can be based on two numerical examples, but it seems that the test of the null hypothesis in Problem II should be carried out as follows:

(*a*) When m, n, r or s are small, with the help of tables prepared on Barnard's lines, based on an ordered classification of the points in the lattice diagram, and giving the true upper bound of the chance that a point (a, b) falls on or beyond the level on which the observed result lies. The particular basis of his classification may, of course, be modified.

(*b*) When m, n, r and s are large, by assuming that the u of equation (22) is a normal deviate with unit standard deviation.

(vii) The classical approach to Problem II

43. It has recently become customary to regard the test of significance applied to data given in a 2×2 table as the limiting case of a χ^2 test with one degree of freedom. But Problem II was originally answered in somewhat different terms. It was noted that if

$$p_1(A) = p_2(A) = p, \tag{23}$$

then the fractions a/m and b/n would both have expectations of p and variances of $p(1-p)/m$ and $p(1-p)/n$, respectively. Hence, if the null hypothesis were true, the difference

$$d = \frac{a}{m} - \frac{b}{n} \tag{24}$$

would have

$$\left.\begin{aligned} \text{mean } d &= 0 \\ \sigma_d &= \sqrt{\left[p(1-p)\left(\frac{1}{m}+\frac{1}{n}\right)\right]} \end{aligned}\right\}. \tag{25}$$

In large samples, therefore, it might be expected that

$$\frac{d}{\sigma_d} = \frac{a/m - b/n}{\sqrt{[p(1-p)\,(1/m+1/n)]}} \tag{26}$$

would be approximately normally distributed. Since by the nature of the problem the common value of p was unknown, an estimate was made from the sample, namely,

$$\hat{p} = \frac{a+b}{m+n} = \frac{r}{N}. \tag{27}$$

Substituting this into equation (26), we have

$$\frac{d}{s_d} = \frac{a/m - b/n}{\sqrt{[(r/N)(1-r/N)\,(1/m+1/n)]}} \tag{28·1}$$

$$= \frac{a - rm/N}{\sqrt{\left(\dfrac{mnrs}{N^3}\right)}}. \tag{28·2}$$

44. The form (28·2) is easily derived from (28·1), if we remember that $b = r-a$, $s = N-r$ and $m+n = N$.* It is seen that the ratio d/s_d is identical with the ratio u of equation (22), except for a factor $\sqrt{[(N-1)/N]}$ which is unimportant in large samples. Thus the classical test is practically identical with that suggested in paras. 40–42 above, though the two tests are differently derived.

* A third alternative form is, of course, $(ad-bc)\sqrt{N}/\sqrt{(mnrs)}$.

(viii) Problem III

45. This may be described as the test for the independence of two characters A and B. It is supposed that the probability that an individual selected at random will possess character A is $p(A)$ and that he will not possess it is $p(\bar{A}) = 1-p(A)$. The corresponding probabilities for character B are $p(B)$ and $p(\bar{B}) = 1-p(B)$. Four alternative combinations of the characters may occur, which may be denoted by AB, $A\bar{B}$, $\bar{A}B$ and $\bar{A}\bar{B}$. The various probabilities are set out in Table 6 A. If the null hypothesis, H_0, specifying the independence of A and B is true, then

$$p(AB) = p(A) \times p(B), \quad p(A\bar{B}) = p(A)\,p(\bar{B}), \quad \text{etc.} \tag{29}$$

To test the hypothesis, we have a random sample of N observations with frequencies of occurrence of the combinations AB, $A\bar{B}$, etc., which may be classified in the 2×2 scheme of Table 6 B. The sampling conditions are such that the probabilities of Table 6 A are the same for all individuals selected, or, in conventional terms, the sample is drawn from an infinite population. Barnard calls this problem that of the double dichotomy.

Table 6 A. *Probabilities*

	A	$\bar{A}$	Total
B	$p(AB)$	$p(\bar{A}B)$	$p(B)$
$\bar{B}$	$p(A\bar{B})$	$p(\bar{A}\bar{B})$	$p(\bar{B})$
Total	$p(A)$	$p(\bar{A})$	1

Table 6 B. *Sample data*

	A	$\bar{A}$	Total
B	a	c	m
$\bar{B}$	b	d	n
Total	r	s	N

46. In Problem III there is only one application of a random process, the selection of N individuals, each one of which must fall into one or other of four alternative categories. If the random process were repeated and another sample of N drawn, not only are the frequencies a, b, c and d free to vary, but also *both* marginal totals, i.e. m may change as well as r. The experimental probability set will therefore contain results (a, b, c, d) restricted by the conditions (i) that none of the frequencies can be negative and (ii) that

$$a+b+c+d = N. \tag{30}$$

Geometrically, as Barnard points out, the set can be represented in 3 dimensions by points at unit intervals within a tetrahedron obtained by placing on top of one another the series of 2-dimensioned lattices of dimensions

$$0 \times n, \quad 1 \times (n-1), \quad 2 \times (n-2), \quad \ldots, \quad (m-1) \times 1, \quad m \times 0. \tag{31}$$

47. We are again testing a composite hypothesis and should like to determine a family of critical surfaces to be used as significance levels, dividing the points within the tetrahedron in such a way that the chance of the sample point (a, b, c, d)* lying outside a given surface L_ϵ is equal to ϵ, whatever the values of the unknown probabilities $p(A)$ and $p(B)$. But again, as in Problem II, owing to the discontinuity in the set of points, there are no 'similar

* In view of the condition (30), the point can be defined by three co-ordinates, e.g. as (a, b, c), (a, b, m) or (a, r, m). In view of the form of equation (32), the last system of co-ordinates will be used.

regions'. We note that if H_0 is true, the probability of the observed result is a term of the multinomial expansion, viz.

$$\frac{N!}{a!\,b!\,c!\,d!}p(AB)^a\,p(A\bar{B})^b\,p(\bar{A}B)^c\,p(\bar{A}\bar{B})^d$$

$$=\frac{N!}{a!\,b!\,c!\,d!}p(A)^{a+b}\,p(B)^{a+c}\,p(\bar{A})^{c+d}\,p(\bar{B})^{b+d}$$

$$=\frac{N!}{m!\,n!}p(B)^m\,(1-p(B))^n\times\frac{N!}{r!\,s!}p(A)^r\,(1-p(A))^s\times\frac{m!\,n!\,r!\,s!}{a!\,b!\,c!\,d!\,N!}$$

$$=P_2\{m\mid p(B),N\}\times P_2\{r\mid p(A),N\}\times P_1\{a\mid N,r,m\}. \tag{32}$$

Here, the notation of para. 30 has been repeated.

48. Thus the probability of obtaining a sample represented by the triplet (a, r, m) may be regarded, if the characters A and B are independent, as the product of three terms:

(i) The probability of drawing m individuals with character B in a random sample of N, i.e. the probability that (a, r, m) falls in a horizontal section of the tetrahedron on which $m=$ constant. This is the $(m+1)$th term in the expansion of the binomial

$$\{(1-p(B))+p(B)\}^N.$$

(ii) The probability of drawing r individuals with character A in a random sample of N, i.e. the probability that (a, r, m) falls on the vertical section of the tetrahedron on which $r=$ constant. This is the $(r+1)$th term in the expansion of

$$\{(1-p(A))+p(A)\}^N.$$

(iii) The probability, given m and r, of the observed partition within the 2×2 table. This term represents the relative probability associated with the points lying along a straight line $m=$ constant, $r=$ constant; it is, of course, the same expression as has arisen in Problems I and II and is proportional to a term in the hypergeometric series $F(-r, -m, n-r+1, 1)$.

49. We are faced with a situation similar to that met under Problem II. Were it possible to cut off from each line on which $m=$ constant, $r=$ constant, a group of points such that

$$\sum_a\,[P_1\{a\mid N,r,m\}]=\epsilon, \tag{33}$$

then the subset of points within the tetrahedron composed of the sum of these groups for all possible combinations of m and r would have the property required of a 'critical region' in a significance test: i.e. the chance that the point (a, r, m) is included in the region, if H_0 is true, would be ϵ whatever values the irrelevant probabilities $p(A)$ and $p(B)$ assumed. However, (33) cannot be satisfied in general, and all that is possible is to define a family of significance contours such that the chance of a sample point falling beyond any one of them, say L_ϵ, is $\leqslant\epsilon$. By using the normal approximation to the sum of the hypergeometric tail-terms with the correction for continuity as described in paras. 35–39 for Problem II, we shall be very much on the safe side, i.e. the formal level of ϵ is likely to be much above the true chance of falling beyond the level, whatever be $p(A)$ or $p(B)$. The presence of the two binomial terms in equation (32) instead of the single term in equation (8·3), makes it likely that the overestimation of ϵ will be greater in Problem III than in II. It is to be expected, therefore, that any any rate when neither m, n, r or s are too small, the better approximation will be obtained by referring the u of equation (22) to the normal probability scale.

50. The handling of Problem III is discussed briefly by Barnard on p. 136 above. There is clearly room for further investigation. The general nature of the approximation

involved is of course that which arises in every χ^2 test for goodness of fit or for independence in an $h \times k$ table, where we replace a distribution consisting of a finite set of probabilities at discrete points in multiple space by a continuous distribution for which integration outside ellipsoidal contours is straightforward.

(ix) General comment

51. The duties of the statistician lie at many levels. He may be required merely to apply an established technique of analysis to an assembly of numerical data and this application may result in a statement, based on probability theory, of a 'level of significance' or a 'confidence interval', which will be used by others. Or he may be called on to share in planning the investigation or experiment which is to provide the data and then to draw conclusions from their analysis which will lead to further action. In this final role he needs to bring into play faculties which are no monopoly of his calling, the qualities of sound judgement which are the characteristics of a well trained, scientific mind. In the weighing of evidence, the result of the statistical analysis, expressed in one or more conventional probability figures, is only one factor in the summing up; as important, may be, is the question of whether the mathematical model is a fair counterpart to the happenings in the observational field. In addition, there will often be much information coming from outside the range of the immediate investigation, yet hardly expressible in numerical terms, which must influence decision.

52. It is perhaps hard experience gained in certain fields of war-time research, where decisions had to be reached on statistical data far less ample than could be wished, which has forced my own attention to this question: What weight do we actually give to the precise value of a probability measure when reaching decisions of first importance? One subject for examination falling under this inquiry is clearly the logical basis of the reasoning process by which judgement is influenced as a result of the application of a test of significance. This was the theme on which this paper opened. The approach illustrated in the pages which followed is a personal one and is set down, with no claim to be the best, in order to provoke thought and discussion. There appears no short route to a right answer in this matter; each individual who hopes to use his own judgement to the full in drawing conclusions from the statistical analysis of sampling data, must decide for himself what he requires of probability theory.

53. In the approach which I have followed and illustrated on the analysis of data classed in a 2×2 table, the appropriate probability set-up is defined by the nature of the random process actually used in the collection of the data. Consideration of this point forms the initial step in the determination of the appropriate test. On this score, what I have termed Problems I, II and III are differentiated. The difference is fundamental and lies at the bottom of the dilemma to which the Barnard-Fisher correspondence in *Nature* drew attention. It can be illustrated on the following data, given in Table 7, where I shall suppose that the effect we are interested in is that making a significantly greater than b.

54. If (a) the results have been obtained by random assignment of Treatment 1 to eighteen out of thirty individuals and Treatment 2 to the remaining twelve, and

(b) we merely ask whether the results are consistent with the hypothesis that the treatments are equivalent as far as these thirty individuals are concerned, so that the difference between the proportions 15/18 and 5/12 may reasonably be ascribed to a chance fluctuation,

(c) we are then concerned with Problem I, i.e. simply with the probabilities associated with the points $(a, 20-a)$ on the diagonal $r = 20$ of Fig. 4. The chance of getting $a \geqslant 15$, if the null hypothesis is true, is 0·0241,* or, using a common phrase, we can speak of the result being significant at the 2·5 % level.

55. On the other hand, if a sample of 18 has been drawn randomly from one population and a sample of 12 independently from a second and we wish to test whether $p_1(A) = p_2(A)$, then it seems to be an artificial procedure to restrict the experimental probability set to the 11 points on the line $r = 20$, i.e. to the values of a: 8, 9, ..., 18. A repetition of the double sampling process could give us a result (a, b) falling at any of the $19 \times 13 = 247$ points in the lattice diagram of Fig. 4. There will be a number of ways of defining a family of significance levels for this 2-dimensioned set; if we adopt that discussed in paras. 40–41, which

Table 7

For problem I	For problem II	Frequency of results		Total
		A	$\bar{A}$	
1st treatment 2nd treatment	Sample from 1st population Sample from 2nd population	$a = 15$ $b = 5$	$c = 3$ $d = 7$	$m = 18$ $n = 12$
	Total	$r = 20$	$s = 10$	$N = 30$

gives as two of its members the dotted, stepped lines shown in Fig. 4, we can say that the chance of a result falling beyond the lower line is certainly less than 0·015.† The observed point, with $a = 15$, $b = 5$ falls beyond the line, so that the result is undoubtedly 'significant at the 1·5 % level'.

56. These two probabilities, 2·5 and 1·5 %, are not the same, but there is no inconsistency in their difference. The character of the two investigations is different and to treat Problem II as though it were Problem I seems to call for a probability set-up which is unnecessarily artificial, when a simpler one is available. Admittedly by getting what seems to me a closer relation between the probability set-up and the experimental procedure, we have sacrificed some simplicity in handling the 2×2 table. But this is only the case when dealing with small numbers. For large numbers the methods of handling Problems I, II and III become, practically, identical.

57. Consider again the heavy shell problem described in para. 7 above. If we are to introduce probability theory, it seems to me that we should regard the problem as one in which we have a sample of $m = 12$ from the possible output of shell made to one design or by one firm and of $n = 8$ from the possible output of a second. This sampling may be hypothetical in that these may be 'pilot' shell, the first off production; nevertheless, this construct is

* For the normal curve approximation, using the correction for continuity, we find

$$u = (15 - \tfrac{1}{2} - 12\cdot 0)/1\cdot 2865 = 1\cdot 943.$$

The proportionate area under the normal curve beyond this deviation is 0·026.

† Table 5, col. (5) shows the largest value of this chance to be 0·0120 for $p = 0\cdot 3$. This figure cannot be much exceeded for other p's though I have not determined the precise maximum. I give 0·015 as a safe-side limit.

clearly less artificial than one in which, on the null hypothesis, we regard the experiment as though it were made on twenty shells, to twelve of which has been randomly assigned the label 'Made by firm X' and to the other eight, 'Made by firm Y'.

58. It is clear that in the heavy shell problem there may be many reasons to doubt whether the rounds fired can be regarded as a random sample from future output. That is why I have emphasized that the exploration which the statistician makes in private will not necessarily be presented in figures at the conference table. In this example, the proportions of successful perforations were 2/12 and 5/8; these put us on the line, $r = 7$, of the lattice diagram for which the hypergeometric probabilities were shown in Fig. 2. The sum of the terms with $a \leqslant 2$ is 5·2 % (normal approximation, using the $\frac{1}{2}$-correction, 5·6 %). This is the chance of getting as great or a greater positive difference, $b-a$, if H_0 were true, treating the case as Problem I. Barnard's method has not yet been extended to cover this case, but if we were to use the large sample method for handling Problem II, described in my paras. 40–41, we should find from equation (22) that

$$u = (2-4{\cdot}2)/1{\cdot}072 = -2{\cdot}05,$$

which puts (a, b) outside the upper 2·5 % level.

59. Were the action taken to be decided automatically by the side of the 5 % level on which the observation point fell, it is clear that the method of analysis used would here be of vital importance. But no responsible statistician, faced with an investigation of this character, would follow an automatic probability rule. The result of either approach would raise considerable doubts as to whether the performance of the first type of shell was as good as that of the second, but without the whole background of the investigation it is impossible to say what the statistician's recommendation as to further action would be.

60. In the example of the proof of anti-tank shot discussed in para. 6, the chance of perforation, p, while varying from plate to plate and batch to batch, will almost certainly not range through the whole interval 0–1. The striking-velocity of the shot would also probably be adjusted so that for average proof-plate and batches, p was near $\frac{1}{2}$. Then the discriminating level (or levels*) set across the 13×13 lattice diagram would be fixed paying regard to the likely variation in p; thus a fairly close upper limit could be calculated to the true probability of (a, b) falling beyond the level if the fresh batch were of the same quality as the standard. This is the upper limit of the risk of segregating the batch wrongly.

61. Precisely similar problems arise for consideration in even more difficult form in the analysis of data arranged in a $h \times k$ table, where h or k or both are > 2. It has become common practice to speak of the solution of this problem in terms of 'fixed marginal totals', but it may be questioned whether the restriction in the experimental probability set implied is generally appropriate. The frequencies in a $h \times k$ table may have been obtained by many different sampling procedures for, as in the 2×2 problem, a single form of tabular presentation will follow from a variety of types of investigation. For most of these, a repetition of the random process of selection would give results with either one or both sets of marginal totals changed.

62. For convenience in solution we may, of course, start by considering the distribution of our test criterion, on the null hypothesis, within the sub-set of results for which the margins

* It is possible that two levels might be taken with the associated proof rules: (i) if (a, b) falls beyond the outer one, reject the batch; (ii) if between outer and inner, fire further rounds; (iii) if within the inner level, accept the batch.

are fixed. If this distribution were the same whatever these fixed values, then the overall, distribution for unrestricted sampling would be the same as that for variation subject to fixed margins. Thus, mathematically, the solution of the partial problem would be a step in the solution of the complete one. But when applying χ^2 analysis to an $h \times k$ table, this result is only true as a large-sample approximation.

63. If we use the mathematical model which it is suggested gives the most direct aid in reasoning from the observations, i.e. that which regards the experimental probability set as generated by a repetition of the random process of selection used in collecting the data, then in the majority of cases we cannot regard the marginal totals as fixed. Thus a rigorous treatment would lead, as in the case of the 2×2 table, to a differentiation into a number of solutions. It is to be hoped, however,* unless the numbers in the margins are very small, that the χ^2 approximation with its appropriate degrees of freedom† will give results which are not misleading. This approximation leads, of course, in the 2×2 table to the reference of the ratio u of equation (22) to the normal probability scale. Some aspects of the approximation in this more general case were discussed by Yates (1934, pp. 233–35).

64. In closing I should like again to acknowledge my indebtedness to Mr G. A. Barnard. Having had the good fortune to discuss these problems with him and see drafts of his work over a period of 2 or 3 years it is difficult to say how many of his ideas have been built unconsciously into my own earlier approach. But I am especially aware of the clarification which his emphasis on the distinction between Problems I, II and III brought to my survey. I am also very grateful to Mr M. G. Kendall, Dr R. C. Geary and Dr B. L. Welch for a number of helpful criticisms, and to Mrs Maxine Merrington for her extensive computing work, which has alone made possible the various numerical illustrations that I have given.

* From the point of view both of the exponents of the fixed marginal and unrestricted marginal approach.

† The statement that, for example, in applying the test of independence of two characters to an $h \times k$ table, the degrees of freedom are $(h-1) \times (k-1)$, does not of course mean that sampling is restricted by fixed marginal totals. All that is implied is that approximately the overall distribution of the χ^2 function of the observations used, is the same as that for sampling within the restricted sub-set; this is because the distribution within each sub-set is approximately independent of the particular marginal totals which define it.

REFERENCES

BARNARD, G. A. (1945*a*). *Nature, Lond.*, **156**, 177.
BARNARD, G. A. (1945*b*). *Nature, Lond.*, **156**, 783.
FISHER, R. A. (1935). *J. Roy. Statist. Soc.* **98**, 39.
FISHER, R. A. (1941). *Science*, **94**, 210.
FISHER, R. A. (1945*a*). *Nature, Lond.*, **156**, 388.
FISHER, R. A. (1945*b*). *Sankhyā*, **7**, 130.
KENDALL, M. G. (1943). *The Advanced Theory of Statistics*, **1**. London: Charles Griffin and Co. Ltd.
NEYMAN, J. & PEARSON, E. S. (1928*a*). *Biometrika*, **20** A, 195.
NEYMAN, J. & PEARSON, E. S. (1928*b*). *Biometrika*, **20** A, 263.
NEYMAN, J. & PEARSON, E. S. (1933). *Philos. Trans.* A, **231**, 289.
NEYMAN, J. & PEARSON, E. S. (1936). *Statist. Res. Mem.* **1**, 113.
NEYMAN, J. & PEARSON, E. S. (1938). *Statist. Res. Mem.* **2**, 25.
PEARSON, K. (1899). *Phil. Mag.* **47**, 236.
PRZYBOROWSKI, J. & WILENSKI, H. (1939). *Biometrika*, **13**, 313.
WILSON, E. B. (1941). *Science*, **93**, 557.
WILSON, E. B. (1942). *Proc. Nat. Acad. Sci., Wash.*, **28**, 94.
YATES, F. (1934). *J. Roy. Statist. Soc.* Suppl. **1**, 217.

APPENDIX

THE NORMAL CURVE APPROXIMATION IN PROBLEM I

1. The following Tables 8 and 9 (A), (B) and (C) show the order of accuracy which results from using the normal curve integral as an approximation to the tail sums in the series

$$P_1\{a \mid N, r, m\} = \frac{m!\,n!\,r!\,s!}{a!\,b!\,c!\,d!\,N!} \qquad (34)$$

the terms of which are proportional to those in the hypergeometric series

$$F(-r, -m, N-m-r+1, 1).$$

Here a is a variable which can assume the range of positive, integral values indicated under (i), (ii) and (iii) in para. 20 above, while N, r and m are fixed. The relation between these quantities and b, c, d, n and s is given in Table 1, para. 17. The method of approximation, using the '$\frac{1}{2}$' correction for continuity, has been discussed in para. 25.

2. Table 8 takes the case of an equal partition, $m = n = \frac{1}{2}N$, and shows the sum of the terms in the expression (34) for which $a \geqslant a_1$ which is also the sum of terms for which $a \leqslant r - a_1$. For $m \neq n$, results are given in Table 9 for $m > n$ and for the following proportionate partitions of N:

$$\text{(A)}\ m = \tfrac{3}{5}N,\quad n = \tfrac{2}{5}N;\quad \text{(B)}\ m = \tfrac{4}{5}N,\quad n = \tfrac{1}{5}N;\quad \text{(C)}\ m = \tfrac{9}{10}N,\quad n = \tfrac{1}{10}N.$$

Here sums of terms at both tails of the series are needed. The sums (or chances of $a \geqslant a_1$ or $\leqslant a_1$) have not been given for all possible values of a_1 but, broadly speaking, for those within the limits where significance is likely to be in question. Sums below 0·0010 have generally been omitted. In each case the true sum of the terms (34) is compared with the approximation from the normal integral.

3. In drawing conclusions from the comparison, we have to decide what degree of accuracy is called for. Clearly the normal integral does not give mathematically exact results to 4 decimal places. On the other hand, except for certain instances where the partition is very unequal ($m = \frac{4}{5}N$ and $\frac{9}{10}N$) and r is small, the order of the approximation may be said to follow that of the series closely. If decisions are made by rule of thumb, according to the side of the 5% or 1% significance level on which a falls, then there are a number of entries in the tables where the approximation would give a on the wrong side. But one may question whether judgement of significance based on a single experiment can in fact be made sensitive to a difference between, say, 0·06 and 0·04 (odds of 16 to 1 and 24 to 1) or between 0·012 and 0·008 (odds of 82 to 1 and 124 to 1) and, given such latitude in accuracy, the approximation will be found generally sufficient. These must be points, however, where personal opinions will differ. Whatever views are held, the tables are sufficiently extensive to make it possible to obtain from them a rough measure of the accuracy of approximation in a wide range of cases.

4. It will be noted that in the symmetrical case ($m = \frac{1}{2}N$) and also when $m = \frac{3}{5}N$ the normal approximation for the tail sum is almost invariably a little too large. Undoubtedly for the symmetrical case an improved approximation could be obtained by modifying the $\frac{1}{2}$ correction used in calculating the ratio of deviation to standard deviation. This second order term would, however, need to vary with the probability level, thus complicating the procedure.

Table 8. *Case of equal partition*, $m = n = \frac{1}{2}N$. *Chance that* $a \geqslant a_1 =$ *chance that* $a \leqslant r - a_1$

Partition		$m=n=50$		$m=n=30$		$m=n=20$		$m=n=15$		$m=n=10$			
r	a_1	True	Normal approx.	True	Normal approx.	True	Normal approx.	True	Normal approx.	True	Normal approx.	a_1	r
30	17	0·2566	0·2574	0·2194	0·2212							17	30
	18	·1376	·1388	·0981	·1002							18	
	19	·0630	·0643	·0348	·0365							19	
	20	·0243	·0253	·0096	·0106							20	
	21	·0078	·0085	·0020	·0024							21	
	22	·0021	·0024									22	
20	12	0·2269	0·2278	0·2060	0·2076	0·1715	0·1745					12	20
	13	·1053	·1068	·0852	·0873	·0564	·0592					13	
	14	·0392	·0408	·0270	·0287	·0128	·0144					14	
	15	·0114	·0126	·0064	·0073	·0019	·0025					15	
	16	·0025	·0031	·0011	·0014							16	
15	9	0·2884	0·2887	0·2760	0·2772	0·2572	0·2595	0·2330	0·2364			9	15
	10	·1312	·1325	·1163	·1185	·0954	·0985	·0715	·0755			10	
	11	·0453	·0473	·0358	·0380	·0242	·0265	·0134	·0156			11	
	12	·0113	·0129	·0077	·0090	·0040	·0049	·0014	·0020			12	
	13	·0019	·0027	·0011	·0016							13	
10	7	0·1589	0·1599	0·1495	0·1514	0·1367	0·1397	0·1226	0·1266	0·0894	0·0955	7	10
	8	·0458	·0486	·0399	·0429	·0324	·0357	·0251	·0285	·0115	·0147	8	
	9	·0078	·0101	·0061	·0081	·0042	·0058	·0026	·0038	·0005	·0011	9	
	10	·0006	·0014	·0004	·0010							10	
7	5	0·2179	0·2177	0·2119	0·2126	0·2038	0·2056	0·1950	0·1980	0·1749	0·1804	5	7
	6	·0558	·0594	·0514	·0553	·0458	·0501	·0401	·0448	·0286	·0338	6	
	7	·0062	·0096	·0053	·0084	·0042	·0068	·0032	·0055	·0015	·0031	7	
5	4	0·1810	0·1806	0·1766	0·1771	0·1709	0·1735	0·1648	0·1677	0·1517	0·1571	4	5
	5	·0281	·0339	·0261	·0320	·0236	·0295	·0211	·0270	·0163	·0220	5	

Table 9. *Case of unequal partition. Chances that $a \leqslant a_1$ and $a \geqslant a_1$*

(A) $m = \frac{3}{5}N$, $n = \frac{2}{5}N$

Partition			$m = 60$, $n = 40$		$m = 36$, $n = 24$		$m = 24$, $n = 16$		$m = 18$, $n = 12$		$m = 12$, $n = 8$				
r	Chance that	a_1	True	Normal approx.	True	Normal approx.	True	Normal approx.	True	Normal approx.	True	Normal approx.	a_1	Chance that	r
30	$a \leqslant a_1$	11	0·0020	0·0019									11	$a \leqslant a_1$	30
		12	·0074	·0074	0·0016	0·0020							12		
		13	·0230	·0231	·0084	·0093	—						13		
		14	·0601	·0604	·0320	·0337	0·0023	0·0050					14		
		15	·1330	·1339	·0936	·0957	·0270	·0329					15		
		16	·2512	·2531	·2148	·2165	·1311	·1348					16		
	$a \geqslant a_1$	20	0·2533	0·2531	0·2148	0·2165	0·1322	0·1348					20	$a \geqslant a_1$	
		21	·1323	·1339	·0936	·0957	·0318	·0329					21		
		22	·0580	·0604	·0320	·0337	·0045	·0050					22		
		23	·0209	·0231	·0084	·0093							23		
		24	·0061	·0074	·0016	·0020							24		
		25	·0014	·0019									25		
20	$a \leqslant a_1$	6	0·0027	0·0026	0·0010	0·0012							6	$a \leqslant a_1$	20
		7	·0114	·0112	·0060	·0063	0·0015	0·0021	—				7		
		8	·0381	·0378	·0255	·0262	·0112	·0128	0·0015	0·0033			8		
		9	·1019	·1021	·0816	·0829	·0526	·0555	·0290	·0260			9		
		10	·2211	·2232	·2005	·2028	·1665	·1695	·1170	·1218			10		
	$a \geqslant a_1$	14	0·2236	0·2232	0·2017	0·2028	0·1665	0·1695	0·1182	0·1218			14	$a \geqslant a_1$	
		15	·0994	·1021	·0798	·0829	·0526	·0555	·0241	·0260			15		
		16	·0341	·0378	·0233	·0262	·0112	·0128	·0026	·0033			16		
		17	·0086	·0112	·0048	·0063	·0015	·0021					17		
		18	·0015	·0026	·0006	·0012							18		
15	$a \leqslant a_1$	4	0·0053	0·0053	0·0032	0·0033	0·0013	0·0015					4	$a \leqslant a_1$	15
		5	·0236	·0233	·0171	·0173	·0098	·0106	0·0038	0·0052			5		
		6	·0776	·0775	·0650	·0657	·0481	·0499	·0301	·0335	—		6		
		7	·1948	·1968	·1804	·1827	·1588	·1618	·1317	·1358	0·0511	0·0616	7		
	$a \geqslant a_1$	11	0·1970	0·1968	0·1814	0·1827	0·1587	0·1618	0·1317	0·1358	0·0578	0·0616	11	$a \geqslant a_1$	
		12	·0734	·0775	·0614	·0657	·0458	·0499	·0301	·0335	·0036	·0051	12		
		13	·0188	·0233	·0138	·0173	·0082	·0106	·0038	·0052	—		13		
		14	·0029	·0053	·0018	·0033	·0008	·0015					14		
10	$a \leqslant a_1$	2	0·0088	0·0089	0·0067	0·0071	0·0045	0·0050	0·0026	0·0033	0·0004	0·0009	2	$a \leqslant a_1$	10
		3	·0457	·0453	·0395	·0398	·0318	·0329	·0241	·0260	·0099	·0131	3		
		4	·1538	·1549	·1447	·1464	·1322	·1348	·1182	·1218	·0849	·0910	4		
	$a \geqslant a_1$	8	0·1539	0·1549	0·1442	0·1464	0·1311	0·1348	0·1170	0·1218	0·0849	0·0910	8	$a \geqslant a_1$	
		9	·0386	·0453	·0334	·0398	·0270	·0329	·0209	·0260	·0099	·0131	9		
		10	·0044	·0089	·0034	·0071	·0023	·0050	·0015	·0033	·0004	·0009	10		
7	$a \leqslant a_1$	0	0·0012	0·0022	0·0009	0·0013	0·0006	0·0010	0·0004	0·0007			0	$a \leqslant a_1$	7
		1	·0156	·0189	·0134	·0140	·0109	·0118	·0086	·0097	0·0044	0·0059	1		
		2	·0884	·0956	·0827	·0832	·0756	·0770	·0681	·0704	·0521	·0564	2		
	$a \geqslant a_1$	6	0·1492	0·1587	0·1426	0·1450	0·1341	0·1378	0·1250	0·1300	0·1056	0·1127	6	$a \geqslant a_1$	
		7	·0241	·0385	·0216	·0306	·0186	·0269	·0156	·0232	·0102	0·0160	7		
5	$a \leqslant a_1$	0	0·0088	0·0099	0·0078	0·0090	0·0066	0·0080	0·0056	0·0070	0·0036	0·0051	0	$a \leqslant a_1$	5
		1	·0816	·0811	·0778	·0781	·0730	·0742	·0681	·0701	·0578	·0616	1		
	$a \geqslant a_1$	5	0·0725	0·0811	0·0690	0·0781	0·0646	0·0742	0·0601	0·0701	0·0511	0·0616	5	$a \geqslant a_1$	

Table 9 (*continued*)

(B) $m = \frac{4}{5}N,\ n = \frac{1}{5}N$

Partition			$m = 80, n = 20$		$m = 48, n = 12$		$m = 32, n = 8$	
r	Chance that	a_1	True	Normal approx.	True	Normal approx.	True	Normal approx.
30	$a \leqslant a_1$	18	0·0018	0·0014				
		19	·0084	·0073	0·0013	0·0020		
		20	·0306	·0288	·0106	·0125		
		21	·0884	·0874	·0521	·0548		
		22	·2046	·2078	·1667	·1685		
	$a \geqslant a_1$	26	0·2092	0·2078	0·1667	0·1685		
		27	·0824	·0874	·0521	·0548		
		28	·0227	·0288	·0106	·0125		
		29	·0039	·0073	·0013	·0020		
		30	·0003	·0014				
20	$a \leqslant a_1$	11	0·0040	0·0026	0·0013	0·0011	—	
		12	·0182	·0148	·0095	·0087	0·0016	0·0031
		13	·0638	·0600	·0460	·0448	·0218	·0255
		14	·1729	·1755	·1523	·1542	·1176	·1208
	$a \geqslant a_1$	18	0·1758	0·1755	0·1522	0·1542	0·1176	0·1208
		19	·0499	·0600	·0371	·0448	·0218	·0255
		20	·0066	·0148	·0041	·0087	·0016	·0031
15	$a \leqslant a_1$	7	0·0018	0·0009	0·0008	0·0004		
		8	·0107	·0074	·0064	·0049	0·0022	0·0024
		9	·0462	·0408	·0355	·0323	·0217	·0219
		10	·1470	·1480	·1329	·1338	·1115	·1133
	$a \geqslant a_1$	14	0·1453	0·1480	0·1294	0·1338	0·1079	0·1133
		15	·0262	·0408	·0206	·0323	·0141	·0219
10	$a \leqslant a_1$	4	0·0039	0·0019	0·0026	0·0013	0·0012	0·0008
		5	·0254	·0191	·0206	·0159	·0145	·0121
		6	·1095	·1068	·1012	·0988	·0893	·0882
	$a \geqslant a_1$	10	0·0951	0·1068	0·0868	0·0988	0·0761	0·0882
7	$a \leqslant a_1$	2	0·0033	0·0013	0·0024	0·0010	0·0015	0·0007
		3	·0282	·0203	·0246	·0181	·0201	·0155
		4	·1408	·1417	·1354	·1364	·1281	·1293
	$a \geqslant a_1$	7	0·1985	0·1910	0·1906	0·1848	0·1805	0·1776
5	$a \leqslant a_1$	1	0·0053	0·0022	0·0045	0·0021	0·0035	0·0016
		2	·0531	·0434	·0499	·0430	·0457	·0383
	$a \geqslant a_1$	5	0·3193	0·2841	0·3135	0·2835	0·3060	0·2776

(C) $m = \frac{9}{10}N,\ n = \frac{1}{10}N$

Partition			$m = 90, n = 10$	
r	Chance that	a_1	True	Normal approx.
30	$a \leqslant a_1$	22	0·0009	0·0006
		23	·0073	·0057
		24	·0388	·0352
		25	·1384	·1388
	$a \geqslant a_1$	29	0·1356	0·1388
		30	·0229	·0352
20	$a \leqslant a_1$	14	0·0039	0·0019
		15	·0254	·0191
		16	·1095	·1068
	$a \geqslant a_1$	20	0·0951	0·1068
15	$a \leqslant a_1$	9	0·0006	0·0001
		10	·0063	·0027
		11	·0408	·0316
		12	·1705	·1765
	$a \geqslant a_1$	15	0·1808	0·1765
10	$a \leqslant a_1$	5	0·0006	0·0001
		6	·0082	·0029
		7	·0600	·0486
		8	·2615	·2902
	$a \geqslant a_1$	10	0·3305	0·2902
7	$a \leqslant a_1$	3	0·0016	0·0003
		4	·0207	·0096
		5	·1442	·1492
	$a \geqslant a_1$	7	0·4667	0·3974
5	$a \leqslant a_1$	2	0·0067	0·0006
		3	·0769	·0538
	$a \geqslant a_1$	5	0·4163	0·5000

2×2 TABLES. A NOTE ON E. S. PEARSON'S PAPER

By G. A. BARNARD

As Prof. Pearson has kindly shown me the proof of his paper, I should like to make the following further remarks.

1. If we have a sample of N from a population in which there is a chance p that an individual will have a character A, we can represent it in the form

$$x_1, x_2, \ldots, x_i, \ldots, x_N,$$

where x_i is 1 or 0 according as to whether the ith member has A or not.* Regarding the x's as quantitative variables, we have by classical results the unbiased estimates

$$\hat{p} = x. = (\Sigma x_i)/N \quad \text{and} \quad \hat{\sigma}^2 = (\Sigma(x_i - x.)^2)/(N-1).$$

If r of the x's are 1, while s are 0, we find

$$\hat{p} = r/N \quad \text{and} \quad \hat{\sigma}^2 = rs/N(N-1).$$

Using this unbiased estimate of variance in Prof. Pearson's para. 43, we get, instead of his (28·2),

$$\frac{d}{s_d} = \frac{a - rm/N}{\sqrt{\dfrac{mnrs}{N^2(N-1)}}}, \tag{1}$$

agreeing exactly with his (22).

2. To carry the argument further, in classical theory, if we have two samples

$$(x_1, x_2, \ldots, x_i, \ldots, x_m) \quad \text{and} \quad (y_1, y_2, \ldots, y_j, \ldots, y_n)$$

to test whether the samples come from the same normal population we take

$$t = \frac{x. - y.}{s} \sqrt{\frac{mn}{m+n}},$$

where $x. = (\Sigma x_i)/m, y. = (\Sigma y_j)/n$, and

$$s^2 = \frac{\Sigma(x_i - x.)^2 + \Sigma(y_j - y.)^2}{m+n-2}, \tag{2}$$

and use tables of the t distribution for $(m+n-2)$ degrees of freedom.

It is common practice to neglect departures from normality in applying this test. If we do so, and apply it to our qualitative case along the lines indicated above, we get

$$t = \frac{a - rm/N}{\sqrt{\dfrac{acn + bdm}{N(N-2)}}},$$

which, if we are justified in our neglect of departures from normality, should be distributed as t on $(N-2)$ degrees of freedom.

* For a similar argument see B. L. Welch (1938, p. 155).

3. To obtain the formula (1) on these lines, we have in effect to commit the well-known fallacy of replacing s^2 as given by (2), by

$$s'^2 = \frac{\Sigma(x_i - m')^2 + \Sigma(y_j - m')^2}{m+n-1}, \tag{3}$$

where $$m' = (\Sigma x_i + \Sigma y_j)/(m+n).$$

We are led to ask why (3) should be approximately correct (and in fact it is better than (2)) in the qualitative case, while (2) is preferred in the quantitative case.

4. The simplest reason for preferring (2) to (3) in the quantitative case is that s'^2 is not independent of $(x. - y.)$, so that the conditions for validity of the t distribution are not satisfied. In our qualitative case this argument loses validity, since neither s^2 nor s'^2 is independent of $(x. - y.)$.

The second reason for preferring (2) to (3) in the quantitative case is more complicated, but for our purposes it reduces essentially to the fact that, in the case of normal distributions, and *only in this case*, the mean and variance of samples are independently distributed, so that the common mean value of the populations, estimated by m', is irrelevant to the test for differences. In our qualitative case, on the other hand, m' contributes to our knowledge of the variance.

5. If we apply Pitman's 'absolute' analogue of the t test to our case, we arrive at the hypergeometric series of Prof. Pearson's Problem I. But Bartlett's argument, showing the convergence of Pitman's test and the t test, will apply here only in very large samples, because of the finite probability of obtaining observed values which coincide.

6. From the above point of view, Prof. Pearson's analysis of his Problem II may be regarded in one sense as an examination of the effect of large departures from normality on the t test. In this light, his conclusions given in paras. 51 and 52 are seen to extend to the t test, as well as to the 2×2 table problem.

7. If I may state my personal attitude, it is that statistics is a branch of applied mathematics, like symbolic logic or hydrodynamics. Examination of foundations is desirable, but it must be remembered that undue emphasis on niceties is a disease to which persons with mathematical training are specially prone. In pure mathematics itself there are disputes on foundations which closely parallel the disputes over the foundations of statistics. The lesson to be drawn is, that while statistics is a most valuable aid to judgement, it cannot wholly replace it.

8. Finally, it must be emphasized that the order of printing of Prof. Pearson's paper and my own reflects Prof. Pearson's generosity rather than the historical order of events. Much of his paper was, unknown to me, given in lectures before the war; whereas my work on the problem began only in 1943. Since then I have owed much both to Prof. Pearson's published work and to discussions which I have been privileged to have with him.

REFERENCE

WELCH, B. L. (1938). *Biometrika*, **30**, 155.

2×2 TABLES; THE POWER FUNCTION OF THE TEST ON A RANDOMIZED EXPERIMENT

By E. S. PEARSON and MAXINE MERRINGTON

1. Introductory

In his discussion of significance tests for 2×2 tables, Barnard (1947) has pointed out how data classified in the form of Table 1 may appear as the outcome of a number of different types of investigation. Differences in point of view which have been expressed regarding the handling of the figures, concern the probability constructs by aid of which the bare numerical data recorded in the table provide a basis for inference. Two lines of approach may be distinguished.

Table 1

	Col. 1	Col. 2	Total
Row 1	a	c	m
Row 2	b	d	n
Total	r	s	N

Following the first, it is considered that for all the types of problem,* the relevant information on the points at issue may be obtained by comparing the observed pattern of cell contents (a, b, c, d) with the set of possible patterns, all giving the marginal totals actually found in the sample. Thus there is only one degree of freedom among the four cell frequencies, and the relevant probability distribution is obtained from the hypergeometric series. This approach can be derived from Fisher's information theory. But without using this theory, a may be referred to the one-dimensioned, conditional set as a convenient practical device, which avoids the introduction of nuisance parameters.

From the point of view of the second approach it is an over-simplification to treat every case providing data in the form of Table 1 as a problem of sampling with fixed marginal totals. It is suggested that the readiness of the mind to assimilate the information provided by the statistical analysis depends on the directness of the relation between the theoretical probability set and the random process of selection introduced in collecting the data. Since the random procedure may have entered in different ways, the appropriate probability constructs may be expected to differ.

It can be argued that, except in the case of small samples, the difference of approach is practically unimportant, and that even here, until tables of the kind which Barnard has in mind are available, the statistician will be forced to draw his conclusions from a table of the conditional distribution, such as that recently prepared by Finney (1948). But there is another aspect to the matter. The published discussion has hitherto been concerned primarily with the sampling distribution of a statistic under the null hypothesis. If we go beyond this

* Three types were discussed by Barnard (1947) and Pearson (1947).

and consider the sensitivity of the test, that is to say, its power to detect differences if they exist, it is at once clear that all problems cannot be treated in the same manner.

In a recent paper, Patnaik (1948) has considered this aspect of what one of us (Pearson, 1947) has termed Problem II and of what Barnard termed the 2×2 comparative trial. This occurs when we inquire whether the probability of an individual bearing a given character A, is the same in two large populations from which random samples of size m and n, respectively, have been drawn. Here, two separate random selections are involved, and the cell contents may be described as having two degrees of freedom. If the two population probabilities are unequal, i.e. $p_1(A) \neq p_2(A)$, the chance that the test will establish a difference at a given significance level α is a function of p_1 and p_2, of m and n and of α. This relationship was explored by Patnaik.

In the present paper we shall consider what Pearson termed Problem I and Barnard the 2×2 independence trial, from this aspect of the power of the test. In this case, only a single process of random selection or partition is called for.

2. Statement of the Problem

For convenience we shall describe the type of experiment we have in mind as one in which two 'treatments', say A and B, are compared; the response is a quantal one, so that an individual either 'reacts' or 'fails to react'. The applications suggested by these terms lie in the biological field, but there is no difficulty in translating the terms of the theoretical picture to fit a case where, for example, the individual is a shell, the two treatments are two types of fuze and the reaction is successful perforation of a steel plate.

In this Problem I, the N individuals available for experiment are divided by a random partition into a group of m which receive treatment A, and a group of $n = N - m$ which receive treatment B. It is then observed that a/m and b/n react in the specified manner. The experiment is self-contained and the random process under complete control; but without further assumptions or knowledge, the inferences that are possible relate only to the reactions of the N individuals to the treatments. This may be all that is called for. Inferences of wider application may be drawn by assuming that the N have been sampled randomly from a population in which we are interested. Or, as is often the case, the experiment may be one of a related series, each experiment in which is self-contained. These, taken as a whole, can form the basis of reasoned conclusions regarding the treatments, conclusions which are not dependent on all groups of individuals having been drawn randomly from a unique population in the rigorous statistical sense. This is the case if the tests are applied to laboratory animals whose susceptibility may change somewhat from time to time. Or, as Barnard has suggested, when an open-air gunnery trial runs over several days of inconstant weather.

The question then is this: confining attention to the group of N individuals, in what sense is it possible to interpret a difference in treatments and how can we measure the power of the test to detect such a difference? Perhaps the most general method of regarding the problem is to suppose that the N individuals fall into four classes:

(i) those who would react if given either treatment, X in number;
(ii) those who would react only if given treatment A, W in number;
(iii) those who would react only if given treatment B, Y in number;
(iv) those who would react to neither treatment, Z in number.

In this way we recognize that every individual does not respond in the same way to a given treatment; that the success of a shell in perforating a plate will depend not only on the fuzing, but on other factors such as strength of shell-case, angle of yaw on striking, the position of the strike on the plate, etc. These latter factors are purposely randomly associated with the two types of fuze under trial.

If m individuals are selected randomly and assigned treatment A and the remaining n assigned treatment B, the resulting partition will be that shown in Table 2a; as, however, we can only observe whether an individual has reacted or not, the figures available for analysis will be in the form of Table 2b.

Table 2a

	React if given A or B	Only react if given A	Only react if given B	React to neither treatment	Total
Treatment A	x_1	w_1	y_1	z_1	m
Treatment B	x_2	w_2	y_2	z_2	n
Total	X	W	Y	Z	N

Table 2b

	React	Fail to react	Total
Treatment A	$x_1+w_1=a$	$y_1+z_1=c$	m
Treatment B	$x_2+y_2=b$	$w_2+z_2=d$	n
Total	$X+w_1+y_2=r$	$Z+w_2+y_1=s$	N

The usual null hypothesis is that the treatments are identical as far as producing a reaction on these N individuals is concerned, i.e. it is the hypothesis that $W = Y = 0$. The test of significance of departure from hypothesis would be applied to the 2×2 Table 2b, and in its exact form consists in referring $a = x_1+w_1$ to the appropriate hypergeometric distribution, with parameters r, N and m. Here, if the sample is not too large, Finney's (1948) table is applicable. More approximately, we can either regard

$$\frac{a-rm/N}{\sqrt{\left(\dfrac{mnrs}{N^2(N-1)}\right)}} \quad \text{as a unit normal deviate, or}$$

$$\frac{(ad-bc)^2N}{mnrs} \quad \text{as a } \chi^2 \text{ with 1 degree of freedom,}$$

making a correction for continuity, if necessary.

It should be noted that if treatment A were regarded as more successful than B when $X+W > X+Y$, then the null hypothesis to test would be that $W-Y=0$. The expectation of the difference $a/m-b/n$ is still zero if $W = Y \neq 0$, but its sampling distribution under random partition can no longer be determined from the marginal totals of Table 2*b*. The experiment as planned is not, in fact, able to distinguish between the cases $W = Y = 0$ and $W-Y=0$; to do so would involve applying both treatments to the same individuals, which will usually be impossible in practice.

Table 3*a*

	React if given A or B	React if given B	React to neither treatment	Total
Treatment A	x_1	y_1	z_1	m
Treatment B	x_2	y_2	z_2	n
Total	X	Y	Z	N

Table 3*b*

	React	Fail to react	Total
Treatment A	$x_1 = a$	$y_1+z_1 = c$	m
Treatment B	$x_2+y_2 = b$	$z_2 = d$	n
Total	$X+y_2 = r$	$Z+y_1 = s$	N

In the discussion which follows we shall suppose that $W = 0$. This may narrow the field of application, but not too seriously. If A is an old treatment and B a new one which it is hoped is an improvement,* we are assuming that B has at least the qualities of A. Thus if B aims at the cure of a disease and A is a control corresponding to 'no treatment', we assume that in no case will B *prevent* a recovery which would have taken place without any treatment at all. With $W = 0$, we have the scheme of Tables 3*a* and *b*. In this case the null hypothesis is that $Y = 0$; the alternative that interests us is that $Y > 0$, so that the statistical test applied to Table 3*b* involves comparing the observed value of a with its lower significance level, or b with its upper level. This critical limit for a may be written $a(\alpha, r, N, m)$, where α is the chance of falling at or below the limit if $Y = 0$. It can be determined either precisely from the hypergeometric or from the normal approximation. If the null hypothesis is not true, $r = X+y_2$ will vary from one random partition to another. Thus the problem is to determine the probability that, when $Y \neq 0$, $a \leqslant a(\alpha, r, N, m)$, where both a and r are random variables.

* For purposes of discussion, we take 'reaction' to be good.

A numerical illustration will help to make the position clear. Thirty small disks were placed in a box, of which $X = 10$ were coloured red, $Y = 10$ coloured green and $Z = 10$ coloured yellow. The disks were divided randomly into two groups A and B each containing $m = n = 15$. In terms of treatment comparisons, reds 'respond to treatment' if they fall into group A, reds and greens if they fall into group B. Four of many possible partitions are shown in the 2×3 tables of row I below; under these are given in row II the corresponding 2×2 tables which contain the numerical data available to the experimenter. He cannot distinguish between greens and yellows in group A or between reds and greens in group B. The null hypothesis is that there were no green disks in the box of 30. Below the 2×2 tables are shown (III) the critical limits corresponding to a nominal 5 % significance level, (IV) the true level or sum of the tail terms and (V) the conclusion that would be drawn. It may be noted that this experimental partition was repeated 50 times and that significance was established, i.e. the presence of green disks inferred, in 20 of these partitions. This is a result which, as will be shown below, agrees closely with expectation.

	Colour ...	R. G. Y.		R. G. Y.		R. G. Y.		R. G. Y.	
I	A	3 6 6	15	5 5 5	15	5 4 6	15	7 3 5	15
	B	7 4 4	15	5 5 5	15	5 6 4	15	3 7 5	15
		10 10 10	30	10 10 10	30	10 10 10	30	10 10 10	30
II		3 12	15	5 10	15	5 10	15	7 8	15
		11 4	15	10 5	15	11 4	15	10 5	15
		14 16	30	15 15	30	16 14	30	17 13	30
III	Rejection level, given r	$a_0 = 4$		$a_0 = 4$		$a_0 = 5$		$a_0 = 5$	
IV	$P\{a \leqslant a_0 \mid r\}$	0·0328		0·0134		0·0328		0·0127	
V	Significant	Yes		No		Yes		No	

The probability that $a \leqslant a(\alpha, r, N, m)$ when $Y \neq 0$ represents the power of the test in the sense of Neyman & Pearson, i.e. the probability of establishing significance at the 100α % level when $Y > 0$. It will be a function not only of Y but of X (or Z). Owing to discontinuity in the distribution of a, it is, of course, impossible to choose $a(\alpha, r, N, m)$ with the same value of α for all r. In our calculations given below we have used what may be termed nominal 5 and 15 % levels, such that the critical limits $a(\alpha, r, N, m)$ are the highest integer values satisfying the inequalities

$$P\{a \leqslant a(\alpha, r, N, m)\} \leqslant \alpha \quad (\alpha = 0{\cdot}05 \text{ and } 0{\cdot}15). \tag{1}$$

We have taken $m = n = \frac{1}{2}N$, supposing that each treatment is given to the same number of individuals. This will usually be the case in a planned experiment with randomization, and as our object is to illustrate certain points which we believe are of general interest, no exhaustive tabulation is called for.

The method of calculation leading to Figs. 2–7 is described in the following section and a discussion of results is given in § 4.

3. Method of Calculation

In a 2×3 table of fixed margins, there are two degrees of freedom. We shall take as independent variables x_1 and y_1. The probability of a particular partition of Table 3*a* is

$$p(x_1, y_1) = \frac{m!\,n!\,X!\,Y!\,Z!}{x_1!\,x_2!\,y_1!\,y_2!\,z_1!\,z_2!\,N!}, \tag{2}$$

where x_2, y_2, z_1 and z_2 can all be expressed in terms of x_1, y_1 and the marginal totals. For mathematical convenience we may regard the partition of Table 3*a* as obtained in two steps, the first determining y_1, the second x_1. In fact, the expression (2) may be written as a product of two parts

$$\frac{m!\,n!\,Y!\,(N-Y)!}{y_1!\,y_2!\,(m-y_1)!\,(n-y_2)!\,N!} \times \frac{X!\,Z!\,(x_1+z_1)!\,(x_2+z_2)!}{x_1!\,x_2!\,z_1!\,z_2!\,(X+Z)!}. \tag{3}$$

The first factor, say $p(y_1)$, is the probability of obtaining y_1 individuals with a character A in a sample of Y drawn randomly, without replacement, from a population of N individuals of whom m have a character A. The second factor, say $p(x_1 \mid y_1)$, is the probability of obtaining x_1 with A in a sample of X drawn, without replacement, from the remaining $N-Y$ individuals, of whom $m-y_1$ now have A. Thus

$$p(x_1 y_1) = p(y_1) \times p(x_1 \mid y_1), \tag{4}$$

and while $p(y_1)$ is the marginal distribution for y_1 of the joint distribution $p(x_1 y_1)$, $p(x_1 \mid y_1)$ is the relative probability distribution of x_1 in the array of constant y_1. Both $p(y_1)$ and $p(x_1 \mid y_1)$ are of hypergeometric type; the joint distribution has been discussed by K. Pearson (1924) who termed it a double hypergeometric series and considered how it might lead to a frequency surface.* He gave some of the momental constants of $p(x_1 \mid y_1)$ which we shall use below; in our present notation, and for the special case $m = n = \tfrac{1}{2}N$, these become

$$\text{Mean } (x_1 \mid y_1) = Xp, \tag{5}$$

$$\text{Variance } (x_1 \mid y_1) = Xpq\frac{Z}{X+Z-1}, \tag{6}$$

$$\beta_1(x_1 \mid y_1) = \frac{(p-q)^2}{Xpq}\frac{\{1-2(X-1)/(X+Z-2)\}^2}{1-(X-1)/(X+Z-1)}, \tag{7}$$

where

$$p = 1-q = (m-y_1)/(N-Y) = (x_1+z_1)/(X+Z). \tag{8}$$

The distribution $p(x_1 y_1)$ is bounded by certain limiting lines, thus:

$$x_1 \leqslant X, \quad y_1 \leqslant Y, \quad m \geqslant x_1 + y_1 \geqslant m - Z. \tag{9}$$

Fig. 1 illustrates the position for the case

$$X = 10, \quad Y = 15, \quad Z = 5, \quad m = n = \tfrac{1}{2}N = 15. \tag{10}$$

In applying the test of significance to the 2×2 Table 3*b*, we shall reject the null hypothesis ($Y = 0$) when

$$x_1 = a \leqslant a(\alpha, r, N, m). \tag{11}$$

But

$$r = X + y_2 = X + Y - y_1. \tag{12}$$

Hence for given X and Y there will be a critical limit in each y_1 array, such that if x_1 fall below the limit, the hypothesis will be rejected. For the marginal values given in (10),

* He had illustrated the distribution many years before (K. Pearson, 1895) in connexion with the correlation between the number of cards of a given suit held by two players at whist.

Fig. 1 shows these rejection limits as a connected line for the nominal level $\alpha = 0{\cdot}05$.* The power of the test for a given X and Y is then the sum of the probabilities $p(x_1 y_1)$ taken over the points of the field outside (or below) this critical boundary. Fig. 4 shows that for this particular case the sum is about 0·85.

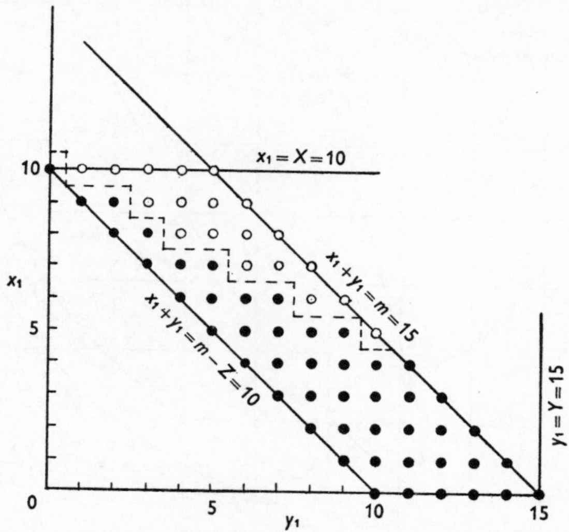

Fig. 1. Illustration for case of partition of 30 individuals into two groups, $m = n = \frac{1}{2}N = 15$; $X = 10$, $Y = 15$, $Z = 5$; nominal significance level, $\alpha = 0{\cdot}05$. The null hypothesis will be rejected at the (x_1, y_1) points marked ●, where $x_1 = a$, $y_1 = 25 - r$.

For small samples the calculations are not very tedious if undertaken systematically, but they become so when N is large. In the case $N = 50$ we have therefore used an approximation based on assuming that the array distributions $p(x_1 \mid y_1)$ can be represented by normal curves with the means and variances of equations (5) and (6). Since, using (8), when $m = \frac{1}{2}N$,

$$q - p = (2y_1 - Y)/(N - Y),$$

where the expectation of y_1 is $\frac{1}{2}Y$, it follows that the β_1 of the array distributions which contain most of the frequency will be small provided that neither X or Z are too small. The accuracy of this normal approximation is illustrated below.

The calculations on which Figs. 2–7 have been based may be summarized as follows:

(i) $N = 20$ *and* 30

Full calculations of the terms of the hypergeometric series

$$\frac{(m!)^2 r!(N-r)!}{a!b!c!d!N!}$$

were made for all values of r, and hence the levels corresponding to the nominal $\alpha = 0{\cdot}05$ and 0·15 were found. This determined the position of the boundary of the critical region as illustrated in Fig. 1 and also provided the terms of the series $p(y_1)$. The expressions $p(x_1 y_1)$ corresponding to points in the critical region were then found and summed for selected values of X, Y and Z, giving the ordinates of the power curves drawn in Figs. 2–5.

* These limits will be found to agree with those in Finney's (1948) table. The relevant section is that for $A = 15 = B$ (in his notation); further, since he takes $a > b$ his (i) a and (ii) b correspond to our (i) $25 - (x_1 + y_1)$ and (ii) x_1. See Appendix, p. 345 below. For example, points in Fig. 1 on the diagonal $x_1 + y_1 = 12$ make Finney's $a = 13$ and for this value he gives the 5 % significance level as $b = 7$; thus all points on this diagonal for which $x_1 \leqslant 7$ fall in the rejection region.

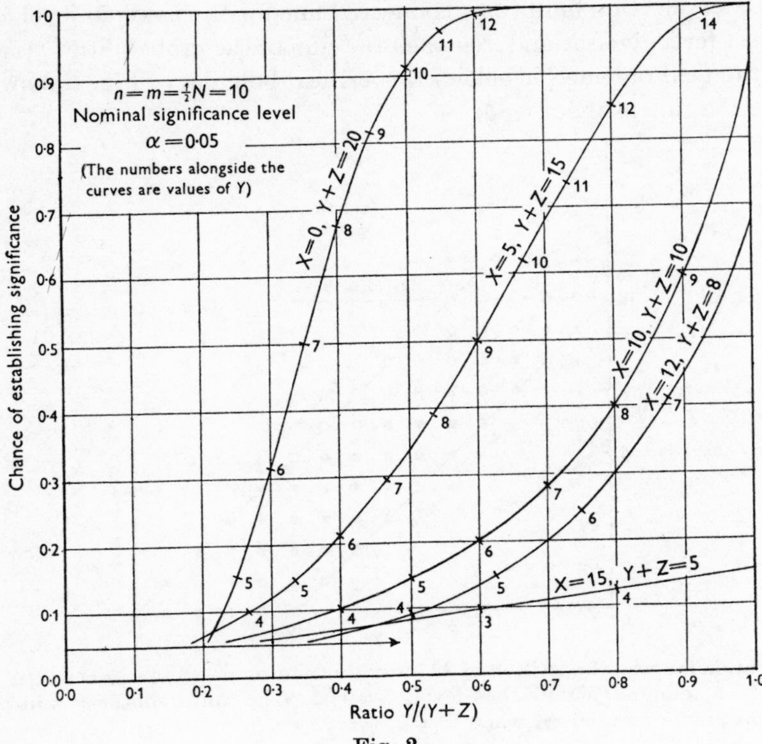
$n=m=\frac{1}{2}N=10$
Nominal significance level
$\alpha=0{\cdot}05$
(The numbers alongside the curves are values of Y)
X=0, Y+Z=20
X=5, Y+Z=15
X=10, Y+Z=10
X=12, Y+Z=8
X=15, Y+Z=5
Chance of establishing significance
Ratio Y/(Y+Z)

Fig. 2

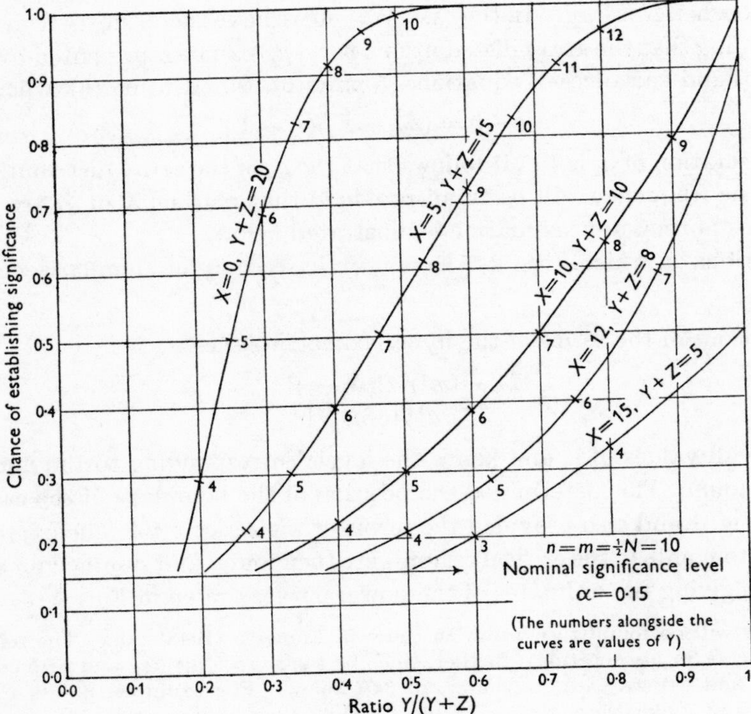
X=0, Y+Z=20
X=5, Y+Z=15
X=10, Y+Z=10
X=12, Y+Z=8
X=15, Y+Z=5
$n=m=\frac{1}{2}N=10$
Nominal significance level
$\alpha=0{\cdot}15$
(The numbers alongside the curves are values of Y)
Chance of establishing significance
Ratio Y/(Y+Z)

Fig. 3

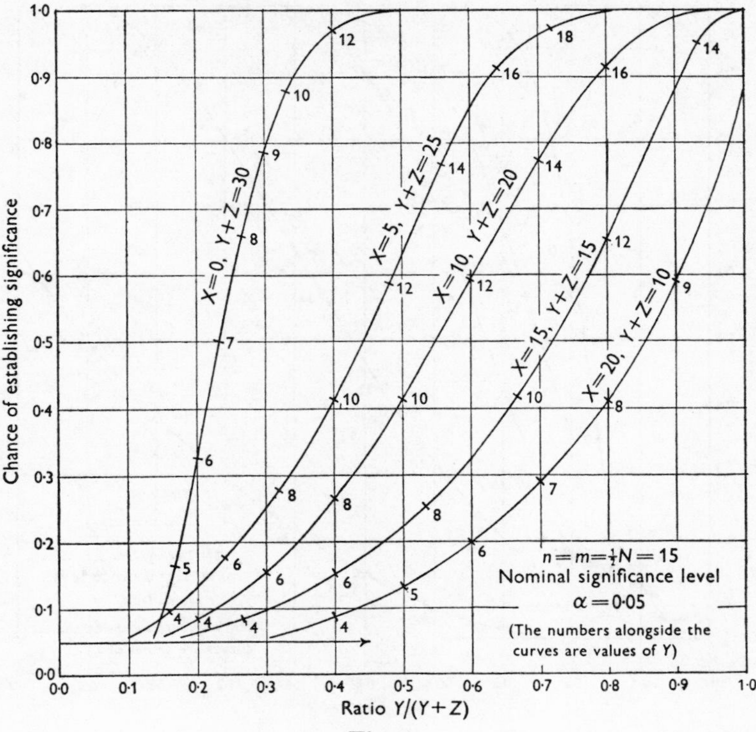

Chance of establishing significance
Ratio $Y/(Y+Z)$
$X=0,\ Y+Z=30$
$X=5,\ Y+Z=25$
$X=10,\ Y+Z=20$
$X=15,\ Y+Z=15$
$X=20,\ Y+Z=10$
$n=m=\frac{1}{2}N=15$
Nominal significance level
$\alpha=0{\cdot}05$
(The numbers alongside the curves are values of Y)

Fig. 4

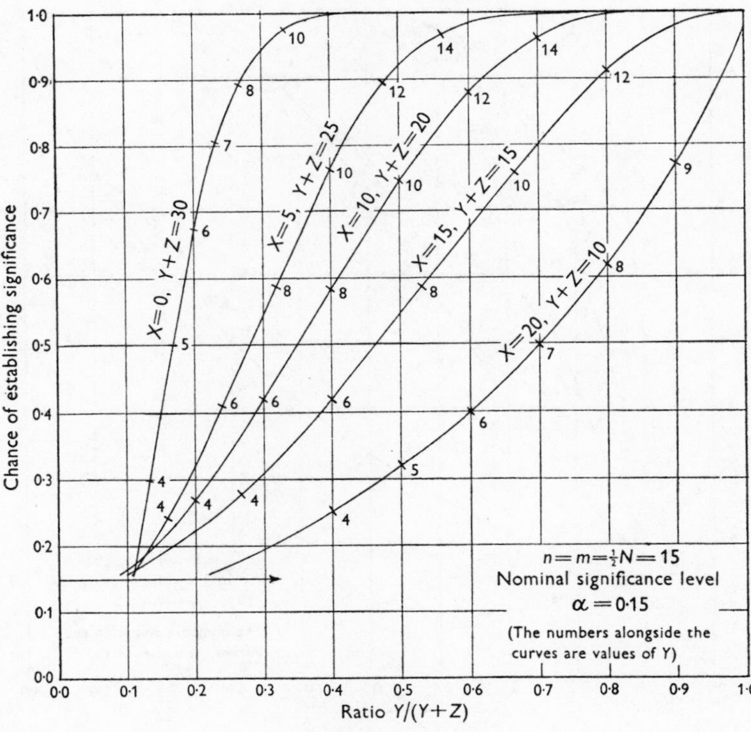

Chance of establishing significance
Ratio $Y/(Y+Z)$
$X=0,\ Y+Z=30$
$X=5,\ Y+Z=25$
$X=10,\ Y+Z=20$
$X=15,\ Y+Z=15$
$X=20,\ Y+Z=10$
$n=m=\frac{1}{2}N=15$
Nominal significance level
$\alpha=0{\cdot}15$
(The numbers alongside the curves are values of Y)

Fig. 5

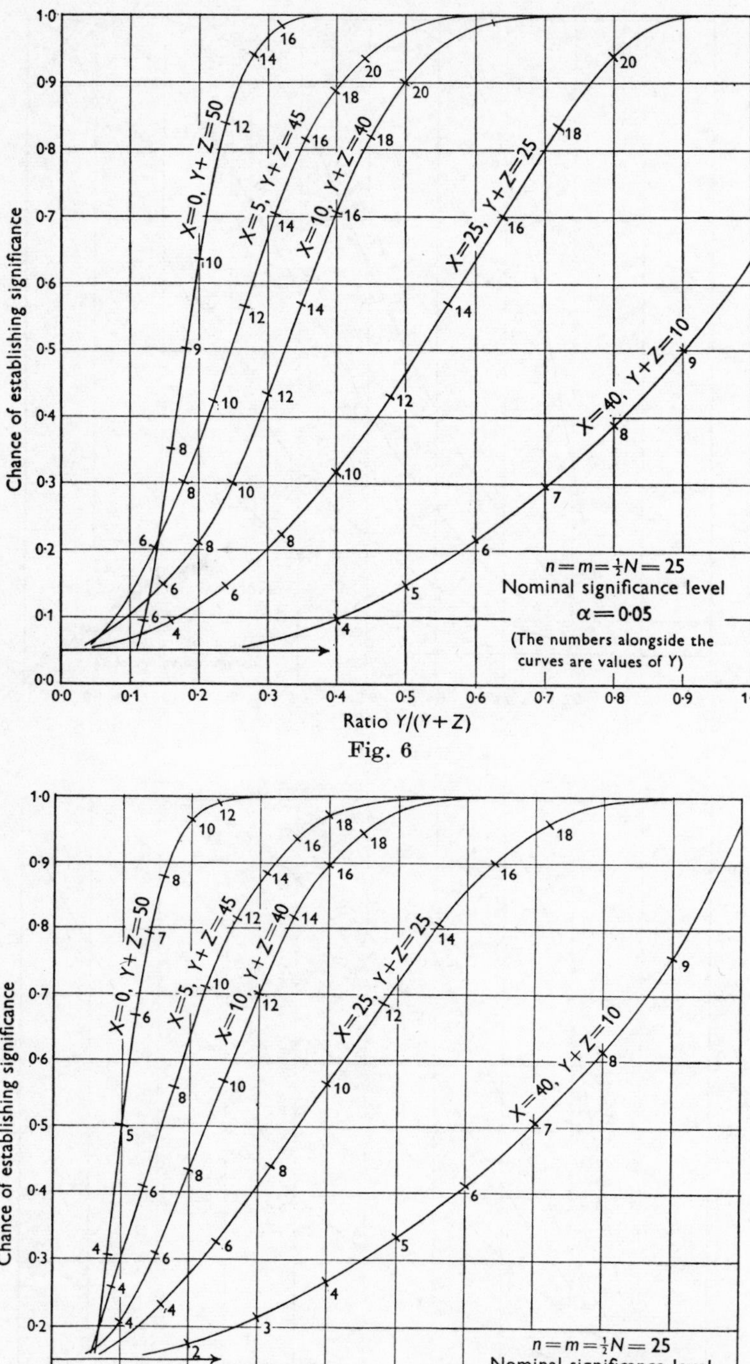
Chance of establishing significance
Ratio Y/(Y+Z)
X=0, Y+Z=50
X=5, Y+Z=45
X=10, Y+Z=40
X=25, Y+Z=25
X=40, Y+Z=10
n=m=½N=25
Nominal significance level
α=0·05
(The numbers alongside the curves are values of Y)

Fig. 6

Chance of establishing significance
Ratio Y/(Y+Z)
X=0, Y+Z=50
X=5, Y+Z=45
X=10, Y+Z=40
X=25, Y+Z=25
X=40, Y+Z=10
n=m=½N=25
Nominal significance level
α=0·15
(The numbers alongside the curves are values of Y)

Fig. 7

(ii) *Check for* $N = 30$

For a number of cases the normal approximation referred to above was also used. This involved finding for each array the integral under the normal curve with mean and variance, (5) and (6), beyond the point $a(\alpha, r, N, m) + 0{\cdot}5$, using a correction for continuity. These integrals were multiplied by the corresponding exact value of $p(y_1)$ and summed for all arrays. A comparison of exact and approximate results is shown in Table 4. From our present point of view the agreement may be regarded as good.

Table 4. *Approximate solution for power function. Case* $m = n = \frac{1}{2}N = 15$

X	Y	$\alpha = 0{\cdot}05$		$\alpha = 0{\cdot}15$	
		True power	Approx.	True power	Approx.
5	2	0·047	0·053	0·121	0·126
	5	·135	·139	·321	·324
	10	·413	·414	·764	·758
	15	·852	·844	·984	·979
	20	·999	·997	1·000	·999
10	2	0·039	0·043	0·166	0·170
	6	·155	·161	·420	·421
	10	·413	·415	·745	·740
	14	·773	·767	·962	·956
	18	·989	·989	1·000	1·000
15	1	0·033	0·036	0·136	0·140
	3	·064	·067	·224	·227
	6	·152	·157	·419	·420
	9	·326	·329	·676	·673
	12	·655	·651	·913	·908
	14	·951	·948	·990	·989

(iii) $N = 50$

Encouraged by the check for $N = 30$, the approximate method was employed throughout in this case, a few checks only being made by the full method, which now becomes rather laborious. The resulting power curves are shown in Figs. 6 and 7.

As N increases above 50, it is probable that further simplifying approximations could be introduced, but these we have not explored. It would also be possible to form diagrams giving contours of constant power, similar to those provided by Patnaik (1948) in his Figs. 2 and 3, for the case where samples are drawn independently from two populations. The parameters corresponding to his p_1 and p_2 would now seem to be X/N and $(X+Y)/N$, the proportion of individuals among the N who would respond to treatments A and B, respectively. A preliminary examination on the basis of the results used to form Figs. 2–7, suggests that the contours corresponding to various values of N, α and the power, may all belong approximately to a single family of curves, as was the case in Patnaik's problem, for $m = n$.

4. Discussion

In the first place some comment is necessary on the significance levels chosen. Owing to the discontinuity which occurs because the cell contents can assume integer values only, the standard levels of 10, 5, 1 %, etc., have not their ordinary meaning. As an example, take the case where $m = n = \frac{1}{2}N = 25$, $r = 16$. On the null hypothesis we have:

$$\begin{aligned} \text{Chance that } a \leqslant 6 &\text{ is } 0{\cdot}182. \\ \leqslant 5 &\text{ is } 0{\cdot}064, \\ \leqslant 4 &\text{ is } 0{\cdot}016, \\ \leqslant 3 &\text{ is } 0{\cdot}003. \end{aligned}$$

Thus if we wish to accept *no more than* a 1 in 20 risk of rejecting the hypothesis when it is true, we should only do so when $a \leqslant 4$. But in practice, if prepared to accept a risk of *about* 1 in 20, we should clearly take $a = 5$ as the limit. Similarly, we should take $a = 4$ for a risk of *about* 1 in 100. Thus we should tend to base our conclusions on the actual tail sum found after the data are collected. But if we use the power function concept to inquire *in advance* how large N must be to make an experiment worth while, then we must think in terms of a specific upper limit or nominal level α. Hence it is important to know how much on the average the true level falls short of the nominal. Table 5 has been prepared to indicate this difference in the cases with $N = 20$, 30 and 50 and for nominal levels of $\alpha = 0{\cdot}05$ and $0{\cdot}15$. Finney's (1948) table also brings this out.*

These upper limit values are well on the safe side, and this may be what is wanted if we attach prime importance to Neyman & Pearson's first kind of error; i.e. to the risk of assuming a difference when none exists. But where it is of first importance to find a new solution, e.g. an improvement in treatment, higher risks in this direction will be accepted in order to avoid the chance of falling into the second kind of error, i.e. of overlooking a real difference when it exists. For this reason our calculations have been made for $\alpha = 0{\cdot}05$ and also for the rather high value $\alpha = 0{\cdot}15$, which, as can be found from Table 5, means on the average† a true level of $\bar{\alpha} = 0{\cdot}057$ for $N = 20$, $\bar{\alpha} = 0{\cdot}082$ for $N = 30$, $\bar{\alpha} = 0{\cdot}089$ for $N = 50$.

Turning to the interpretation of the diagrams, it must be emphasized again that the frequencies X, Y and Z will of course not be known; the purpose of the charts is to show for certain sample sizes, the combinations of these three frequencies needed to give a reasonable chance of establishing a significant treatment difference. If the investigation has the positive objective of establishing the value of new methods, it will naturally be hoped that the comparative experiment will establish statistical significance. If, with the knowledge available, it can be shown that an experiment of given magnitude is very unlikely to lead to a significant result, then it may be a waste of time to proceed on this scale. We think that the results presented in the diagrams will be helpful in this type of review.

If treatment A has already been in use, some information will be available as to the likely value of X/N, the proportion of individuals in a group of N who would react to A. We shall at least know whether it is more likely to be 0 or $\frac{1}{2}$. The ratio $Y/(Y+Z)$ used as the abscissa for the power curves measures the headway which the new treatment B could make in causing a satisfactory response among individuals with whom treatment A fails. Again, the experimenter will generally have some idea of what he hopes the treatment will achieve.

* See Appendix, p. 345 below.

† Giving equal weight to all values of r.

He may know, for example, that $Y/(Y+Z)$ is unlikely to exceed 0·25, and yet be clear that even if it were no larger than this the introduction of B would be amply justified. Here Figs. 4 and 5 show that, for $m = n = 15$, were $X = 0$ (treatment A ineffective*) and $Y/(Y+Z) = 8/30 = 0{\cdot}27$, the chance of establishing significance is about 0·66 at the nominal 5 % level and 0·89 at the nominal 0·15 % level. But if X were 10, or one-third of the group of $N = 30$ were responsive to the old treatment then, though 5 of the remaining 20 would

Table 5. *Showing for the case* $m = n = \frac{1}{2}N$: (i) *the critical limits* $a_0(\alpha, r, N, m)$ *for nominal significance levels* $\alpha = 0{\cdot}05$ *and* 0·15; (ii) *the true chance that* $a \leqslant a_0(\alpha, r, N, m)$

r	$N=20$				$N=30$				$N=50$			
	$\alpha=0{\cdot}05$		$\alpha=0{\cdot}15$		$\alpha=0{\cdot}05$		$\alpha=0{\cdot}15$		$\alpha=0{\cdot}05$		$\alpha=0{\cdot}15$	
	a_0	True chance	a_0	True chance	a_0	True chance	a_0	True chance	a_0	True chance	a_0	True chance
3	—	—	0	0·105	—	—	0	0·112	—	—	0	0·117
4	0	0·043	0	0·043	0	0·050	0	0·050	—	—	0	0·055
5	0	0·016	0	0·016	0	0·021	0	0·021	0	0·025	0	0·025
6	0	0·005	1	0·070	0	0·008	1	0·084	0	0·011	1	0·095
7	1	0·029	1	0·029	1	0·040	1	0·040	1	0·049	1	0·049
8	1	0·010	2	0·085	1	0·018	2	0·107	1	0·024	2	0·123
9	2	0·035	2	0·035	1	0·007	2	0·054	1	0·012	2	0·069
10	2	0·012	3	0·089	2	0·025	3	0·123	2	0·037	3	0·144
11	—	—	—	—	2	0·010	3	0·064	2	0·019	3	0·085
12	—	—	—	—	3	0·030	4	0·132	3	0·048	3	0·048
13	—	—	—	—	3	0·013	4	0·070	3	0·025	4	0·098
14	—	—	—	—	4	0·033	5	0·136	3	0·013	4	0·057
15	—	—	—	—	4	0·013	5	0·071	4	0·031	5	0·108
16	—	—	—	—	—	—	—	—	4	0·016	5	0·064
17	—	—	—	—	—	—	—	—	5	0·038	6	0·119
18	—	—	—	—	—	—	—	—	5	0·021	6	0·072
19	—	—	—	—	—	—	—	—	6	0·042	7	0·124
20	—	—	—	—	—	—	—	—	6	0·023	7	0·077
21	—	—	—	—	—	—	—	—	7	0·044	8	0·128
22	—	—	—	—	—	—	—	—	7	0·024	8	0·079
23	—	—	—	—	—	—	—	—	8	0·046	9	0·131
24	—	—	—	—	—	—	—	—	8	0·025	9	0·081
25	—	—	—	—	—	—	—	—	9	0·046	10	0·131

For $r > \frac{1}{2}N$ the true chance for r is the same as that for $N-r$, while $a_0(\alpha, r, N, m) = r - m + a_0(\alpha, N-r, N, m)$.

react if given treatment B ($Y/(Y+Z) = 0{\cdot}25$), the experiment will most probably be inconclusive. This is because the power of the test is now only 0·12 and 0·34, respectively, at the 5 and 15 % levels.

If we regard $Y/(Y+Z)$ as the measure of effectiveness, the existence of X reduces the chance of establishing significance. We need not express effectiveness in this way, but the numerical data given in the charts associating power with the partition of N in X, Y and Z, makes it possible to express the position in any terms considered more appropriate.

As a further example, we may take the case where out of $N = 30$ individuals, $X = 10$ would react to treatment A and $X + Y = 20$ to treatment B. This might well be regarded

* At least, ineffective on the 30 individuals selected for the experiment.

as an eminently satisfactory result. But Figs. 4 and 5 show that the chance of distinguishing this case from one in which $Y = 0$ is only 0·41 at the 5 % level and 0·74 at the 15 % level.* If now we make a rough interpolation in Figs. 6 and 7 between the power curves for $X = 10$ and $X = 25$, it is seen that using 50 individuals for the experiment, then were $X = Y = 17$ (keeping the same proportions as before) there would be a chance of about 0·76 of establishing significance at the 5 % level and of about 0·92 at the 15 % level. There are likely to be circumstances where, with this knowledge, it would rightly be concluded that while a comparative experiment on two sets of 15 individuals would not be worth undertaking, an experiment using two sets of 25 would be.

Another point which the diagrams bring out is the dilemma which faces the medical research worker who wishes to establish his conclusions on a scientific basis, but has a strong conviction that a new treatment will be effective in reducing pain, hastening recovery or even saving life. Dealing with a hospital population of varying susceptibilities and with other changes in external conditions from time to time, it may be impossible to make comparisons which could be accepted indisputably between (*a*) successes in the past, using treatment A, and (*b*) successes at the moment using treatment B. Yet if a controlled, comparative test is carried out, it is seen that to provide a conclusive result the number of patients in the group Y must be considerable, perhaps 10, 16 or even 20. And yet, on the average, $\frac{1}{2}Y$ of these patients will be assigned the old treatment. Even if the belief in treatment B is based on intuition rather than evidence, considerations of ethics are likely to outweigh the urge to plan an experiment which makes a valid scientific comparison possible.

In conclusion, we freely admit that the presentation given in Figs. 2–7 cannot be regarded as a final one. It does, however, provide enough material for the statistician to consider whether the approach is practically useful and, hence, whether its extension and possible simplification are desirable.

REFERENCES

Barnard, G. A. (1947). *Biometrika*, **34**, 123.
Finney, D. J. (1948). *Biometrika*, **35**, 145.
Patnaik, P. B. (1948). *Biometrika*, **35**, 157.
Pearson, E. S. (1947). *Biometrika*, **34**, 139.
Pearson, K. (1895). *Philos. Trans.* A, **186**, 411.
Pearson, K. (1924). *Biometrika*, **16**, 172.

* In the experiment with disks referred to on p. 335 above, in 20 partitions out of 50 significance was established at the 5 % level and in 40 out of 50 at the 15 % level, results clearly consistent with these theoretical chances.

APPENDIX

Note on the arrangement of D. J. Finney's table (*Biometrika*, **35**, 145–56)

In the present paper we have been mainly concerned with a lower significance level for a, for a given value of $r = a+b$. This limiting value of a is determined by the sum of the tail terms in a hypergeometric series. Thus in Fig. 8 below, for $m = n = \frac{1}{2}N = 15$, when $r = 13$, what we have termed the nominal lower 5 % significance level for a is 3 and when $r = 12$ it is also 3. This is because the sum of the chances of a assuming values of 0, 1, 2 and 3 on the null hypothesis is 0·0127 in the former case and 0·0301 in the latter, while it would be over 0·05 if we included the chance that $a = 4$. On this basis, the stepped line indicates the position of the significance level for different values of r.

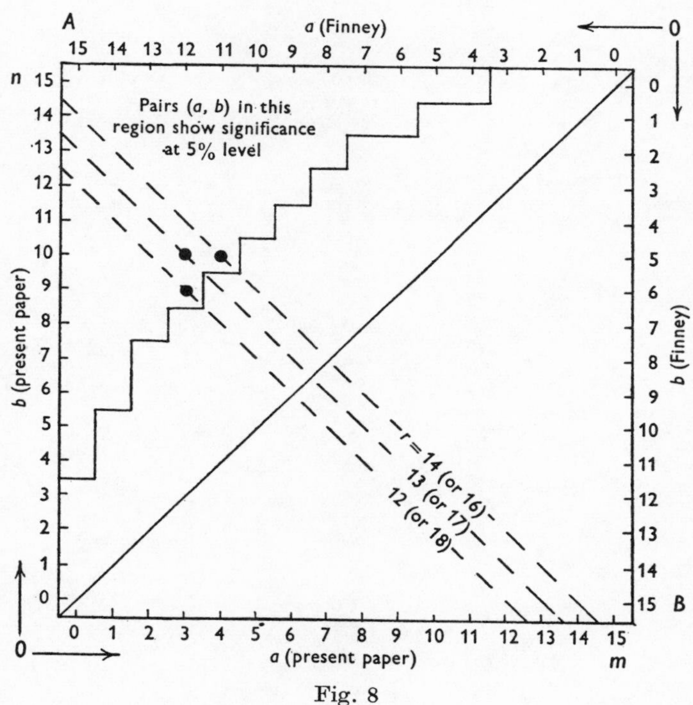

Fig. 8

In Finney's arrangement, when dealing with the single-tail test, $a/A \geqslant b/B$, where $A = m$ and $B = n$. Thus in Fig. 8 the scales of a and b must be reversed. His table is not entered with r, but shows for a given a the highest value of b which is just significant at the 5 % level. Thus when $A = B = 15$, for $a = 11$ he gives $b = 5$, and for $a = 12$ he gives $b = 6$. These points correspond to $r = 16$, $a = 11$ and $r = 18$, $a = 12$ in the diagram. It will be seen that on this basis an entry for the point $a = 12$, $b = 5$ on the intermediate diagonal with $r = 17$ is unnecessary and space is saved in tabulation. But there is no difference whatsoever in the basic calculations leading to Finney's table and to the special results we have given in Table 5 above.

ON QUESTIONS RAISED BY THE COMBINATION OF TESTS BASED ON DISCONTINUOUS DISTRIBUTIONS

By E. S. PEARSON

1. Introduction

In statistical practice it often happens that we wish to combine the results of a number of independent experiments which have all been planned to test a common hypothesis. Thus, for example, several experiments comparing two treatments may have been carried out, but owing to differences in error variance or to other changes in conditions between experiments, it is not possible to pool all the data together. The overall test calls therefore for the combination of a number of independent tests of significance. As was first pointed out by Fisher (1932, §21·1), when dealing with continuous variables an overall test may be obtained very simply by an application of the probability integral transformation, which may be defined in the following general terms.

Let $p(x)$ be the probability density function of a continuous random variable x in the interval $a \leqslant x \leqslant b$, where $p(x) = 0$ for $x < a$ or $x > b$. Then if we write

$$y = \int_a^x p(x)\,dx, \tag{1}$$

y is uniformly distributed in the interval (0, 1) and $z = -2\log_e y$ is distributed as χ^2 with $\nu = 2$ degrees of freedom, that is to say,

$$p(z) = \tfrac{1}{2}e^{-\frac{1}{2}z}. \tag{2}$$

Similarly

$$1-y = \int_x^b p(x)\,dx \tag{3}$$

will have the same distribution. Further, if M is the median value of x, such that

$$\int_a^M p(x)\,dx = \int_M^b p(x)\,dx = 0{\cdot}5$$

and y' is defined as follows:

$$\left.\begin{aligned} y' &= 2\int_a^x p(x)\,dx \quad \text{if} \quad x \leqslant M,\\ &= 2\int_x^b p(x)\,dx \quad \text{if} \quad x > M, \end{aligned}\right\} \tag{4}$$

then y' is also uniformly distributed in (0, 1) and $-2\log_e y'$ will have the χ^2 distribution with $\nu = 2$. If now $x_i (i = 1, 2, \ldots, k)$ are k independent random variables with probability density functions $p_i(x)$, $a_i \leqslant x_i \leqslant b_i$ and if y_i and y'_i are defined as in (1) and (4) above, it follows that:

$$\text{(i)}\ Q_1 = -2\sum_{i=1}^k \log_e y_i, \quad \text{(ii)}\ Q_2 = -2\sum_{i=1}^k \log(1-y_i), \quad \text{(iii)}\ Q_3 = -2\sum_{i=1}^k \log_e y'_i, \tag{5}$$

are each distributed as χ^2 with $\nu = 2k$ degrees of freedom.

The application of these results to the combination of independent tests of significance is straightforward. x_i will be one of k independent test statistics, $p(x_i \mid H_0)$ will be its probability density distribution if the hypothesis tested is true and

$$\text{(1)}\quad y_i \quad \text{or} \quad 1-y_i, \qquad \text{(2)}\quad y'_i$$

will be used according to whether it is appropriate to take the component tests in (1) asymmetrical (single-tailed) or (2) symmetrical (double-tailed) form.

This comprehensive test is not, however, immediately applicable if the distribution of x is discontinuous. The matter was recently discussed by Lancaster (1949), who pointed out the importance of having such a test available in a situation often met where the relevant probability distributions are either binomial, Poisson or (for the case of 2×2 tables) hypergeometric and where the number of observations in any single group may be very small. Lancaster proposed for the discontinuous case two modifications of the standard test, leading to statistics whose sampling distributions were approximately those of χ^2. The effect of discontinuity has also been considered in greater detail by David & Johnson (1950). The work of these writers was aimed at providing more accurate approximations, in terms of the probability integral of a continuous variable, of what is still a discontinuous distribution. A much more radical method of attack, however, follows from a simple extension of the procedure discussed by Eudey (1949), Stevens (1950) and Tocher (1950) in recent papers. This consists in the simple if unconventional device of adding by a separate 'random experiment' a continuous variable (say u) to the original discrete variable (X) and so obtaining a continuous variable (x) to which the methods for the continuous variables outlined above may be accurately applied.

The possibility of this conversion has been recognized by statisticians for a number of years; it was recently raised and discussed in a paper read by Anscombe to the Royal Statistical Society (1948). But Eudey, Stevens and Tocher, in the papers referred to, have investigated from different angles, and rather more fully than before, the consequences of applying such a procedure. Its adoption would be accompanied by very great advantages, particularly in the case of interval estimation and in the problem of combining independent tests of significance. There are, however, a number of objections to its use, which many statisticians would regard as decisive. The object of the present paper is, first, to illustrate the method and its connexion with Lancaster's proposal and, afterwards, to discuss the objections and their relation to theories of probability.

2. Outline of the conversion device

Let X be a discontinuous random variable which can assume values $0, 1, \ldots, X, \ldots$ with probabilities $f(0), f(1), \ldots, f(X), \ldots$. Write

$$F(X) = \sum_{t=0}^{X} f(t). \tag{6}$$

Let u be a continuous random variable, independent of X, and uniformly distributed in $(0, 1)$. Write

$$x = X + u. \tag{7}$$

Then, using x_0, X_0 and u_0 to denote particular observed values of the variables,

$$\Pr\{x \leqslant x_0\} = \Pr\{X < X_0\} + u_0 f(X_0) = F(X_0 - 1) + u_0 f(X_0).$$

If we now take

$$y(X, u) = F(X-1) + uf(X), \tag{8}$$

it will follow that y is a continuous random variable uniformly distributed in $(0, 1)$. In practice, X is the random variable whose value is determined by the experiment proper, while u is determined by an 'auxiliary experiment' which may be most easily performed by selecting a number from a table of random digits.

The following is an illustration of the procedure. The probabilities associated with the possible partitions within the 2×2 table

X	—	5
—	—	5
6	4	10

are given by the hypergeometric function

$$= \frac{5!\,5!\,6!\,4!}{X!\,(6-X)!\,(5-X)!\,(X-1)!\,10!}. \tag{9}$$

Thus we have the following table:

X	$f(X)$	$F(X)$
1	$\frac{1}{42}=0{\cdot}0238$	0·0238
2	$\frac{5}{21}=0{\cdot}2381$	0·2619
3	$\frac{10}{21}=0{\cdot}4762$	0·7381
4	$\frac{5}{21}=0{\cdot}2381$	0·9762
5	$\frac{1}{42}=0{\cdot}0238$	1·0000

In Fig. 1 the five discrete ordinates ending in small circles represent the distribution of X, while that of $x = X+u$ is represented by the probability histogram in which the discrete probability value at X is spread out uniformly over the interval $(X, X+1)$. Suppose the observed value of X is 2 and that the random selection of a two-figure number is 82; then $x = 2{\cdot}82$. In the type of application discussed by Stevens (1950), where fiducial or confidence limits for an unknown parameter are required, the value of x will be what is directly needed.

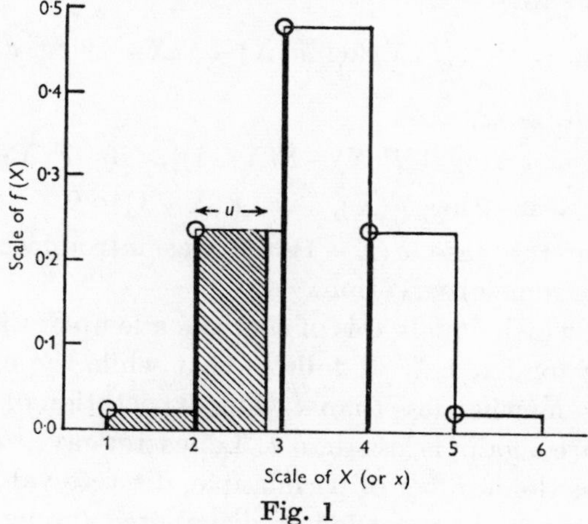

Fig. 1

When dealing with statistical tests we need, however, the probability integral of x, or the $y(X,u)$ of equation (8). This is most easily obtained in the following manner. For the example given above, with $X = 2$, it is seen that

$$F(X-1) = F(1) = 0{\cdot}0238, \quad F(X) = F(2) = 0{\cdot}2619.$$

In a series of four-digit, random numbers, any number between 0238 and 2618 is equally likely to occur. If then we run down a column of these numbers and select the first one occurring in the range 0238–2618, this, when divided by 10,000, may be taken as $y(2,u)$.

For example, if the random number is 2186, then $y(2, u) = 0{\cdot}2186$ and is proportional to the shaded area shown on the left of the histogram in Fig. 1. u, if needed, could be found from

$$u = \frac{0{\cdot}2186 - 0{\cdot}0238}{0{\cdot}2381} = 0{\cdot}818.$$

It will be noted that if the double act of sampling is repeated, i.e. of selecting X in accordance with the law (9) and then determining u by the random number process, there will be an equal probability of y assuming any one of the 10,000 numbers 0000–9999.

It follows that if the hypothesis specifying the probability law $f(X)$ is correct,

$$z = -2\log_e y(X, u)$$

will be distributed as χ^2 with 2 degrees of freedom, and, further, that a series of independent tests may be combined as indicated in §1 above.

3. Comparison with Lancaster's tests

For a given result of the experiment, i.e. for fixed X, the distribution of $z = -2\log_e y(X, u)$ for variation in the random element u in $(0, 1)$ will be that of a truncated section of an exponential curve. Thus the minimum and maximum values for z, attained when $u = 1$ and 0, respectively, are given by

$$\text{Min.}\, z = -2\log_e F(X), \quad \text{Max.}\, z = -2\log_e F(X-1). \tag{10}$$

Lancaster (1949), although not considering the introduction of u, suggested the use of two statistics which are, in fact, (a) the expectation or mean value, and (b) the median value of z. Since

$$y(X, u) = F(X-1) + uf(X) = e^{-\frac{1}{2}z}, \tag{11}$$

we obtain the following results:

(a) *Mean z or Lancaster's* χ^2_m:

$$\bar{z} = \int_0^1 z\,du = 2 - 2\{F(X)\log_e F(X) - F(X-1)\log_e F(X-1)\}/f(X). \tag{12}$$

(b) *Median z or Lancaster's* χ'^2_m.

$$\text{Median } z = -2\log_e \tfrac{1}{2}\{F(X) + F(X-1)\}, \quad \text{if} \quad F(X-1) \neq 0, \tag{13}$$

$$= 2 - 2\log_e F(X), \quad \text{if} \quad F(X-1) = 0. \tag{13a}$$

The definition (13a) in the case $F(X-1) = 0$ was introduced by Lancaster so that $\chi'^2_m = \chi^2_m$ when X is the extreme observation.

The total variance of z, which equals 4, is of course made up of the variance of $\bar{z} = \chi^2_m$ and the variance of z about $\bar{z}$ for fixed X. It follows that while the expectation of $\bar{z}$ is 2, the variance is bound to be somewhat less than 4. The expectation of *median* $z = \chi'^2_m$ is a little less than 2, and its variance, again, is less than 4. Lancaster gave some numerical examples, and concluded that unless the number of permissible, discrete values for X was very small indeed, both χ^2_m and χ'^2_m might be regarded as distributed (under the null hypothesis) as a χ^2 with 2 degrees of freedom. Independent tests, each yielding a value of χ^2_m (or χ'^2_m), could therefore, he suggested, be combined by summing these values as outlined in §1 above. The use of χ'^2_m, rather than χ^2_m, would, he thought, be preferred in practice because it could be more easily calculated. It should be noted that χ'^2_m corresponds to $-2\log_e u$ in David & Johnson's notation (1950, p. 42).

The examples given in §4 below will illustrate, in particular cases, the relation between these different quantities. A more critical discussion of their use and interpretation will be reserved for §5.

4. Illustrative examples

The methods of analysis which have been suggested will be compared on three examples. In the present section, only the calculations will be presented, the interpretation and critical comment on the results being left to § 5.

Example I. The data were obtained in course of an investigation in progress at the Safety in Mines Research and Testing Branch of the Ministry of Fuel and Power, concerning the relative safety of mining explosives. Table 1 shows the result of six separate experiments comparing two explosives, A and B, under a number of different conditions. The cartridges of explosive are fixed in a gas chamber and a record is made of whether each shot results in an ignition (E) or non-ignition (not-E). The weight of cartridge and the conditions of the explosion were varied in the different comparisons, so that it is not possible to pool the results. The problem is to consider whether, taken as a whole, there is evidence that

Table 1. *Safety in Mines data*

Comparison	Explosive A		Explosive B	
	Ignitions	Total shots	Ignitions	Total shots
1	8	10	5	5
2	2	10	13	15
3	4	5	5	5
4	1	5	1	10
5	1	5	0	10
6	0	10	4	6

explosive A is safer than B under the conditions of the experiments.* The result of each comparative trial may be represented in a 2×2 table; for example, for comparison 1, we have

	E	Not-E	Total
A	$X = 8$	2	10
B	5	0	5
	13	2	15

On the hypothesis of no difference, the conditional distribution of X (no. of ignitions for explosive A) for fixed margins will be of hypergeometric form, and the $F(X)$ of equation (6) will be the lower tail sum of this series.

The problem is one which seems to require a comprehensive test of the null hypothesis, sensitive to detect a trend in the direction of A being safer than B. With these very small frequencies conventional methods will give rise to inaccuracies which are difficult to assess, and it is here that the introduction of the random u-element provides a solution which, if it were otherwise acceptable, is mathematically correct.

The results of the analysis are summarized in Table 2. Cols. (2) and (3) give the tail sums, calculated from the appropriate hypergeometric series; col. (4) shows the random number,

* The rather fuller data actually collected at the station made it possible to subdivide the results into three series of comparisons within each of which only the weight of charge varied. It was then possible to apply probit analysis technique.

lying between $F(X-1)$ and $F(X)$, determined as described on p. 385 above.* Col. (5) gives the transformed variable z, which on the null hypothesis will be distributed exactly as χ^2 with 2 degrees of freedom. Cols. (6) and (7) give Lancaster's 'mean' and 'median' value χ^2 determined from equations (12) and (13). Cols. (8) and (9) show the extreme values that z would have assumed had the random number drawn given u as 1 or 0.

Table 2. *Analysis of data in Example* 1

Comparison (1)	$F(X-1)$ (2)	$F(X)$ (3)	$y(X, u)$ (4)	$z=-2\log_e y$ (5)	$\bar{z}=\chi_m^2$ (6)	Med. $z=\chi_m'^2$ (7)	Min. z (8)	Max. z (9)
1	0	0·4286	0·0051	10·56	3·69	3·69	1·69	∞
2	0·0005	0·00149	0·00107	13·68	14·80	14·34	13·02	19·97
3	0	0·5000	0·0907	4·80	3·39	3·39	1·39	∞
4	0·4286	0·9048	0·8804	0·25	0·86	0·81	0·20	1·69
5	0·6667	1·0000	0·9846	0·03	0·38	0·36	0·00	0·81
6	0	0·00820	0·00490	10·64	11·61	11·61	9·61	∞
Total				39·96	34·73	34·20	25·91	∞
$P(\chi^2)$ ($\nu=12$)				$<0·001$	$<0·001$	$<0·001$	0·011	0

At the bottom of the table are given the sums of cols. (5)–(9), and the probability, $P(\chi^2)$, of obtaining a value of χ^2 as large or larger than this sum value, for $\nu = 12$ degrees of freedom. Points which may be noted are:

(1) In three comparisons the observed X falls at the lowest term of the appropriate hypergeometric series; hence $F(X-1) = 0$. The luck of the draw might therefore make y zero or, at any rate, exceedingly small. The upper limit for z has therefore been denoted as ∞ for these cases.

(2) Median z is slightly less than $\bar{z}$, except in the cases where $F(X-1) = 0$, when they are equal.

(3) The comprehensive test, whether applied exactly to the sum of the six values of $z = -2\log_e y(X, u)$ or approximately to the sum of Lancaster's χ^2's, establishes significance at the 1 in 1000 level, and even supposing the exceedingly unlikely result that each z had its minimum possible value, the total χ^2 would have been 25·91, and so at the 1 % level.

(4) The largest contributions to the total χ^2 come from the comparisons 2 and 6.

Example II. The data are the result of an investigation, described by Rothschild (1949), into the effect of small electric currents on the fertilizing capacity of bull semen, used for artificial insemination of heifers. After collection, each sample of semen was divided into two equal portions; one portion had an electric current passed through it, following a method suggested for the measurement of sperm activity; the other portion was not so treated. The treated and untreated portions were then used to inseminate heifers; effectiveness was measured by the number of heifers which did not become pregnant, as judged by their being returned by the owners for re-insemination. In Table 3, this is the meaning of the column

* The seven numbers were determined by opening Kendall & Babington Smith's (1939) Table of Random Sampling Numbers at random and running down a column to find the first number, treated as a decimal fraction, lying between $F(X-1)$ and $F(X)$.

headed 'Returns'; a significantly greater proportion of returns among heifers for which the treated semen had been used would imply that the electrical test procedure was harmful.

As the samples, leading to the results in Table 3, might be heterogeneous it was considered that the figures should not be pooled by merely adding the columns. In the paper quoted, Rothschild used a method of analysis suggested by R. A. Fisher involving the angular transformation for binomial variables. There is, of course, some approximation involved in this, and it is of interest to apply the same methods as have been used in Example I above.

Table 3. *Rothschild data*

Sample	Inseminations with untreated semen		Inseminations with treated semen	
	Returns	Total	Returns	Total
1	5	11	1	9
2	3	9	4	9
3	3	12	3	5
4	6	11	3	9
5	4	10	0	5
6	3	11	1	5
7	1	4	3	6

Table 4. *First analysis of data in Example II*

Sample (1)	$F(X-1)$ (2)	$F(X)$ (3)	$y(X, u)$ (4)	$z=-2\log_e y$ (5)	$\bar{z}=\chi_m^2$ (6)	Med. $z=\chi_m'^2$ (7)	Min. z (8)	Max. z (9)
1	0·8808	0·9881	0·9867	0·03	0·14	0·14	0·02	0·25
2	0·1674	0·5000	0·4099	1·78	2·28	2·20	1·39	3·57
3	0·0276	0·2054	0·1031	4·54	4·54	4·30	3·17	7·18
4	0·6890	0·9201	0·7802	0·50	0·46	0·44	0·17	0·74
5	0·8462	1·0000	0·9906	0·02	0·16	0·16	0·00	0·33
6	0·3654	0·8187	0·4871	1·44	1·10	1·05	0·40	2·01
7	0·0714	0·4524	0·2511	2·76	2·89	2·68	1·59	5·28
Total				11·07	11·57	10·97	6·74	19·36
$P(\chi^2)$ $(\nu=14)$				0·68	0·64	0·69	0·94	0·15

With the figures as arranged, X will denote the number of returns in the second column of the table and we want a comprehensive test of the null hypothesis, sensitive to detect a trend in the direction of the treatment causing an increased proportion of returns. Table 4 shows a similar analysis to Table 2, $F(X)$ being the lower tail-sum of the appropriate hypergeometric series. We note that:

(1) In this case the luck of the draw has actually placed $\Sigma(z)$ between $\Sigma(\bar{z})$ and Σ (median z).

(2) The comprehensive test gives no suggestion of significance, whichever criterion is used. This would have been the conclusion even in the unlikely event of $\Sigma(z)$ attaining its maximum value.

(3) The test used by Rothschild leads to a standardized normal deviate ξ, large positive values of which would have indicated that the electrical treatment was harmful. He found that $\xi = -1{\cdot}22$,* so that the $P(\xi)$, comparable to the $P(\chi^2)$ of the present tests, equalled 0·89.

It is clear, therefore, that there is no evidence, when the results are considered as a whole, that the treatment reduces the fertilizing capacity of the semen. A casual inspection of the figures in Table 3 does, however, suggest that there might be some heterogeneity present in the sense that in some cases it is the treated and in others the untreated material that appears to give considerably the better result. This point may be investigated by using the double-tailed or symmetrical test based on the y' defined in equation (4) above. Thus

$$\left.\begin{aligned} y'(X,u) &= 2y(X,u) \quad \text{if} \quad y(X,u) \leqslant 0{\cdot}5 \\ &= 2(1-y(X,u)) \quad \text{if} \quad y(X,u) > 0{\cdot}5, \\ \text{and} \qquad z &= -2\log_e y'(X,u). \end{aligned}\right\} \tag{14}$$

Similarly, for Lancaster's median z, we should take

$$\left.\begin{aligned} \chi'^2_m &= -2\log_e\{F(X)+F(X-1)\}, \quad \text{if} \quad \tfrac{1}{2}\{F(X)+F(X-1)\} \leqslant 0{\cdot}5 \\ &= -2\log_e\{2-F(X)-F(X-1)\}, \quad \text{if} \quad \tfrac{1}{2}\{F(X)+F(X-1)\} > 0{\cdot}5. \end{aligned}\right\} \tag{15}$$

The result of applying this analysis is shown in Table 5 for z and median z. For the former, the same random values of u have been taken as in Table 4. In this case, owing to the chance association of rather large values of u with the large values of X in samples 1 and 5, the total χ^2 for z is considerably larger than for median z. Significance could not be claimed, even with the χ^2 of 21·83, but the example brings out the point which must be faced in the discussion that the 'luck of the draw' for the u-values is bound sometimes to put $\Sigma(z)$ beyond a significance level not exceeded by either of Lancaster's statistics, and vice versa.

Table 5. *Second analysis of data in Example II*

Sample	$y'(X, u)$	$z = -2\log_e y'$	Med. $z = \chi'^2_m$
1	0·0266	7·25	4·06
2	0·8198	0·40	0·81
3	0·2062	3·16	2·91
4	0·4396	1·64	1·88
5	0·0188	7·95	3·74
6	0·9742	0·05	0·41
7	0·5022	1·38	1·29
Total		21·83	15·10
$P(\chi^2)$ ($\nu = 14$)		0·083	0·37

Example III. In this illustration the distribution of X on the null hypothesis follows the binomial and not the hypergeometric series. The problem is of a type which may often arise in comparing frequencies of rare events. The data have been taken for purposes of illustration from those collected in a much fuller investigation into traffic accidents undertaken by the Road Research Laboratory (described by Manning, 1949). In Table 6, cols. (3) and (4) show, respectively, the number of cyclists (a_1) and motor-cyclists (a_2) involved in accidents leading to personal injury on sections* of five main roads near London during the period June

* The figure is given in his paper as $+1{\cdot}22$, but the sign appears to be in error.

1946 to May 1947. Since the vehicle mileage of these two types of road-user will have been different, the figures are not comparable as they stand. Cols. (6) and (7) give rough estimates, M_1 and M_2, in millions of miles, of the appropriate total vehicle mileage during the year on the sections of the roads considered. If vehicles are involved in accidents in a random manner, it might be expected that a_1 and a_2 would be Poisson variables with expectations m_1 and m_2. If that is the case we might ask the following question: Allowing for the difference in vehicle mileage (but not for differences in speed governing the vehicle-hours on the road), is there evidence from these data that the risk of accident is less for a pedal-cyclist than for a motor-cyclist?

Table 6. *Road Research data*

Comparison	Road	Vehicles involved in accidents			Estimated vehicle mileage in millions		$\lambda = \frac{M_1}{M_1+M_2}$
		Cycles (a_1)	Motor-cycles (a_2)	$r = a_1 + a_2$	Cycles (M_1)	Motor-cycles (M_2)	
(1)	(2)	(3)	(4)	(5)	(6)	(7)	(8)
1	R_1	5	4	9	1·69	0·80	0·68
2	R_2	2	2	4	1·80	0·50	0·78
3	R_3	3	1	4	1·82	0·33	0·85
4	R_4	4	3	7	1·79	0·57	0·76
5	R_5	3	5	8	1·56	0·54	0·74

Formally, the problem is that of testing the hypothesis that $m_1/m_2 = M_1/M_2$, making the test sensitive to alternatives $m_1/m_2 < M_1/M_2$. It is known† that if a_1 and a_2 are independent Poisson variables, then on the null hypothesis and within the conditional set of samples for which $a_1 + a_2 = r$ is constant, a_1 follows a binomial $(\overline{1-\lambda+\lambda})^r$, where $\lambda = M_1/(M_1+M_2)$. In our general theory we may put $a_1 = X$, so that $f(X)$ is a binomial term. By adding the random element u we shall have the $y(X, u)$ of equation (8) uniformly distributed in (0, 1), that is to say, it has a distribution freed from dependence on the restriction $a_1 + a_2 = r =$ constant. The comprehensive test is obtained as before by summing $z = -2\log_e y(X, u)$ for each comparison.

The results of the analysis are shown in Table 7. $F(X)$ and $F(X-1)$ are the lower tail-sums of the binomials $(\overline{1-\lambda+\lambda})^r$ with $X = a_1$ and using the values of λ given in col. (8) of Table 6. It will be seen that there is relatively little difference between $\Sigma(z)$, $\Sigma(\bar{z})$ and Σ (Med. z) and that, taken as a whole, we should conclude that the risk of accident per vehicle mile was less for a cyclist than for a motor-cyclist. This result is amply confirmed by the fuller data. It will be noticed, however, that the result would have been inconclusive had we confined our attention to the first four sections of road; the relevant figures are shown at the bottom of the table.

It should be emphasized that the application of this method to these particular data is perhaps not altogether justifiable, partly because the estimates of the vehicle mileage, M_1

* Between 6 and 15 miles long.

† See, for example, Pearson (1948) for a discussion of the test and references. Also, for another solution, see Haldane (1948).

and M_2, were very rough, but also because the frequencies a_1 and a_2 may not have been independent, if more than one vehicle was involved in the same accident. However, data of similar type where a_1 and a_2 are independent and small, and where $\lambda = m_1/(m_1+m_2)$ can be fairly closely estimated, are of quite common occurrence. If the λ's are not the same for all comparisons, then the overall test proposed, if acceptable, avoids all complications arising from the discrete character of the original Poisson distributions.

Table 7. *Analysis of data in Example III*

Comparison (1)	$F(X-1)$ (2)	$F(X)$ (3)	$y(X, u)$ (4)	$z=-2\log_e y$ (5)	$\bar{z}=\chi^2_m$ (6)	Med. $z=\chi'^2_m$ (7)	Min. z (8)	Max. z (9)
1	0·1252	0·3173	0·2413	2·84	3·09	3·02	2·30	4·16
2	0·0356	0·2122	0·1003	4·60	4·38	4·18	3·10	6·67
3	0·1095	0·4780	0·2983	2·42	2·61	2·45	1·48	4·42
4	0·0617	0·2231	0·1447	3·87	4·02	3·90	3·00	5·57
5	0·00172	0·01224	0·00397	11·06	10·17	9·91	8·81	12·73
Total, 1–5				24·79	24·27	23·46	18·69	33·55
$P(\chi^2)$ ($\nu=10$)				0·006	0·007	0·009	0·045	<0·001
Total, 1–4				13·73	14·10	13·55	9·88	20·82
$P(\chi^2)$ ($\nu=8$)				0·090	0·080	0·095	0·27	0·008

5. Discussion

(5·1) *The case, for and against*

Before examining obvious objections to the adoption of statistical tests involving the introduction of this additional random element, it may be well to summarize what is gained by their use.

(*a*) In the first place we have secured for discontinuous distributions one objective which is commonly regarded as desirable in a test of significance. If we follow the rule of procedure laid down, we know precisely the chance of rejecting the null hypothesis when it is true; in other words, we have an exact significance level and do not have to be content with using an upper bound to this risk.

(*b*) This result may hardly be considered necessary in the case of a single comparison, where a knowledge of the numerical values of $F(X-1)$ and $F(X)$ should provide all that the statistician needs on purely probability grounds to make up his mind on whether to reject the null hypothesis or not. But as soon as we wish to draw a broad conclusion from a number of independent tests, the advantage of an overall test criterion having a simply determined, continuous probability integral becomes apparent.

(*c*) While it is true that the use of Lancaster's statistics or of angular or other similar transformations provides variables whose distributions can be fairly closely represented by known, continuous distributions, there must always be some doubt of the 'closeness' when dealing with small frequencies. To illustrate this I have calculated for the combination of samples 5, 6 and 7 of Example II, the possible values that $\bar{z}_5$, $\bar{z}_6$ and $\bar{z}_7$ (i.e. the χ^2_m values) might assume, keeping the marginal totals of the corresponding 2×2 tables fixed at the observed values as follows:

Sample 5			Sample 6			Sample 7		
X	—	10	X	—	11	X	—	4
—	—	5	—	—	5	—	—	6
4	11	15	4	12	16	4	6	10

Assigning to each value of X its appropriate hypergeometric probability, it was possible to calculate the chance that

$$S = \bar{z}_5 + \bar{z}_6 + \bar{z}_7$$

exceeds (*a*) the 5 % and (*b*) the 1 % level of significance for a χ^2 having 6 degrees of freedom. The result was as follows:

	5 %	1 %
χ^2 significance level	12·592	16·812
No. of values of S exceeding this level	59	34
Chance of S exceeding this level	0·0429	0·0089

The differences between 0·05 and 0·0429, 0·01 and 0·0089 are in this case small, but as long as χ^2_m, or any other criterion used, can assume only discrete values, the element of uncertainty will be present.

(*d*) Since the distribution of $\Sigma(z) = \Sigma\{-2\log_e y(X, u)\}$ is the same within every conditional set, e.g. whatever be the marginal values of the 2×2 tables, differences in point of view as to the reference set to which the test should be related, which have led to some controversy, become irrelevant.

(*e*) In the case of a single comparison, Tocher (1950) has shown that if we require a test region of fixed 'size' then, in spite of the introduction of the random element, the test is more powerful in the sense of Neyman and Pearson than any other test. The extent to which the comprehensive test also possesses optimum properties of this kind has not so far been explored.

(*f*) It is sometimes necessary to compare the efficiency of two statistical tests, one or both of which depend on a statistic having a discontinuous distribution. Difficulties then arise in adjusting the critical regions to be of the same size, e.g. so that both correspond to a 5 % level of significance. The introduction of u would avoid this difficulty.

(*g*) If the values of $F(X-1)$ and $F(X)$ have to be calculated, and this may be necessary in any analysis of small frequencies, $y(X, u)$ is found immediately if random number tables are available. The overall test is therefore as quick to carry out as that based on Lancaster's χ'^2_m and is a good deal quicker than that based on χ^2_m.

However, even when these advantages have been considered, it is impossible to deny that the introduction of the random element strikes a discordant note in statistical practice, not only because it is unfamiliar but because it appears to offend some common-sense principle. Although in the examples given above it has turned out that the conclusions based on z are the same as those based on χ^2_m or χ'^2_m, it is clear that this will sometimes not be the case; expressed crudely, the idea that a decision should depend on what could be described as a toss-up made after the true experimental results are available, is certainly difficult to accept. Yet it is doubtful whether we can dismiss straight away this type of procedure as impossible, for the implications run deeper than at first sight appears. There is a conflict of attitudes of mind which is not easily solved. As M. G. Kendall wrote in a recent article on 'Reconciliation of theories of probability' (1949, p. 103): 'We are concerned not only with the relationship of theory with the external world but also with the relationship between our calculus and the way we think.'

The two main attitudes held to-day towards the theory of probability both result from an attempt to define the probability number scale so that it may readily be put in gear with common processes of rational thought. For one school, the degree of confidence in a proposition, a quantity varying with the nature and extent of the evidence, provides the basic notion to which the numerical scale should be adjusted. The other school notes how in ordinary life a knowledge of the relative frequency of occurrence of a particular class of events in a series of repetitions has again and again an influence on conduct; it therefore suggests that it is through its link with relative frequency that a numerical probability measure has the most direct meaning for the human mind.

An intriguing characteristic of the problem posed by the introduction of this 'last-minute' random element is that it shows that most of us, whether we regard ourselves as 'frequentists' or not, to use Kendall's term, are in fact influenced by the primitive idea on which Jeffreys's theory is based. If we are at first repelled by the suggestion of using this device it is, I think, because we feel instinctively that having completed the experiment proper, the relevant information on which to reach a rational conclusion must be available without an appeal to any list of random numbers. But the recognition of this fact does not, of course, necessarily imply acceptance of the view that degree of belief can be represented on a numerical scale.

Elsewhere in this issue of the journal, Barnard (1950, p. 207) has suggested that there should be a difference between the theory to be used in planning an experiment in advance and that required in drawing inferences after the results are known. The first is the theory of probability, related closely to relative frequency, the second is the theory of likelihood. But it seems difficult to accept this solution; for if the planning is based on the consequences that will result from following a rule of statistical procedure, e.g. is based on a study of the power function of a test and then, having obtained our results, we do not follow the first rule but another, based on likelihoods, what is the meaning of the planning?

(5·2) *Introduction of the random element into the problem of interval estimation*

It may be helpful at this point to consider the proposal made by Eudey (1949) and Stevens (1950), in its special application to the binomial. If X is the number of individuals bearing a character A in a sample of size n drawn randomly from a much larger population in which a proportion p possess A and $q = 1-p$ do not, then $f(X)$ will be a term in the expansion of the binomial $(q+p)^n$. The problem of calculating from X a confidence or fiducial interval for p was first attacked by Clopper & Pearson (1934), who provided some charts from which the interval could be roughly calculated. Later Stevens (Fisher & Yates, 1942, Table VIII *i*) provided an alternative solution with tables. In both cases it was only possible to associate with the intervals the lower bound of the probability that the interval would include the unknown value of p, i.e. the upper bound of the risk of non-inclusion or error. Thus, as Stevens points out, the implication remained that the limits provided were unnecessarily wide and might in some way be narrowed until the stipulated risk was reached. This result can be achieved by using the continuous variable $x = X+u$ in place of X and then, on replacing the upper bound of the risk by an exact risk of error, the interval is invariably narrowed. In Fig. 2 are plotted the boundaries of the confidence belt for $n = 10$ and risk of error 0·20 (or confidence coefficient 0·80) tabled by Stevens (1950, p. 126). For a given p the two limiting values for $x = X+u$ are those obtained by regarding the binomial as a probability histogram as in Fig. 1, and then cutting off the 0·10 tail areas, by dividing the blocks as required in proportional parts. Using the current method based on X only, we make use of the discrete points indicated by small circles.*

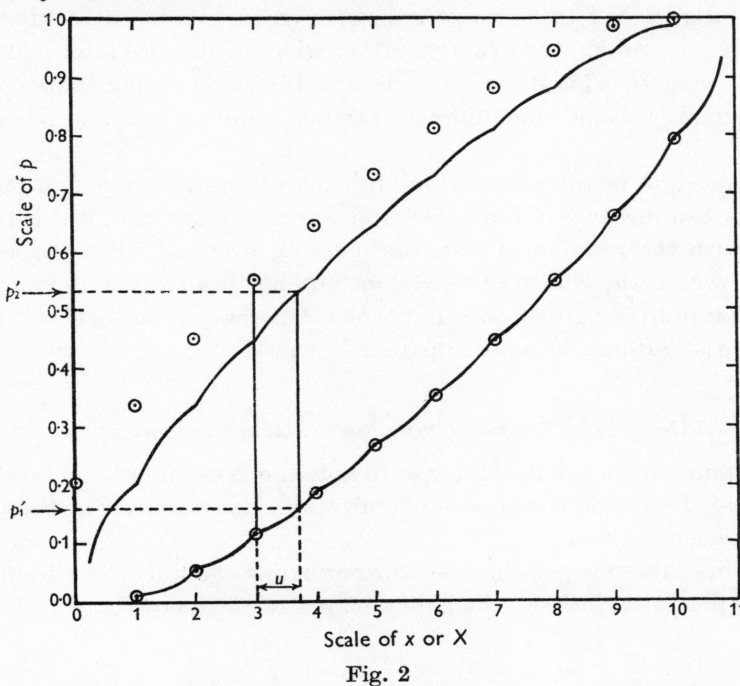

Fig. 2

As an example, suppose three individuals in a sample of ten possess a character A. By the current method the confidence limits p_1 and p_2 are given by the circled points on the ordinate at $X = 3$. Thus we can make the statement

$$0\cdot116 \leqslant p \leqslant 0\cdot552$$

with a probability of at least 0·80 of being correct. Using Stevens's procedure we select a random number in (0, 1); suppose it is 0·74, then $x = 3\cdot74$ and we find from the bounding curves that $p_1' = 0\cdot161$, $p_2' = 0\cdot534$. Hence the statement becomes

$$0\cdot161 \leqslant p \leqslant 0\cdot534,$$

and the associated confidence coefficient is exactly 0·80. The interval is reduced from 0·436 to 0·373, and both limits have been pulled in.

It seems true to say that those who have accepted and understood the principle of confidence interval estimation have regarded the method as a useful technique whose adoption means no more and no less than this: that in long-run use of the method in statistical practice

* For convenience, in Clopper & Pearson's charts (1934), these points were joined by continuous curves, whose ordinates could, however, only be used at integral values of the abscissa.

It should be noted that Eudey (1949), who derives a shortest unbiased confidence interval in Neyman's sense, gives a confidence belt which is rather differently placed with regard to the Clopper-Pearson points (see his Fig. 13).

(whether in binomial or other problems) the interval will include the unknown parameter in about the expected number of cases.* If it was previously accepted as a technique with this property, its essential character is not altered by the addition of Stevens's random element, and since, as a result, the interval is narrower and the risk of error made more precise, it would appear unreasonable to refuse the improvement if it were made available in suitable tables. On the confidence interval approach (though not on the fiducial) alternative estimators giving different intervals for the same data may be used. Thus it is accepted that statistician A, using range or mean range for rapidity in calculation to estimate σ, will get a different and, on the average, rather wider confidence interval for an unknown mean than statistician B, using standard deviation. It would therefore not appear anomalous that in the binomial problem using different random numbers u, A and B will find different intervals for p.

It appears, indeed, to be the case that in problems of estimation, where generally all that we ask for is a broad measure of reliability and where any decision, if it is to follow, is not closely linked with the result of a test, the method proposed will not meet with strong objection. It is where the choice of a random number has to be followed at once in the statistical procedure by a verdict on significance that the conflict between the frequentist and non-frequentist outlook becomes apparent.

(5·3) *Other tests involving last-moment randomization*

Before a final summing up, it is of interest to note the existence of certain other statistical procedures where the introduction of randomization, not essential to the conduct of the experiment, has been suggested.

Geary (1935), in examining possible tests for normality of a univariate frequency distribution, suggested (p. 316) a statistic which may be written as follows:

$$w_{n-1} = \sum_{i=1}^{n-1} |y_i| \Big/ \left\{(n-1)\sqrt{\sum_{i=1}^{n-1} y_i^2}\right\},$$

where (on the hypothesis tested) y_i $(i = 1, 2, \ldots, n-1)$ are $n-1$ independent normally distributed linear functions of the n observations x_i. He also provided some tables of the probability integral of w_{n-1} for small values of n. The y_i were not symmetrical functions of the x_i, for example,

$$y_1 = (x_1 - x_2)/\sqrt{2}, \quad y_2 = (x_1 + x_2 - 2x_3)/\sqrt{6}, \text{ etc.},$$

so that the x's had to be ordered in a random manner before the y's could be calculated. Thus w_{n-1} would assume different values for the $n\,!$ possible permutations of the x_i. If the observations were collected in some natural random order, this could be used in calculating y_i. Otherwise, a process of randomization was required.

Scheffé (1943) has proposed a test of the hypothesis that the means are equal in two normal populations from which two independent samples of size n_1 and $n_2 \geqslant n_1$, respectively, have been drawn, where no assumption is made of equal population variances. This test requires a random pairing of n_1 of the observations from the second sample with the n_1 of the first sample. Again, if the observations are not recorded in a random order, randomization is needed before the pairing is carried out, and the numerical value of the test statistic will depend on the outcome of this process.

* Or, for the discontinuous case in rather more than the nominal expected number of cases.

The range or difference between extreme observations in a sample has been used as a means of estimating σ. For a given total number of observations, N, the accuracy of estimation may often be improved considerably if the observations are broken up into a number, m, of equal groups each containing n (say 5–10) observations and a mean range is calculated. Recently, Lord (1947, 1950) has suggested a form of modified t-test, in which the root mean-square estimate of σ is replaced by a range estimate. If the number of observations exceeds, say $N = 10$, the efficiency of the test, i.e. its power to detect differences in mean values, may be considerably increased by breaking the observations from which σ is to be estimated into groups and calculating a mean range. But this subdivision must be a random one. If, from the nature of the problem, we are confident that the observations come to hand in a random order, then we can find the range of the 1st n, the 2nd n and so on, take an average and use Lord's test. But if we are not sure that the variations among the observations are independent of order, we must introduce some random procedure on purpose to group them. Thus the estimate of σ and hence the value of the test statistic will depend on this final randomization.

Here then we are faced with a dilemma. Is it justifiable to use Lord's test when there is an obvious grouping of the observations inherent in the form of the data, but not so when artificial randomization is necessary? Or, if the test is legitimate in both cases, what is the essential difference between using randomization here and in the tests suggested earlier in this paper? Alternatively, are all tests based on mean range to be condemned? One may note that in the range test some little effort is involved in randomly grouping the observations and finding the mean range, so that we do not readily have before us a number of alternative values of the test criterion. In the case of the binomial or hypergeometric we can get as many values of u, and therefore of $x = X+u$, as we please by merely looking further down the column of random numbers. This suggests a levity in approaching a decision on significance which offends our sense of scientific propriety! But the difference between a more concealed and more blatant form of tossing up may vanish when viewed in perspective.

(5·4) *Conclusion*

This paper has raised more questions than it has answered. 'The way we think' is so much a personal matter that it would be presumptuous to claim one right way of regarding the randomization procedure described in the earlier sections of the paper. Just as views have changed with time on the propriety of introducing a random element which would not otherwise be there, into the conduct of an experiment, so it is possible that with time the instinctive objection to using a random number *after* the experiment proper is completed may disappear. Cases will always arise from time to time where it is evident that the luck of the draw has made the u elements in the x's pull against the X elements, so that a result becomes significant that we judge should not, or vice versa. But it is also true that a random draw made *before* the experiment is sometimes found to lead to an arrangement, e.g. of plots, which it is realized will be likely, if accepted, to render that particular experiment inconclusive or biased. No doubt, in such cases, practical common sense prevails and chance is invoked a second time. This problem is always present when artificial randomization is employed, and it was with this difficulty in mind that W. S. Gosset in his last statistical paper ('Student', 1937) advocated the greater use of balanced in place of randomized designs.

The long-run verdict on this form of comprehensive test for discontinuous variables will depend on many factors, among which utility is likely to carry much weight. The test is often required as a rough foot rule where more detailed consideration might involve weighting the different series. Thus, for a small number of series, Lancaster's suggestion of adding the values of

$$\chi_m'^2 = \text{Med.}\, z = -2 \log_e \tfrac{1}{2}\{F(X) + F(X-1)\}$$

may meet all needs. Once the $F(X)$ have been found, this test is quick to apply and is conservative, in that it is rather less likely to claim significance than the nominal probability level suggests. On the other hand, if many series are to be combined, the risk of accumulation in the bias and the subnormal variation of $\chi_m'^2$ may swing the choice to $\Sigma\{-2\log_e y(X, u)\}$. The present paper has included a number of examples which make possible some study of the behaviour of the test based on $y(X, u)$; but the reader may well prefer to suspend judgement until he has had opportunity of making his own comparisons.

Finally, one point seems clear; to condemn the procedure out of hand may involve, for consistency, ruling out of court a number of other techniques which have been or are being accepted into current statistical practice.

The author is indebted to Mr J. W. Gibson of the Safety in Mines Research and Testing Branch of the Ministry of Fuel and Power and to Dr F. Garwood of the Road Research Laboratory for supplying him with the original data used in Tables 1 and 6 respectively.

REFERENCES

Anscombe, F. U. (1948). *J. R. Statist. Soc.* A, **109**, 181.
Barnard, G. A. (1950). *Biometrika*, **37**, 203.
Clopper, C. J. & Pearson, E. S. (1934). *Biometrika*, **26**, 404.
David, F. N. & Johnson, N. L. (1950). *Biometrika*, **37**, 42.
Eudey, M. W. (1949). Technical Report No. 13, Statistical Laboratory, University of California.
Fisher, R. A. (1932). *Statistical Methods for Research Workers*, 4th ed. London and Edinburgh: Oliver and Boyd.
Fisher, R. A. & Yates, F. (1942). *Statistical Tables for Biological, Agricultural and Medical Research*, 2nd ed. London and Edinburgh: Oliver and Boyd.
Geary, R. C. (1935). *Biometrika*, **27**, 310.
Haldane, J. B. S. (1948). *Biometrika*, **35**, 297.
Kendall, M. G. (1949). *Biometrika*, **36**, 101.
Kendall, M. G. & Babington Smith, B. (1939). *Tracts for Computers*, no. 24. Cambridge University Press.
Lancaster, H. O. (1949). *Biometrika*, **36**, 370.
Lord, E. (1947). *Biometrika*, **34**, 41.
Lord, E. (1950). *Biometrika*, **37**, 64.
Manning, J. R. (1949). Unpublished Report.
Pearson, E. S. (1948). *Biometrika*, **35**, 301.
Rothschild, Lord (1949). *J. Agric. Sci.* **39**, 294.
Scheffé, H. (1943). *Ann. Math. Statist.* **14**, 1.
Stevens, W. L. (1950). *Biometrika*, **37**, 117.
'Student' (W. S. Gosset) (1937). *Biometrika*, **29**, 363.
Tocher, K. D. (1950). *Biometrika*, **37**, 130.

THE TIME INTERVALS BETWEEN INDUSTRIAL ACCIDENTS

THE TIME INTERVALS BETWEEN INDUSTRIAL ACCIDENTS

By B. A. MAGUIRE, E. S. PEARSON and A. H. A. WYNN

1. Introduction

Statistical methods have been used for many years for studying the frequency of occurrence of accidents in fixed intervals of time. Statisticians are familiar with the use by Bortkiewicz (1898) of the Poisson distribution to analyse the numbers of men in ten Prussian army corps killed by the kick of a horse, quoted, for example, by Yule (1922) and still being quoted in text-books (Jeffreys, 1948). Again, the series of papers describing research on industrial accidents published by the Industrial Health Research Board, which began with a paper by Greenwood & Woods (1919), are based on the analysis of the frequency of accidents occurring in fixed intervals of time.

It is, however, a characteristic of an accident that it occurs at a particular instant of time, which is often recorded. Thus the basic data consist of a sequence of ordered intervals of varying length. Analysis may therefore be applied to the time intervals between accidents rather than to the frequencies of accidents occurring in successive fixed intervals of time. Which of the alternative methods of analysis is the most efficient will depend on the type of question we are asking and the assumptions regarding the data which we are prepared to make. Under certain conditions the two methods of attack are clearly equivalent. Thus if we are prepared to assume that accidents are taking place at random in time and at a constant average rate, we shall obtain the same estimate of this rate* either from the average number of accidents occurring in successive fixed time intervals or from the average length of the varying interval between the accidents.

When, however, a more detailed analysis is required, as, for example, in testing for changes with time, it seems likely (provided accurate interval data are available) that methods of analysis based on these will be more powerful than those often employed using only the accident frequencies in relatively long fixed intervals of time. This advantage will lie partly in the fact that for an analysis to be sensitive to changes in time it must be able to handle observations in small groups, and an exact distribution theory for the continuous variable (the interval) is available, where it does not exist in manageable form for the discontinuous variable (the frequency or count). In the present paper, however, we are not concerned with a comparison of the efficiency of the two methods of attack, but rather with an examination of available methods of handling the interval analysis.

Any conclusion about the accident liability of a single individual must always be based on very small numbers even in unusually dangerous occupations. Serious accidents of particular kinds, such as explosions in mines, are fortunately infrequent. The extent to which any body of accident statistics may be usefully analysed depends in part upon the power of the statistical methods to generalize from these small numbers. The loss of information entailed in compiling accident frequencies in fixed intervals of time may, therefore, seriously reduce the usefulness of the records.

* Apart from a marginal difference due to the fact that the time stretch considered may not be precisely the same in the two cases.

In routine accident control it is important for a manager to have the earliest possible indication of a significant change in the expectation of accident. Administrative measures may have been taken to reduce accidents; it is important to have the earliest possible indication of the effect of these measures. Analysis of the time intervals between accidents may provide an earlier indication of an improvement than any analysis of accident frequency.

Failure in the past to use time-interval analysis for research on industrial accidents has been partly due to the more complicated records necessary and to the difficulty of defining intervals. This paper is not concerned with these practical difficulties but introduces a discussion of the many statistical techniques which are available for the analysis of time-interval data if the practical difficulties can be overcome.

There is one note of caution which should be raised. If we take for consideration the sample of intervals between accidents occurring in a given period of time, e.g. in a year, the data are in some degree selected. For instance, no intervals of a year or more can be included in the sample. While this should not affect the theory seriously, provided the average interval is short compared to the fixed period, the matter is one requiring investigation.

2. The exponential distribution

It was shown by Whitworth (1901) that if the expectation of events per unit time is constant, then the time intervals between events are exponentially distributed. If E is the expectation of accidents per unit time, then the probability density function of time intervals may be written

$$f(t) = E\,e^{-Et}. \tag{1}$$

For this distribution, both mean and standard deviation equal $1/E$.

Table 1. *Time intervals in days between explosions in mines, involving more than 10 men killed, from 6 December 1875 to 29 May 1951*

378	286	871	66
36	114	48	291
15	108	123	4
31	188	457	369
215	233	498	338
11	28	49	336
137	22	131	19
4	61	182	329
15	78	255	330
72	99	195	312
96	326	224	171
124	275	566	145
50	54	390	75
120	217	72	364
203	113	228	37
176	32	271	19
55	23	208	156
93	151	517	47
59	361	1613	129
315	312	54	1630
59	354	326	29
61	58	1312	217
1	275	348	7
13	78	745	18
189	17	217	1357
345	1205	120	(complete interval
20	644	275	to 29 May 1951)
81	467	20	

Mean time interval = 241 days.

Table 1 gives the time intervals between explosions in mines in Great Britain involving the loss of ten lives or more since 1875. In Fig. 1 these intervals are shown to be approximately exponentially distributed. A study of other sequences of industrial accidents shows that the time intervals are usually exponentially distributed to at least a rough approximation.

Table 2. *Time intervals in days between successive compensable accidents in one district of a mine*

3	2	4	8	3
23	0	0	2	12
0	0	0	0	10
0	2	2	1	4
2	3	1	1	0
3	0	1	8	3
0	0	1	0	2
2	0	1	0	2
1	0	8	0	0
0	0	0	1	0
1	3	0	8	14
0	4	2	3	1
0	2	0	0	4
0	3	2	2	8
0	5	2	0	
1	0	0	1	
0	0	2	1	
1	2	0	3	
3	4	0	2	
2	5	2	0	
1	0	8	4	

Mean time interval = 2·2653 days.

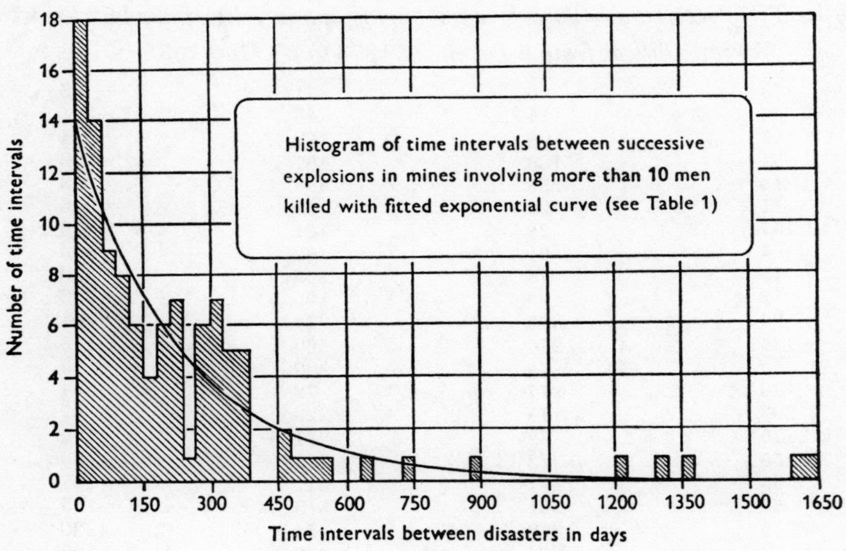

Fig. 1.

Table 2 gives the time interval between successive accidents for one shift in a section of a mine. Fig. 2 shows that the distribution is approximately exponential.

If the risk of accident were constant, the exponential distribution would be a good fit. In order to show that there have been changes in risk or expectation of accident, tests of homogeneity or goodness of fit are required for an exponential distribution. This method of attack has been suggested by various writers including Bortkiewicz (1898), Morant (1920), Neyman & Pearson (1928) and Sukhatme (1936).

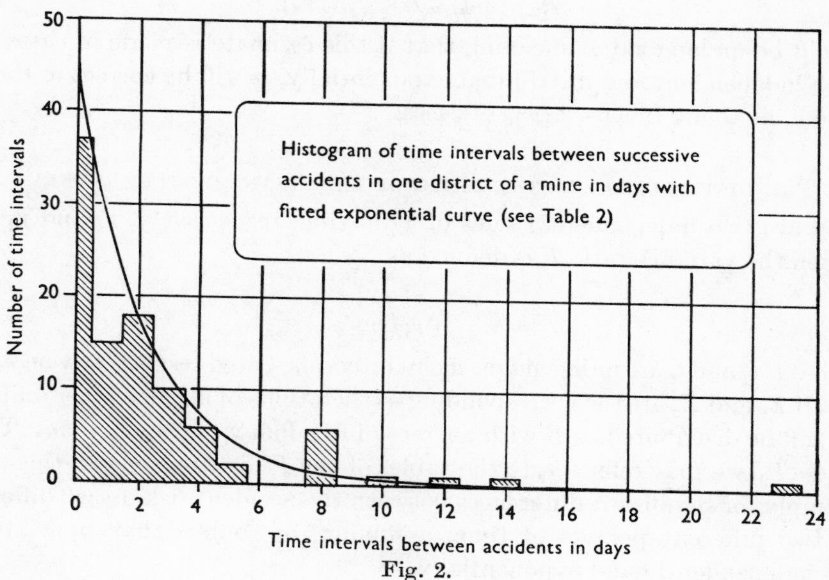

Fig. 2.

The exponential distribution has also been used in a more generalized form which assumes that following each event there is a 'closed period', t_0, during which another event cannot occur; (1) then becomes

$$f(t) = E\, e^{-E(t-t_0)}. \tag{2}$$

This distribution has been applied by various writers, including Sukhatme (1936), to the analysis of the time intervals between telephone calls. No useful application to the study of industrial accidents appears, however, to have been discovered so far, and the simpler distribution (1), where $t_0 = 0$, appears adequate for accident analysis.

3. The distribution of the sum and mean of time intervals

It may be shown that if time intervals are exponentially distributed, then both the sum, T, and the mean, $\bar{t}$, of n intervals have a Pearson type III distribution. The distribution of the sum of n intervals, say T, is

$$f(T) = \frac{(ET)^{n-1}\, e^{-ET}\, E}{(n-1)!}. \tag{3}$$

The distribution of the mean of n intervals, say $\bar{t}$, is

$$f(\bar{t}) = \frac{(nE\bar{t})^{n-1}\, e^{-nE\bar{t}}\, nE}{(n-1)!}. \tag{4}$$

The distribution (4) has a mean of $1/E$ and standard deviation of $1/(\sqrt{(n)}\,E)$; as n becomes large, this distribution tends to the normal form. $\bar{t}$ is also a sufficient estimator of $1/E$.

It follows from the form of equations (1) and (4) that $2Et$ and $2nE\bar{t}$ are distributed as χ^2 with degrees of freedom $\nu = 2$ and $\nu = 2n$, respectively. This means that well-known properties of the χ^2-distribution and of related functions, as well as existing tables, may be employed in accident interval analysis. For example, $\bar{t}$ may be used to provide confidence limits for an unknown value of E. Thus if $\chi^2_{1-\alpha}$ and χ^2_α are the lower and upper 100α % points of the distribution of χ^2, having $\nu = 2n$ degrees of freedom, there is a probability of $1-2\alpha$ that

$$\chi^2_{1-\alpha}/(2n\bar{t}) \leqslant E \leqslant \chi^2_\alpha/(2n\bar{t}).$$

This should be understood as meaning that if this estimate is made in cases where the intervals are independent and distributed exponentially, it will be correct in the long run, whatever be n, in about $100(1-2\alpha)$ % of cases.

4. The distribution of the ratio of the means of time intervals

If χ^2_1 and χ^2_2 are two independent values of χ^2 having, respectively, ν_1 and ν_2 degrees of freedom, then the variance ratio F is defined as

$$F = \frac{\chi^2_1}{\nu_1}\Big/\frac{\chi^2_2}{\nu_2}.$$

It follows that if $\bar{t}_1$ and $\bar{t}_2$ are independent mean intervals, based respectively on n_1 and n_2 intervals, and if E_1 and E_2 are the corresponding expectations of accidents per unit time, then $E_1\bar{t}_1/(E_2\bar{t}_2)$ will be distributed as F with degrees of freedom $\nu_1 = 2n_1$, $\nu_2 = 2n_2$. Thus to test whether $E_1 = E_2$, we may refer $\bar{t}_1/\bar{t}_2$ to the tables of the F-distribution. In this way we can test very simply for significant differences between the accident risk in two different places or during two different periods of time, assuming, of course, that time intervals are distributed independently and exponentially.

Thus when operations started on a particular working face in a mine there were seven compensable accidents with a mean time interval of 32 days. New machinery was then introduced and there were twelve further accidents with a mean time interval of 21 days. The ratio $32/21 = 1{\cdot}52$. The 10 % point for F is $1{\cdot}86$ for $\nu_1 = 2\times(7-1) = 12$ and $\nu_2 = 2\times(12-1) = 22$ degrees of freedom. The evidence from these data that the introduction of machinery has increased the expectation of accident is thus very weak.

As indicated in the preceding section, we may also obtain confidence limits for E or $1/E$ based, say, on the value of $\bar{t} = 21$ days observed after new machinery had been introduced. For $\nu = 22$ the lower and upper 5% points for χ^2 are $12{\cdot}34$ and $33{\cdot}92$ respectively. Hence we may state that

$$\frac{22\times 21}{33{\cdot}92} \leqslant \frac{1}{E} \leqslant \frac{22\times 21}{12{\cdot}34} \quad \text{or} \quad 13{\cdot}6 \leqslant \frac{1}{E} \leqslant 37{\cdot}4 \text{ days}$$

with a probability of $1-2\times 0{\cdot}05 = 0{\cdot}90$ of being correct, provided that the intervals follow the exponential law.

As a further illustration, consider the following case. A district in a mine had been working for over two years and there had been sixty-three compensable accidents. The mean time interval was 13·7 days. It became necessary to transfer a group of men to a new district replacing the experienced men by new face workers. Immediately after the change there were five accidents with a mean interval of 1·8 days. The ratio of the means is $F = 7{\cdot}6$; the numbers of degrees of freedom for F are 124 and 8, which give a 1% point of about 4·9. The change resulted, therefore, in a highly significant increase in the expectation of accident.

5. The extreme observations in samples from an exponential distribution

The χ^2 and F-distribution may both be usefully applied to the analysis of time intervals between accidents. Their application depends, however, on the assumption of homogeneity.

Particular tests for homogeneity may be based on the distribution of the extreme intervals. Range tests are particularly useful for indicating significantly long periods of immunity from accident. Thus in Table 1 it will be noted that there are intervals of 1613 and 1630 days between disasters. Is there evidence that the risk of disaster was lower during these periods?

(a) *Distribution of* $t_n/(n\bar{t})$

If t_n is the largest among n independent time intervals and $\bar{t}$ the mean of the n intervals, then if we let $g = t_n/(n\bar{t})$, the probability that g exceeds a given value G is shown by Fisher (1929) to be

$$\Pr\{g > G\} = n(1-G)^{n-1} - \tfrac{1}{2}n(n-1)(1-2G)^{n-1} + \ldots + (-1)^{k-1}\frac{n!}{k!(n-k)!}(1-kG)^{n-1},$$

where k is the largest integer less than $1/G$. 5 and 1 % significance levels for g up to $n = 50$ have been tabulated by Fisher (1929, 1950), who has shown that a good approximation can often be obtained from the first term of the series.

Application to data in Table 1. Here $n = 109$, $\bar{t} = 241$, $t_n = 1630$. The significant value of g at the 5 % significance level is $g_{\cdot 05} = 0{\cdot}068703$. Hence t_n is significant if

$$t_n \geqslant g_{\cdot 05} \times n\bar{t} = 1805 \text{ days}.$$

Our longest interval, 1630, is therefore not significant at the 5 % level.

Application to data in Table 2. $n = 98$, $n\bar{t} = 222$, $t_n = 23$. We find that $g = 0{\cdot}1036$, and from the formula above, of which the first term is sufficient,

$$\Pr\{g > 0{\cdot}1036\} = 0{\cdot}0024,$$

so that having regard to the mean of 2·27 days, the largest interval of 27 days is clearly significant.

(b) *Distribution of* t_n/t_1

Hartley (1951) has recently considered the ratio, $F_{\text{max.}} = s^2_{\text{max.}}/s^2_{\text{min.}}$, where $s^2_{\text{max.}}$ and $s^2_{\text{min.}}$ are the largest and smallest out of k independent mean-square estimates of variance each based on the same number of degrees of freedom ν. He has also shown that when $\nu = 2$

$$\Pr\{F_{\text{max.}} \leqslant F\} = k\int_0^\infty e^{-x}(e^{-x} - e^{-Fx})^{k-1}\,dx. \tag{5}$$

Clearly if t_n and t_1 are the largest and smallest of n time intervals, their ratio t_n/t_1 will follow Hartley's distribution (5). It must be remembered, however, that relatively small inaccuracies due to recording the shortest interval to the nearest day, week or month have a large influence on the value of t_n/t_1.

In Table 1 the ratio $t_n/t_1 = 1630/1$, which is not significant at the 5 % level. However, since t_1, recorded to the nearest day, is given in this case as 1, we can only say that $0{\cdot}5 < t_1 < 1{\cdot}5$; thus $F_{\text{max.}}$ may lie between 3260 and 1087. Indeed the shortest time interval may in practical cases often be recorded as zero, as in the list of intervals in Table 2 between successive accidents in one district of a mine. It is therefore not likely that the ratio t_n/t_1 will be found very useful in this field of application.

The distributions of t_n and $t_n - t_1$ may be useful if there is a satisfactory basis for assuming a hypothetical value for the expectation of accidents.

(c) *Distribution of* t_n

We have for t_n
$$\Pr\{t_n > \tau\} = 1-(1-e^{-E\tau})^n, \tag{6}$$
where E is the expectation of accidents per unit time.

Application to data in Table 1. $n = 109, E = 0{\cdot}004150$. We find from (6) that with 109 observations the 5 % significance level of Et_n is 7·5268. Thus if the true value of E were as found for this 75-year period, the 5 % significance level for the largest interval would be 1813 days. The observed value, $t_n = 1630$, falls within this limit. It also falls within the 10 % limit, calculated on the same basis.

Application to data in Table 2. $n = 98$, $E = 0{\cdot}4414$. The 5 % significance level of Et_n is 7·4866. Using the observed E, this gives 16·96 as the significant value of t_n. The largest interval, 23, falls beyond this level.

This test as applied in these illustrations, is of course not exact, as E has been determined from the data.

(d) *Distribution of* $t_n - t_1$

For the variate $y = t_n - t_1$, we have
$$\Pr\{y > Y\} = \int_Y^\infty (n-1)\, Ee^{-EY}\,(1-e^{-EY})^{n-2}\,dY$$
$$= 1-(1-e^{-EY})^{n-1}, \tag{7}$$
a result very similar to (6) except that $n-1$ replaces n. If n is large these tests are very nearly the same. For n small it may be that the test based on $t_n - t_1$ is more powerful.

6. The M-test

Tests may be applied to discover whether there is any significant tendency for intervals to succeed one another in groups, sometimes longer, sometimes shorter. A failure of the overall distribution of intervals to correspond with the exponential might be due to such a tendency; within short periods the exponential law might hold but E might change from period to period. The whole sequence may be broken into k groups of n successive intervals and may be tested for a significant difference between the k mean intervals, these mean intervals being each estimates of $1/E$.

If $\bar{t}_i$ is the mean interval in the ith group of n consecutive intervals ($i = 1, 2, \ldots, k$), where the intervals are exponentially distributed with parameter E_i, then the probability density function for $\bar{t}_i$ is given by
$$f(\bar{t}_i)\, d\bar{t}_i = \frac{1}{\Gamma(n)} (nE_i\bar{t}_i)^{n-1}\, e^{-n\bar{t}_iE_i}\, d(nE_i\bar{t}_i) \tag{8}$$
or $2nE_i\bar{t}_i$ is distributed like χ^2 with $\nu = 2n$ degrees of freedom, i.e. the mean intervals $\bar{t}_1, \bar{t}_2, \ldots, \bar{t}_k$ of the k groups of n successive intervals will, on our hypothesis, be distributed independently as
$$\chi^2/(2E_in).$$

If the data are homogeneous, the E_i will be equal. This can be examined by using the standard test for homogeneity of variances in samples from a normal population, commonly called Bartlett's test, though in the case of equal groups it is identical with the test given by Neyman and Pearson in 1931.*

* See note on p. 180 added in proof.

The test criterion to be calculated is*

$$M = 2nk\left\{\log_e\left(\frac{1}{k}\sum_{i=1}^{k}\bar{t}_i\right) - \frac{1}{k}\sum_{i=1}^{k}(\log_e\bar{t}_i)\right\}$$

$$= 2nk\left\{\log_e\left(\frac{1}{k}\sum_i T_i\right) - \frac{1}{k}\sum_i \log_e T_i\right\}, \tag{9}$$

where $T_i = n\bar{t}_i$ is the sum of n intervals in the ith group. Bartlett (1937) shows that M/C is distributed approximately as χ^2 with $\nu = k-1$, where

$$C = 1+(k+1)/(6nk). \tag{10}$$

For n small and $k \leqslant 15$, the tables computed by Thompson & Merrington (1946) give the 5 and 1 % points for M.

If ν is large we may have to make use of the fact that, to a good approximation, $\sqrt{(2\chi^2)} - \sqrt{(2\nu-1)}$ is a normal deviate with unit standard deviation. The M-test may also be used when the numbers of intervals in each group are unequal, the necessary modifications to equation (9) being given in the papers quoted.

The data of Table 2 were broken up into fourteen consecutive groups of $n = 7$ intervals, the fourteen sums, T_i, calculated and M obtained from equation (9) as follows:

$$M = 196\,(\log_{10} 2{\cdot}2653 - \tfrac{1}{14}3{\cdot}99028)\log_e 10$$
$$= 31{\cdot}639.$$

Further, $C = 1+15/(6\times 98) = 1{\cdot}0255$.

Hence $M/C = 30{\cdot}85$ with 13 degrees of freedom. Regarded as χ^2, M/C is just significant at the 0·5 % level. There appears therefore to be evidence of fluctuations in accident expectation with time during the period considered.

The M-test may also be applied to single intervals, i.e. when $n = 1$, but here, in practice, the application may be impossible if the record gives zero intervals making some values of $\log_e T_i = -\infty$. Table 1 contains no zeros, and we find that the set of single intervals is just significant at the 10 % level, M being 155·589. Thus the evidence that E is varying is slight.

It will be noticed that the results of applying the M-test in this section confirm those obtained with the g-test in § 5 above; the intervals in Table 1 are consistent with a constant accident expectation while those in Table 2 are not.

If a sequence of intervals is broken up into small groups in the way suggested and M calculated, we are perhaps using the best method available of testing whether the intervals follow a common exponential law and are arranged in random order. The test does, however, involve an arbitrary element in the sense that the division points separating the group of n intervals and the value of n itself are at the statistician's choice. In the ideal test this element would be eliminated; but to derive such a test more thought may be needed as to the kind of alternatives to homogeneity which may be expected to occur.

7. A FURTHER EXAMPLE

We shall take as an example to which several methods of analysis may be applied some data for the intervals between accidents causing fatalities in the mines of Great Britain. The seven lists in Table 3 correspond to the seven divisions of the National Coal Board and

* In Bartlett's (1937) notation, $M = -2\log_e \mu$.

the units of time are days. The period covered is 245 days in 1950. The first and last intervals in each division are not intervals between accidents, but between the start of the period and the first accident and between the last accident and the end of the period; they must therefore be omitted from any interval analysis.

Table 3

Div. 1		Div. 2			Div. 3		Div. 4	Div. 5		Div. 6		Div. 7		
16	2	4	13	8	12	0	16	21	4	7	3	17	2	0
3	2	9	4	4	1	13	8	2	5	9	20	2	1	1
1	6	0	0	1	7	2	24	15	1	10	7	4	7	1
0	14	11	3	3	1	13	6	1	13	4	12	1	4	15
7	10	1	4	2	4	7	5	5	6	2	0	2	1	2
7	2	12	4	3	5	5	14	1	9	6	23	0	0	5
20	2	0	15	4	9	11	2	9	3	9	13	6	5	3
6	2	0	0	3	6	0	11	1	—	14	19	1	3	14
1	7	1	5	0	5	0	8	0	—	0	12	4	6	2
20	3	2	8	5	8	3	16	17	—	7	—	2	6	5
5	15	26	3	0	2	8	8	0	—	0	—	0	0	24
10	13	2	3	2	13	5	98	1	—	5	—	0	1	0
4	4	4	1	13	8	1	1	24	—	1	—	14	7	1
6	8	4	0	2	1	13	3	14	—	14	—	2	3	0
19	—	6	1	3	1	18	16	4	—	2	—	10	5	8
1	—	0	0	0	4	17	9	9	—	9	—	2	2	—
9	—	5	5	3	3	5	—	20	—	8	—	5	0	—
16	—	0	3	0	6	—	—	14	—	2	—	9	0	—
0	—	0	1	9	11	—	—	1	—	5	—	6	0	—
2	—	2	4	0	11	—	—	1	—	10	—	13	2	—
2	—	5	2	7	6	—	—	44	—	12	—	8	1	—

If we are prepared to assume that accidents occur randomly in time and that the accident expectation was constant within a division during the 245 days, and merely want to test whether there is evidence that the rate differs between divisions, we may apply the simple χ^2 test to the total number of accidents. Here we assume that the frequency of accidents in a fixed period of time is a Poisson variable. The frequency of accidents in each division, $n_j, j = 1, 2, \ldots, 7$, is given in Table 4, and we find that

$$\chi^2 = \sum_{j=1}^{7} (n_j - \bar{n})^2 \Big/ \bar{n} = 44{\cdot}23 \text{ with } \nu = 6,$$

where $\bar{n} = 37{\cdot}14$ is the average number of accidents. This result is clearly very significant so that we must conclude that the differences among the n_j are real.*

Allowing, therefore, E to vary between divisions, we may ask whether the intervals within a division appear to follow the exponential law of equation (1), with values of E_j which may differ. A rapid check on this is obtained from Fisher's g-test, the necessary information being given in Table 4, where as before t_n is the largest of n intervals in a division, T is the sum of the intervals and $g = t_n/T$.† The number of intervals for the jth division is, of course, $n_j - 1$.

For $n_j - 1 < 50$, 5 and 1 % significance levels are shown, taken from Fisher's (1950) table. For the other two cases, the probability level corresponding to the observed g is shown. The

* Even when Division 4 with its exceptional interval of 98 days is omitted, $\chi^2 = 26{\cdot}22$ with $\nu = 5$ is still a highly significant value.

† The suffices j, which strictly should be given, have been dropped for simplicity.

only exceptional result is for Division 4, where g exceeds the 1 % level; this draws attention to the single long interval of 98 days. None of the other six values of g are significant at the 5 % level. The exponential distribution has, of course, a very long 'tail', and the test is mainly helping us to determine whether apparently outlying observations are, in fact, exceptional. To derive a more critical test of departure from the exponential, we must specify the form of departure to which it is wished that the test should be sensitive.

The M-test may also be applied to these data. Allowing for between-divisional differences in E_j, it searches for fluctuations in accident risk during the course of the 245-day period. Omitting the first and last intervals, we have summed the intervals within each division into k consecutive groups of $n = 4$, omitting the last intervals where the total number was not a multiple of 4. The results are shown in Table 5, where M and the Bartlett corrective factor C have been defined in equations (9) and (10). The only value of χ^2 which can be regarded as significant is that for Division 7 which falls just beyond the 0·5 % point. When the 7 values of χ^2 are summed, we find that for $\nu = 54$

$$\Pr\{\chi^2 > 74{\cdot}20\} = 0{\cdot}036.$$

Table 4

Division (j)	n_j	t_n	T	g	Significance levels 5 %	1 %	
1	34	20	221	0·0905	0·1835	0·2237	
2	62	26	234	0·1111	—	—	$\Pr\{g > 0{\cdot}1111\} = 0{\cdot}057$
3	37	18	228	0·0789	0·1712	0·2086	
4	15	98	220	0·4455	0·3517	0·4272	
5	27	44	221	0·1991	0·2212	0·2699	
6	29	23	226	0·1018	0·2088	0·2547	
7	56	24	220	0·1091	—		$\Pr\{g > 0{\cdot}1091\} = 0{\cdot}105$

Table 5

Division	k	M	C	$\chi^2 = M/C$	$\nu = k-1$
1	8	5·41	1·047	5·17	7
2	15	18·66	1·044	17·87	14
3	9	8·12	1·046	7·76	8
4	3	3·88	1·056	3·67	2
5	6	6·92	1·049	6·60	5
6	7	4·50	1·048	4·30	6
7	13	30·13	1·045	28·83	12
			Total	74·20	54

Without Division 7, the χ^2's sum to 45·32 which for 42 degrees of freedom is not exceptional.

Have we any justification in concluding that the intervals for Division 7 show significant changes in risk? We are faced here with the arbitrary character referred to above of our selection of the consecutive group of four intervals. If instead of taking the groups

2, 4, 1, 2), (0, 6, 1, 4), ..., we start two intervals later with (1, 2, 0, 6), (1, 4, 2, 0), ..., and proceed as before we obtain

$$\chi^2 = M/C = 17\cdot 58,$$

a value which, for $\nu = 12$, is not significant at the 10 % level. In other cases, which we have examined, shifting the position of the grouping divisions has not led to so large a change in χ^2. However, the limitation of the test must be recognized. In this case we cannot apply the test to single intervals and so avoid ambiguity (as was possible in examining the data in Table 1) because of the presence of zero intervals in the data as recorded.

Finally, we think it must be concluded that:

(*a*) there is definite evidence of differences in accident expectation between Divisions;

(*b*) the interval of 98 days in Division 4 is exceptional;

(*c*) apart from this we have not established inconsistency with the hypothesis that the intervals are randomly and exponentially distributed within a division.

8. Variations in the expectation

If E is the expectation of accidents per unit time and is a constant parameter, it has been shown that the distribution of time intervals between events is exponential and is given by the probability density function

$$f(t) = E\,e^{-Et}. \tag{1}$$

The distribution of accidents per unit time is the well known Poisson distribution which is discontinuous, the probability of r accidents in time τ being

$$p(r) = \frac{e^{-E\tau}\,(E\tau)^r}{r!}. \tag{11}$$

If E is itself a random variable with probability density function $h(E)$, $0 < E < \infty$, (1) may be transformed to give a new distribution of time intervals

$$f(t) = \int_{E=0}^{\infty} Eh(E)\,e^{-Et}\,dE. \tag{12}$$

This will be recognized as the Laplace transform. The tables of Laplace transforms and the considerable literature on their application to quite different problems may find some application to the analysis of interval distributions. See for example Carslaw & Jaeger (1941) and Doetsch (1947). Again, if E is a variable with probability distribution $h(E)$ as above, (11) may similarly be transformed to give the probability of intervals in time τ

$$p(r) = \frac{\tau^r}{r!}\int_0^{\infty} E^r h(E)\,e^{-E\tau}\,dE. \tag{13}$$

(13) is also a Laplace transform.

As an example, E may be assumed to be distributed in Pearson type III form

$$h(E) = \frac{c^q}{(q-1)!}E^{q-1}\,e^{-cE}. \tag{14}$$

Substitution in (12) and integration gives

$$f(t) = \frac{q}{c}\left(1+\frac{t}{c}\right)^{-(q+1)}. \tag{15}$$

This J-shaped curve is a form of the Pearson type XI distribution. Substitution of the Pearson type III distribution (14) in (13) gives the general term of the negative binomial distribution found by Greenwood & Yule (1920):

$$f(r) = \left(\frac{c}{c+1}\right)^q \frac{q(q+1)\dots(q+r-1)}{r!\,(c+1)^r}, \tag{16}$$

where τ is taken to be unity. The Pearson type XI distribution is thus seen to be the distribution of the time intervals between events which have a negative binomial frequency distribution and a Pearson type III probability distribution of the expectation of events per unit time.

Every distribution of time intervals is seen to have two related distributions; the frequency distribution of events in fixed intervals of time, and the frequency distribution of the expectation of events per unit time. Their relationship is stated in general terms by (12) and (13).

9. CONCLUSIONS

It is apparent that many statistical tests, often already developed and tabulated for other purposes, may be usefully adapted to analyse industrial accident data if the difficulties of collecting and recording can be overcome.

None of the tests described in this paper demonstrates lack of homogeneity in the series of time intervals in Table 1. No significance attaches to the long intervals of 1613 and 1630 days or to the short intervals of 1 and 4 days. Such extremes might well occur during a period of 76 years even if the expectation of accident were constant. It is not suggested, however, that these tests are exhaustive or are the most sensitive that could be devised. Further, the conclusions only apply to one class of explosions in mines; milder explosions involving one man or more killed, or serious disasters involving fifty or more men killed may not provide homogeneous series. A thorough study of time intervals between explosions in mines would take into consideration the number of men killed and the number at risk.

It has been seen that the time intervals in Table 2 are not homogeneous. The range test, in particular, provides a method of identifying a time interval when the risk of accident was sufficiently low.

The problems of industrial accident control are statistically analogous to those of industrial quality control and similar practical techniques, including sequential procedures, can almost certainly be developed to help in their solution. There are, however, very important differences between quality control and accident control. It is easy to define categories of accident in which men are killed or in which men receive compensation, but many accidents are difficult to place in satisfactory categories. The problems of accidents are more human and more complicated than those of quality control. It is usually more important to extract the maximum amount of information from industrial accident data than from the data obtained from inspectors' samples. In quality control the size of sample can be chosen, but in accident control the data must be examined from a sample which may be any size and cannot be chosen by the investigator. Finally, accidents happen at a particular time and, as the time of occurrence is a valuable part of the data, techniques based on the analysis of time intervals, unfamiliar in quality control, are needed.

The analysis of intervals may not only be used to study events distributed in time, but points distributed in space. The exponential distribution was, indeed, probably first used to describe the distribution of free paths of molecules of a perfect gas. The analysis of intervals may be usefully applied to a much wider range of problems than hitherto.

Acknowledgement is made to the Ministry of Fuel and Power for permission to publish this paper.

REFERENCES

BARTLETT, M. S. (1937). *Proc. Roy. Soc.* A, **160**, 268.

BORTKIEWICZ, L. (1898). *Bull. Inst. Statist.* **20** (2).

CARSLAW, H. S. & JAEGER, J. C. (1941). *Operational Methods in Applied Mathematics.* Oxford: Clarendon Press.

DOETSCH, G. (1947). *Tabellen zur Laplace Transformation und Anleitung zum Gebrauch.* Berlin: Springer.

FISHER, R. A. (1929). *Proc. Roy. Soc.* A, **125**, 54.

FISHER, R. A. (1950). *Contributions to Mathematical Statistics,* 16, 59*a*. London: Chapman and Hall.

GREENWOOD, M. (1946). *J.R. Statist. Soc.* **109**, 85.

GREENWOOD, M. & WOODS, H. M. (1919). *Industrial Fatigue Research Board Report,* 4. H.M.S.O.

GREENWOOD, M. & YULE, G. U. (1920). *J.R. Statist. Soc.* **83**, 255.

HARTLEY, H. O. (1951). *Biometrika,* **37**, 271.

JEFFREYS, H. (1948). *The Theory of Probability,* 2nd ed. Oxford University Press.

MORAN, P. A. P. (1951). *J.R. Statist. Soc.,* Series B, **13**, 147.

MORANT, G. M. (1920). *Biometrika,* **13**, 309.

NEYMAN, J. & PEARSON, E. S. (1928). *Biometrika,* **20**A, 175.

NEYMAN, J. & PEARSON, E. S. (1931). *Bull. Int. Acad. Cracovie,* A, 460.

SUKHATME, P. V. (1936). *Statist. Res. Mem.* **1**, 94.

THOMPSON, C. M. & MERRINGTON, M. (1946). *Biometrika,* **33**, 296.

WHITWORTH, W. A. (1901). *Choice and Chance,* 5th ed. Cambridge: Deighton Bell and Co.

YULE, G. U. (1922). *J.R. Statist. Soc.* **85**, 95.

Note added in proof. The publication of a recent paper by Moran (1951) has drawn our attention to the fact that in the discussion following a paper by Greenwood (1946), regarding industrial accidents, Bartlett suggested that known tests for homogeneity of variances could be used in the analysis of random time intervals. In his paper, Moran supposes that as an alternative to the exponential distribution of time intervals of equation (1), the probability density function has the Type III form

$$f(t) = (pE)^p \, e^{-pEt} t^{p-1}/\Gamma(p).$$

He then shows that in testing the hypothesis that $p=1$, i.e. that equation (1) is true against this class of alternatives, the likelihood ratio criterion will be a function of the M of equation (9), with $n=1$.

The departure from randomness which Moran contemplates is, of course, different from that which we have considered, i.e. a situation in which the accident expectation E may change from time to time, but the distribution of t remains exponential.

Further notes on the analysis of accident data

By B. A. MAGUIRE, E. S. PEARSON AND A. H. A. WYNN

1. We are very glad that Prof. Barnard (1953) has drawn attention in the preceding paper to the fact that the Kolmogoroff test may be used very simply to establish departure from randomness in a series of events occurring in sequence, either in time or space*. The figure reproduced below illustrates diagrammatically the application of the test to the accident data from our earlier paper (Maguire, Pearson & Wynn, 1952) used by Barnard. If t_i, measured in days from 6 December 1875, represents the time of occurrence of the ith accident following that which occurred at $t = 0$, then the 110 cumulative sample points (t_i, i), $i = 0, 1, \ldots, 109$, have been plotted (section A–B of the chart). A central, continuous line joins the first and last points (0, 0) and (t_n, n), where $n = 109$, $t_{109} = T = 26{,}263$; this is the theoretical cumulative line. Two parallel 'control' lines have been drawn on each side of this line at distances (measured parallel to the axis of i) of $\pm 1\cdot 6276\sqrt{n} = \pm 17\cdot 0$ forming a significance belt.

2. The Kolmogoroff theorem states that if the accidents have occurred at random with constant expectation during the period T, then the probability is approximately only 0·01 that the track of the cumulative points (t_i, i) will pass outside this belt. The points cross the upper limit of the belt where $i = 34$, $t = 3931$. Birnbaum (1952) has shown that when $n \geqslant 100$ there is good agreement as far out in the tail as the 1 % point between the true and the limiting distributions of the Kolmogoroff statistic. If we may assume that the approximation is also adequate at more extreme limits, it is possible to make use of Smirnoff's (1939, 1948) table of the limiting probability integral. This shows that

$$nD_n = \text{maximum}\,|\,nt_i/T - i\,|,$$

which is 24·6 at $i = 53$, is also significant at the 0·001 % level. It is quite clear, therefore, as Barnard points out, that there is evidence of very significant departure from randomness, the average interval having increased during the period.

3. Before following up one or two points concerning methods of analysis suggested by Barnard's note, it is perhaps desirable to say a few words about the particular accident data of this example. The figures are taken from Table 1 of our 1952 paper and show the intervals between mining accidents in Great Britain due to explosions involving more than ten men killed, during the 75-year period 1875–1950. They were introduced to illustrate certain points in our discussion—for example, the use of the following two tests of the hypothesis that the overall distribution of 109 intervals was consistent with sampling from a single exponential population:

(*a*) the M-test (heterogeneity of variance) applied to single intervals,

(*b*) Fisher's g-test, based on the ratio of the longest interval to the average interval.

Neither test established a significant departure from the exponential law.

4. Although we might and perhaps should have proceeded further, we did not in fact attempt to analyse these data further in the paper, i.e. we did not examine for changes in accident expectation within the period. The result brought out by the Kolmogoroff test, namely, that the accident intervals were shorter at the beginning than at the end of the period, can also be established quite simply by using another test which we gave (Maguire *et al.* 1952, p. 172) but did not use on these data. If T_1 is the time covered by the first 54 accidents and T_2 the time covered by the next 54, then

$$T_1 = t_{54} - t_0 = 8042, \quad T_2 = t_{108} - t_{54} = 16864.$$

* Some remarks of Bartlett (1949, p. 216) are also of interest in this connexion.

If the accidents have occurred randomly with constant expectation, T_2/T_1 should be distributed as a variance ratio, F, with degrees of freedom $\nu_1 = \nu_2 = 108$. But $F = 16864/8042 = 2{\cdot}10$, which is significant at the 0·1 % level.

5. To study the changes that may have occurred in the risk of explosions in mines would involve the consideration of a very complex story, and it would be out of place to make the attempt here. The following summary, however, gives a broad picture of what seems to have occurred. There appears to have been a substantial improvement in mine safety from 1870–90, and the average gravity of explosions, as judged from the number of casualties per explosion, was less in the period 1920–50 than between 1890–1920, but the frequency of explosions was not reduced; on the other hand, there may have been some increase in the risk of explosion in recent years in relation to coal output, the number of men in employment and the number of mines being worked, but this has not been fully investigated by the authors. There has been a considerable reduction in mining accidents in some other important categories.

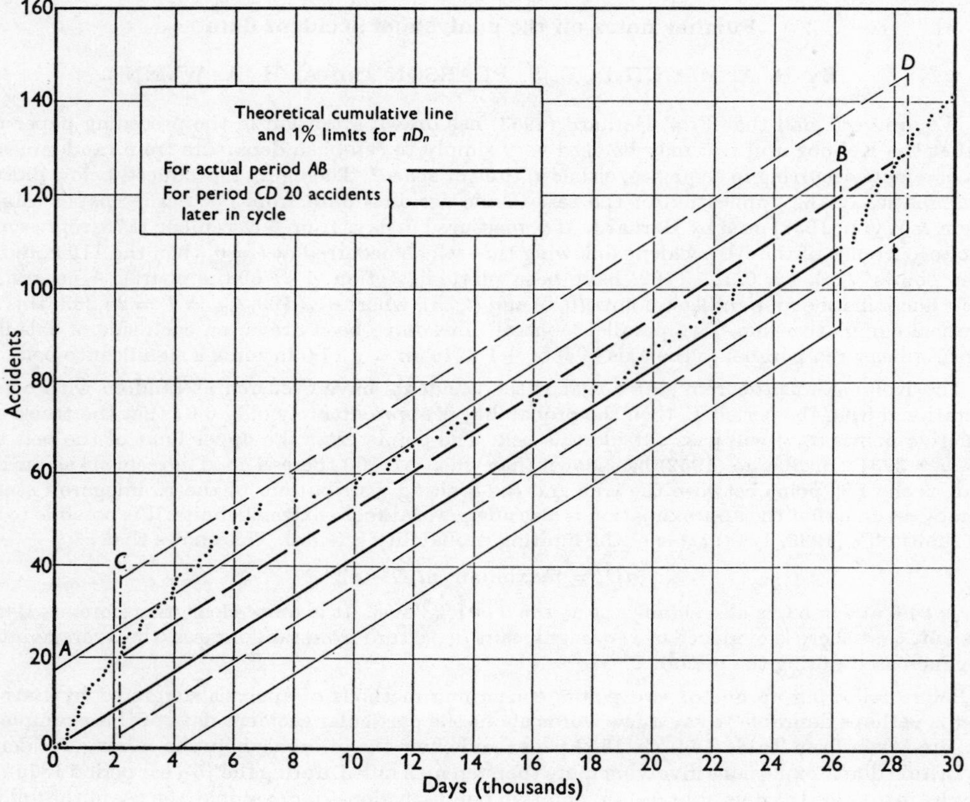

6. As Barnard has pointed out, the Kolmogoroff test is likely to be efficient in detecting a monotonic change in the risk $\lambda(t)$ whether this is of exponential character or follows a linear trend. Under these conditions, the plot of the cumulative points (t_i, i) moves away from the cumulative line and then comes back again in a single broad sweep. If $\lambda(t)$ does not change monotonically the position may, however, be very different, since the track of the cumulative points may now cross the theoretical line several times and never reach the boundary of the belt. For example, under certain conditions $\lambda(t)$ might fluctuate as an autoregressive function; we might then arrange the sequence of intervals in a closed cycle and look for a test for detecting changes in $\lambda(t)$ which is independent of any particular starting-point in the cycle.

7. In the diagram we have introduced this idea by adding the 1st, 2nd, 3rd, ..., etc., intervals after the 109th. If now we apply the Kolmogoroff test to the stretch CD instead of AB, i.e. to the 110 accidents of the cycle starting at the 20th accident of the original series, the expectation line and the two parallel 0·5 % limits are as shown by broken lines. The track of cumulative sample points now never passes

outside the 99 % belt and significance would not be established by the test. The maximum value of $|nt_i/T - i|$ is now 13·3, which (using the limiting distribution of Smirnoff) falls near the 8 % significance level.

8. Although the calculation is somewhat laborious with n so large, it is of interest to consider the application of a further test which is allied to that of Kolmogoroff, namely, the ω^2-test developed by Cramér (1928), von Mises (1931) and Smirnoff (1936). If $F(x)$ is the continuous cumulative frequency function of a random variable x specified by the hypothesis tested, and if $x_1, x_2, \ldots, x_n$ are n observed values of x arranged in ascending order of magnitude, then

$$\omega^2 = \frac{1}{12n^2} + \frac{1}{n}\sum_{i=1}^{n}\left\{F(x_i) - \frac{2i-1}{2n}\right\}^2. \tag{1}$$

For the case where the distribution of $x = t$ is rectangular in the interval $(0, T)$, $F(x_i) = F(t_i) = t_i/T$ and we may write

$$n\omega^2 = \frac{1}{12n} + \frac{1}{n^2}\sum_{i=1}^{n}\{nt_i/T - (i-0\cdot5)\}^2. \tag{2}$$

Thus, while the Kolmogoroff test uses the maximum value of n times the difference $t_i/T - i/n$, the ω^2 test uses the sum of squares of the n differences $d_i = t_i/T - (2i-1)/(2n)$. It will be seen that if the pattern of the n events is reproduced on a line of unit length, then d_i is the amount by which the ith point is displaced from the corresponding point in the regular series

$$1/(2n),\ 3/(2n),\ \ldots\ (2i-1)/(2n),\ \ldots\ (2n-1)/(2n).$$

Thus if denser concentrations of points alternate with stretches of rarer occurrence, ω^2 may increase significantly above expectation.

9. The first two moments of $n\omega^2$ have been known for some time, but we are indebted to Mr B. A. M. Thomas* for expressions for the 3rd and 4th moments about the mean. Thus we have for the first four moments:

$$\left.\begin{aligned} \mu_1' &= \frac{1}{6}, & \mu_2 &= \frac{4n-3}{180n}, \\ \mu_3 &= \frac{32n^2-61n+30}{3780n^2}, & \mu_4 &= \frac{496n^3-1532n^2+1671n-630}{75600n^3}. \end{aligned}\right\} \tag{3}$$

The distribution is very far from normal. It will be found that when $n \to \infty$ the limiting values of the moments agree with the values of the cumulants of the limiting distribution of $n\omega^2$ given by Anderson & Darling (1952). The use of these moments in deriving an approximation to the distribution of $n\omega^2$ in relatively small samples requires much fuller consideration, but the following values of the standard deviation and the moment ratios $\beta_1 = \mu_3^2/\mu_2^3$ and $\beta_2 = \mu_4/\mu_2^2$, which we owe to Thomas, show that when $n = 109$ the distribution of $n\omega^2$ must be approaching the limiting form:

n	S.D.	β_1	β_2
10	0·143	5·53	11·23
20	0·146	6·03	12·24
50	0·148	6·33	12·87
100	0·149	6·43	13·08
1000	0·149	6·52	13·26
∞	0·149	6·53	13·29

We shall therefore use below the percentage points of the limiting distribution tabled by Anderson & Darling (1952, p. 203), in particular

5 %	4 %	1 %	0·1 %
0·461	0·499	0·743	1·168

* The results were included in an essay presented as part of the Examination for the B.Sc. Special Degree of the University of London (1952).

10. We have now calculated $n\omega^2$ from equation (2)* for the $n = 109$ accident times t_i considered previously, (*a*) starting from the zero point at 6 December 1875 and (*b*) from the date of the 20th accident in the artificial cycle described in para. 7. We then find for (*a*) and (*b*):

(*a*) $n\omega^2 = 1{\cdot}541$, which is a value far beyond the 0·1 % significance level given above;

(*b*) $n\omega^2 = 0{\cdot}474$, a result significant at the 5 % (but not at the 4 %) level.

It follows that for the present data, in its original form, both the Kolmogoroff and ω^2-test give very clear evidence of departure from randomness. When, however, the intervals are arranged in cyclical form and the analysis starts at the 20th accident, the former test does not, and the latter does, establish significance at the 5 % level.

11. It would not be legitimate to make any general comparison of the two tests on the basis of these special results. One broad conclusion, however, may, we think, be drawn. As one of us has emphasized before (Pearson, 1942), while it seems attractive to transform a statistical problem into one of testing whether a sample has been drawn from a rectangular population, it is still not possible to determine the most efficient test to use for the purpose unless we can formulate the type of departure from the rectangle that is likely to arise. It appears that the Kolmogoroff test will only be powerful in detecting certain kinds of variation in $\lambda(t)$ and a similar position will hold for the ω^2-test.

REFERENCES

Anderson, T. W. & Darling, D. A. (1952). *Ann. Math. Statist.* **23**, 193–212.
Barnard, G. A. (1953). *Biometrika*, **40**, 212.
Bartlett, M. S. (1949). *J. Roy. Statist. Soc.* B, **11**, 211.
Birnbaum, Z. W. (1952). *J. Amer. Statist. Ass.* **47**, 425–41.
Cramér, H. (1928). *Skand. Aktuar. Tidskr.* **11**, 13–74, 141–80.
Maguire, B. A., Pearson, E. S. & Wynn, A. H. A. (1952). *Biometrika*, **39**, 168–80.
von Mises, R. (1931). *Wahrscheinlichkeitsrechnung*. Vienna: Deuticke.
Pearson, E. S. (1942). *Biometrika*, **32**, 311–16.
Smirnoff, N. V. (1936). *C.R. Acad. Sci., Paris*, **202**, 449.
Smirnoff, N. V. (1939). *Bull. Math. Univ. Moscou*, **2**, fasc. 2.
Smirnoff, N. V. (1948). *Ann. Math. Statist.* **19**, 279–81.

Some aspects of the geometry of statistics

The use of visual presentation in understanding the theory and application of mathematical statistics

Some aspects of the geometry of statistics

The use of visual presentation in understanding the theory and application of mathematical statistics

[The Inaugural Address of the PRESIDENT, PROFESSOR E. S. PEARSON, C.B.E., delivered to the ROYAL STATISTICAL SOCIETY, on 18 January, 1956]

1. INTRODUCTION

The main title which I have chosen for this address was suggested by an incident in the early stages of development of mathematical statistics in England. In the year 1890, Karl Pearson, then Professor of Applied Mathematics at University College, London, was appointed to the part-time professorship in Geometry at Gresham College in the City of London. Whatever may have been the original intentions of Sir Thomas Gresham, the duties of one of his seven professors 300 years after the founding of his College seem to have consisted in giving some dozen end-of-the-day lectures each year to a semi-popular audience. The first eight lectures which Pearson gave on the 'Scope and Methods of Science' were later developed into his book *The Grammar of Science*; these lectures were, however, followed by twelve on 'The Geometry of Statistics', twelve on 'The Laws of Chance' and finally in 1893–94 by ten on 'The Geometry of Chance'.*

It appears from the summaries that the lectures on the Geometry of Statistics were mainly concerned with methods of visual presentation of what may be termed descriptive statistics. Two years later, however, when the elements of a theory of mathematical statistics were already taking shape in Gower Street, with the development of the properties of the binomial and the hypergeometric series, of the normal distribution and of compound and skew frequency curves, the evening lectures given at Gresham College had changed their emphasis. The audiences were encouraged to carry out a variety of sampling experiments whose results were compared with theory, the whole being illustrated by models and wall diagrams, some of which survive with us at University College today.

The graphical approach was a characteristic feature of Pearson's teaching of Applied Mathematics; it appeared in his courses on geometrical drawing and projection, on graphical mechanics and in the drawing office classes which he conducted for engineering students right up till 1911. It was natural that he should extend this approach to Statistics. In the summary to his first lecture on the Geometry of Statistics he noted:

> Contest of geometry and arithmetic as scientific tools in dealing with physical and social phenomena. Erroneous opinion that geometry is only a means of popular representation; it is a fundamental method of investigating and analysing statistical material.

Today our statistical theory and the techniques of analysis which we apply to numerical data are based on mathematical models of far greater complexity and refinement than could be imagined 65 years ago. But if the model is more elaborate, it becomes all the more difficult to judge whether it fits the data as a whole. In last February's discussion before the Society

* For the syllabuses of these lectures, see E. S. Pearson (1938), Appendix II.

on 'The Teaching of Mathematical Statistics at University Level', Professor D. G. Champernowne remarked:

> ...that theory (of mathematical statistics) is solely concerned with working out the properties of the theoretical models—whereas what matters—and what in one sense is most difficult—is deciding what theoretical model best corresponds to the real world situation to which statistical methods must be applied. There is great danger that mathematical pupils will imagine that a knowledge of mathematical statistics alone makes a statistician.

I have little doubt that, where this is possible, a visual survey of the 'pattern' of his data provides the statistician who is trained to extract a meaning from diagrams with the quickest method of checking whether the model he proposes to use is likely to be appropriate or not. That understanding can be achieved through visual aids may be regarded as a proposition so obvious that it needs no restatement by me; yet there is much evidence that the average mathematically-trained student who forms today the raw material of our classes in mathematical statistics is not too well endowed with visual imagination. How far, one may ask, is this a question of teaching both at school and at university level? Later in the discussion just mentioned Professor M. G. Kendall referred to the question of *how* to teach statistics.

> University teachers, [he said], are unique among professional men in having no training whatsoever in their profession. They have to learn by experience and some of them never do learn. One would expect that in such circumstances a good deal of thought would have been given to the technique by which statistical ideas should be introduced to students. Perhaps it has, but if so the results have not been made available for general use.

My remarks today may be regarded in part as an answer to Professor Kendall's challenge. In broad terms we may accept the thesis that appropriate methods of visual presentation can play an important part in helping the statistician in ways such as these: in understanding the meaning of his arithmetical results; in avoiding mistakes through lack of fit of his models; in saving time; and in providing what is often the best means of making clear his methods of analysis to the non-statistician. But the prestige of arithmetical procedures based on algebraic formulae is deeply entrenched in our lecture courses and our text-books, so that few mathematical statisticians will use to the full their visual faculties unless they are trained to do so. In a matter of this kind one can speak confidently only from personal experience, but I believe that the intellectual stimulus which can come from use of the visual imagination may be very great. In the course of my own statistical training I remember two points at which diagrams formed the key to my understanding of a great tract of territory.

At the very beginning of his lectures on correlation my father would describe the difference between what he termed the physicist's conception of a law of relationship between two variables and the statistician's concept of correlation. He would draw on one part of the blackboard a straight line or curve with a few points lying closely on either side of it. $y = f(x)$ represented the law and the points fell off the curve only through what would be termed errors of observation. Next to this he drew a great belt of dots or crosses suggesting what we now would call a bivariate probability density distribution, and he told us how the statistician's problem was to describe this belt as he found it. One could see in this diagram the meaning of two regression lines and of array distributions which might be described in terms of their standard deviations and their shape. Here, in a picture, was a model of a correlation distribution in which to my mind one could *see* the properties as a whole far more surely than one could extract them from an algebraically expressed function $p(x, y)$.

My second flash of understanding developed from the small diagram on p. 509 of R. A. Fisher's 1915 paper in Vol. 10 of *Biometrika.* While the main part of this paper was concerned with the distribution of the correlation coefficient, this diagram introduced me to that fruitful idea, adequately grasped in terms of 3-dimensional geometry of the relation of a mean, a standard deviation, and Student's ratio to a plane, a cylinder and a cone. One *saw*, also why, when the space was filled with the probability density distribution of 'normal' variation with its spherical density contours, then and then only problems of distribution theory became beautifully simple. One could see, too, in geometrical terms, how the methods of the analysis of variance consisted in a skilful rotation of axes, so as to separate and compare the appropriate projections of a vector.

I am told that I have been fortunately endowed with an extra amount of visual imagination, and that it is unfair for me to expect others of my staff or students to be helped by statistical geometry. But while it may be true that most mathematicians cannot see things in pictures, indeed may have a better method of grasping the fit of their models to data than I have, they find difficulty in telling me how they get this overall grasp of the appropriateness of a fit. At any rate I feel justified in setting down some of my own pictures. That even in the field of Pure Mathematics, where no question arises of fitting a model to observational data, the value of visual presentation is recognized, is well illustrated in Hilbert and Cohn-Vosser's *Geometry and the Imagination** (1932). This book is filled with well drawn diagrams illustrating the properties of 3-dimensional curves and surfaces. In the first paragraph to his Preface, Hilbert wrote as follows:

> In mathematics, as in any scientific research, we find two tendencies present. On the one hand, the tendency towards *abstraction* seeks to crystallize the *logical* relations inherent in the maze of material in a systematic and orderly manner. On the other hand, the tendency towards *intuitive understanding* fosters a more immediate grasp of the objects one studies, a live *rapport* with them, so to speak, which stresses the concrete meaning of their relations.

And later:

> With the aid of visual imagination we can illuminate the manifold facts and problems of geometry, and beyond this it is possible in many cases to depict the geometric outline of the methods of investigation and proof, without necessarily entering into details connected with the strict definitions of concepts and with the actual calculations.

These passages bring out clearly some of the aspects of the geometry of statistics which I have in mind. The function of visual presentation in fostering in the mathematician a lively understanding of his data; the power of a geometrical outline to help the non-mathematical practitioner in grasping the meaning of the techniques of analysis. In the following sections I shall endeavour to illustrate my theme with a few selected examples. For much of what I shall say I could use as text the introductory paragraph of chapter II of R. A. Fisher's (1925) *Statistical Methods for Research Workers*, which runs as follows:

> The preliminary examination of most data is facilitated by the use of diagrams. Diagrams prove nothing, but bring outstanding features readily to the eye; they are therefore no substitute for such critical tests as may be applied to the data, but are valuable in suggesting such tests, and in explaining the conclusions founded upon them.

* A translation was issued by the Chelsea Publishing Company, New York, in 1952 from which I have quoted.

2. Geometry and teaching

2·1. *Training in the visual approach*

I shall later be concerned with stressing the value of diagrams to the practising statistician as companions to arithmetic in extracting the meaning from data, but there is no doubt that their function in teaching is also an important one. This is partly from the help they can give towards understanding mathematical models, by describing their properties in geometric as well as algebraic terms. But if the student is to turn into a statistician who makes full use of diagrams in the analysis of observations he will generally need some training in the visual approach to data. Even if the mathematically-minded student believes that he can himself dispense with any form of visual aid, he may regret later in his career that he had not given more thought to what may prove the surest means of communication open to him with some of his non-mathematical clients or colleagues.

Many openings can be found for encouraging the use of the visual imagination in connexion with the common distributions and tests used in statistical sampling theory. I shall start by taking two illustrations which concern Student's t-distribution.

2·2. *The difference between two means*

Authorities have differed widely in the philosophy of their approach to tests of significance. Fig. 1 presents a series of steps in the development of one possible train of reasoning by which we apply the t-test to draw conclusions about the significance of the difference between two mean values.

At the top we see two population distributions to each of which a normal curve has been fitted. The variable is the depth of sapwood in inches measured in telephone poles supplied by two companies;* below these two distributions the dots represent two random samples of 10 observations, based on measurements of poles from each source of supply. We ask: 'would these 20 observations alone give us reason for doubting that the means in the two populations are the same?'.

Assuming that the variability in the two populations is approximately equal—and the full data shows this to be the case—we calculate Student's t, that is the ratio of the difference between the sample means to the pooled estimate of the standard error of the difference. For this particular pair of samples, $t = 2{\cdot}53$.

In the next section of the diagram this value of 2·53 is related to the distribution which the t-ratio would follow if the population means were the same; it is seen that it lies between the 5% and 1% points (using the two-tailed test with 18 degrees of freedom). In this case two samples of 10 observations would have been sufficient to make the statistician suspect a difference in population means, but it is natural to ask: 'would this generally be so?'. In other words, given two populations with the degree of overlap illustrated in the top section of the diagram [(Difference between population means)/(standard deviation) $= 0{\cdot}76/0{\cdot}60 = 1{\cdot}27$] what is the probability that the t-test based on two samples of 10 will establish a difference in means, using either (a) the 5%, or (b) the 1% level of significance?

The answer is given mathematically by the so-called non-central distribution of t shown as the lowest curve. Tables or charts (e.g. Pearson & Hartley, 1954, table 10) indicate that the area under this curve lying outside the 5% and 1% limits of the standard t-curve

* The figures are Bell Telephone Company data originally used by Dr W. A. Shewhart.

drawn above it are 0·76 and 0·49 respectively. In other words, the probability of establishing significance is (*a*) 0·76, (*b*) 0·49.

To drive home the meaning of this argument pictorially, 19 further pairs of samples of 10 were drawn randomly from the two populations and the 20 values of Student's t (the first value of 2·53 is drawn as an open circle) have been plotted at the foot of the diagram;

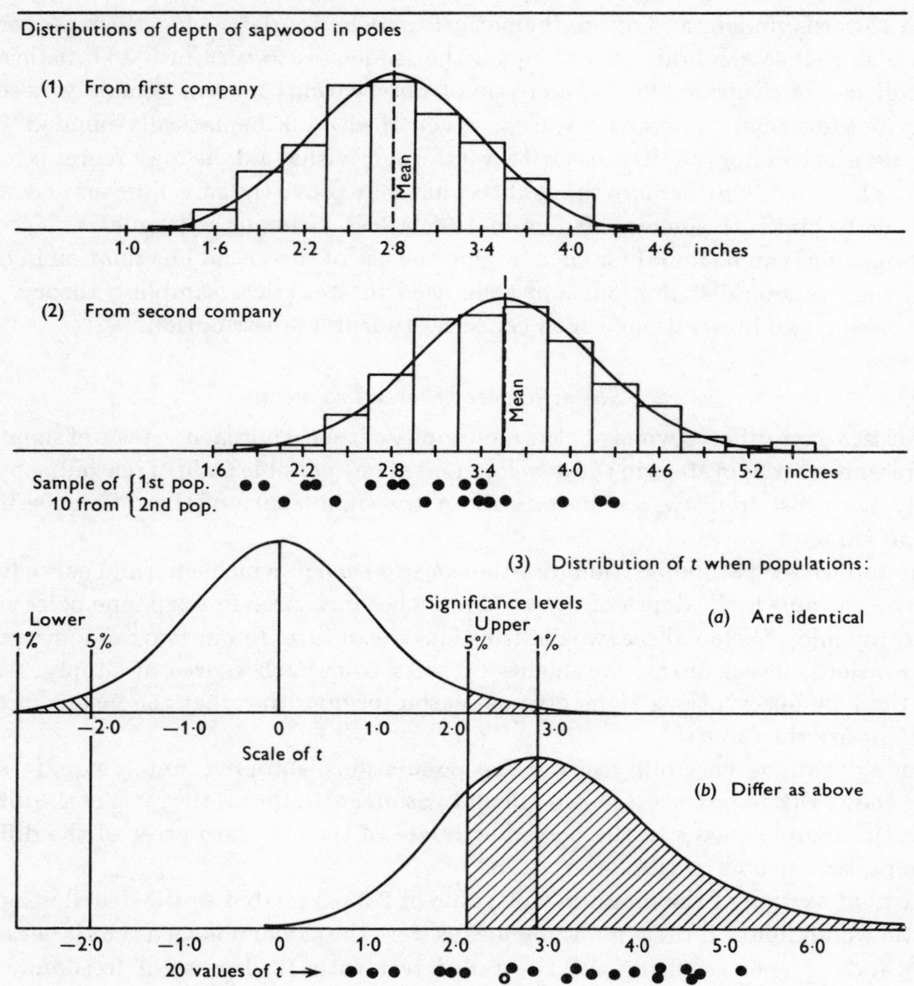

Fig. 1. Student's t-test applied to two sample means.

14 out of 20 fall beyond the 5 % significance level, and 11 out of 20 beyond the 1 % results in good agreement with the expectations of mathematical theory, i.e. 15·2 and 9·8.

This argument is, of course, very familiar to statisticians, but I have purposely set it out at some length in order to show how Fig. 1, which could easily be reproduced as a class wall diagram, summarizes the underlying properties of the test. Not only so, but it provides points of departure for comment on the adequacy of the mathematical model and the ways in which it may fail. What will happen, it may be asked, if the two population distributions are not well represented by normal curves or have very different variances? How much will the central and non-central t-distributions shown below be modified? Upon this depends what Box has termed the robustness of the test.

There can be little doubt that summary diagrams of this kind have their value for the mathematical statistician in training as well as for the non-mathematician, who besides using tables of significance levels is seeking for a broad understanding of statistical ideas.

2·3. *The geometry of two and three dimensions*

My second figure relates to a situation where the visual imagination, extended through two to three dimensions, can help the geometrically minded to 'understand' in a flash what can only be proved algebraically at considerable length. It follows from R. A. Fisher's geometrical identification of the mean and standard deviation (1915, p. 509) already referred to and relates again to a form of Student's t-test.

Suppose that x_1, x_2—and for 3-dimensional representation x_1, x_2, x_3—represents a random sample of 2 (or 3) observations from a normal population, with mean zero and standard deviation σ. Possible samples will be represented by a cluster of points surrounding the origin, 0, in 2 (or 3) dimensions such as are shown in Fig. 2a. Since the probability density law takes the form

$$p(x_1, x_2) = \frac{1}{2\pi\sigma^2}\exp\{-\tfrac{1}{2}(x_1^2+x_2^2)/\sigma^2\}$$

it follows that the contours of this probability distribution are circular or, in 3 dimensions, spherical. If the value of σ is unknown, the probability contours will remain the same, but we shall not know what may be termed the scale of radial concentration about 0.

Suppose that we are uncertain whether the population mean of x is zero, thinking that it may have some unknown positive value, $\mu > 0$. If this is so, in 2 dimensions, the sample point (x_1, x_2) may be described as one of a possible cluster centred at (μ, μ) on the axis $x_1 = x_2$, for which the density contours will also be circular. This situation again is suggested in Fig. 2a. In the approach commonly followed for testing the hypothesis that $\mu = 0$, on the basis of a given sample, having the alternative $\mu > 0$ in mind, we specify a rejection region in the space such that:

(a) if the observed sample point falls within this region, we reject the hypothesis;

(b) the probability of the point falling in this region, if $\mu = 0$, has some small value α.

Now if σ is unknown, geometrical considerations show that the rejection region can only satisfy (b), whatever be σ, if it is built up of elementary regions each containing a fraction α of every circular (or for 3 dimensions, spherical) contour of equal density centred at 0. The horn-shaped regions suggested by the lines AOA' and COC' for 2 and 3 dimensions in Fig. 2 are constructed in this way. But how shall we choose between the infinite number of regions which would satisfy requirement (b)?

It appears desirable to choose that region which

(c) will give the greatest chance of rejecting the hypothesis $\mu = 0$ when in fact μ has any other value greater than zero.

Since for $\mu > 0$, the probability density distribution has circular (or spherical) symmetry about some point on the diagonal axis $x_1 = x_2$ (or $x_1 = x_2 = x_3$), it appears to be intuitively established that the rejection region satisfying conditions (c) must be directed symmetrically up this diagonal axis—as the area between two straight lines BOB' in Fig. 2a, or as the volume inside the cone DOD' with circular cross-section in Fig. 2b.

But from Fisher's geometrical result the boundaries of these regions are precisely the

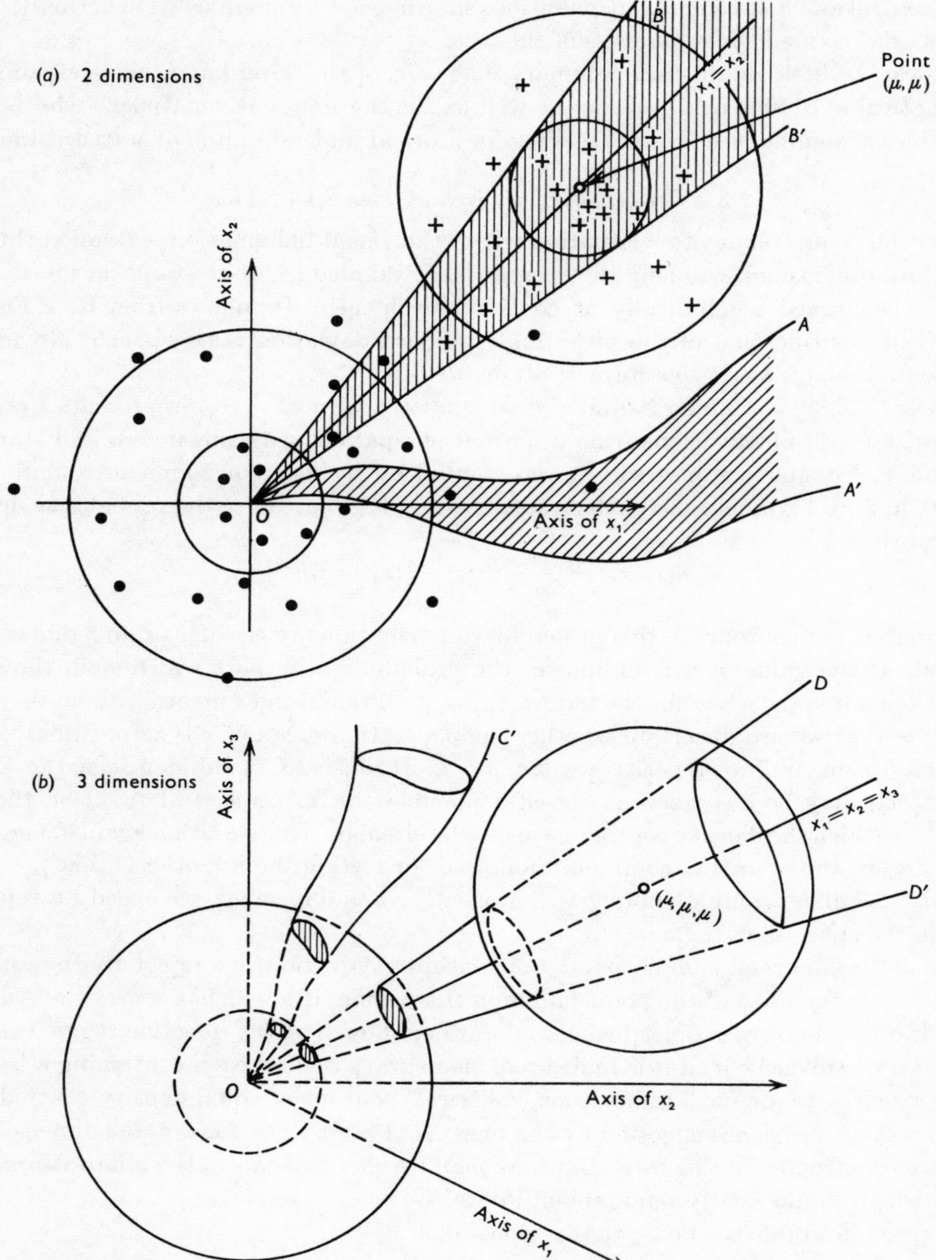

Fig. 2. Geometric presentation of Student's test.

surfaces on which Student's t-ratio is constant and *within* which t exceeds the boundary value. For the case of 3 dimensions

$$t = \sqrt{(6)}\,\bar{x}/\sqrt{\{\Sigma(x_i - \bar{x})^2\}} \quad \text{where} \quad \bar{x} = \tfrac{1}{3}(x_1 + x_2 + x_3).$$

This result, that Student's ratio provides what has been termed the uniformly most powerful test of the hypothesis specified, can of course be proved in general by algebraic methods. But I am doubtful whether the more conventional proof can provide the same mental satisfaction as an approach by which we seem to see the result must be true by an appeal to our visual imagination!

2·4. *The shape of Edgeworth curves*

The previous examples have been concerned with the interpretation of statistical tests in terms of the concept of repeated sampling. My next example is of a different character.

In recent years it has been common to use Gram-Charlier and Edgeworth curves to represent the distribution of the variable in the parent population when exploring the effect of

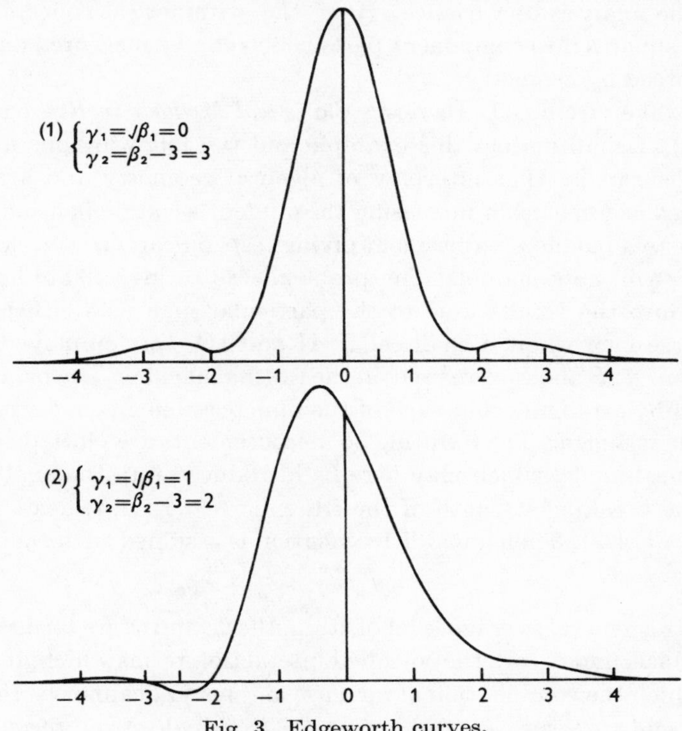

Fig. 3. Edgeworth curves.

departure from normality on standard statistical procedures, such as those of the analysis of variance. This has been done because the use of the mathematical forms involved renders algebraic treatment possible, even if sometimes laborious. Thus it is assumed that an Edgeworth curve of the form

$$f(x) = e^{-\frac{1}{2}x^2}/\sqrt{(2\pi)}\left\{1+\frac{1}{3!}\gamma_1 H_3(x)+\frac{1}{4!}\gamma_2 H_4(x)+\frac{1}{3.4!}\gamma_1^2 H_6(x)\right\}$$

can be used to represent the population, where

$$\gamma_1 = \sqrt{\beta_1} = \kappa_3/\kappa_2^{\frac{3}{2}}, \quad \gamma_2 = \beta_2 - 3 = \kappa_4/\kappa_2^2$$

are the usual moment ratios of the distribution and $H_3(x)$, $H_4(x)$ and $H_6(x)$ are Hermite polynomials in x.

But there has not always been evidence in the published papers that the authors have examined the shapes of the distributions falling within the range of the γ_1, γ_2 values which they have discussed. Thus the two curves of Fig. 3 have γ-values (0, 3 and 1, 2) which have been included within the range of some of these investigations. It is probable that certain broad conclusions about the robustness of tests can be drawn by stretching departure from normality into shapes containing small negative frequencies and subsidiary bumps, but if the writers had been trained always to *look* at the shapes of frequency distributions and probability curves before starting to use them, they would hardly have included such forms in their discussion without some comment.

2·5. *Diagrams showing component parts in the analysis of variance*

One of the statistical fields in which visual aids to understanding have always seemed to me valuable is the analysis of variance. Here, the arithmetical concept of the partition of a total sum of squares into component parts which can be measured and compared may be usefully reinforced by geometry.

My example is taken from O. L. Davies' s *Statistical Methods in Research and Production* (1947, pp. 90–93). I shall discuss this example and the following one at some length to illustrate what I mean by that interplay of algebra, geometry and arithmetic which I believe can be used as a means of increasing the student's comprehension.

The data relate to a balanced experiment giving tests on compressive strength of cement mortar, cast into $\frac{1}{2}$ in. cube moulds. The problem was to investigate how far a personal element entered into the results, due to the particular men who either mixed or tested the material. Three men whom I shall call I, II and III were employed as 'mixers' and three different men, A, B and C were used on the testing machine. The balance in the experiment was secured by arranging that each of the nine possible mixer-tester pairs dealt with four cubes of cement mortar. The resulting 36 measurements are plotted as circles in Fig. 4.

The mathematical model which may here be introduced into the analysis is as follows. y_{mti} represents the breaking strength of the ith cube ($i = 1, \ldots, 4$) dealt with by mixer m and tester $t\,(m, t = 1, 2, 3)$. Then an additive relation is assumed such that

$$y_{mti} = \alpha + \beta_m + \gamma_t + \delta_{mt} + z_{mti}, \tag{1}$$

where α represents a general average level of strength, β_m and γ_t are terms due to individual mixer and tester bias, and δ_{mt} are the so-called interaction terms which, if present, measure the amount by which the combination of mixer m and tester t cannot be represented by the sum of two independent terms, β_m and γ_t. z_{mti} is a residual 'error' term which cannot be accounted for by systematic biases.

As a counterpart to the idealized equation (1) we can form an identity with estimated components:*

$$y_{mti} \equiv \underset{(\alpha)}{y_{\ldots}} + \underset{(\beta_m)}{(y_{m..} - y_{\ldots})} + \underset{(\gamma_t)}{(y_{.t.} - y_{\ldots})} + \underset{(\delta_{mt})}{(y_{mt.} - y_{m..} - y_{.t.} + y_{\ldots})} + \underset{(z_{mti})}{(y_{mti} - y_{mt.})}. \tag{2}$$

The standard analysis of variance table given in Table 1 provides in arithmetical form the partition of the total sum of squares about the grand mean, represented by the identity

$$\begin{aligned} \Sigma(y_{mti} - y_{\ldots})^2 &\equiv \Sigma(y_{m..} - y_{\ldots})^2 + \Sigma(y_{.t.} - y_{\ldots})^2 \\ \text{or} \quad S \quad &= \quad S_1 \quad + \quad S_2 \\ &\quad + \Sigma(y_{mt.} - y_{m..} - y_{.t.} + y_{\ldots})^2 + \Sigma(y_{mti} - y_{mt.})^2. \\ &\quad + \quad S_3 \quad + \quad S_4 \end{aligned} \tag{3}$$

* Here the mean values have their customary meaning, i.e. $y_{\ldots}$ is the grand mean of the 36 observations, $y_{m..}$ the mean of the 12 cubes prepared by mixer m, $y_{.t.}$ of those broken by tester t, and $y_{mt.}$ of the 4 cubes dealt with by m and t in combination.

Table 1. *Analysis of variance for tests on Portland cement*

Source of variation	Sum of squares	Degrees of freedom	Mean square	Variance ratio
Between mixers	$S_1 = 8{,}965$	2	4,482	$F_1 = \frac{S_1}{2} \div \frac{S_4}{27} = 1{\cdot}63$
Between testers	$S_2 = 25{,}061$	2	12,530	$F_2 = \frac{S_2}{2} \div \frac{S_4}{27} = 4{\cdot}56$
Mixer-tester interaction	$S_3 = 6{,}638$	4	1,659	$F_3 = \frac{S_3}{4} \div \frac{S_4}{27} = 0{\cdot}60$
Residual (within groups of 4 observations)	$S_4 = 74{,}155$	27	2,746	—
Total	$S = 114{,}819$	35		

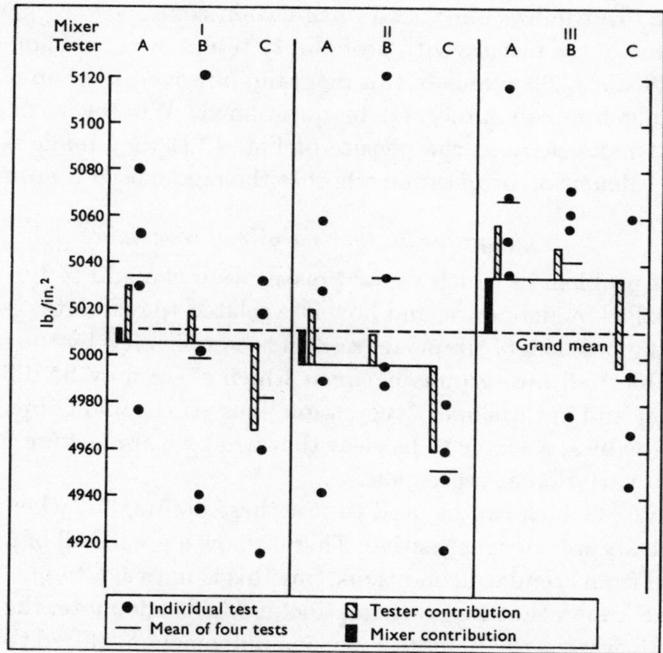

Fig. 4. Tests on samples of Portland cement. ●, Individual test; —, mean of four tests; ▨, tester contribution; ■, mixer contribution.

Inferences are drawn in the usual way by a comparison of the mean squares calculated from this analysis. Thus we find* no evidence for interaction nor for any effect due to the different mixers but there is a definite suggestion of tester bias.

How now can geometry help us in understanding? Fig. 4 illustrates just how the sums of squares set out in equation (2) and Table 1 are made up. Starting from the 36 observational spots we see the mean value for each group of four observations marked by a short horizontal stroke. The residual S_4 of the table is the sum of squares of the 36 distances between

* By referring the variance ratios F shown in Table 1 to appropriate significance tables.

each spot and the corresponding column mean. We may now start from the other end and build up towards these nine column means as in equation (2).

First we have the level of the grand mean at $y_{...} = 5012$. On to this we add three steps representing the estimated mixer biases, -7, -15 and 22, drawn as the solid-line components. On to these are added the three estimated tester biases, 24, 13 and -37, which are drawn (three times over) as the hatched-line components.* Do these two sets of additive components, a mixer and a tester term, adequately represent the situation? This will depend on how nearly the ends of the hatched blocks fit on to the nine column means, where 'nearness' has to be judged in terms of the residual variation. The nine differences (*viz.* 6, -19, 13; -16, 24, -8; 10, -5, -5) squared, summed and multiplied by four† give the interaction sum of squares, S_3 of Table 1.

The visual picture of Fig. 4 cannot by itself provide an answer to the investigation. From it we can see the meaning of the arithmetical analysis—can note, for example, how the three tester biases, estimated as 24, 13 and -37, are more important than the three mixer biases of -7, -15 and 22. But unless our visual imagination could be very highly trained so as to link the impression of the picture with probability tables, we could not safely attempt an assessment of significance. The value of this diagram, however, in giving a clearer meaning to arithmetic and algebra, can surely not be questioned? Whatever conclusions we draw from Table 1 must make sense in the picture of Fig. 4. If they make nonsense, we shall suspect an error in calculation or question whether the model used is appropriate.

2·6. *Diagrams for the analysis of covariance*

An allied type of problem in which visual presentation can add to the understanding of what our mathematical model means and how it is related to real data, is in the analysis of covariance. Here the problem of simple regression is complicated by the fact that the pairs of correlated variables fall into groups between which there may be differences in mean-values, in variability and in the slope of regression lines. If the main objective is to look for differences in mean values, we have to be clear that what we are looking for is not obscured by heterogeneity in variation or regression.

There are procedures which can be used to test these points, but when few observations are available such tests are very insensitive. There is now a good deal of information on the effects of departure from standard conditions, but this is not easy to put into precise form. When asked how he knows that his mathematical model is adequate, the practising statistician will perhaps answer that it is a matter of using judgement acquired through experience, by getting the feel of the data by a process which is partly intuitional. The beginner cannot have this confidence in his own judgement, but is there any surer way for him to acquire it than by making a practice of plotting his data and thinking round the picture in the light of what he knows of theoretical work on the robustness of statistical tests? Again, therefore, as in the preceding example, I shall venture to describe this process of 'thinking round' in a little detail.

My illustration is based on the figures given in Table 2; these fall into four groups, each containing 10 pairs of correlated observations, x_{ti}, y_{ti} $(t = 1, 2, 3, 4;\ i = 1, 2, \ldots, 10)$. They may be supposed to represent the weights (in lb.) of 40 animals, x before and y after a period

* We could equally well have added the tester biases first and then put the mixer biases on top of these.

† Since each of the four observations in a column provides an identical interaction contribution.

of feeding with one of four special diets. The problem is to find out whether gain in weight is influenced by diet.

The x, y points have been plotted in four separate charts, one for each diet in Fig. 5; on these charts we can as a first step usefully show as reference lines the overall mean value for the 40 observations $x_{..} = 47{\cdot}1$, $y_{..} = 78{\cdot}5$. Apart from the obvious correlation between x and y, we see at once that the initial mean weights, x, of the animals in the four groups differed considerably. This can be regarded as bad planning, but the difference being there can be allowed for.

Table 2. *Initial weight* (x) *and final weight* (y) *in lb. of* 40 *animals*, 10 *of which were fed on each of four different diets*

	Diet A_1		Diet A_2		Diet A_3		Diet A_4	
	x	y	x	y	x	y	x	y
	39	75	60	96	53	92	60	98
	48	74	56	91	50	91	53	94
	42	72	51	90	54	82	51	90
	45	70	53	86	48	80	48	90
	41	66	62	86	44	80	53	89
	37	64	46	80	47	75	58	87
	36	62	51	80	41	71	54	84
	41	59	54	80	36	70	44	82
	32	58	46	75	45	70	51	80
	39	58	44	72	32	64	40	77
Mean	40·0	65·8	52·3	83·6	45·0	77·5	51·2	87·1

The mathematical model to be used in the analysis of covariance supposes (i) that the regression of y on x within each group is linear, (ii) that the variation of y for given x about these regressions is normal; (iii) that for all four groups, and whatever the x value, the variance of y about the regression line is the same. If we draw in the four regression straight lines fitted to each of the sets of 10 observations (shown as broken lines in the diagram) with slopes

$$b_1 = 0{\cdot}94, \quad b_2 = 0{\cdot}97, \quad b_3 = 1{\cdot}10 \quad \text{and} \quad b_4 = 0{\cdot}75$$

we have the data fully displayed for inspection. The general conclusion drawn from study of these pictures must I think be that, when examining for differences in mean growth, there is no reason to doubt the usefulness of a model which involves the conditions (i), (ii) and (iii).* Further that it would be neither necessary nor profitable in this case to apply arithmetical tests of this assumption.

The diagram, however, might have shown a different state of affairs, one in which there was a strong suggestion of heterogeneity due to a few discrepant observations, or of departure from linearity in some or all of the group. It might then be difficult to decide how to proceed, but, however tiresome this may be, if conclusions are to be true to the real data we must not allow all evidence of anomaly to be buried within a conventional arithmetical procedure.

Having drawn Fig. 5 in the first instance to check the mathematical model, it may next be used to give an added meaning to the analysis which we have now accepted as appropriate. We are considering possibilities that:

* As is frequently the case in problems of growth, we should anticipate that the variance of y would increase with x. Such an effect, if present in these data, does not appear to be sufficient to make nonsense of condition (iii).

(*a*) The only difference between the groups lies in the x-values—the initial weights—so that the whole set of 40 points vary about a common regression line representing an average increase in weight during the period of observation, which is the same for all diets. This regression is estimated by the line with slope b_0 drawn through the common grand mean $x_{..}, y_{..}$ on each chart. (This is the line fitted to the 40 pooled observations.)

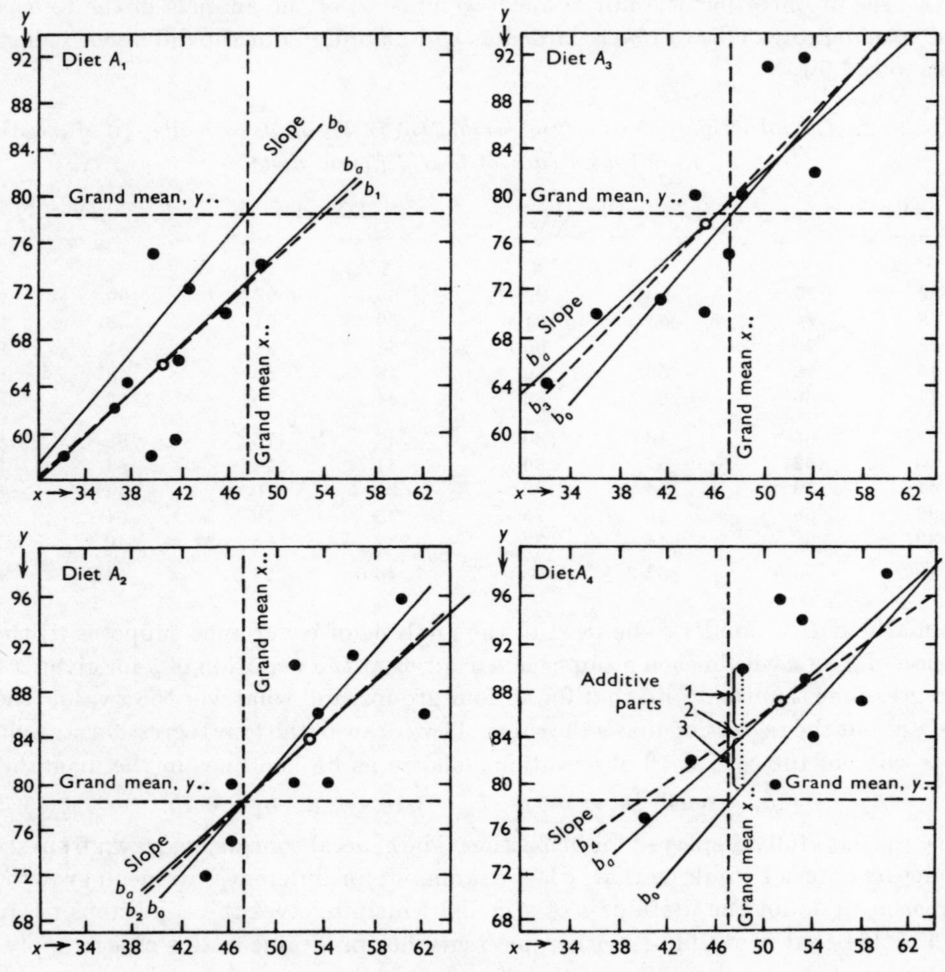

Fig. 5. Analysis of covariance.

(*b*) There is a differential effect of diet, so that the displacements of the mean points $x_{\iota.}, y_{\iota.}$ (represented by open circles in each chart) are not consistent with chance fluctuation from a common line; but the slope of the regression of y on x is the same for all diets. This common slope is estimated by b_a.

(*c*) The rate of growth varies with diet so that we may have to consider four regression slopes, estimated by b_1, b_2, b_3 and b_4. To compare numerically with these four estimates quoted above, we have:

$$b_0 = 1{\cdot}22, \quad b_a = 0{\cdot}95.$$

With this picture in front of us, we can ask what exactly are the components whose sums of squares S_1, S_2 and S_3 are given in Table 3 below? For one observation pair (x, y) in the fourth group of 10, the diagram shows the three component parts which have been squared and summed for all 40 observations. They are distances, parallel to the y axis, between:

(1) observation point and the corresponding point on the line with slope $b_t (t = 1, 2, \ldots, 4)$ drawn through the group mean;

(2) the lines with slopes b_t and b_a drawn through the group mean;

(3) the line with slope b_a drawn through the group mean and that with slope b_0 drawn through the grand mean.

If we say that a comparison of the sums of squares of these components provides the appropriate means of distinguishing between the possibilities (*a*), (*b*) and (*c*) set out above, we are making an appeal to the imagination through the visual faculty. Mathematical theory has shown that we can make these comparisons most neatly by dividing each sum of squares by its appropriate degrees of freedom and referring to standard tables of the variance ratio F or of its logarithm. But the essential comparison appears geometrically in this diagram as the sum of squares of the three parts of a distance.

Table 3. *Analysis of the data in Table 2*

Variation due to	Sum of squares	Degrees of freedom	Mean squares
Deviations within each group from regressions b_t	$S_1 = 859{\cdot}2$	32	26·85
Differences among regressions b_t	$S_2 = 23{\cdot}0$	3	7·67
Deviations within groups from common regression b_a	$S_1 + S_2 = 882{\cdot}2$	35	25·21
Differences among corrected group means	$S_3 = 424{\cdot}5$	3	141·50
Total deviations about $y = y_{..} + b_0(x - x_{..})$	1306·7	38	

The arithmetical analysis summarized in Table 3 shows that $F = S_2/3 \div S_1/32 \doteq 0{\cdot}286$ is not significantly large (nor exceptionally small) so that there is no ground for discarding the hypothesis that there is a common regression slope for all four diets. On the other hand $F = S_3/3 \div (S_1 + S_2)/35 = 5{\cdot}61$ is definitely significant, so that the displacement of the four group means from the common line

$$y = y_{..} + b_0(x - x_{..})$$

is clearly real. These conclusions obtained from the arithmetic are seen to be reasonable from the diagram.

What further question we ask about the established differences in effect of diet will depend on details of the experiment. If, as in the case of sheep trials for which data were given by R. A. Fisher (1947, Table 29·1), the treatments A_2 and A_3 represent the addition of two different constituents to the normal diet A_1, while A_4 represents the addition of both A_2 and A_3, we can examine for the significance of the two main effects and for the presence of a possible interaction. The diagram does, indeed, suggest that such additive main effects are present.

3. Seeing the data as a whole

3·1. *Diagrams and text-books*

I have described some of the ways in which I believe that visual aids may be of value in teaching the mathematical theory of statistics and in showing how its models are brought into relation with real data. I want now to add something about the importance of diagrams to the trained statistician as a means of helping him, in Hilbert's words, to keep in live *rapport* with his data.

The only published evidence of the way in which practising statisticians handle their data comes from the examples given in text-books or in papers dealing with the development of new methodology. Here it must be admitted that one finds but little evidence that statisticians examine geometrically what I shall term the pattern of their data before analysing them arithmetically. Certainly, publishers and editors are inclined to discourage frequent use of illustrations because of expense, but it is doubtful whether many of the writers of statistical text-books would find it easy to make full use of diagrams even if their publishers would allow them. The use of the visual imagination is rarely required by the mathematician and many of the authors of statistical texts have been primarily mathematicians.

In looking through these published numerical examples it is common to find instances where inspection by diagram would have enabled the author to add something of value to his comments and, sometimes, to avoid misinterpretation. These published examples are, of course, generally introduced to illustrate the working out of an arithmetical procedure based on the use of some mathematical model, and if the data used do not fit the model precisely the illustration of procedure may be none the less valuable. As mathematical statisticians we have no doubt most of us been concerned in illustrating new theory on data that are not altogether suitable. Recognizing this, I would disclaim any specific criticism of the writers whose data I shall now make use of. The examples were admirable for their purpose; I am using them for another purpose.

3·2. *Example* 1

My first example in this series is taken from *The Design and Analysis of Industrial Experiments* edited by O. L. Davies (1954, Example 4·4, pp. 124–30, 142–4) where it is used to illustrate methods of investigating the errors involved in sampling and analysing a compound material. The data reproduced in Table 4 are concerned with the chemical analysis of fertilizer for percentage of potash. Eight batches, each contained in a number of bags, were sampled by inserting an auger into a bag chosen at random from each batch. The sampling was repeated next day so as to give two independent samples, S_1 and S_2, from every batch. Each sample was then carefully divided into two sub-samples, the first sent to one laboratory to be analysed by method A, the second to another laboratory for analysis by method R.

Table 4. *Giving percentage potash determined from samples, by two methods*

Sample ...	S_1		S_2	
Method ...	A	R	A	R
Batch 1	15·6	15·5	15·5	15·4
2	15·4	14·9	15·2	15·0
3	15·3	15·4	14·6	14·6
4	15·0	15·5	15·0	15·5
5	15·5	15·0	15·4	15·1
6	14·8	14·8	15·0	14·8
7	14·9	15·0	14·9	15·3
8	15·0	15·8	15·2	15·8

Let us now look at the plot of the data in Fig. 6. What first do we note? That with the exception of batch 3 the difference between the two results for a given batch, using the *same* method of analysis (either A *or* R) is small; this difference can be ascribed to two sources.

(i) Reproducibility in chemical analysis; the authors have reason to believe that this may be assumed to be the same for both methods of analysis, and they represent the variability by a standard error σ_0.

(ii) The error of sampling involved in taking two auger samples from each batch, and represented by σ_1.

But inspection of the diagram shows that there is clearly another type of error present. The determinations by methods A and R differ considerably; sometimes those for A are greater than those for R, sometimes the reverse (here again batch 3 is exceptional). Clearly there is some bias which is not constant, and this variability in bias may be represented by

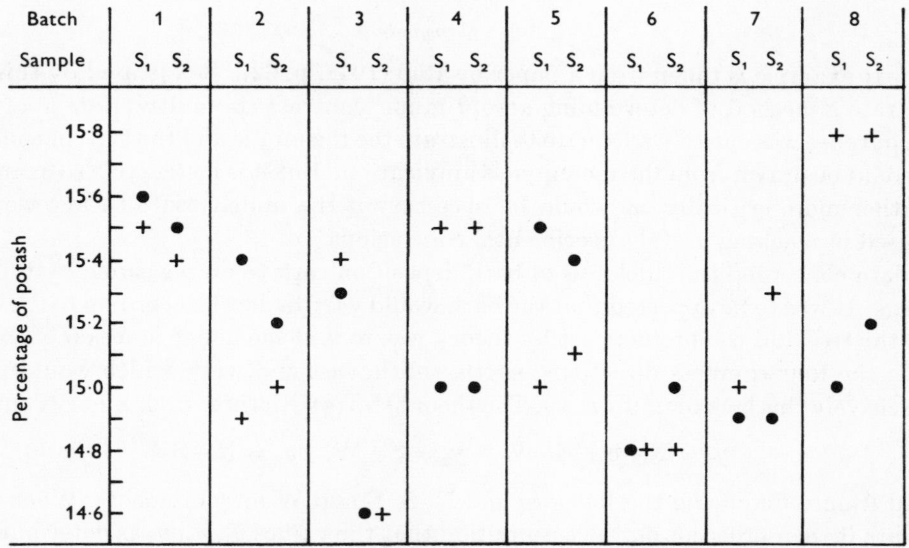

Fig. 6. Errors of sampling and chemical analysis.
Result of analysis by: method A, ●; method R, +.

a standard error, σ_2. To explain the phenomenon we have to appeal to information about the analytical processes. We are told that while A is a very accurate but lengthy method, R involves a much quicker technique but the results may vary considerably from batch to batch, perhaps being influenced by another constituent (other than potash) present in variable amounts in the batches of fertilizer.

Thus apart from batch-to-batch variation for which the diagram suggests some evidence, there are three standard errors to estimate, σ_0, σ_1 and σ_2. If we omit batch 3 from consideration a study of the pattern of points suggests at once (a) a large value for σ_2 (the spots are sometimes consistently well above, sometimes below the crosses), and (b) a value for σ_0 which is likely to be larger than for σ_1, as there is no consistent evidence that when one sample gives a higher reading than the other for method A it also does so for method R and vice versa. The result for batch 3 is, however, obviously exceptional since here a very large between-sample difference is consistently picked out by the two methods of analysis.

This immediately suggests that the statistical analysis should be carried out both with and without batch 3. It is unnecessary to give the analysis of variance tables, but they lead to the estimates:

From eight batches (as in Davies)

$$\hat{\sigma}_0 = 0{\cdot}098, \quad \hat{\sigma}_1 = 0{\cdot}184, \quad \hat{\sigma}_2 = 0{\cdot}378.$$

Omitting batch 3 $\quad \hat{\sigma}_0 = 0{\cdot}103$, $\hat{\sigma}_1$ negligible*, $\hat{\sigma}_2 = 0{\cdot}410$.

It is clear therefore that the figures for batch 3 play a predominating part in determining the estimate of the error in sampling measured by σ_1. The preliminary examination by diagram shows that this is likely to be the case before any arithmetical analysis is undertaken. What the implications of this anomaly are it would be for the statistician dealing with the investigation to decide.

3·3. *Example* 2

My next example is taken from a paper by Rao (1948, p. 62). It was used by this author to illustrate a method of determining an optimum 'contrast' in multivariate analysis and for this purpose was entirely adequate to illustrate the technique and the type of conclusions which could be drawn from the technique's application. But it is instructive to examine the data rather more critically, as would be necessary if the multivariate theory were to be safely used in reaching useful experimental conclusions.

The data concerned the thickness of bark deposit on cork trees, measured by the weight of borings. It was to be expected that the bark would vary in depth according to the orientation on the tree and the problem set by theory was to find the linear function of the thicknesses in the four compass directions, north, south, east and west, which would pick out most decisively this lack of uniformity. The theory starts with three preliminary contrasting variables

$$y_1 = \mathrm{N}+\mathrm{S}-\mathrm{E}-\mathrm{W}, \quad y_2 = \mathrm{S}-\mathrm{W}, \quad y_3 = \mathrm{N}-\mathrm{S}$$

obtained from differencing the four original N, S, E and W measurements. When applied to the data it then proceeds on the assumption that the values y_1, y_2, y_3 as determined from measurements on 28 cork trees growing in a block of plantations may be regarded as a sample of three normally correlated variables.

The original measurements in the four orientations have been plotted in Fig. 7. We see first of all the large differences between trees, but this main effect will be eliminated in the differences y_1, y_2 and y_3. We are not given any information about the order in which the 28 trees are numbered, but the eye is a sensitive instrument and it leaves us with the strong impression that, besides the very noticeable between-tree differences, there are differences in pattern (i.e. in the magnitude and sign of the y-values) which are associated with this ordering.

The question here raised by visual examination of pattern, is whether without further subdivision the data would be sufficiently homogeneous to justify useful conclusions being drawn from them by application of multivariate normal theory.† It would not be profitable

* The estimate of $\sigma_0^2 + 2\sigma_1^2$ is less than that of σ_0^2.

† It may be noted that if we apply Geary's (1936) criterion for kurtosis based on the ratio of the mean deviation to the standard deviation to this sample of 28 observations, we find that the distribution of y_1 is significantly leptokurtic at the 5% level and that of y_3 significantly platykurtic at the 1% level. These results also suggest possible lack of homogeneity.

to follow out this example further, but taken to this stage only it emphasizes the importance of some preliminary study of the statistical uniformity of data when several variables are used.

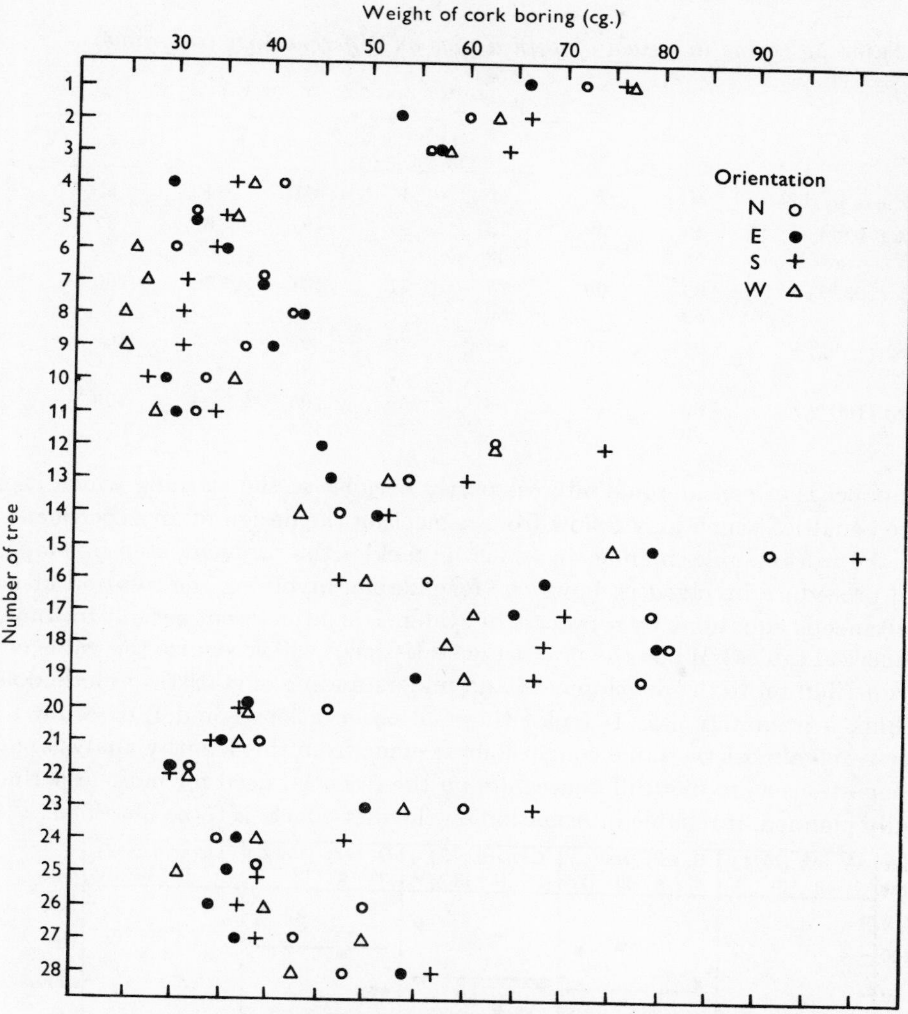

Fig. 7. Measurements of bark on cork trees.
Orientation: N, ○; E, ●; S, +; W, △.

3·4. *Example* 3

A paper by Stevens (1948) provides another example which is relevant to the present discussion. He is concerned with developing an arithmetical procedure which may be applied systematically to test for any effects or interaction in experimental data collected under conditions where there has been a complete breakdown of the usual orthogonality restrictions. The data used are given in Table 5. They relate to an experiment (quoting from Stevens's paper) 'designed to observe the effect on the growth of guinea-pigs of four diets distinguished by the four types of wheat which they included:

A = soft (70 %), B = soft (100 %), C = hard (70 %), D = hard (100 %).

The guinea-pigs were of two sexes and drawn from four litters, so there are three factors: sex, diet and litter.' The experiment is therefore tri-factorial and, as the table shows, presents a complete lack of orthogonality.

Table 5. *Gains in weight of guinea-pigs on different diets (in grams)*

	Litter and sex (M. or F.)							
	I		II		III		IV	
Type of wheat in diet	M.	F.	M.	F.	M.	F.	M.	F.
A = soft (70%)	43	58	73	—	81	62	67	71
	58		59					
B = soft (100%)	93	60	75	71	101	76	100	—
	83		89					
C = hard (70%)	91	70	85	70	92	—	106	73
				58	88			
D = hard (100%)	89	—	98	69	105	—	109	76
	89			72	108			

Stevens's paper is of considerable interest partly because of the warning which it gives of the severe penalties which may follow from neglecting the design of an experiment and partly from the workmanlike manner in which he tackles the problem, step by step. The arithmetical procedure involved is, however, formidable, involving the solution of many sets of simultaneous equations by a process of systematic adjustment set out in some ten pages of numerical tables! While the practising statistician will recognize the value of this paper as a contribution to the development and understanding of statistical methodology, he may I think legitimately ask: If I plot these 36 observations could I, or could I not, very quickly reach almost the same conclusions as come from this lengthy analysis: (*a*) on tentative suggestions as to diet differences, (*b*) on the essential need for more experiment, more carefully planned, if reliable information on the diet effects is to be obtained?

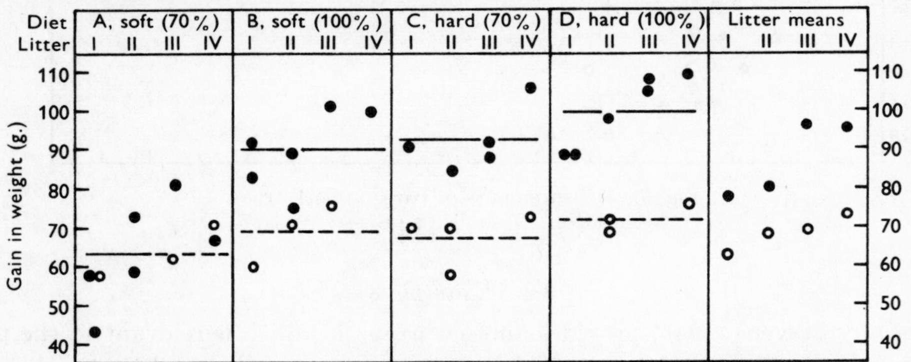

Fig. 8. Gains in weight of guinea-pigs receiving different diets. Individual gains in weight: male, ●; female, ○. Diet means: male, —; female, – – –.

The gains in weight from Table 5 have been plotted in Fig. 8. I wonder whether any trained statistician after studying the spot pattern would reach very different conclusions from those I did, noting down points as follows from my diagram before reading the conclusions which Stevens extracts from his analysis?

(i) There is a definite litter effect shown among the males, i.e. litters III and IV show greater increases in weight than I and II. It is unlikely that any litter × diet interaction could be established.

(ii) It is unlikely that a litter effect could be established among the females, although such a trend as appears resembles that for the males.

(iii) The most noticeable characteristic of the data is that, for the males, diet *A* is definitely inferior to the other three diets.

(iv) There is no similar effect which could be established for the females, although here, too, the average gain for diet *A* is in fact a little less than for *B*, *C*, and *D*.

(v) As a result, the gain in weight for diet *A* appears to be the same for both sexes, but for the other three diets there is a marked difference between the males and females. Thus there seems to be a diet × sex interaction.

(vi) It is possible that there is a real advantage in 'hardness' over 'softness' in the wheat, and in '100 %' over '70 %'; the data are consistent with this, but it is the differences for males between *A* on the one hand and *B*, *C*, *D* on the other which overshadows all else.

It will be found that Stevens's analysis brings out just these points; the advantage of his treatment, of course, is that he can present his conclusions more precisely in terms of probabilities. For example, he finds that the diet × sex interaction is just significant at the 5 % level. But in the matter of any positive contribution to the study of the effect of diet on guinea-pigs, he can only tell us that the results are inconclusive. Thus in connexion with the diet × sex interaction he remarks that the observations are 'consistent with either of the following hypotheses, indeed with many others:

(*a*) That the difference between male and female is the same on diets *B*, *C*, *D* but different on *A*.

(*b*) That the sex difference between male and female increases steadily with the response of either sex, i.e. the "better" the diet, the more the male will outstrip the female.'

However we look at things, what is needed is further trial.

In making this comparison between the use of a diagram and the full arithmetical analysis of Stevens's data, I must emphasize that I would not normally suggest that visual inspection of a plot should be substituted for precise analysis. My contention is that a study of a diagram must always add something to our understanding of the results of analysis and that in cases where the analysis, to be exact, must be very lengthy the diagram with certain simple exploratory calculations* may suffice for all practical purposes.

4. Concluding remarks

Regarding geometry very broadly as a branch of science concerned with the presentation of both mathematical facts and observational material in a form in which their properties can be studied and illuminated with the aid of visual imagination, I have suggested that it has a part to play in various ways in the field of statistics. Geometry may first be useful in teaching ; sometimes as an alternative to algebra as a means of establishing mathematical theory; sometimes in illustrating the relation between probability theory and random sampling; sometimes in making clear how a mathematical model fits a set of observational data.

* It will be noted from Table 5 that there are nine pairs of animals, each member of which was of the same litter and sex and received the same diet. The nine differences readily provide an estimate of error which can be used as a rough foot-rule in exploring the significance of possible effects.

Beyond this I have considered how, in the practical interpretation of data, in the process of learning what the material means, examination of an appropriate diagram can supplement the usual arithmetical analysis, largely because only by this means is it easy to see the data as a whole. By suggesting that much can be learnt in this way, I run the risk of being accused of encouraging slapdash methods of handling statistical data, a step against the tradition of 60 years' development of statistics as a science. But there is also danger in the ease with which a standard text-book technique can be applied uncritically to observations to which the model does not fit. I am not suggesting that the visual imagination can replace hard calculation and the use of tables of probability functions. My thesis is that arithmetic and geometry are complementary.

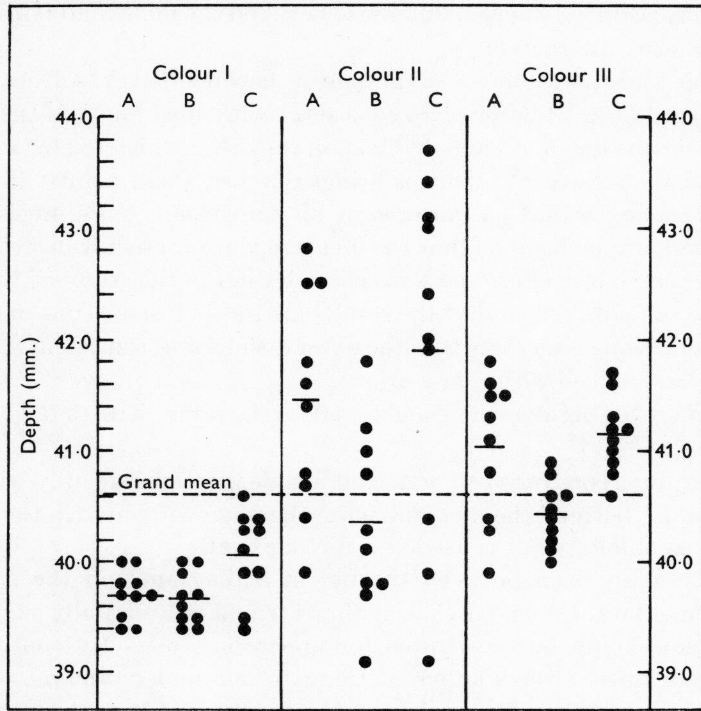

Fig. 9. Matching of dye colours by three observers, A, B and C.

The extremes to be avoided can be emphasized by considering two final diagrams. The first, Fig. 9, is a plot with mean values added of a part of more extensive data given a few years ago in a University of London statistics practical examination. The figures are readings obtained from a colorimeter used for standardization purposes in the manufacture of industrial dyes. One cell of the instrument contains a fixed depth of a standard solution and the observer tries to make a colour match by adjusting the depth of solution in a second cell by means of a plunger. The diagram shows the adjusted depths in the second cell when the standard depth was 40 mm. In the figures here shown, each of three observers A, B and C made 10 matches with three colours. The candidates were asked to analyse and make a report on these data.

The diagram (which presents only about one-fifth of the total material provided) shows several things as obvious and others which it may be worth following up more carefully.

Among the obvious things is the evidence that reproducibility in matching varies tremendously with the colour used. Although it should have been clear that no investigation of this kind could start before the observations had been looked at as a whole, the four or five students who attempted this question applied straight away an analysis of variance procedure which supposed that the standard deviation in each of the colour-observer groups was the same. These students had been urged more than once to look at their data before plunging into arithmetical analysis. If they cast common sense to the winds, was it from examination nervousness or the fault of a habit of mind, encouraged perhaps by school mathematics teaching and apparently confirmed by statistical text-books—an obstinate belief that diagram drawing is only an occupation for the mathematical beginner?

But if diagrams often give pointers of where to go in analysis and if they can sometimes establish results without need of arithmetical confirmation, it is unlikely that the most highly endowed statistical eye could ever be a substitute for the more objective probability measures based on calculation. Nevertheless there are some interesting questions involved here, concerning the sensitivity of the eye in picking out effects that are probably real and the relation of this sensitivity to conventional significance levels. My last diagram bears on these points.

Some little while ago I made a number of random samplings of different types and plotted the results for inspection. Fig. 10 contain six samples from a series in which five observations of a normal variable, y, fall into each of six arrays. All the samples were randomly drawn from a distribution in which there was a linear regression of y on x rising from left to right. I have drawn in the array means and the grand mean for each sample, quantities which can be easily calculated, but have not inserted the estimated sample regression lines. What conclusions could be drawn by inspection from any of these samples about the regression of y upon x?

It is likely that there would be general agreement among statisticians that:

(*a*) sample *B* 8 provides no justification for rejecting the hypothesis of independence;

(*b*) sample *B* 17 gives definite evidence of the existence of regression.

In these two instances, if a snap decision was needed, we should feel able to dispense with a test; but should we feel able to do this in any of the other four cases? A diagram of this type seems to bring out well the need for an objective test, and it could also be useful in teaching in getting across the idea of significance.

In fact, all six samples were drawn randomly from a distribution where there was linear regression of y upon x, measured by a slope of $\beta = 1{\cdot}31$, and on applying Student's test for the significance of the sample regressions, we have:

Sample	*B* 8	13	16	20	18	17
Slope, b	0·34	0·73	0·91	1·22	1·15	1·89
t_0	0·69	1·38	1·63	1·81	2·76	4·55
$P\{t \geqslant t_0 \mid \beta = 0\}$*	0·25	0·09	0·06	0·04	0·005	$< 0{\cdot}001$

* That is, the probability that t could exceed the observed value, t_0, if the population regression line were horizontal with $\beta = 0$.

A comparison of this table with Fig. 10 leaves us with some interesting questions to turn over. Can we—indeed should we—ever base a conclusion on arithmetical analysis which we cannot at the same time see from inspection makes sense? Were a statistician to make the habit of relating to an appropriate diagram the probability level determined by every test of significance he applies, would he gradually acquire a more sensitive eye so that in time he could make a very shrewd guess from a diagram as to whether an effect were significant, let us say at about the 5% level? Would the same result apply to the confidence interval associated with an estimate? Would this be a dangerous faculty to acquire, because it might lead to the abandonment of objectivity? Or would the gain in understanding outweigh any risk of misuse of the visual imagination? These are questions which I shall not attempt to answer, but I think they have an interest for us whether as teachers or practising statisticians.

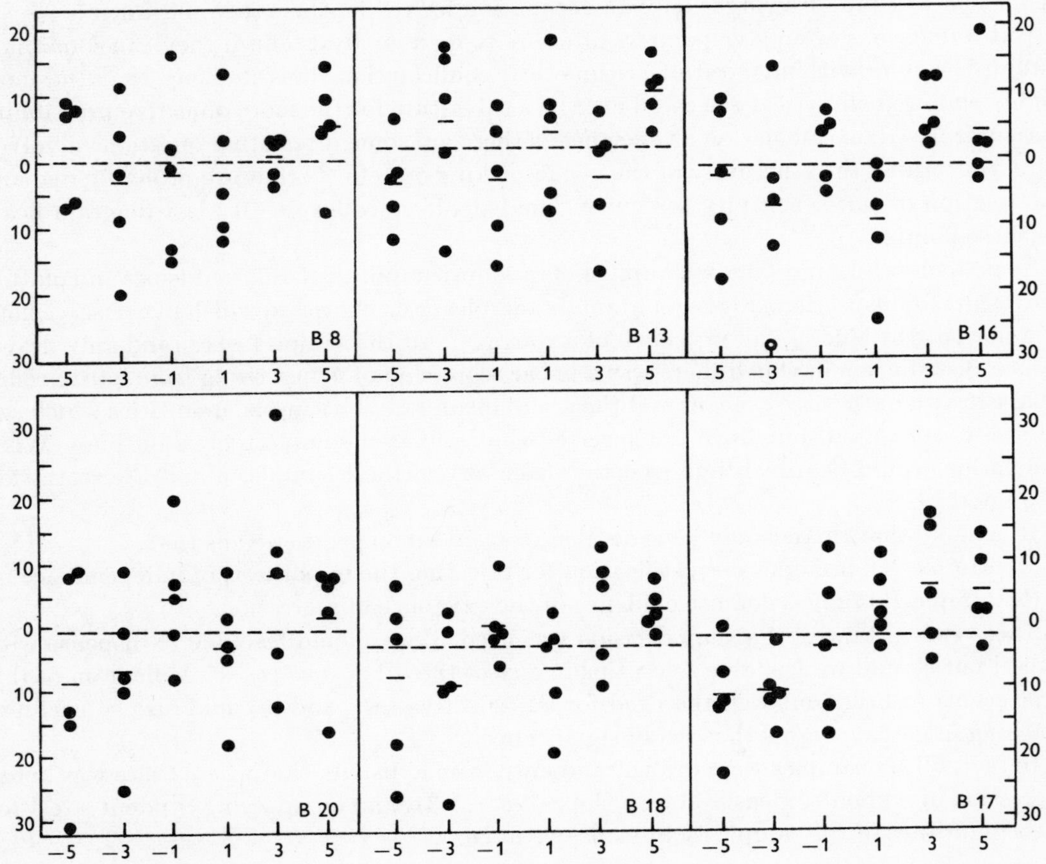

Fig. 10. Six random samples of 30. Is the regression significant?

The account which I have given has been necessarily to a large extent a personal one. I have taken a particular range of statistical problems which may well be regarded as somewhat limited, and have described how within this field the study of diagrams has helped me. Of this help I have no doubt whatsoever; as a teacher, help in seeing that a student's arithmetical results are probably right or certainly wrong; as an editor, help in understanding the purpose of an algebraic *tour de force*, by plotting the numerical data which the author has introduced to illustrate his results; help even without pencil and paper by seeing, through a kind of mental imagery, the character of mathematical problems to be solved. In general the mathematically-trained mind works no doubt in other ways, but the job of the average mathematical statistician is to learn from observational data with the help of mathematical tools. I am suggesting that in this process full understanding can only be obtained through visual aid and that if this is so, both in teaching and in writing of books, we need to give a good deal more consideration than we seem to do at present to what was once described as the 'geometry of statistics' and the 'geometry of chance'. This is the thought with which I should like to leave you.

REFERENCES

DAVIES, O. L. (editor) (1947). *Statistical Methods in Research and Production.* Edinburgh: Oliver and Boyd.

DAVIES, O. L. (editor) (1954). *Design and Analysis of Industrial Experiments.* Edinburgh: Oliver and Boyd.

FISHER, R. A. (1915). Distribution of the correlation coefficient. *Biometrika*, **10**, 507–21.

FISHER, R. A. (1925). *Statistical Methods for Research Workers* (1st edition). Edinburgh: Oliver and Boyd.

FISHER, R. A. (1947). *The Design of Experiments.* 4th ed. Edinburgh: Oliver and Boyd.

GEARY, R. C. (1936). Moments of the ratio of the mean deviation to the standard deviation for normal samples. *Biometrika*, **28**, 295–303.

HILBERT, D. & COHN-VOSSER, S. (1952). *Geometry and the Imagination.* New York: Chelsea Publishing Co. (translation of original *Anschauliche Geometrie* of 1932).

PEARSON, E. S. (1938). *Karl Pearson. An Appreciation of Some Aspects of his Life and Work.* Cambridge University Press.

PEARSON, E. S. & HARTLEY, H. O. (1954). *Biometrika Tables for Statisticians.* **1**. Cambridge University Press.

RAO, C. R. (1948). Tests of significance in multivariate analysis. *Biometrika*, **35**, 58–79.

STEVENS, W. L. (1948). Statistical analysis of a non-orthogonal trifactorial experiment. *Biometrika*, **35**, 346–67.

Some thoughts on statistical inference*

By E. S. PEARSON
University College London

1. Introduction

A few weeks ago, before leaving England I found some notes of various talks which I had given on a visit to the United States paid 30 years ago. In a lecture which I delivered here, at Cornell, in early May 1931 I seem to have used some words which it is perhaps rather bold of me to quote today before a Meeting of the Institute of Mathematical Statistics. Still, I will do it because I suppose that after all I am the same kind of person now as I was then! I used words like these: 'I sometimes think that Statistics is becoming far too mathematical, and that it is a relief to turn to the many simple, unsolved problems which can be discussed in terms only of means and standard deviations.'

It is evident from the context that the problems I was thinking of were concerned with what I might call the philosophy of statistical inference, whose principles and relationships can often be discussed most clearly in terms of simple situations. When I was here in 1931 the work of Neyman and myself was in an early stage; we spoke of the class of admissible alternative hypotheses and we were deriving tests using the likelihood ratio principle. But the idea of the power function and of the uniformly most powerful test was still in embryo, coming to birth at meetings contrived here or there in Europe or in correspondence carried on between Warsaw and London.

I must confess that the older I get, the more difficult I find it to be positive in this matter of statistical inference, but I have felt that as you have invited me to address you here on what is nearly the 30th anniversary of an earlier visit, I should try to formulate some of my thoughts on the relation between the Neyman–Pearson theory and fresh views on inference that are current today. I do this the more readily because I believe rather strongly in the value of emphasizing continuity as well as differences in statistical philosophy. I am convinced that if we can only get to the bottom of the way in which similar situations are tackled by different approaches, all I believe lying within the broad path of development of our subject, our understanding will gain in richness—gain in a way which can never happen if we waste energy in trying to establish that we are right and the other fellow is wrong!

2. Some historical reflexions on the development of the Neyman–Pearson theory

Allow me therefore to start with a few historical remarks. There is perhaps in current literature a tendency to speak of the Neyman–Pearson contributions as some static system, rather than as part of the historical process of development of thought on statistical theory which is and will always go on. Neyman and Pearson were after all very much persons of their time. They built on things which they found in the middle 1920's:

* Received 28 July 1961; revised 12 December 1961. This article contains the substance of an invited paper read before the Regional Meeting of the Institute of Mathematical Statistics held at Cornell University, 21 April 1961.

(*a*) The way of thinking which had found acceptance for a number of years among practising statisticians, which included the use of tail areas of the distributions of test statistics.

(*b*) The classical tradition that, somehow, prior probabilities should be introduced numerically into a solution—a tradition which can certainly be traced in the writings of Karl Pearson and of Student, but to which perhaps only lip service was then being paid.

(*c*) The tremendous impact of R. A. Fisher. His criticism of Bayes's Theorem and his use of Likelihood.

(*d*) His geometrical representation in multiple space, out of which readily came the concept of alternative critical regions in a sample space.

(*e*) His tables of 5 and 1% significance levels, which lent themselves to the idea of choice, in advance of experiment, of the risk of the 'first kind of error' which the experimenter was prepared to take.

(*f*) His emphasis on the importance of planning an experiment, which led naturally to the examination of the power function, both in choosing the size of sample so as to enable worthwhile results to be achieved, and in determining the most appropriate test.

(*g*) Then, too, there were a number of common-sense contributions from that great practising statistician, Student, some in correspondence, some in personal discussion.

What Neyman and I experienced, as no doubt do the exponents of any new line of thought on inference, was a dissatisfaction with the logical basis—or lack of it—which seemed to underlie the choice and construction of statistical tests. We found this not only in the theoretical work of what was then called the Biometric School, but also in some of R. A. Fisher's writing, in so far as we could follow its underlying philosophy. We tried therefore to develop a set of principles having a mathematical basis which it seemed to us led to a rational choice of statistical procedures when faced with certain types of problem in the analysis and interpretation of data. Put in another way, we were seeking how to bring probability theory into gear with the way we think as rational human beings. No doubt because the scope of application of statistical methods was much narrower in those days, the emphasis which we gave to certain types of situation may now seem out of balance.

We were certainly aware that inferences must make use of prior information and that decisions must take account of utilities, but after some considerable thought and discussion round these matters we came to the conclusion, rightly or wrongly, that it was so rarely possible to give sure numerical values to these entities, that our line of approach must proceed otherwise.* Thus we came down on the side of using only probability measures which could be related to relative frequency. Of necessity, as it seemed to us, we left in our mathematical model a gap for the exercise of a more intuitive process of personal judgement in such matters—to use our terminology—as the choice of the most likely class of admissible hypotheses, the appropriate significance level, the magnitude of worthwhile effects and the balance of utilities.

We also considered how far inferences and decisions could be based on the values of likelihood ratios and we first obtained for the critical or rejection regions, those bounded by contours in the sample space on which the appropriate likelihood ratio was constant. But looking back I think it is clear why we regarded the integral of probability density within (or

* This is perhaps the central problem over which opinions differ. In setting down my thoughts on some of the difficulties to be faced my purpose is not to nail a flag to any mast, but to encourage discussion which may in the end lead to a clearing up of certain dusty corners of our minds.

beyond) a contour as more meaningful than the likelihood ratio—more readily brought into gear with the particular process of reasoning we followed.

The reason was this. We were regarding the ideal statistical procedure as one in which preliminary planning and subsequent interpretation were closely linked together—formed part of a single whole. It was in this connexion that integrals over regions of the sample space were required. Certainly, we were much less interested in dealing with situations where the data are thrown at the statistician and he is asked to draw a conclusion. I have the impression that there is here a point which is often overlooked; I will come back to this in the example which I propose to discuss shortly.

3. The subjectivist approach

As I have said, these choices of Neyman and myself were deliberate, although at that time the issues may not have been as clearly before us as they are presented today. The up to date subjectivist or Bayesian considers that this was the wrong choice. He believes that unless the statistician attempts to express his notions of prior probability and his utility functions in a form which can be inserted into a mathematical mechanism, geared with his way of thought, he is falling down on his job. The ideas of the Bayesian are not of course new; what is new I think is the more precise formulation of the theory in mathematical terms and its application to a much wider range of situations than the nineteenth-century users of inverse probability methods could have dreamed of.

If I am asked how I regard the views of writers on subjective probability, my answer is this: the approach of Professor Savage and others strikes me as extremely illuminating in a variety of ways and I certainly welcome further exploration along these lines. At the same time I must admit that there are some fundamental parts of the mechanism of subjective probability theory which simply will not at present get into gear with the way *I* think any more than they did 30 years ago. May be this is because I am getting old and have settled into a certain routine of thought—or may be I have some justification for an instinctive hunch that some things cannot always work. I do not pretend to know the answer.

Let me however illustrate some of my difficulties very briefly.

(*a*) We are told that 'if one is being consistent, there is a prior distribution'. 'A subjectivist feels that the prior distribution means something about the state of his mind and that he can discover it by introspection.' But does this mean that if introspection fails to produce for me a stable and meaningful prior distribution which can be expressed in terms of numbers, I must give up the use of statistical method?

(*b*) Again, it is an attractive hypothesis that Bayesian probabilities 'only differ between individuals because individuals are differently informed; but with common knowledge we have common Bayesian probabilities'. Of course it is possible to define conceptual Bayesian probabilities and the 'rational man' in this way, but how to establish that all this bears a close relation to reality?

It seems to me that in many situations, if I received no more relevant knowledge in the interval and could forget the figures I had produced before, I might quote at intervals widely different Bayesian probabilities for the same set of states, simply because I should be attempting what would be for me impossible and resorting to guesswork. It is difficult to see how the matter could be put to experimental test. Of course the range of problems is very great. At one end we have the case where a prior distribution can be closely related to past observation; at the other, it has to be determined almost entirely by introspection or (because we do not trust our introspection) by the introduction of some formal mathematical function, in Jeffreys's manner, to get the model started. In the same way utility and loss functions have sometimes a clear objective foundation, but must sometimes be formulated on a purely subjectivist basis.

To have a unified mathematical model of the mind's way of working in all these varied situations is certainly intellectually attractive. But is it always meaningful? I think that there is always this question at the back of my mind; can it really lead to my own clear thinking to put at the very foundation of the mathematical structure used in acquiring knowledge, functions about whose form I have often such imprecise ideas?

4. THE PROBLEM OF KING HIERO'S CROWN

To make these reflexions more concrete I will try to illustrate both the illumination and some of the difficulties of the subjectivist approach as they strike me, on an example, the broad lines of which originate from Professor L. J. Savage, who introduced it during a two-day discussion meeting at Birkbeck College, London, nearly two years ago.* The example whose scope I have somewhat enlarged, though no doubt expressed in rather simplified terms, seems to me to represent a type of situation which is not altogether unusual.

Savage has called it the problem of *King Hiero's Crown*. Briefly, the legend as brought up to date is this:

(*a*) King Hiero has ordered a new crown and he believes that the goldsmiths may have adulterated the gold, either with lead or with silver.

(*b*) Archimedes has hit on the idea (presumably unknown to the goldsmiths) of determining the density of the crown by weighing it and a specimen of pure gold in air and in water.

(*c*) By this test, Archimedes is estimating a quantity λ by means of a measure x (which may be the mean of n independent test results, X_i).

(*d*) For pure gold $\lambda = 0$, for lead $\lambda > 0$, for silver $\lambda < 0$.

(*e*) Archimedes has found by earlier experiment that from weighing to weighing x will vary normally about λ with known standard error σ. (σ may equal $\Sigma/\sqrt{n}$ where Σ is the standard error of a single observation.)

The King attaches some credence to the possibility that there is no cheating ($\lambda = 0$), and associates this with a prior probability I. $\bar{I} = 1-I$ is the prior probability of cheating, and the prior distribution of λ, conditional on cheating, is $\pi(\lambda)$. If I' and $\bar{I}'$ are the posterior probabilities of no cheating and cheating, respectively, then it may be shown that

$$\frac{\bar{I}'}{I'} = \frac{\bar{I}}{I}\frac{\sigma}{\phi(x/\sigma)}\cdot\int_{-\infty}^{\infty}\pi(\lambda)\,\phi\left(\frac{x-\lambda}{\sigma}\right)\frac{d\lambda}{\sigma}, \tag{1}$$

where ϕ is the standardized Normal probability density function.

If $\pi(\lambda)$ is nearly uniform over a sufficiently long range having regard to σ, then (1) becomes approximately

$$\frac{\bar{I}'}{I'} = \frac{\bar{I}}{I}\frac{\sigma}{\phi(x/\sigma)}\pi(x). \tag{2}$$

Notice that in this model no attempt is made to introduce the degree of guilt nor to balance the utility of hanging innocent goldsmiths against allowing guilty ones to go free. As

* *Later Note*. Professor Savage's talk and the discussion which followed have since been published with the title *The Foundations of Statistical Inference*, Methuen's Monographs on Applied Probability and Statistics, 1962.

Savage has pointed out to me, it is quite possible and elegant mathematically to introduce a utility function into the problem. But I think that the example, without this complication, represents a common type of problem in which the consequences of the two different kinds of mistaken conclusions are incommensurable in terms of any readily acceptable numbers. I had thought it likely that Hiero would decide not to execute unless the odds against innocence were high, perhaps 25 to 1, or 10 to 1. But Professor Savage points out to me that a likely royal view in Hiero's days would be that the goldsmiths should be hanged unless the odds on their innocence were very high!

5. Numerical illustration of the theory

In the calculations illustrated by Figs. 1 and 2, I have first taken six different prior distributions. For cases 1–3, $\bar{I}/I = 4{:}1$ and for cases 4–6, $\bar{I}/I = 1{:}1$. Two values for σ have been taken:

$\sigma = 0{\cdot}25$, which might correspond, say, to $n = 4$, $\Sigma = 0{\cdot}5$;

$\sigma = 0{\cdot}10$, corresponding to $n = 25$, $\Sigma = 0{\cdot}5$.

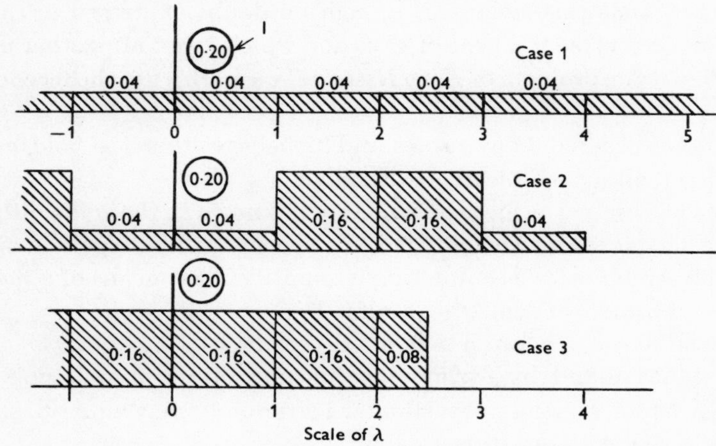

Fig. 1. Prior distribution of λ for cases 1–3.

Note: the numbers associated with the shaded blocks are the integrals of $\bar{I}\pi(\lambda)$ for unit (or in one case half-unit) intervals of λ.

For these values of σ if we explore only the case where $\lambda \geqslant 0$ it is not necessary to specify the form of $\pi(\lambda)$ outside a certain section of the λ-scale, but we can if we like suppose $\pi(\lambda)$ to be symmetrical about $\lambda = 0$. *Within the range shown*,* it was supposed that:

for cases 1 and 4, $\quad \pi(\lambda) = 0{\cdot}05$ for $-1 \leqslant \lambda \leqslant 4$,

2 and 5, $\quad \pi(\lambda) = 0{\cdot}05$ for $-1 \leqslant \lambda \leqslant 1$

$\quad = 0{\cdot}20$ for $1 < \lambda \leqslant 3$

$\quad = 0{\cdot}05$ for $3 < \lambda \leqslant 4$,

3 and 6, $\quad \pi(\lambda) = 0{\cdot}20$ for $-1 \leqslant \lambda \leqslant 2{\cdot}5$

$\quad = 0$ for $\lambda > 2{\cdot}5$.

* It will be noticed that I have not committed myself to the form of $\pi(\lambda)$ outside the range of λ needed in my discussion. This explains, for example, why I have not defined $\pi(\lambda)$ for $\lambda < -1$.

Cases 1 and 4 correspond to a situation in which the King's opinion about the extent of cheating, if it has occurred, is very 'diffuse'. Thus it could be that $\pi(\lambda) = 0{\cdot}05$ for $-10 \leqslant \lambda \leqslant 10$.

Cases 2 and 5, might represent the position if the King argued as follows: On the one hand the goldsmiths will not risk including so much base metal that it might be obvious; on the other it will hardly seem to them worthwhile adulterating the gold to only a small extent.

Cases 3 and 6 use an intermediate form for $\pi(\lambda)$.

The crude step functions were of course introduced to simplify the calculations. Fig. 1 illustrates the prior distributions for cases 1–3 only: the value of $I = 0{\cdot}2$ is given and also the integral of $\bar{I}\pi(\lambda) = 0{\cdot}8\pi(\lambda)$ over unit (or $\frac{1}{2}$ unit) intervals of λ.

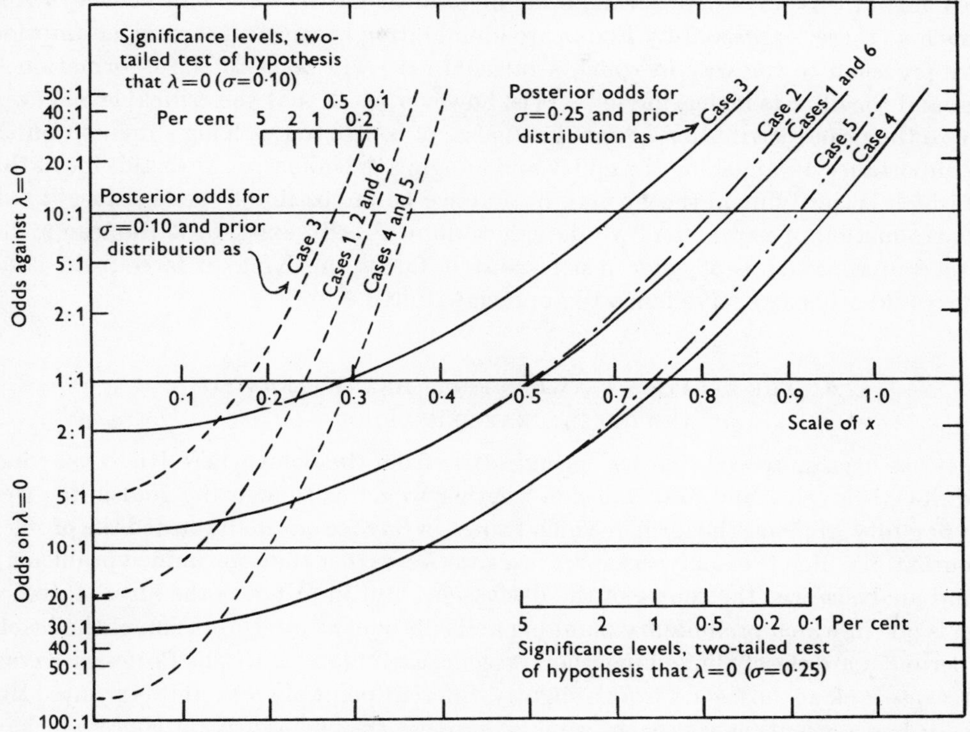

Fig. 2. Curves for posterior odds plotted against x, the estimator of λ.

In Fig. 2 are shown the posterior odds derived from equation (1), or, where adequate, using equation (2). Also included are scales showing significance levels for a two-tailed test of the hypothesis that $\lambda = 0$; e.g. for $\sigma = 0{\cdot}25$ the 5 % levels of the two-tailed test fall at $x = \pm 0{\cdot}25 \times 1{\cdot}96 = \pm 0{\cdot}49$. The values of $\bar{I}'/I'$ for cases 1 and 6 are the same, since within the range of x considered equation (2) is appropriate and $\bar{I}\pi(x)/I$ has the same value for both cases.

Accepting equations (1) and (2) as meaningful, consider a few of the points brought out by Fig. 2:

(*a*) If $\sigma = 0{\cdot}25$ and the King is of opinion that the posterior odds on guilt should be at least 10 to 1 before he hangs the goldsmiths, the critical value for z will fall at $x_c = 0{\cdot}61$ for case 3 (corresponding to the $1{\cdot}5\,\%$ significance level to the null hypothesis test) and at $x_c = 0{\cdot}85$ (corresponding to the $0{\cdot}07\,\%$ significance level) for case 4. In other words, if as in case 4 the King believes that the goldsmiths are as likely to cheat as not ($I = \bar{I}$) and that if they cheat the odds are 9 to 1 that $|\lambda| > 1$, he can afford to put the critical x-level much further out than in case 3.

(*b*) On the other hand, he may have an entirely different outlook on what is just and on the value of human life where a King's position is concerned. He may, therefore, decide to hang unless the posterior odds are at least 10 to 1 in favour of innocence and so will always hang in cases 1–3 and 6 and will hang unless $x < x_c = 0{\cdot}38$ in cases 4 and 5. Conventional significance levels have here no bearing on his decision.

(*c*) With $n = 25$, $\sigma = 0{\cdot}10$ the relation between posterior odds and the scale of significance levels is clearly not the same as for $n = 4$, $\sigma = 0{\cdot}25$.

Approached in this way there seems to me no doubt that the lessons to be drawn from results such as these, suggested by Fig. 2, are illuminating because on certain assumptions they give precision to the way in which a rational man will react to the information he possesses and the objects he has in view. It is, however, clear that the critical level is very sensitive to the prior distribution adopted and also, of course to the King's opinion on the relative importance of punishing the guilty and hanging the innocent. Does this mean that a model which is clarifying in theory may in practice be impossible to use because it calls for the introduction of parameters whose values do not really exist, or is the lesson that this method of approach is of value just because it forces the King to face up to issues which he would otherwise have failed to appreciate fully?

6. The relation between preliminary planning and subsequent behaviour

So far it has been supposed that the legend starts from the point where Hiero has views on I and $\pi(\lambda)$, is given x and has to decide whether to act as though the goldsmiths were innocent or guilty; this was the form in which Professor Savage originally stated the problem in the context in which the analysis aspect of statistics, rather than the unified problems of design and analysis, was the centre of the discussion. But in so far as the ideal statistical situation is one in which preliminary planning and subsequent interpretation of the results of an experiment are closely linked together, it seems useful (and with this Professor Savage fully agrees) to look at the legend from a slightly different point of view. If it is granted that Archimedes has a scientific approach, we may suppose that he and King Hiero will have thought round their method of testing the goldsmiths *before* x is known to them. They must, indeed, do some preliminary thinking, for if they have not pretty clear views on the values they will give to I and $\pi(\lambda)$ before x is known, they will find it hard to be unprejudiced in assigning values for these expressions afterwards. Thus it is likely that a survey of possibilities somewhat of the kind presented in my diagrams would have been carried out, perhaps while the goldsmiths were putting the finishing touches to the crown.

In this survey, we can imagine Hiero remarking somewhat as follows: 'You say that if we make four weighings of the crown ($\sigma = 0{\cdot}25$) and if we agree on values for I and $\pi(\lambda)$ as, say, in case 2, then the odds will be at least 10 to 1 against innocence if $x > 0{\cdot}71$. So perhaps we might fix this as the critical value for hanging. But tell me, Archimedes, if we do take $0{\cdot}71$ what is the probability that (i) we shall hang innocent men, (ii) shall let off guilty men when they have actually adulterated the gold to the extent, say, of $\lambda = 1, 0{\cdot}75, 0{\cdot}5$?'

Archimedes of course might answer: 'Your Majesty, you have accepted a prior distribution $\pi(\lambda)$ which makes a value of $|\lambda| < 1$ most improbable; you should not therefore ask this question.'

To which the King might reply: 'Pray give me the answer which I asked for Archimedes. I am far too uncertain whether the particular prior distribution which we sketched out has any sure justification behind it.'

Archimedes must therefore consider the operating characteristic or power function of the rule suggested. He will find in answer to Hiero's questions that if $\sigma = 0{\cdot}25$,

$$\Pr\{|x| > 0{\cdot}71 | \lambda = 0\} = 0{\cdot}0045, \tag{i}$$

$$\left.\begin{aligned} \Pr\{x < 0{\cdot}71 | \lambda = 0{\cdot}5\} &= 0{\cdot}80, \\ \Pr\{x < 0{\cdot}71 | \lambda = 0{\cdot}75\} &= 0{\cdot}44, \\ \Pr\{x < 0{\cdot}71 | \lambda = 1{\cdot}0\} &= 0{\cdot}12. \end{aligned}\right\} \tag{ii}$$

This position the King may consider to be entirely unsatisfactory because of the large chance of failing to detect an amount of adulteration which he considers to be highly criminal.* He is neither prepared to rely on any prior distribution for λ nor does Archimedes's suggestion to formulate a value function appeal to him because he doubts whether this, too, would stand a critical scrutiny. So perhaps he will accept more readily a different specification of his wishes.

If Archimedes were to tell him that by making 25 rather than four measurements ($\sigma = 0{\cdot}10$) and setting the critical value x_c at $0{\cdot}25$, (*a*) the probability of hanging innocent men is about $0{\cdot}01$, (*b*) the probability of letting off men who have taken $\lambda = 0{\cdot}5$ has the same value, he might say: 'I realise, Archimedes, that the figures which you have put into this statement are somewhat arbitrary, but in my opinion they provide a solution which I can understand and accept as reasonable.'

This reply of Hiero might be described as that of a man who after much thought finds one kind of arbitrary choice more meaningful than another. He would in short have come to the conclusion that it would be easier to specify his wishes in terms of an 'indifference value' for λ at, say $0{\cdot}25$ and of two risks (possibly but not necessarily equal), associated with wrong decisions when $\lambda = 0$ and $\lambda = 0{\cdot}5$.

7. CONCLUSION

Having got this far I have reached a point where I am told by my Bayesian friends that we must try 'to see as clearly as we can by reflexion and introspection where the appeal of such a solution lies'.† This is good counsel to which I have no objection; indeed my main purpose in venturing on this talk was to come to such a point where it was agreed that there were difficulties of many kinds which should be discussed jointly and dispassionately. But clearly I have had my say for today and must go no further now. Time might have counted for Hiero and Archimedes too, and they, as well as working statisticians of to-day, might have had to call off further philosophical discussion and adopt a solution which was intelligible to them and in their judgement reasonable.

* Presumably Hiero would regard *any* adulteration as criminal, but he might feel that by including only a small amount of silver or lead the men would have gained no profit adequate to outweigh their continual fear of later discovery.

† In preparing this paper for publication, I quote the words of a very fair-minded referee.

Some problems arising in approximating to probability distributions, using moments†

By E. S. PEARSON
University College London

1. Introduction

In the history of the development of statistical distribution theory there have been many instances where it has been possible to determine the sampling moments of the distribution of a statistic, without any immediate prospect of deriving the mathematical distribution itself in explicit form. Two examples of this are the distributions of (i) the Cramér–von Mises–Simirnoff statistic W_N^2 (or $N\omega^2$)‡ and (ii) the standardized fourth moment $b_2 = m_4/m_2^2$ in samples from a normal universe (where m_s is the sth central sample moment). In so far as there may be a number of alternative mathematical forms which could be used to approximate the unknown true distribution, the question arises as to how to select between them. Suppose, for example, that we take two different frequency functions each having the same first four moments as the unknown true distribution, should we expect that the empirical function whose higher moments are the closer to the true values will give the better representation? And what do we mean by better representation?

In so far as a distribution can be represented by a Gram–Charlier or Fisher–Cornish type of expansion we might expect in theory that agreement in moments would lead to agreement in probability integrals, but it is well known that questions of the convergence of such expansions arise in the case of distributions which are far from normal. The distributions (i) and (ii) referred to above are indeed extremely leptokurtic.

In the following paper it is proposed to draw together several hitherto unpublished investigations, some dating back a number of years, which bear on these points. In particular, we shall:

(*a*) Consider the proportionate contributions, arising from different parts of the parent frequency, to each of the first six moments of certain selected distributions.

(*b*) Make a comparison of the distribution functions of three leptokurtic distributions, namely (i) the Pearson type IV, (ii) the non-central t, and (iii) Johnson's S_U, when their first four moments have identical values.

(*c*) Apply some of the conclusions drawn from the studies (*a*) and (*b*) to the problem of determining significance points for the moment ratio statistics $\sqrt{b_1} = m_3/m_2^{\frac{3}{2}}$ and $b_2 = m_4/m_2^2$ used in testing for departure from normality.

To help the comparison of distributions, we shall represent them as points on a (β_1, β_2) chart as illustrated in Figs. 2 and 3, where

$$\sqrt{\beta_1} = \gamma_1 = \mu_3/\mu_2^{\frac{3}{2}}, \quad \beta_2 = \gamma_2 + 3 = \mu_4/\mu_2^2,$$

μ_s being the sth moment about the population mean.

† This paper is in part based on work first published by the author in Report no. 47 (1961) issued by the Statistical Techniques Research Group, Princeton University, Princeton, N.J.

‡ For a recent discussion on the use of frequency curves in representing this distribution, see Pearson & Stephens (1962).

2. The contribution to moments from the tails of a distribution

The diminishing utility of increasingly high moments as a means of graduating observational data by a frequency curve becomes obvious when calculating such moments; we realize quickly what an effect the presence or absence of a single extreme observation can have on the value of even a third or fourth moment. But when we are concerned with representing one mathematical function by another the conditions under which moments or cumulants are useful are less clear cut.

The problem can be examined from a number of angles. The illustrations given in Tables 1 and 2 below have been taken from some unpublished work of C. Mishra (1955). Suppose that the frequency function $f(x)$ is contained between the limits h and k, so that

$$\int_h^k f(x) = 1.$$

We shall suppose the mean to be at $x = \xi$ so that

$$\mu_s = \int_h^k (x-\xi)^s f(x)\,dx.$$

Further, the upper and lower 100α % points of the distribution, say x_α and x'_α will be defined by

$$\alpha = \int_{x_\alpha}^k f(x)\,dx = \int_h^{x'_\alpha} f(x)\,dx.$$

Tables 1 and 2 give for a variety of distributions the ratios, expressed as percentages,

$$\int_{x_\alpha}^k (x-\xi)^s f(x)\,dx/\mu_s \quad \text{and} \quad \int_h^{x'_\alpha} (x-\xi)^s f(x)\,dx/\mu_s$$

for $\alpha = 0{\cdot}01$ and $0{\cdot}001$. In the case of the symmetrical distributions the two integrals will of course be equal and if

$$\xi = 0, \quad x'_\alpha = -x_\alpha.$$

The symmetrical distributions of Table 1 are: (*a*) the rectangular or uniform distribution; (*b*) the Pearson type II or

$$f(x) = \frac{1}{B(\frac{1}{2}, m+1)}(1-x^2)^m \quad (-1 \leqslant x \leqslant 1); \tag{1}$$

with $m = 3{\cdot}5$; (*c*) the normal distribution; (*d*) and (*e*) the type VII or Student's t distribution

$$f(x) = \frac{1}{B(\frac{1}{2}, m-\frac{1}{2})}(1+x^2)^{-m} \quad (-\infty < x < \infty), \tag{2}$$

with $m = 4{\cdot}5$, $3{\cdot}0$. The asymmetrical type V distributions of Table 2 are those of the reciprocal of χ^2, or

$$f(x) = \frac{1}{\Gamma(m-1)} x^{-m} e^{-1/x} \quad (0 \leqslant x < \infty), \tag{3}$$

with $m = 45{\cdot}2$, $25{\cdot}6$, $15{\cdot}6$ and $10{\cdot}6$, respectively.

Table 1 shows how, as we proceed from flat-topped distributions with abrupt terminals, through the normal to the very long-tailed distribution of Student's t, with 5 degrees of freedom, the contributions to the moments are derived increasingly from the extreme tails of the frequency function. Even for the normal curve, 61 % of μ_6 is made up from the integral in the two tails falling beyond the 1 % points.

For the skew distributions in Table 2 the odd moments μ_3 and μ_5 are added. Here, what is particularly noticeable is the small contribution (negative for odd moments) made by the steep tail. As would be expected, the predominance of the long drawn out tail increases with the order of moment and with the increase in β_1 and β_2. These distributions are of some interest because their beta coefficients are not very different from those of the distributions of the moment ratio b_2 in samples of size n from a normal population discussed in § 4·2 below (see Fig. 3). For $n = 40$, b_2 has beta coefficients (2·75, 8·78) nearly corresponding to those of the fourth distribution in Table 2 (i.e. 2·79, 9·01). In Fig. 1 we consider this case in rather greater detail.

Table 1. *Symmetrical distributions. Contributions to μ_s from beyond the* 100α % *point (single tail)*

Population β_2	α	Percentage contribution to μ_2	μ_4	μ_6
1·8	0·001	0·3	0·5	0·7
(rectangle)	·01	2·9	4·8	6·6
2·5	0·001	0·7	2·1	4·4
	·01	5·6	12·8	20·9
3·0	0·001	1·1	4·5	10·8
(normal)	·01	7·2	18·4	30·5
4·5	0·001	2·2	12·8	34·4
(t, $\nu = 8$)	·01	10·1	29·2	45·2
9·0	0·001	3·6	28·3	μ_6 is
(t, $\nu = 5$)	·01	13·0	40·1	infinite

Table 2. *Asymmetrical (type V) distributions. Contributions to μ_s from beyond the* 100α % *points (single tail)*

Population β_1	β_2	m		α	Percentage contribution to μ_2	μ_4	μ_6	μ_3	μ_5
0·40	3·76	45·2	Upper	0·001	2·2	13·8	39·8	16·8	33·9
				·01	11·7	41·5	76·4	66·2	79·1
			Lower	·01	4·4	5·4	2·8	−15·1	−5·7
				·001	0·6	1·0	0·6	−2·4	−1·2
0·77	4·51	25·6	Upper	0·001	2·8	19·4	52·2	17·6	40·0
				·01	13·8	50·9	84·6	62·1	80·7
			Lower	·01	3·8	3·2	0·9	−8·3	−2·2
				·001	0·5	0·6	0·2	−1·3	−0·5
1·50	6·03	15·6	Upper	0·001	3·8	28·3	68·3	20·4	51·2
				·01	16·9	62·4	92·4	62·4	85·7
			Lower	·01	3·0	1·6	0·2	−4·4	−0·7
				·001	0·4	0·3	0·1	−0·6	−0·1
2·79	9·01	10·6	Upper	0·001	5·4	40·9	85·0	25·5	66·8
				·01	21·0	74·2	97·4	66·0	91·9
			Lower	·01	2·4	0·7	0·0	−2·3	−0·2
				·001	0·3	0·1	0·0	−0·3	−0·0

Below the frequency distribution itself we have plotted the function

$$c(x) = (x-\xi)^s f(x)/\mu_s$$

for $s = 2, 3, \ldots, 6$. The diagram shows clearly how the higher moments of an asymmetrical, long-tailed distribution depend on the form of the frequency distribution in a region of the tail which may be of no practical interest to us.

Even the third and fourth moments may depend very largely upon contributions from the tails. Mishra illustrated this in another way by truncating certain distributions at the upper and lower 0·1 % points and comparing the original beta coefficients with those calculated from the truncated distributions. Some of his results are shown in Table 3. It is evident, particularly as far as β_2 is concerned, that for leptokurtic distributions the tail is wagging the dog!

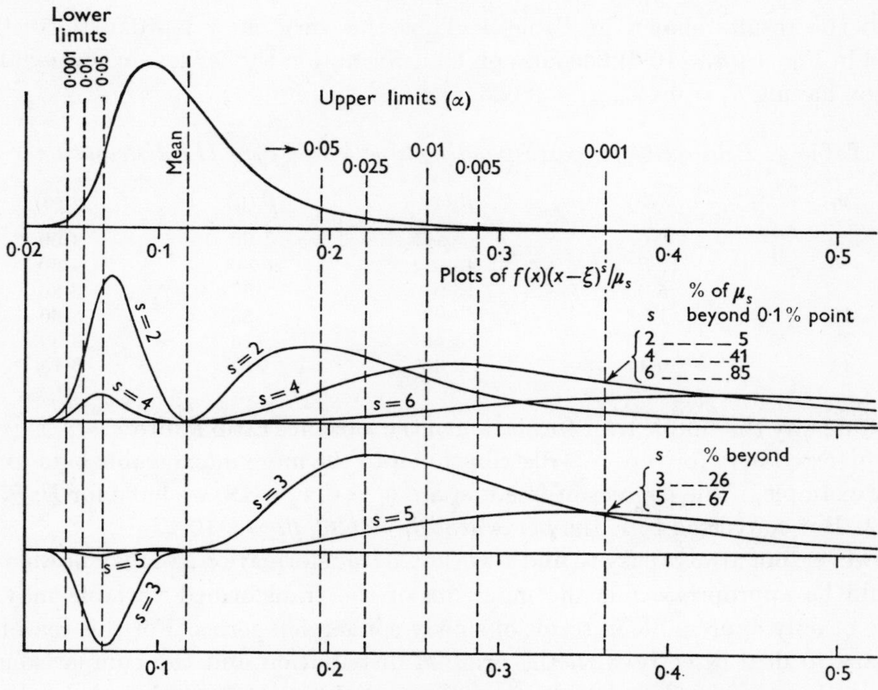

Fig. 1. Distribution $f(x) = 1/[\Gamma(m-1)]\, x^{-m} e^{-1/x}$ for $m = 10{\cdot}6$.

Table 3. *Effect on the beta ratios of truncating a distribution at the two 0·1 % points* ($\alpha = 0{\cdot}001$)

Symmetrical Pearson distributions			Asymmetrical type V distributions			
Degrees of freedom for 't'	Original β_2	β_2 after truncation	Original β_1	Original β_2	After truncation β_1	After truncation β_2
—	2·5	2·46	0·40	3·76	0·32	3·39
∞	3·0	2·86	0·77	4·51	0·60	3·86
12	3·75	3·32	1·50	6·03	1·10	4·68
8	4·5	3·65	2·79	9·01	1·86	5·96
6	6·0	4·09				
5	9·0	4·54				

Undoubtedly one moral to be drawn from these results is that if we wish to find an approximating function for a leptokurtic distribution, we should if possible find a transformation of the variable which makes the distribution more manageable. For example, the transformation $x = 1/u$ turns the type V distribution of equation (3) into the type III or gamma form

$$f(u) = \frac{1}{\Gamma(m-1)} u^{m-2} e^{-u} \quad (0 \leqslant u < \infty). \tag{4}$$

Further, the corresponding (β_1, β_2) coefficients are as follows:

$$\beta_1(x) = \frac{16(m-3)}{(m-4)^2}, \qquad \beta(u) = \frac{4}{m-1},$$

$$\beta_2(x) = 3 + \frac{6(5m-16)}{(m-4)(m-5)}, \quad \beta_2(u) = 3 + \frac{6}{m-1},$$

leading to the results shown in Table 4. Thus the very skew leptokurtic distribution illustrated in Fig. 1 ($m = 10{\cdot}6$) becomes on transformation the far less exceptional gamma distribution having $\beta_1 = 0{\cdot}417$, $\beta_2 = 3{\cdot}625$.

Table 4. *Beta ratios for corresponding type V and type III distributions*

m	$\beta_1(x)$	$\beta_2(x)$	$\beta_1(u)$	$\beta_2(u)$
5	32·0	∞	1·00	4·50
6	12·0	45·0	0·80	4·20
8	5·0	15·0	·57	3·86
13	1·98	7·08	·33	3·50
21	1·00	4·96	·20	3·30
41	0·44	3·85	·10	3·15

In the same way the simple transformation of the variance ratio F into $x = \nu_1 F/(\nu_2 + \nu_1 F)$ turns the inverted beta (or type VI) distribution into the more manageable beta (or type I) form. For example, if the degrees of freedom are $\nu_1 = 6$, $\nu_2 = 18$, we have for F: $\beta_1 = 4{\cdot}62$, $\beta_2 = 12{\cdot}52$. But converted to x, the betas are: $\beta_1 = 0{\cdot}35$, $\beta_2 = 3{\cdot}10$.

It is, however, not always easy to find a workable transformation; we may be able to guess what would be appropriate but the moments of the transformed variable may not be obtainable or only expressible in terms of slowly convergent series. For this reason it may be necessary to deal directly with the original distribution and the comparisons in the following section were undertaken to throw some light on the relations between certain alternative functions available over a considerable area of the (β_1, β_2) field.

3. A comparison of leptokurtic distributions having the same first four moments

The region in the (β_1, β_2) field with which we shall be concerned is shown in Fig. 2 and comparisons will be made at the ten points indicated by the letters $A, B, \ldots, J$. The distribution forms considered are:

(i) *The Pearson-type curves*, which all arise from the solution of the differential equation

$$\frac{df(x)}{dx}\bigg/ f(x) = \frac{-(x+c_1)}{c_0 + c_1 x + c_2 x^2}. \tag{5}$$

Over the greater part of the area considered the solution takes the form of type IV, namely

$$f(x) = c(1+x^2)^{-m} \exp[-d \tan^{-1} x]. \tag{6}$$

The type IV area lies between the axis, $\beta_1 = 0$, where the parameter d is equal to zero and the equation takes the form of Student's t-distribution of equation (2), and the type V line representing the distributions of equation (3). Two of the points in Fig. 2, G and J, lie in the type VI or inverted beta area. However, the tables recently completed by N. L. Johnson & Eric Nixon† make it possible to find, given $\sqrt{\beta_1}$ and β_2, any one of fifteen standardized percentage points of Pearson curves without the need of specifying the particular solution of the differential equation (5) which is appropriate. For these curves also, the standardized 5th and 6th moments or cumulants are readily obtained in terms of β_1 and β_2 (see Appendix).

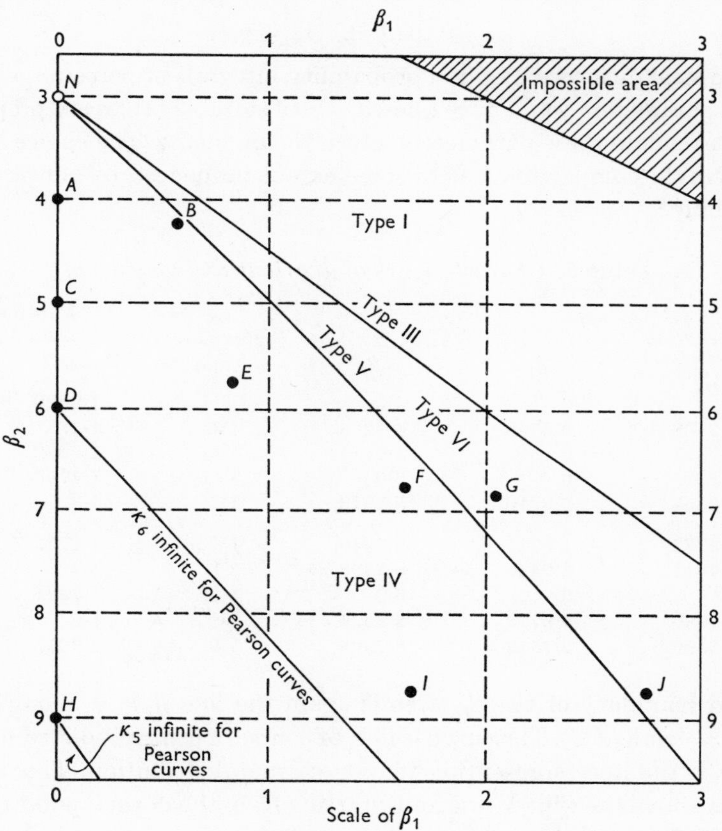

Fig. 2. Diagram showing the ten points at which comparisons are made.

(ii) *The non-central t distribution.* The close similarity between this distribution and the type IV has been pointed out by Merrington & Pearson (1958). The curves are identical along the boundary $\beta_1 = 0$; the right-hand boundary (in the sense of Fig. 2) for non-central t is a curve representing distributions of the reciprocal of χ which lies close to and below the type V (reciprocal of χ^2) line. The points G and J in Fig. 2 lie a little outside the non-central t area.

† These tables which will be published shortly were calculated on the Ferranti Mercury Computer of the University of London. The process used involved a double integration of the differential equation (5) and therefore did not make use explicitly of the many types of solution. Further computations by Dr D. E. Amos of the Sandia Corporation have extended the original scope of the tables to include J- and U-shaped distributions.

The standardized percentage points and the values of κ_5/σ^5 and κ_6/σ^6 for non-central t have been calculated for me at the Sandia Corporation.† The kappas were computed mechanically from the well-known expressions for the moments about the origin (cf. Hogben, Pinkham & Wilk, 1961).

(iii) *The S_U distribution of N. L. Johnson* (1949). The defining relation for this distribution is

$$Z = \gamma + \delta \sinh^{-1} x \quad (-\infty < x < \infty), \tag{7}$$

where Z is a $N(0, 1)$ variable. The moments of S_U up to the sixth are given in the Appendix in terms of the two modified parameters

$$\omega = \exp(\delta^{-2}), \quad \Omega = \gamma/\delta.$$

It is of course straightforward to find probability integrals or percentage points of an S_U curve, once the parameters γ and δ are known. Until suitable tables are prepared, however, it is difficult to calculate these parameters, given the moments. The choice of certain of the ten points used in the comparison was to some extent influenced by considerations of simplicity in handling S_U.

Table 5. *Characteristics of distributions considered*

Case	$\sqrt{\beta_1}$	β_1	β_2	Pearson type	Parameters of S_U ω	Ω
A	0	0	4·0	VII	1·2039	0
B	0·7588	0·5758	4·2268	IV	1·1	1·0
C	0	0	5·0	VII	1·3522	0
D	0	0	6·0	VII	1·4705	0
E	0·9064	0·8216	5·7813	IV	1·3	0·5
F	1·2772	1·6311	6·7740	IV	1·2777	0·8755
G	1·4311	2·0480	6·8496	VI	1·2	∞
H	0	0	9·0	VII	1·7321	0
I	1·2930	1·6719	8·7534	IV	1·5	0·5
J	1·6596	2·7542	8·7808	VI	1·3273	1·2395

The left-hand boundary of the S_U area is again the line $\beta_1 = 0$; along this γ (and Ω) vanish, so that $x = \sinh(Z/\delta)$. The curve is not, of course, a central t-distribution. The right-hand boundary is the line representing the log-normal distribution. This is not shown in Fig. 2, but it lies above the type V line and, starting from the normal point ($\beta_1 = 0, \beta_1 = 3$), passes through the point G shown in the diagram.

The particular distributions considered. The ten (β_1, β_2) points selected are not spread out over the area in an ideally regular pattern, but since heavy computational labour was involved use was made of certain distributions on which work had already been done. The characteristics of the distributions are shown in Table 5. A, C, D and H are symmetrical distributions of increasing long tailedness. B, E and I were picked out of others on which Draper (1952) had made some calculations; G is a log-normal distribution having a simple value for ω; F and J have the same values of β_1 and β_2 as the distribution of the moment ratio $b_2 = m_4/m_2^2$ when samples of $n = 100$ and 40, respectively, are drawn from a normal population.

† Dr D. B. Owen of Sandia is in the course of preparing extensive tables of this function. The expressions for the 5th and 6th cumulants were derived and programmed under his direction by Mrs Marjorie Endres.

In Table 6 are given the standardized cumulants, κ_5/σ^5 and κ_6/σ^6, for each of the three types of distribution (i), (ii) and (iii)† at the ten selected points and also the ratios of these standardized cumulants for distributions (ii) and (iii) to that for (i). The following points will be noted:

(*a*) Where distributions (i) and (ii) are not identical, i.e. for *B*, *E*, *F* and *I* the values of the 5th and 6th cumulants for the Pearson curve (i) lie between those for non-central *t* (ii) and S_U (iii), but are invariably nearer to (ii).

(*b*) The kappas for the distributions (i) and (iii) (Pearson and S_U) appear to be most alike (the ratio (i)/(iii) nearest to unity) towards the log-normal line, i.e. at *G*, and next at *B* and *J*, a point noticed by Dennis (1954) and differ more and more as we move away from this line in a 'south westerly' direction.

Table 6. *Standardized* 5*th and* 6*th cumulants*

Case	κ_5/σ^5	Ratio	κ_6/σ^6	Ratio	Case	κ_5/σ^6	Ratio	κ_6/σ^6	Ratio
A (i), (ii)	0	—	10·00	—	*E* (i)	13·72	—	116·94	—
(iii)	—	—	7·17	0·72	(ii)	13·85	1·01	122·63	1·05
					(iii)	11·22	0·82	70·36	0·60
C (i), (ii)	0	—	80·00	—					
(iii)	—	—	33·61	0·42	*F* (i)	18·95	—	147·90	—
					(ii)	19·31	1·02	157·18	1·06
D (i), (ii)	0	—	∞	—	(iii)	17·23	0·91	113·34	0·77
(iii)	—	—	87·21	0					
					G (i)	16·30	—	98·72	—
H (i), (ii)	0	—	∞	—	(iii)	15·98	0·98	92·57	0·94
(iii)	—	—	496·0	0					
					I (i)	52·37	—	1437·8	—
B (i)	3·09	—	10·82	—	(ii)	54·59	1·04	2066·7	1·44
(ii)	3·12	1·01	11·10	1·03	(iii)	36·58	0·70	384·2	0·27
(iii)	2·94	0·95	9·65	0·89					
					J (i)	34·40	—	321·85	—
					(iii)	32·22	0·94	261·40	0·81

The figures in the columns headed 'ratio' are the ratios of the standardized cumulants (ii)/(i) and/or (iii)/(i), where (i) is Pearson curve, (ii) non-central *t*, (iii) S_U.

Table 7 gives for each distribution the upper and lower standardized percentage points

$$X_\alpha = (x_\alpha - \xi)/\sigma,$$

where ξ and σ are as before the mean and standard deviation, and x_α is the value of the abscissa x at which the ordinate cuts off a tail area α from the frequency function. Following the practice adopted in a number of tables and also used by Johnson & Nixon, we have taken

$$\alpha = 0{\cdot}50,\ 0{\cdot}25,\ 0{\cdot}10,\ 0{\cdot}05,\ 0{\cdot}025,\ 0{\cdot}01,\ 0{\cdot}005,\ 0{\cdot}0025.$$

All the figures for asymmetrical Pearson curves were obtained by interpolation in the Johnson–Nixon tables; they will certainly sometimes be in error by a unit in the third decimal place. The figures for the central and non-central *t*-distributions were computed at

† For the symmetrical distributions *A*, *C*, *D* and *H* the distributions (i) and (ii) are identical; for points *G* and *J* there is no non-central *t* distribution as we are outside its area.

the Sandia Corporation and are cut down from values calculated to considerably greater accuracy. Given the values of the parameters in equation (7), the standardized percentage points for S_U were easily calculated.

Table 7. *Standardized percentage points* X_α

Upper percentage points

Case		50	25	10	5	2·5	1	0·5	0·25
A	(i), (ii)	0	0·626	1·227	1·621	1·993	2·472	2·835	3·203
	(iii)		−5	−2	2	8	15	17	17
C	(i), (ii)	0	0·601	1·196	1·601	1·998	2·534	2·958	3·405
	(iii)		−12	−9	2	17	38	51	59
D	(i), (ii)	0	0·586	1·176	1·587	1·998	2·566	3·027	3·525
	(iii)		−20	−18	−2	23	60	87	108
H	(i), (ii)	0	0·563	1·143	1·561	1·991	2·606	3·123	3·697
	(iii)		−42	−44	−17	29	109	177	245
B	(i)	−0·111	0·577	1·306	1·803	2·277	2·885	3·339	3·793
	(ii)	−1	1	1	0	−1	−1	−1	−1
	(iii)	−2	−1	1	3	4	5	5	1
E	(i)	−0·105	0·543	1·254	1·765	2·280	2·982	3·542	4·133
	(ii)	−1	0	1	1	−1	−1	−2	−3
	(iii)	−4	−13	−6	7	20	38	45	45
F	(i)	−0·159	0·507	1·272	1·833	2·400	3·175	3·789	4·433
	(ii)	1	2	1	0	−2	−5	−6	−6
	(iii)	1	−10	−7	1	11	24	31	34
G	(i)	−0·196	0·489	1·295	1·884	2·475	3·269	3·886	4·521
	(iii)	1	−3	−3	0	3	7	9	10
I	(i)	−0·128	0·499	1·222	1·766	2·334	3·141	3·809	4·536
	(ii)	−1	2	4	3	1	−2	−5	−9
	(iii)	−1	−25	−23	−3	24	66	95	117
J	(i)	−0·202	0·461	1·263	1·869	2·492	3·356	4·048	4·779
	(iii)	3	−8	−9	−3	5	20	29	36

Lower percentage points

Case		25	10	5	2·5	1	0·5	0·25
B	(i)	−0·704	−1·169	−1·423	−1·631	−1·861	−2·011	−2·145
	(ii)	1	0	−1	0	1	3	5
	(iii)	3	4	2	−1	−7	−14	−23
E	(i)	−0·666	−1·135	−1·415	−1·661	−1·960	−2·174	−2·384
	(ii)	−1	0	2	3	3	2	0
	(iii)	12	16	10	−6	−39	−72	−111
F	(i)	−0·690	−1·089	−1·303	−1·477	−1·669	−1·794	−1·909
	(ii)	−1	−2	0	3	9	13	20
	(iii)	13	13	4	−14	−48	−83	−124
G	(i)	−0·709	−1·057	−1·223	−1·344	−1·465	−1·535	−1·590
	(iii)	3	2	−2	−8	−15	−21	−30
I	(i)	−0·653	−1·087	−1·345	−1·577	−1·864	−2·074	−2·285
	(ii)	−2	0	2	5	10	11	11
	(iii)	29	33	12	−25	−97	−169	−255
J	(i)	−0·693	−1·029	−1·194	−1·316	−1·442	−1·517	−1·581
	(iii)	13	9	−3	−25	−61	−96	−133

(i) Pearson curve percentage points. The corrections in rows (ii) and (iii) when added to figure in row (i) give the percentage points of non-central t and S_U, respectively. The column headings are in percentages, i.e. 100α.

The table only shows the full values for the Pearson curves: values for (ii), non-central t, and (iii), S_U, can be obtained by adding the differences in the rows marked (ii) and (iii) respectively. E.g. the lower standardized 0·5 % point for S_U, in case F, is

$$-1{\cdot}794-0{\cdot}083 = -1{\cdot}877.$$

A number of interesting points are suggested by a study of Table 7:

(*a*) Where a comparison is possible, at B, E, F and I, the agreement between the position of the percentage points of the (i) type IV and (ii) non-central t distributions is remarkable. At the upper tail, the greatest discrepancy is 0·009 of the standard deviation and at the lower tail, 0·02; both these differences are at the extreme, 0·25 % points. This agreement confirms the conclusions of Merrington & Pearson (1958).

(*b*) There is considerably more disagreement between the percentage points of the (i) type IV and (iii) S_U distributions. The differences are greater in the lower, steeper tail.

(*c*) There is a striking agreement in the position of both upper and lower 5 % points for all three distributions. Near here a cross-over is clearly occurring in the cumulative distributions of (i) and (iii).

(*d*) There is also excellent agreement in the position of the medians of the distributions; again, there will be here another cross-over in the cumulative distributions of (i) and (iii).

(*e*) As far as these necessarily limited results go, we do find, on comparison of Tables 6 and 7, that the distributions whose κ_5 and κ_6 are the more alike, show the better agreement in the position of percentage points. Consider, for example, the three points H, I and J which have nearly the same β_2 values but very different values of β_1. As we pass from H through I to J, the values of κ_6/σ^6 for the Pearson and S_U distributions get closer (ratios (i)/(iii) from Table 6 are 0, 0·27 and 0·81 respectively). At the same time the percentage point values for (i) and (iii) approach one another, e.g.

		H	I	J
Difference (iii) – (i)	For upper 1 % points	0·109	0·066	0·020
	For lower 1 % points	–0·109	–0·097	–0·061
Difference (iii) – (i)	For upper 0·25 % points	0·245	0·117	0·036
	For lower 0·25 % points	–0·245	–0·255	–0·133

(*f*) In §2 it was shown that for a distribution very similar to the Pearson distribution J, a 67 % contribution to μ_5 and an 85 % contribution to μ_6 came from that part of the tail of the parent distribution falling beyond the upper 0·1 % point. Nevertheless, it seems clear, as illustrated above, that the values of these high moments do provide a guide to the agreement of the cumulative distributions at less extreme points. We are of course dealing only with particular cases, and it may be possible to find situations where matching of κ_5 and κ_6 would not result in best agreement, say, at the more abrupt tail of a distribution.

4. An illustration from the distributions used in tests for normality

To put some of these suggestions to practical account, it is of interest to turn to a problem in which a search for the higher moments was undertaken almost entirely with a view to determining the sampling distributions of two statistics. This was the problem of providing tests for normality based either on the moment ratios

$$\sqrt{b_1} = m_3/m_2^{\frac{3}{2}}, \quad b_2 = m_4/m_2^2,$$

or, alternatively, on the related k-statistic ratios

$$g_1 = k_3/k_2^{\frac{3}{2}}, \quad g_2 = k_4/k_2^2$$

in samples of n independent observations drawn from a normal population.

R. A. Fisher's (1928) great break-through in the combinatorial field was followed by a series of papers applying his methods in the 'tests for normality' problem. He himself (1930) derived the 2nd, 4th and 6th cumulants of the (symmetrical) distribution of g_1, and the first four cumulants of g_2. Pepper (1932) obtained the 8th moment of g_1, Hsu & Lawley (1940) obtained the 5th and 6th moments of b_2 and, finally, Geary & Worlledge (1947) obtained its 7th moment.

The sum total of the effort involved in these investigations was very great, and yet it cannot be said that the objective was ever fully achieved. The difficulties involved in the problem as the sample size becomes small are evidenced by the papers of McKay (1933*a*, *b*) and Geary (1947*a*, *b*).

4·1. *The case of* $\sqrt{b_1}$

In Table 8 are given the true values of $\beta_2 = \mu_4/\sigma^4$, μ_6/σ^6 and μ_8/σ^8 for the distribution of $\sqrt{b_1}$ in samples of $n = 25, 50, 75, 100$ and also the last two of these ratios for the t-distribution (Pearson type VII) having the correct β_2 value. For $n \geqslant 50$ it is seen that there is fairly close agreement between the higher ratios for the true and the t distribution, so that we

Table 8. *Moment ratios of* $\sqrt{b_1}$ *in normal samples of size n*

n	$\mu_4/\sigma^4 = \beta_2$	μ_6/σ^6 True	μ_6/σ^6 Type VII approx.	μ_8/σ^8 True	μ_8/σ^8 Type VII approx.
25	3·5783	25·48	26·44	297·0	359·2
50	3·4525	23·42	23·39	267·4	269·9
75	3·3511	21·38	21·20	223·8	216·4
100	3·2844	20·04	19·86	195·4	187·8

Table 9. *Percentage points for* $\sqrt{b_1}$ *when* $n = 25$

		5 %	1 %	μ_6/σ^6	μ_8/σ^8
Two moment fits	Type VII or t	0·710	1·057	26·44	359·2
	S_U	·711	1·059	25·90	—
Four moment fit (Hansmann)		·711	1·059	25·48	297·0

might hope that from this sample size upwards, at least, the latter would provide a good approximating function to the unknown true distribution. At $n = 25$ the 8th moment ratio for the t distribution is however considerably greater than the true value. In this case Williams (1935) introduced as an alternative approximation a distribution belonging to the system of symmetrical curves derived by Hansmann (1934) from a differential equation analogous to that of the Pearson system.

Hansmann found that the solution of the equation

$$\frac{1}{y}\frac{dy}{dX} = \frac{X}{b_0 + b_2 X^2 + b_4 X^4},$$

where the origin is at the mean and $X = x/\sigma$, takes a variety of forms of which

$$y = y_0 \left\{\frac{p \pm X^2}{q \pm X^2}\right\}^k \tag{8}$$

is typical. The values of the parameters depend on the first four even moments.

Using the true moments up to μ_8 for the case $n = 25$, Williams fitted the equation (8) and found 5 and 1 % points for $\sqrt{b_1}$ by quadrature. It is also possible to fit Johnson's symmetrical

S_U curve having the correct variance and β_2, an ω value of 1·1273 and $\mu_6/\sigma^6 = 25{\cdot}90$.† The results are summarized in Table 9. It is interesting to note the intermediate position of the S_U distribution both as regards these two percentage points and the μ_6/σ^6 value.

The percentage points for $\sqrt{b_1}$ given in *Biometrika Tables for Statisticians*, Table 34 *a*, for $n = 25\,(5)\,50\,(10)\,100\ldots$, were obtained from the t-distribution approximation, except for $n = 25$ where Williams's results from fitting the Hansmann curve were introduced. Clearly a little further exploration would be desirable to determine at what sample size the three methods of approximation give identical values to, say, three decimal places, although we cannot be sure that the approximation using the correct μ_6/σ^6 and μ_8/σ^8 is the most accurate of the three.

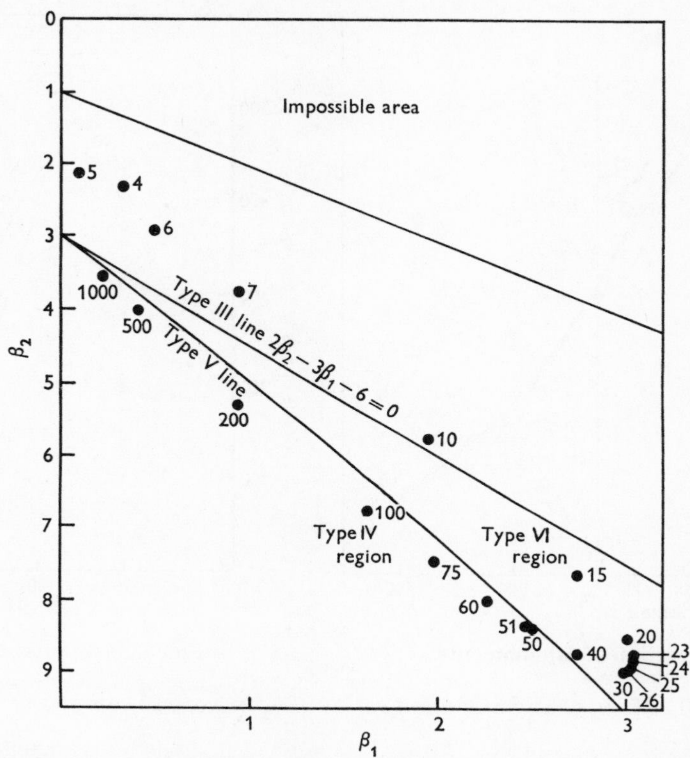

Fig. 3. (β_1, β_2) points for the distribution of b_2 in samples from a normal distribution.

4·2. *The case of* b_2

This problem is more interesting, but more difficult to handle. In Fig. 3, taken from C. T. Hsu's unpublished M.Sc. Thesis (1939), the (β_1, β_2) points of b_2 are plotted. It will be seen that they lie on a sinuous curve which first approaches symmetry at $n = 5$, then becomes more and more skew until about $n = 25$ where the plot finally turns back towards the normal point. Even when $n = 200$, however, the distribution is far from normal. Values of the moment ratios for certain values of n between 25 and 200 are shown in Table 10; Hsu's μ_5 and μ_6 have been converted to κ_5 and κ_6 using the relations

$$\frac{\kappa_5}{\sigma^5} = \frac{\mu_5}{\sigma^5} - 10\sqrt{\beta_1}, \quad \frac{\kappa_6}{\sigma^6} = \frac{\mu_6}{\sigma^6} - 15\beta_2 - 10\beta_1 + 30.$$

† Johnson (1949) gave a general expression from which the 8th moment of a symmetrical S_U distribution could be derived as a function of ω. I did not, however, go further than use the expression for μ_6 given in the Appendix below.

It will be seen from Fig. 3 that some of these beta points fall in the Pearson type VI, others within the type IV region.

C. T. Hsu's method of approach was to compare with the true values, the 5th and 6th moments for distributions from other systems having correct lower moments. Figs. 4 and 5 are also based on diagrams reproduced in his Thesis. On these diagrams are added points for S_U distributions for the cases $n = 40$ and 100. The curves on the diagrams labelled type V are for the distributions of that type having the correct β_1, but not the correct β_2. Fig. 3 shows that for $n > 30$ the true beta points never lie far from the type V line, and this suggested to Hsu a possible method of approximation.

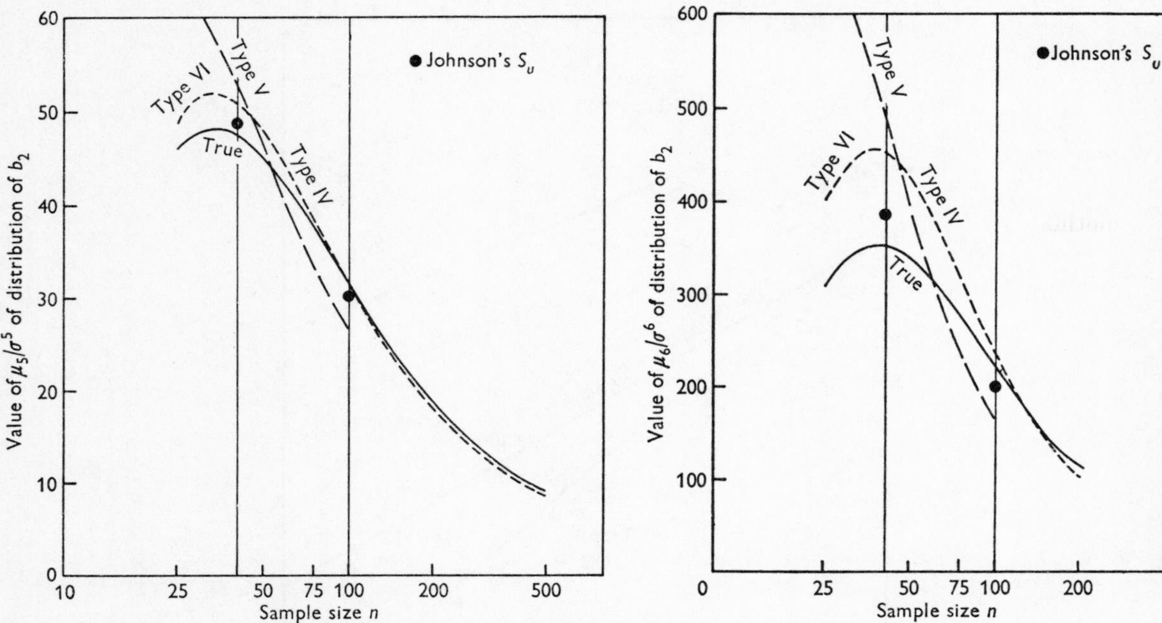

Fig. 4. Comparison of 5th moments.

Fig. 5. Comparison of 6th moments.

Table 10. *Moment and cumulant ratios of* b_2 *in normal samples of size* n

n	$\sqrt{\beta_1}$	β_1	β_2	μ_5/σ^5	κ_5/σ^5	μ_6/σ^6	κ_6/σ^6
25	1·75	3·05	8·90	46·1	28·7	309	175
40	1·66	2·75	8·78	47·6	31·0	352	223
60	1·51	2·27	8·03	42·0	26·9	314	201
100	1·28	1·63	6·77	31·4	18·7	221	133
200	0·97	0·94	5·25	18·7	9·0	112	54

Further comments will be concerned only with the distributions for $n = 40$ and 100, for which the true values of β_1, β_2 are those corresponding to cases J and F, respectively, discussed in § 3. Table 11 compares the true values of the standardized 5th and 6th cumulants with those of the three approximating distributions having the same β_1, β_2 values.

It is seen from this table, as is also evident from Figs. 4 and 5, that:

(*a*) At $n = 40$ these higher cumulants for S_U are closer to the true values than are those of the Pearson type VI.

(*b*) At $n = 100$ the Pearson curve (now type IV) has the closest values of the three alternatives.

Table 12 rounds off the discussion, giving for each distribution six upper and six lower percentage points for b_2 obtained from the relation

$$(b_2)_\alpha = \text{mean } b_2 + X_\alpha \times \text{standard deviation of } b_2,$$

where the X_α are the standardized percentage points for cases J and F already given in Table 7.

The results are only given to two decimal places which would be adequate for a test of significance. It will be noted that:

(*a*) At $n = 100$, the figures derived from the non-central t approximation never differ by more than 0·01 from those for the Pearson curve.

(*b*) Agreement between the S_U and Pearson approximations is better at the upper than at the lower tails of the distributions.

(*c*) It is only at the latter and for the 0·5 and 0·25 % points that the differences between these two approximations become appreciable.

Table 11. *Higher cumulants of approximating distributions for* b_2

Distribution	$n = 40$		$n = 100$	
	κ_5/σ^5	κ_6/σ^6	κ_5/σ^5	κ_6/σ^6
True	31·0	223	18·7	133
Pearson VI or IV	34·4	322	18·9	148
Non-central t	—	—	19·3	157
S_U	32·2	261	17·2	113

Table 12. *Percentage points for* b_2 *from three 4-moment approximations*

Percentage point	$n = 40$ Lower (i)	$n = 40$ Lower (iii)	$n = 40$ Upper (i)	$n = 40$ Upper (iii)	$n = 100$ Lower (i)	$n = 100$ Lower (ii)	$n = 100$ Lower (iii)	$n = 100$ Upper (i)	$n = 100$ Upper (ii)	$n = 100$ Upper (iii)
10	2·19	2·20	3·67	3·66	2·45	2·44	2·45	3·52	3·52	3·52
5	2·09	2·08	4·06	4·06	2·35	2·35	2·35	3·77	3·77	3·77
2·5	2·01	1·99	4·46	4·46	2·27	2·27	2·26	4·03	4·03	4·04
1	1·93	1·89	5·02	5·03	2·18	2·19	2·16	4·38	4·38	4·40
0·5	1·88	1·81	5·46	5·48	2·12	2·13	2·09	4·66	4·66	4·68
0·25	1·84	1·75	5·93	5·96	2·07	2·08	2·02	4·96	4·95	4·97

Approximations: (i) Pearson curve (VI and IV); (ii) non-central t; (iii) S_U.

Following from the comparison of the higher cumulants in Table 11 it might be thought that the S_U values were the safer bet when $n = 40$ and the type VI or inverted beta values when $n = 100$. But if we recall the insignificant contribution to these 5th and 6th moments which came from the lower tail region in the case of the rather similar curve of Fig. 1, we can hardly feel confident that the distribution with the most accurate values of these moments provides the best fit at the steep tail, particularly when $n = 40$.

It can perhaps be argued that the largest differences between approximations shown in Table 11 are not of importance, although at $n = 40$ the lower 0·25 % point for one approximation falls inside the 0·5 % point for the other. The result is however 'untidy' from the table-making point of view. In *Biometrika Tables for Statisticians*, Table 34*c*, the difficulty was avoided by giving 5 and 1 % points only when $n \geqslant 200$. The present comparisons suggest that the table could be carried down to $n = 100$, and perhaps further, using some rough method of interpolating between the approximations on the basis of the higher cumulant values.

Various attempts have been made to work with a transformed variable. For example, the closeness of the (β_1, β_2) points to the type V line suggest that the reciprocal of b_2 would be more nearly normally distributed; we do not, however, know the negative moments of b_2. Presumably the cumulants of $\log b_2$ could be expressed as a series in inverse powers of n, having coefficients depending on the known first seven cumulants of b_2, but here difficulties of convergence might well arise. The theoretical problem is therefore still unsolved; it is of some interest in being not alone of its kind.

5. Discussion

The separate investigations brought together in this paper have all been concerned with different aspects of the general question of how best to approximate to an unknown frequency function, given a knowledge of its moments. The problem was particularly in evidence in the case of the statistics $\sqrt{b_1}$ and b_2 for which, in the 1930's, a considerable number of moments had been derived after much labour, and yet it was not very clear how to make best use of them.

Statisticians working in the field of distribution theory have been accustomed to make use of Gram–Charlier, Edgeworth or Cornish–Fisher types of expansion, but the distributions represented in Figs. 2 or 3 fall almost entirely outside the area in which these expansions have been proved effective. In a recent paper Fisher & Cornish (1960) illustrated the accuracy of their expansion by taking the case of a χ^2, a t and a z distribution. They presented auxiliary tables with enough coefficients and enough significant figures to give 4-decimal-place accuracy for the percentage points of χ^2 and t having $\nu \geqslant 30$ degrees of freedom and of z having $\nu_1 \geqslant 24$, $\nu_2 \geqslant 60$. But the corresponding area in the (β_1, β_2) plane of Figs. 2 or 3 lies within the small triangle bounded by the axis of β_2, the type III line and the line $\beta_2 = 3{\cdot}5$. The distributions we are considering all lie well outside this area.

One solution is clearly to transform the variable so as to make its distribution more amenable; it was for this reason that Fisher took $z = \frac{1}{2}\log_e F$ as the basis of his significance tables for use in the analysis of variance. The present work has been carried out in the belief that it is not always easy to find or handle an appropriate transformation so that more knowledge of the characteristics of these long-tailed distributions is needed. It is hoped that the studies described here, though clearly inconclusive, add something to our knowledge.

Experience has suggested that we can go a long way in the process of approximation if we make the distribution used have the correct values of its first four moments, but the limits of the usefulness of this approach are hard to define. In § 3 it has been shown that of three types of curve having identical first four moments, there is very close correspondence between the Pearson curve and the distribution of non-central t; in this case it must be remembered that the equation to both distributions contains a similar factor, $(1+x^2)^{-m}$. However, for many purposes the agreement between the S_U distribution and the other two would also be regarded as good.

In terms of the displacement of standardized percentage points agreement is better for skew distributions at the long tail than at the steep tail. Because of the higher values of $d\alpha/dx$ at the steep tail, a given displacement also means more at this tail than at the long one. For example, for case I (see Table 7) the 0·5 % point of S_U (at $-2{\cdot}243$) is nearly as far out from the mean as the 0·25 % point of type IV (at $-2·285$) and for case J it is in fact further out ($-1·613$ against $-1·581$); the effect of shifts at the corresponding upper-tail points are of much less consequence.

Linked with this phenomenon it has been found that, for a number of the more abnormal distributions considered, (*a*) the contributions to the higher moments from the steep tail are quite negligible, (*b*) the greater part of the contribution comes from a region in the long tail which may lie well beyond that part of the distributions in which we are generally interested in practice. Nevertheless, as far as the limited evidence presented here goes, values of the standardized 5th and 6th moments do provide some guide to the degree of correspondence between distributions in the more central range of the curve.

The agreement between the positions of the medians and of the upper and lower 5 % points of different types of distribution has also been brought out, a point no doubt recognized elsewhere by other statisticians.

The usefulness of the 'moment fit' in providing good approximations at the long tail, but failing at the steep tail, is well illustrated in an even more extreme example than those discussed here. The limiting distribution of the Cramér–von Mises–Smirnoff statistic W_N^2 as $N \to \infty$ has beta coefficients: $\beta_1 = 6·53$, $\beta_2 = 13·29$. It can be represented reasonably well by a Johnson S_B curve having the correct first four moments (see Pearson & Stephens, 1962). Both distributions have a zero ordinate at the abrupt terminal. On the other hand, in standardized form, the corresponding 4-moment Pearson curve has the equation

$$f(x) = \text{constant} \times x^{-36·960}(x-6·0882)^{-0·2905} \quad (6·0882 \leqslant x < \infty). \tag{9}$$

This is a J-shaped curve with infinite ordinate at the start so that it is clearly quite inappropriate to use in approximating to W_∞^2 for low values. But it provides a good approximation in the long upper tail, at any rate as far as the 5 and 1 % points are concerned. We have in fact for W_∞^2, after appropriate transformation of equation (9):

	5 %	1 %
Anderson and Darling's true values	0·461	0·743
From S_B approximation	·457	·746
From equation (9)	·462	·738

The scope of this paper has been confined to a particular region of the (β_1, β_2) plane. It is probable that for distributions whose range is limited at both ends, e.g. for the beta or type I distribution, the situation will be rather different. It is planned to carry out some comparisons in this region.

The results collected in this paper owe much to the labours of a number of graduate students who have worked in the Department of Statistics, University College London, during the past 30 years. In particular the author must mention Mr C. T. Hsu (with whom he has long lost touch) and Dr C. Mishra, whose University of London Theses have neither of them been so far published. To all those he would like to express his warm thanks.

He is also particularly grateful to Professor N. L. Johnson and Mr Eric Nixon for their table computation which has made it easy, in a way never possible before, to obtain standardized deviates for a wide range of Pearson curves; and to Dr D. B. Owen, Dr D. E. Amos and Mrs Marjorie Endres of the Sandia Corporation, Albuquerque, New Mexico, for providing him with great promptitude and to a high degree of accuracy with the data for the non-central t distribution needed in § 3.

Finally he would like to make clear that it was the welcome opportunity provided to him by Professor J. W. Tukey of a 2-month visit to the Statistical Techniques Research Group at Princeton University which encouraged him to put together much of the material and to write it up in preliminary form for the Group's Report no. 47 (1961).

References

Dennis, K. E. R. (1954). University of London M.Sc. Thesis (unpublished).

Draper, J. (1952). Properties of distributions resulting from certain simple transformations of the normal distribution. *Biometrika*, **39**, 290–301.

Fisher, R. A. (1928). Moments and product moments of sampling distributions. *Proc. Lond. Math. Soc.* (Series 2), **30**, 199–238.

Fisher, R. A. (1930). The moments of the distribution for normal samples of measures of departure from normality. *Proc. Roy. Soc.* A, **130**, 16–28.

Fisher, R. A. & Cornish, E. A. (1960). The percentile points of distributions having known cumulants. *Technometrics*, **2**, 209–25.

Geary, R. C. (1947*a*). The frequency distribution of $\sqrt{b_1}$ for samples of all sizes drawn at random from a normal population. *Biometrika*, **34**, 68–97.

Geary, R. C. (1947*b*). Testing for normality. *Biometrika*, **34**, 209–42.

Geary, R. C. & Worlledge, J. P. G. (1947). On the computation of universal moments of tests of statistical normality derived from samples drawn at random from a normal universe. Application to the calculation of the seventh moment of b_2. *Biometrika*, **34**, 98–110. (Correction, **37**, 189.)

Hansmann, G. H. (1934). On certain non-normal symmetrical frequency distributions. *Biometrika*, **26**, 129–95.

Hogben, D., Pinkham, R. S. & Wilk, M. B. (1961). The moments of the non-central *t* distribution. *Biometrika*, **48**, 465–8.

Hsu, C. T. (1939). University of London M.Sc. Thesis (unpublished).

Hsu, C. T. & Lawley, D. N. (1940). The derivation of the 5th and 6th moments of the distribution of b_2 in samples from a normal population. *Biometrika*, **31**, 238–48.

Johnson, N. L. (1949). Systems of frequency curves generated by methods of translation. *Biometrika*, **36**, 149–76.

McKay, A. T. (1933*a*). The distribution of $\sqrt{b_1}$ in samples of four from a normal universe. *Biometrika*, **25**, 204–10.

McKay, A. T. (1933*b*). The distribution of b_2 in samples of four from a normal universe. *Biometrika*, **25**, 411–5.

Merrington, Maxine & Pearson, E. S. (1958). An approximation to the distribution of non-central *t*. *Biometrika*, **45**, 484–91.

Mishra, C. (1955). University of London Ph.D. Thesis (unpublished).

Pearson, E. S. & Stephens, M. A. (1962). The goodness-of-fit tests based on W_N^2 and U_N^2. *Biometrika*, **49**, 397–402.

Pepper, J. (1932). The sampling distribution of the third moment coefficient—an experiment. *Biometrika*, **24**, 55–84.

Williams, P. (1935). Note on the sampling distribution of $\sqrt{b_1}$, where the population is normal. *Biometrika*, **27**, 269–71.

Appendix

(1) *Expressions for the 5th and 6th standardized moments and cumulants of Pearson curves in terms of β_1 and β_2*

Write
$$\theta = (2\beta_2 - 3\beta_1 - 6)/(\beta_2 + 3),$$
then
$$\frac{\mu_5}{\sigma^5} = \frac{2\sqrt{\beta_1}\{\beta_2 + 2 + \theta\}}{1-\theta},$$
$$\frac{\mu_6}{\sigma^6} = \frac{5\{\sqrt{\beta_1}\,\mu_5/\sigma^5 + (2+\theta)\,\beta_2\}}{2-3\theta}.$$
In cumulant notation
$$\gamma_1 = \sqrt{\beta_1}, \quad \gamma_2 = \beta_2 - 3,$$
$$\frac{\kappa_5}{\sigma^5} = \frac{\mu_5}{\sigma^5} - 10\gamma_1, \quad \frac{\kappa_6}{\sigma^6} = \frac{\mu_6}{\sigma^6} - 15\gamma_2 - 10\gamma_1^2 - 15.$$

(2) *The moments of Johnson's S_U distribution, expressed in terms of the parameters ω and Ω*

$$\mu_1 = -\omega^{\frac{1}{2}}\sinh\Omega,$$
$$\mu_2 = \tfrac{1}{2}(\omega-1)(\omega\cosh 2\Omega + 1),$$
$$\mu_3 = -\tfrac{1}{4}\omega^{\frac{1}{2}}(\omega-1)^2\{\omega(\omega+2)\sinh 3\Omega + 3\sinh\Omega\},$$
$$\mu_4 = \tfrac{1}{8}(\omega-1)^2\{\omega^2(\omega^4+2\omega^3+3\omega^2-3)\cosh 4\Omega + 4\omega^2(\omega+2)\cosh 2\Omega + 3(2\omega+1)\},$$
$$\mu_5 = -\tfrac{1}{16}\omega^{\frac{1}{2}}\{\omega^2(\omega^{10}-5\omega^6+10\omega^3-10\omega+4)\sinh 5\Omega + 5\omega(\omega^7-4\omega^4-\omega^3+6\omega^2-2)\sinh 3\Omega$$
$$+10(\omega^5-4\omega^3+2\omega^2+3\omega-2)\sinh\Omega\},$$
$$\mu_6 = \tfrac{1}{32}\{\omega^3(\omega^{15}-6\omega^{10}+15\omega^6-2\omega^3+15\omega-5)\cosh 6\Omega$$
$$+6\omega^2(\omega^{11}-5\omega^7-\omega^6+10\omega^4+5\omega^3-10\omega^2-5\omega+5)\cosh 4\Omega$$
$$+15\omega(\omega^8-4\omega^5-2\omega^4+7\omega^3+3\omega^2-7\omega+2)\cosh 2\Omega + 10(2\omega^6-6\omega^4-\omega^3+9\omega^2-3\omega-1)\}.$$

The defining relation for the S_U distribution is
$$Z = \gamma + \delta\sinh^{-1}x \quad (-\infty < x < \infty),$$
where Z is a $N(0,1)$ variable and
$$\omega = \exp\delta^{-2}, \quad \Omega = \gamma/\delta.$$
The equations for the first four moments are taken from Johnson (1949) and those for μ_5 and μ_6 from Dennis (1954).

Comparison of tests for randomness of points on a line

By E. S. PEARSON
University College London

1. Introduction

The following paper should be regarded as a companion to papers by Watson (1961), Pearson & Stephens (1962) and Stephens (1963). In the first of these papers Watson has listed four goodness-of-fit tests based on various measures of the difference between a specified continuous distribution function $F(x)$ and the sample distribution function $F_N(x)$ where, on the hypothesis tested, $x_1, x_2, \ldots, x_N$ is a random sample from the population specified by $F(x)$. Denoting the four test statistics by W_N^2, D_N, U_N^2 and V_N, we have

$$W_N^2 = N\int_{-\infty}^{\infty} \{F_N(x) - F(x)\}^2\, dF(x), \tag{1}$$

$$D_N = \sup_{-\infty \leqslant x \leqslant \infty} |F_N(x) - F(x)|, \tag{2}$$

$$U_N^2 = N\int_{-\infty}^{\infty} \left\{F_N(x) - F(x) - \int_{-\infty}^{\infty} [F_N(y) - F(y)]\, dF(y)\right\}^2 dF(x), \tag{3}$$

$$V_N = \sup_{-\infty \leqslant x \leqslant \infty} \{F_N(x) - F(x)\} - \inf_{-\infty \leqslant x \leqslant \infty} \{F_N(x) - F(x)\}. \tag{4}$$

The asymptotic distributions under the null hypothesis of all four statistics are known, and it is clear that the convergence of the cumulative distributions to their asymptotic forms is unusually rapid. Tables for determining the significance of D_N in finite samples were given by Birnbaum (1952), while Pearson & Stephens and Stephens, in the papers cited above, have made some progress in the determining the pre-asymptotic behaviour of W_N^2 and U_N^2. In the present paper the use of the four tests will be compared on several sets of data which the author has collected in the past for illustrative purposes.

2. Adjustment to test for randomness of points on a line

Since distributions of the four statistics are, on the null hypothesis, independent of $F(x)$, it is convenient to write

(*a*) $x_{(1)} \leqslant x_{(2)} \leqslant \ldots \leqslant x_{(N)}$ for the ordered observations, and
(*b*) $v_i = F(x_{(i)}) \quad (i = 1, 2, \ldots, N)$.

Then the statistics assume the forms

$$W_N^2 = \sum_{i=1}^{N} \left(\frac{2i-1}{2N} - v_i\right)^2 + \frac{1}{12N}, \tag{5}$$

$$D_N = \sup_{0 \leqslant v_i \leqslant 1} \left|\frac{i}{N} - v_i\right|, \tag{6}$$

$$U_N^2 = \sum_{i=1}^{N} \left(\frac{2i-1}{2N} - v_i\right)^2 - N(\bar{v} - 0{\cdot}5)^2 + \frac{1}{12N}, \tag{7}$$

$$V_N = \sup_{0 \leqslant v_i \leqslant 1} \left(\frac{i}{N} - v_i\right) - \inf_{0 \leqslant v_i \leqslant 1} \left(\frac{i}{N} - v_i\right), \tag{8}$$

where $\bar{v} = \sum_i v_i/N$.

In this standardized form we may regard the tests as concerned with the hypothesis that N points are randomly and independently distributed on the unit line (0, 1). Since the distributions of U_N^2 and V_N as defined in equations (2) and (4) have been shown to be independent of the origin for x, these two statistics may also be used to test the randomness of points on a circle. The V_N test was in fact developed by Kuiper (1960) to examine a theory that the flights of birds were random in direction. The illustrations considered below are not, however, concerned with this circular problem, all four tests being compared on the unit line.

It is perhaps instructive to start with a geometrical interpretation of the relationship between the tests. For this purpose the data of Example 1 (given in the Appendix) have been used. These relate to 20 consecutive observations of warp breaks on a loom. The distance along the warp was measured in units of 100 'picks'.† We may denote the distance from the starting point of observation to the ith break by t_i ($i = 1, 2, \ldots, 20$). The total length of warp within which the $N = 20$ breaks occurred being $T = 1520$, we write

$$v_i = t_i/T, \tag{9}$$

so that $0 \leqslant v \leqslant 1$.

Fig. 1 shows the step function of the observations plotted within a square frame to axes v_i, i/N. Below is shown the plot of the 20 points which, owing to close proximity in some instances, could not be drawn exactly on a line. A typical value of the differences

$$d_i = (2i-1)/(2N) - v_i \tag{10}$$

is shown for $i = 7$. The 20 differences when squared and summed, with the addition of $1/(12N)$, form the W_N^2 of equation (5). They clearly provided one measure of the total departure of the step function from the diagonal $v_i = i/N$.

The largest values of W_N^2 will arise when there is a general shift of the points towards one or other end of the line, so that all the differences d_i are either positive or negative. This is a situation which would arise, in terms of the original problem specified in § 1 above, if the true probability density function for $x, f(x)$, differed in the main from the hypothetical form, say $f_0(x)$, by a shift in location.

For points on a circle, the maximum value of U_N^2 occurs when all points coincide. This means that on the line it occurs either (i) when they all coincide at one end or at any other point, or (ii) when the points are in two arbitrary sized groups, one at each end of the line. Thus in terms of the original problem a large U_N^2 may be a sign that the variance of $f(x)$ is considerably larger or considerably smaller than the variance assumed, but U_N^2 is clearly sensitive to changes both in the mean and the variance of $f(x)$.

Fig. 1 indicates also the lengths $\sup(i/N - v_i)$ and $\inf(i/N - v_i)$ which provide values for the D_N and V_N of equations (6) and (8); in fact, for this example

$$D_N = 0{\cdot}356, \quad V_N = 0{\cdot}438.$$

D_N has the character of an extreme value and V_N of a range, although not precisely the maximum absolute value and the range of the d_i as these last differences are measured from half way up the 'step'. It might be expected that D_N would be most effective in establishing differences under the conditions where W_N^2 is effective and V_N where U_N^2 is effective.

As soon as the problem which was originally defined in terms of the x's is translated into that of testing for randomness of points on a line, it becomes clear that there will be many alternative tests of this hypothesis. We might, for example, cut the line into several

† A 'pick' is a weft thread and 100 picks occupy between 1 and 2 in. of warp.

equal parts, count the number of points in each part and apply a χ^2 test, the hypothesis tested specifying that the chance of a point falling in each part is the same. Or we could use tests based on the intervals between neighbouring points or between every kth point. Apart from simplicity in application, the most appropriate choice between tests must depend on the alternatives to the null hypothesis to which the user wishes the test to be most sensitive. If they are not distributed randomly, for example, what particular type of long-run clustering on the line does he expect?

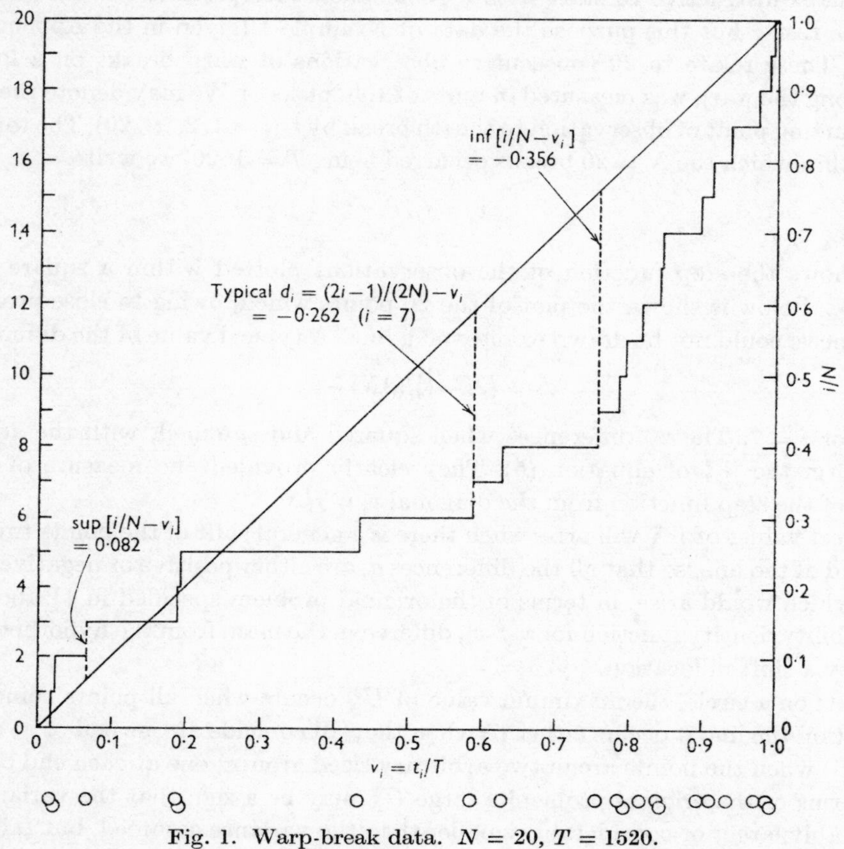

Fig. 1. Warp-break data. $N = 20$, $T = 1520$.

Some early work following this line of thought was described by the present writer in a paper of 1938; since then a very considerable literature has appeared on the subject of alternative tests, though a study of comparative power has always proved difficult. In the present paper attention will be confined to the four test statistics given above. By applying these to eight illustrative examples, some light is thrown on the performance characteristics of the tests.

3. The illustrative examples

In all cases the data are in the form of points on a line, i.e. we shall be concerned with the equations (5)–(8), not (1)–(4). The original data are recorded in an Appendix, in case any reader should care to use them in further comparisons. The following notation is used: N = no. of observations; T = total length of line or period of observation; t_i the distance of the ith ordered observation from one end of the line and, lastly, $v_i = t_i/T$.

Example 1. These are the warp break records used in Fig. 1. The data were taken from among similar series sent me some years ago by Mr L. H. C. Tippett from Shirley Institute records; $N = 20$.

Example 2. The times of road accidents, involving at least two vehicles, which occurred in an English country town during the 68 days 7 March to 14 May 1950; the unit is 24 hr. Data provided by Dr F. Garwood of the Road Research Laboratories; $N = 19$.

Example 3. Fatal accidents in coal mines. The data are taken from Table 1 of Maguire, Pearson & Wynn (1952). This table records the intervals in days between explosions in British mines, involving more than 10 men killed, in the period 6 December 1875 to 29 May 1951. The section selected covers $N = 50$ accidents which occurred between the years 1881 and 1913 and includes all intervals in the earlier table between the 21st (recorded as 59 days) and the 69th (recorded as 390 days). The total period used is $T = 11{,}136$ and $t_1 = 155$, $T - t_{50} = 44$.

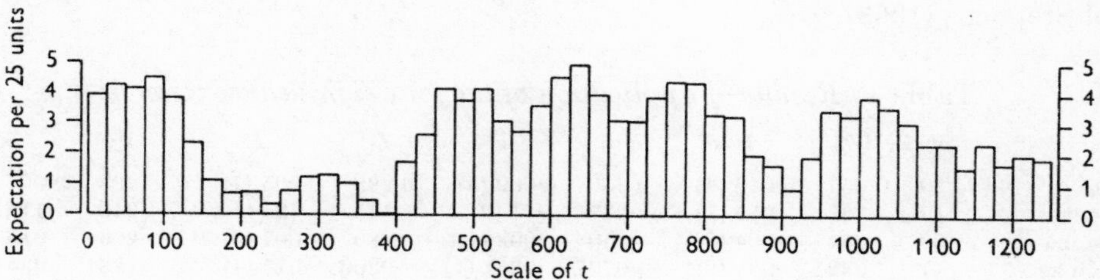

Fig. 2. Expectations from autoregressive scheme (Examples 5–8).

Example 4. The dates of death of the Kings and Queens of England during the 900-year period 1050–1950 A.D. The unit is 1 year; $N = 41$. It is not of course to be expected that the intervals, i.e. the lengths of reigns, would behave like independent, negative exponential variables. We might expect, for example, a negative correlation between the lengths of successive reigns; if a king reigned for a long time, his son would be old when he in turn succeeded. The point of interest was whether the tests would pick out the abnormality of the series.

Examples 5–8. These are four independent artificial series constructed on the following basis. The idea was to use a sampling model in which the expectation of an event remained constant for a short section or period of time and then changed, the expectations in successive sections being determined by an autoregressive scheme. In this way it seemed possible to represent a situation which must often occur in practice, where the expectations do not vary in a regular periodic manner nor with a clear secular trend, but nevertheless with some degree of correlation. How successful, it could then be asked, would these tests be in detecting that the expectation was changing?

A total length of $T = 1250$ equal units was divided into 50 sections of 25 units. Associated with each section was a probability p_j ($j = 1, 2, \ldots, 50$) derived from the first 50 terms, u_j, of M. G. Kendall's (1949, p. 270) autoregressive series $5a$ by the equation

$$p_j = (100 + u_j)/1000.$$

The resulting expectations, $m_j = 25p_j$, in successive sections of $25\,t$-units are shown in Fig. 2.

The series was then constructed with the help of a table of random numbers, making the probability that an event occurred in each of the first 25 unit intervals equal p_1 ($= 0{\cdot}157$)

and that it failed to occur, $1-p_1\,(=0{\cdot}843)$; in each of the next 25 intervals the probability of occurrence was $p_2\,(=0{\cdot}169)$; and so on for the 50 sets of 25 unit intervals. The procedure was carried through four times independently, using the same 50 values of p_j;† the results were the four series of Examples 5–8, with $N = 152$, 145, 130, and 138, respectively, and $T = 1250$. Since only a single event could occur in each unit interval, the procedure was to this extent coarse-grained.

The four statistics W_N^2, D_N, U_N^2 and V_N were then calculated for each example and a level of significance, either exactly or approximately, determined as follows:

W_N^2: by rough interpolation between Anderson & Darling's (1952) asymptotic probability levels and the empirical values for $N = 10$ given by Pearson & Stephens (1962).

D_N: using the Smirnov (1948) asymptotic values and Tables 1 and 2 of the paper by Birnbaum (1952).

U_N^2: using the asymptotic formula given by Watson (1961, equation (22)) and the empirical results of Stephens (1963).

Table 1. *Results of application of the four significance tests*

Ex.	Data		N	W_N^2	P	D_N	P	U_N^2	P	V_N	P	$\bar{v}$
1	Warp breaks		20	0·655	0·016 (4)	0·356	0·009 (3)	0·298	0·005 (1)	0·438	0·007 (2)	0·634
2	Road accidents		19	·398	·075 (1)	·267	·11 (2)	·145	·12 (4)	·346	·11 (3)	·615
3	Mine explosions		50	·884	·004 (2)	·250	·003 (1)	·280	·007 (3)	·266	·015 (4)	·390
4	Deaths of Kings and Queens		41	·0324	·03* (2)	·0707	·025* (1)	·0300	·07* (4)	·1234	·034* (3)	·508
5	Autoregressive schemes	(i)	152	0·400	0·072 (4)	0·119	0·028 (3)	0·299	0·005 (1)	0·156	0·014 (2)	0·526
6		(ii)	145	·192	·28 (3)	·074	·40 (4)	·192	·045 (1)	·141	·054 (2)	·501
7		(iii)	130	·296	·14 (3)	·100	·15 (4)	·218	·027 (2)	·185	·004 (1)	·476
8		(iv)	138	·609	·022 (4)	·146	·006 (3)	·604	·00001 (2)	·241	·000005 (1)	·494

The column headed P gives the probability, on the null hypothesis, of exceeding the observed value of the test statistic except for Example 4, where the probabilities of falling below it, marked with an asterisk, are given. The figures in parentheses are the rankings of P for each example.

V_N: using the large sample formula for the probability integral given by Kuiper (1960) and quoted by Watson (1961, equation (5)). Although this formula has three terms, the first being unity and the third of which is expressed so as to contain a factor $N^{-\frac{1}{2}}$, this third term was not found to be negligible compared with the second, e.g. for Example 5 with $N = 152$ the second term was $-0{\cdot}0167$ and the third was $0{\cdot}0030$. There seems to be no evidence, therefore, that the next term in N^{-1} will be entirely negligible in series of the size we are considering, and the tail areas quoted in Table 1 for V_N may be subject to some error.

The results of applying the tests are summarized in Table 1. The values of W_N^2 were calculated from equation (5), where the v_i's are the ratios t_i/T obtained from the Appendix. U_N^2 was then found by subtracting $N(\bar{v}-0{\cdot}5)^2$ from W_N^2, the values of $\bar{v}$ being given in the last column of the table.

4. Discussion of results in Table 1

That most of the results are significant is not of course surprising, since the examples were chosen after studying their 'spot patterns', in the expectation that they might illustrate features of interest. The following points are noted:

† It might, of course, have been more instructive to take a fresh series of u_j values from Kendall's series each time.

(4·1). For each example Table 1 shows in parentheses the ranking of the four tests in ascending order of the tail-area integrals. While it would be wrong to place too much weight on these rankings, it is interesting to note that in every case W_N^2 and D_N, U_N^2 and V_N pair off in the sense that the members of each pair hold either the 1st and 2nd or else the 3rd and 4th places in 'order of significance'. In other words, the members of a pair make a similar response to the pattern of points. This was to be expected, as the first pair have the character of a second moment about a fixed origin and the distance of an extreme from that origin; the second pair of a variance and a range.

(4·2). Again, in broad terms and as far as these examples go, the statistician's inferences drawn from either member of a pair would have been very much the same. This suggests that in so far as they are easier to determine, he might well be content to use D_N or V_N rather

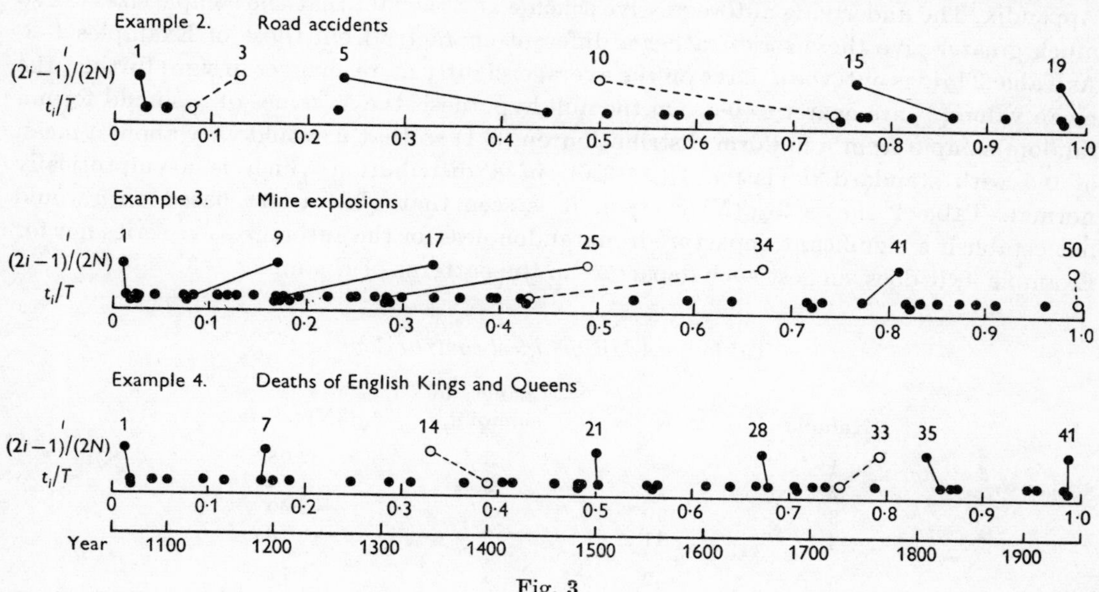

Fig. 3

than W_N^2 or U_N^2. Although a good many of the individual differences may have to be found to determine for certain where their upper and lower bounds occur, there may be a good deal of saving in time if the calculation of the N squares $\{(2_i - 1)/(2N) - v_i\}^2$ can be avoided.

(4·3). The plot of the warp breaks of Example 1 has been given in Fig. 1. As a visual presentation may be helpful in a comparison of the tests, Fig. 3 has been drawn to show the plotted points for Examples 2–4. The lower line of circles in each diagram shows the observed $v_i = t_i/T$, while the upper line shows certain selected values of $(2i-1)/(2N)$ linked with the corresponding v_i below. These linkages show the trend of the displacements from regularity in the pattern. The greatest positive and negative displacements are indicated by broken lines joining open circles; the numerical values of the differences d_i must be increased by $\frac{1}{2}i/N$ to obtain sup $(i/N - v_i)$ and inf $(i/N - v_i)$.

(4·4). In none of the examples is there a large shift of the points towards one end of the line of a kind which might put W_N^2 and D_N at considerable advantage over U_N^2 and V_N. The shift is perhaps most marked in the case of the mining explosions (which were more frequent in the early years of the period), but even here U_N^2 gives nearly as significant a result as W_N^2.

(4·5). In contrast to the first three examples, we have the case of the dates of death of the Kings and Queens (Example 4). Here the variation about the points $(2i-1)/(2N)$ is subnormal and as shown in Table 1 all four test statistics are on the verge of significance at the lower end of their distributions (P-values between 0·03 and 0·07). It is interesting to find that the otherwise obvious inappropriateness of the random model is picked out in this way. While a visual inspection of the spot pattern for the mine explosions would certainly suggest lack of randomness in time, it is more doubtful whether mere inspection of the Kings' and Queens' pattern would have suggested too great regularity. Our eyes are probably not practised in the detection of subnormal variation!

(4·6). Owing to the greater length of the series, the four artificial samples have not been plotted. The raw data from which the plots could be made, however, are given in the Appendix. The underlying autoregressive scheme and the fact that the sample sizes are so much greater give these series rather a different character from those of Examples 1–3. As Table 2 brings out, the d_i have on the average slightly more changes in sign; further, the mean values, $\bar{v}$, are nearer to 0·5. On the null hypothesis the N values of v_i should form a random sample from a uniform distribution on (0, 1) so that $\bar{v}$ should vary about a mean of 0·5 with standard deviation $1/\{2\sqrt{(3N)}\}$ in a distribution which is asymptotically normal. Table 2 shows $2\sqrt{(3N)}\,(\bar{v}-0{\cdot}5)$; it is seen that while a test based on $\bar{v}$ would not establish a significant departure from randomness for the autoregressive series nor for Example 4, it does suggest such departure in the patterns of Examples 1–3.

Table 2. *Additional test comparisons*

Example	N	Changes in sign of d_i	$2\sqrt{(3N)}\,(\bar{v}-0{\cdot}5)$
1	20	3	2·08
2	19	2	1·74
3	50	2	−2·69
4	41	9	0·18
5	152	3	1·11
6	145	7	0·04
7	130	2	−0·95
8	138	3	−0·24

(4·7). It is therefore interesting to find that the U_N^2 and V_N tests are in every one of these autoregressive samples more sensitive to the fluctuations than are W_N^2 and D_N. Whether the V_N test would be as sensitive as U_N^2, indeed whether either would be sensitive, in a case where the fluctuations were of shorter duration than those illustrated in Fig. 2, it is clearly not possible to say on the present evidence.

5. The relation between W_N^2, U_N^2 and $\bar{v}$

I am indebted to Dr D. J. Bartholomew for pointing out that it is possible to throw some further light on the relationship between W_N^2, U_N^2 and $\bar{v}$, the mean of the v_i. If we write

$$R_N^2 = N\bar{d}^2 = N(0{\cdot}5-\bar{v})^2$$

then

$$W_N^2 = U_N^2 + R_N^2. \tag{11}$$

The variance of R_N^2 under the null hypothesis depends on the moments of the mean of a sample of N observations from a rectangular distribution. It can be shown that

$$\operatorname{var}(R_N^2) = \frac{5N-3}{360N}.$$

From earlier work we know that

$$\operatorname{var}(W_N^2) = \frac{4N-3}{180N}, \quad \operatorname{var}(U_N^2) = \frac{N-1}{360N}.$$

We have, therefore, the information to determine the correlations between these three statistics from relations of the form

$$\operatorname{var}(W_N^2) = \operatorname{var}(U_N^2) + \operatorname{var}(R_N^2) + 2\operatorname{cov}(U_N^2, R_N^2). \tag{12}$$

In fact, we find the following expressions for these coefficients, to which we have assigned numerical values for the cases $N = 10$ and $N = \infty$.

	$N = 10$	$N = \infty$
$\rho(W_N^2, U_N^2) = \sqrt{\left(\frac{2(N-1)}{4N-3}\right)}$	0·697	0·707
$\rho(W_N^2, R_N^2) = \frac{(3N-2)\sqrt{2}}{\sqrt{\{(4N-3)(5N-3)\}}}$	0·950	0·949
$\rho(U_N^2, R_N^2) = \sqrt{\left(\frac{N-1}{5N-3}\right)}$	0·438	0·447

It is of course difficult to know how to interpret these figures when the distributions involved are so skew, but they suggest that while W_N^2 adds little to what is given by R_N^2 (or by $\bar{v}$), U_N^2 will provide additional information.

In this connexion it is of interest to note that if the N values of x form a sample from an exponential distribution

$$f(v) = ae^{av}/(e^a - 1), \quad (0 \leqslant v \leqslant 1,\ a > 0) \tag{13}$$

rather than from a rectangle, then the test based on $\bar{v}$ is the uniformly most powerful test of the hypothesis that $a = 0$, against alternatives $a > 0$. It follows that if departure from randomness is of the character implied by (13), showing as a shift of the points towards one end of the line, $\bar{v}$ will be more likely than W_N^2 to establish significance. Although for small departures from randomness, at any rate, $\bar{v}^2$ and W_N^2 are highly correlated it is clear that the former statistic has the advantage of being by far the more easily calculated.

6. Summary

(6·1). The discussion in this paper has been confined to the case where the data are in the form of points on a line, and where the null hypothesis of constant expectation and independence can be completely specified. This is equivalent to the case of sampling from a uniform distribution for which $F(x) = x$, $(0 \leqslant x \leqslant 1)$. Until more progress has been made in determining how tests of the difference between $F_N(x)$ and $F(x)$ can be used when a specified class of probability density function has been fitted to the observations, it seems that the four statistics considered will be more likely to be used in the forms of equations (5)–(8) rather than (1)–(4).

(6·2). While there must be types of departure from randomness for which the simpler tests based on maximum and minimum differences are less powerful than those based on the sums of squares, on the examples chosen D_N has given a smaller P-value than W_N^2 on 5 out of 8 occasions and V_N than U_N^2 on 4 out of 8.

(6·3). Again, as far as these examples are concerned the statistics U_N^2 and V_N (both of which can also be used in the circular case) have come out on the whole more sensitive to departures from randomness than the longer established W_N^2 and D_N statistics. In situations, not included here, where departure from randomness takes the form of a marked crowding up of the points towards one end of the line only, the latter tests might be expected to be more powerful than the former. However, in such cases it is likely that the much simpler test which consists (if N is not too small) in referring $2\sqrt{(3N)}\,(\bar{v}-0{\cdot}5)$ to a normal probability scale, will on the average establish significance as well or better.

(6·4). While all this evidence is pointing towards Kuiper's V_N as a very 'good buy', it is clearly desirable to find out a little more about the accuracy of the expression for its probability integral when N is as low as 10 or 20.

(6·5). Finally, it must be emphasized again that the numerical work and illustrative diagrams given in this paper can establish nothing firmly; they have been presented in the hope that they will help to make clearer some problems which need more precise solution.

References

Anderson, T. W. & Darling, D. A. (1952). Asymptotic theory of certain goodness-of-fit criteria based on stochastic processes. *Ann. Math. Statist.* **23**, 193–212.

Birnbaum, Z. W. (1952). Numerical tabulation of the distribution of Kolmogorov's statistic for finite sample size. *J. Amer. Statist. Ass.* **47**, 425–40.

Kendall, M. G. (1949). Tables of autoregressive series. *Biometrika*, **36**, 267–89.

Kuiper, N. H. (1960). Tests concerning random points on a circle. *Proc. Koninkl. Nederl. Akad. Van Wettenschappen*, Series A, **63**, 38–47.

Maguire, B. A., Pearson, E. S. & Wynn, A. H. A. (1952). The time intervals between industrial accidents. *Biometrika*, **39**, 168–80.

Pearson, E. S. (1938). The probability integral transformation for testing goodness-of-fit and combining independent tests of significance. *Biometrika*, **30**, 134–48.

Pearson, E. S. & Stephens, M. A. (1962). The goodness-of-fit tests based on W_N^2 and U_N^2. *Biometrika*, **49**, 397–402.

Smirnov, N. V. (1948). Table for estimating the goodness-of-fit of empirical distributions. *Ann. Math. Statist.* **19**, 279–81.

Stephens, M. A. (1963). The distribution of the goodness-of-fit statistic U_N^2. I. *Biometrika*, **50**, 303–13.

Watson, G. S. (1961). Goodness-of-fit tests on a circle. *Biometrika*, **48**, 109–14.

APPENDIX

Values of t_i ($i = 1, 2, \ldots, N$) for eight examples

i	Warp breaks Ex. 1
1	30
2	36
3	104
4	286
5	291
6	658
7	893
8	955
9	1,149
10	1,195
11	1,208
12	1,240
13	1,277
14	1,282
15	1,363
16	1,384
17	1,421
18	1,477
19	1,504
20	1,510
T	1,520

i	Road accidents Ex. 2
1	2·3
2	3·7
3	5·4
4	15·7
5	30·4
6	34·5
7	38·5
8	39·5
9	41·7
10	50·4
11	50·8
12	52·3
13	52·7
14	55·8
15	58·7
16	62·4
17	66·3
18	66·4
19	67·6
T	68·0

i	Mine explosions Ex. 3	Kings and Queens Ex. 4	Autoregressive series Ex. 5	Ex. 6	Ex. 7	Ex. 8	i
1	155	16	19	10	1	3	1
2	214	17	25	17	10	10	2
3	275	37	29	29	15	12	3
4	276	50	32	33	17	30	4
5	289	85	34	36	23	35	5
6	478	104	37	37	30	38	6
7	823	139	41	38	33	46	7
8	843	149	46	39	40	50	8
9	924	166	69	44	41	54	9
10	1,210	222	77	48	45	77	10
11	1,324	257	82	49	56	81	11
12	1,432	277	86	50	59	82	12
13	1,620	327	89	58	61	83	13
14	1,853	349	100	59	66	90	14
15	1,881	363	102	61	73	94	15
16	1,903	372	104	67	87	97	16
17	1,964	411	106	78	93	105	17
18	2,042	433	118	90	96	109	18
19	2,141	433	123	91	99	121	19
20	2,467	435	137	102	107	125	20
21	2,742	459	162	111	118	132	21
22	2,796	497	177	115	124	137	22
23	3,013	503	184	118	125	175	23
24	3,126	508	188	131	132	190	24
25	3,158	553	219	139	133	263	25
26	3,181	575	277	148	134	290	26
27	3,332	599	284	149	142	294	27
28	3,693	610	302	160	144	319	28
29	4,005	635	315	173	179	321	29
30	4,359	638	340	180	236	353	30
31	4,417	652	362	196	285	437	31
32	4,692	664	403	197	286	463	32
33	4,770	677	405	225	309	464	33
34	4,787	710	410	282	338	474	34
35	5,992	770	428	285	379	482	35
36	6,616	780	429	309	440	484	36
37	7,103	787	435	326	450	487	37
38	7,974	851	438	412	462	488	38
39	8,022	860	450	414	465	501	39
40	8,145	885	453	415	467	505	40
41	8,602	886	456	421	468	508	41
42	9,100	—	459	435	471	509	42
43	9,149	—	462	447	474	510	43
44	9,280	—	465	453	476	513	44
45	9,462	—	473	467	481	524	45
46	9,717	—	487	473	485	533	46
47	9,912	—	495	474	490	545	47
48	10,136	—	501	478	491	558	48
49	10,702	—	503	479	492	563	49
50	11,092	—	507	490	496	565	50
T	11,136	900					

APPENDIX (*cont.*)

Autoregressive series (*cont.*)

i	Ex. 5	Ex. 6	Ex. 7	Ex. 8	i	Ex. 5	Ex. 6	Ex. 7	Ex. 8	i	Ex. 5
51	508	493	518	567	101	832	846	899	824	151	1,227
52	510	500	520	568	102	835	849	914	828	152	1,228
53	513	501	548	572	103	840	857	930	831		
54	518	502	550	577	104	846	861	940	840	T for all autoregressive series	1,250
55	530	503	551	578	105	849	870	953	845		
56	534	514	555	582	106	860	885	960	852		
57	554	537	564	591	107	862	917	966	953		
58	555	544	581	594	108	872	918	969	860		
59	570	550	588	595	109	875	919	981	868		
60	574	551	594	598	110	877	929	994	883		
61	597	558	596	606	111	879	954	1,002	931		
62	605	579	602	607	112	895	958	1,008	952		
63	624	591	607	611	113	897	961	1,016	964		
64	630	601	611	614	114	907	964	1,031	974		
65	635	629	614	615	115	908	966	1,039	977		
66	648	630	617	616	116	922	970	1,041	984		
67	650	631	622	617	117	938	981	1,045	991		
68	651	635	627	623	118	943	983	1,051	992		
69	653	637	636	626	119	961	989	1,060	997		
70	667	640	650	630	120	970	991	1,062	1,003		
71	669	641	665	634	121	986	1,001	1,074	1,015		
72	671	643	680	639	122	992	1,008	1,077	1,016		
73	675	650	685	642	123	993	1,015	1,086	1,019		
74	678	664	697	643	124	995	1,030	1,111	1,036		
75	680	667	698	661	125	999	1,037	1,167	1,039		
76	681	694	712	665	126	1,000	1,060	1,173	1,047		
77	708	705	713	668	127	1,005	1,069	1,182	1,058		
78	713	730	714	672	128	1,010	1,071	1,195	1,060		
79	726	736	725	674	129	1,016	1,075	1,203	1,073		
80	729	741	740	676	130	1,024	1,077	1,239	1,084		
81	731	744	746	677	131	1,035	1,095	—	1,093		
82	737	752	751	684	132	1,039	1,099	—	1,097		
83	739	764	752	687	133	1,047	1,106	—	1,115		
84	741	765	753	688	134	1,076	1,108	—	1,119		
85	745	768	766	690	135	1,090	1,114	—	1,181		
86	748	770	769	691	136	1,099	1,130	—	1,233		
87	754	783	770	700	137	1,109	1,157	—	1,244		
88	755	784	784	708	138	1,112	1,167	—	1,250		
89	761	787	785	717	139	1,119	1,210				
90	762	789	786	729	140	1,120	1,211				
91	772	790	789	737	141	1,128	1,228				
92	775	797	794	738	142	1,142	1,238				
93	784	808	797	748	143	1,165	1,239				
94	785	809	804	752	144	1,166	1,242				
95	799	816	808	753	145	1,171	1,244				
96	801	817	815	783	146	1,183					
97	807	819	827	790	147	1,199					
98	810	821	839	804	148	1,209					
99	820	827	893	807	149	1,210					
100	826	838	896	814	150	1,217					

A statistician's place in assessing the likely operational performance of army weapons and equipment

A statistician's place in assessing the likely operational performance of army weapons and equipment*

By E. S. PEARSON
University College London

1. The background of this paper

It has been a special honour to receive an invitation from the organizing committee of this Conference to make the journey from England and to address you to-day. In thinking how I could best repay the compliment, it seemed to me that I should look for a subject in illustrating which I could draw on my own particular experiences, gained in working for the British armed services both during and since the Second World War. From 1939 to 1946 I was attached, with a number of members of the University College London Statistics Department, to the British Ordnance Board. This is an organization of some historic interest for I believe its foundation can be traced back to an appointment made in 1414, the year before the Battle of Agincourt! It is now concerned with certain aspects of the development and acceptance of weapons for both the Army, the Navy and the Air Force. Then, for some years after the war, I was a member of the Ordnance Board Anti-aircraft Lethality Committee and very recently I have been pulled back to be chairman of an advisory committee concerned with the general problem of assessment in connexion with army weapons and equipment.

My main experience was with the subject which has been described as terminal ballistics and in particular with the lethal effectiveness of anti-aircraft fire. We were concerned also with field artillery fire and with the medium and small bombs of those days, in so far as fragmentation of the casing rather than blast played an important part in their effectiveness. It is of course true that the weapons and the army requirements of 15–20 years ago have been to a large extent out-dated, but if I make my main topic today a piece of historical recording, it is because I believe that a number of general principles and lessons emerge from such a study which are still relevant to the practice of experimentation and analysis in Army Research today.

It seemed to me that there were two advantages in taking illustrations from the Second World War experience. In the first place I could speak of matters about which I had the 'feel' from first-hand knowledge and so perhaps could be more interesting as well as convincing in any arguments put forward. Secondly, it was easier to be factual without running into the danger of using classified material. What I shall try to do, therefore, is to give you first some account of the difficulties with which we were faced in the years 1939–45 in constructing a model which could be used to help determine how to improve the effectiveness of anti-aircraft fire. In describing this problem, it should be possible to indicate a number of lessons which are still relevant in a much wider field. There are also many points of difference which it will be instructive to emphasize.

* An address given at the Eighth Conference on the Design of Experiments in Army Research, Development and Testing. Washington D.C., October 1962.

2. THE STATISTICIAN'S PLACE

I should perhaps confess straight away that I shall say very little about statistics or about what is commonly thought of as the design of experiments. To this extent you may think that the leading phrase in the title of this paper is misleading, unless you interpret the words in the personal sense as referring to the statistician who is giving this address! But there is, I think, a point here which I should like to make. At the fourth of this series of Conferences, held in 1958, Dr A. W. Kimball read a paper with the title: 'Errors of the 3rd kind in statistical consulting'; in this he discussed and illustrated the fault of giving a perfectly sound statistical answer to a problem which is not the real one needing solution.

Many of us are I think conscious of what might perhaps be called an error of a 4th kind; that which the statistician makes when he allows his interest in the statistical elements of a problem and its potential for statistical elegance and sophistication to obscure what should be his prime objective, the solution of the real matter at issue. The fault is not so much that wrong statistical methods are used (Kimball's 3rd kind of error) but that the situation does not justify the use of any refined statistical methods at all until the outstanding problem has been solved of obtaining data which are both relevant and reliable. The statistician, indeed, is called upon to be a scientist in the fullest sense of that term—to apply scientific method, not merely statistical techniques, to the job on hand.

When he has completed some piece of mathematical or arithmetical analysis, he needs to ask himself searchingly: does this answer make sense? I can recall, as no doubt some of you can too, war-time reports which appeared both in my country and in yours, containing a pretty piece of algebraic development or some standard analysis of variance, the conclusions from which obviously did not make sense. Perhaps such reports from youthful enthusiasts would never have appeared but for the inevitable shortage of experienced and critical supervision in rapidly expanding organizations. They were likely, however, to discourage the idea that mathematics or statistics were of value in problems of weapon development and testing, because the experienced non-statistical layman, the military or naval technical officer who had the feel of the problems, could see at once that the data would not bear the confident interpretation which was often placed on them.

Certainly in my own experience at the Ordnance Board it was the physical difficulty in securing meaningful experimental data which had always to be faced. There was very little opportunity for design as it is understood in agricultural or biological trials. There was no paramount function for the application of advanced statistics—we used to say that the only statistical tools which were needed were the normal distribution in 1, 2 and 3 dimensions, the Poisson and the bionomial. But it is true to say that the statistician's training, with the understanding which should follow of the meaning of variation and correlation, of randomness and probability, with its emphasis on the importance of adopting a critical outlook on assumptions—all this is likely to provide an excellent preparation for the kind of work we are discussing, but on one essential condition—that the training has been carried out in conjunction with practical application to data analysis. The trend in the teaching of mathematical statistics at our universities today is often increasingly away from any real application to data.

There is another point which I think is worth emphasizing. One of the surest ways to cure the statistician from any tendency to over-sophistication is to arrange that he is present at experiments or trials, the data from which he is to use. In this respect we were lucky in

England; we attended firing trials on the Shoeburyness Ranges, we were hot on the scene after bombs had been dropped on parked aircraft, trucks and wooden dummies in slit trenches on a special bombing range in the New Forest, and—as a wartime experience—we might happen to be present at a gun-site when German aircraft were the target. Under such conditions it is easier to come to grips with the meaning and limitations of data.

3. The anti-aircraft problem

First let me try to put this problem into its setting of 20 or more years ago. As far as the Ordnance Board group was concerned, we had not to consider the problems of the deployment of guns, of the acquisition of targets, of the handling of mass attacks or other important tactical matters. These were questions for the Anti-aircraft Command and its Operational Research Section which was formed in the summer of 1940. Our work was closely related to the question of design, to understand more clearly the individual relationship between predictor, gun, shell, fuse and enemy target in order to advise what improvements were possible and likely to be worthwhile.

In this field of research where the terminal action in which one is interested may be taking place several thousand feet above ground, no overall experiment bringing in all the factors concerned is conceivable; the reasons for this are so obvious that I do not need to list them. As a consequence, it is absolutely essential to construct a mathematical model of the terminal engagement, and then to consider how the parameters of this model may best be estimated. As in so many other problems of military science the model, even if necessarily simplified, serves as an essential means of defining the relationships of the situation, showing how research investigation can be broken into separate pieces and emphasizing at what points our lack of sure information is greatest and most hampering.

Let me now outline the problem and its solution in some detail, first describing the *mathematical model* and then discussing the three main headings under which gaps in knowledge had to be filled, namely:

(i) *Positioning errors* (until the introduction of the radar proximity fuze in 1943–44 it was easy to combine the error of the time fuze with the predictor, gun-laying and ballistic errors).

(ii) *Fragmentation characteristics of the shell.*

(iii) *Target vulnerability.*

The difficulties which had to be overcome, largely through ignorance of physical properties in this hitherto unexplored field, are I think sufficiently instructive to be worth including as part of the story. Much the same problems were I know faced later on (building perhaps on our experience) in Section T of the Applied Physics Laboratory at Silver Spring and the associated Proving Ground near Albuquerque, where research and trial work was carried out for the U.S. Navy. I did not myself have any direct contact with U.S. Army investigations.

4. The mathematical model

The first simplified model which was used involved:

(*a*) A three-dimensional normal distribution of positioning errors about the target, with a major axis along the shell trajectory and the standard errors in directions perpendicular to this axis equal, i.e. the density contours were taken to be ellipsoids with circular cross-sections in planes perpendicular to the principal axis.

(b) A main fragment zone lying between two cones whose axis was that of the shell axis and the trajectory at time of burst, and a small subsidiary nose cone. The density of fragments within the main zone was not of course uniform, though it might be treated as such for a first approximation. For any zone within which the average density of fragments of a given penetrating power could be regarded as constant, the probability distribution of strikes was taken as Poisson.

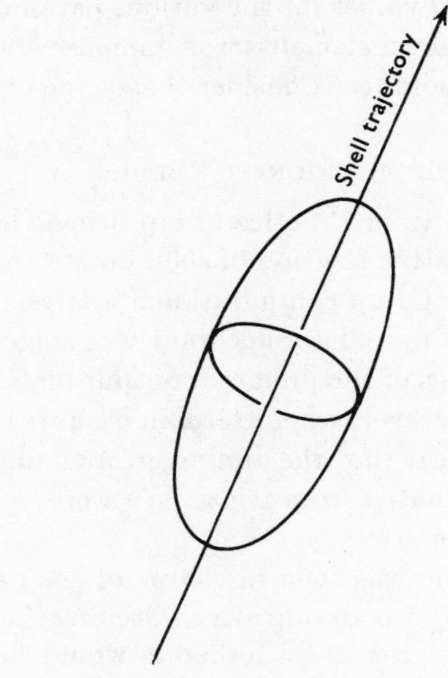

Fig. 1

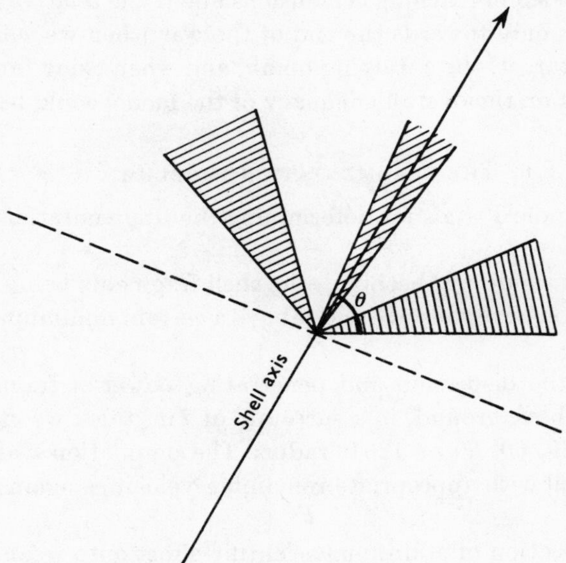

Fig. 2

(*c*) For the aircraft, we first used what was termed an 'equivalent vulnerable target' represented by a sphere of a few feet in radius such that its 'perforation' by at least one 'lethal' shell fragment would result in a kill. Later, this representation had to be treated in more detail.

This simple model based on the trivariate normal and the Poisson distributions, with bounding surfaces consisting of ellipsoids, cones and spheres was amenable to computation, provided that meaningful numerical values for the various parameters could be estimated. But the task of filling in these unknown elements was immense and for a time the more we learnt, the more we realized our ignorance. Consider then some of the gaps to be filled.

5. The positioning errors

The original data were collected from Practice Camp firings, at towed 'sleeves', using kine-theodolites to measure the relative position of shell bursts and target. This was much too slow a target and the Practice Camp computational analysis was not very accurate. Later, in April 1940, a special trial of predictor accuracy was staged, following a free flying aircraft, and using camera recordings of the predictor output dials synchronized with kine-theodolites tracking the target. However, when German aircraft began to come over England later in 1940, it was at once clear that the aiming errors under operational conditions were much greater than those estimated from trials. We were up against the problem of increased operator inaccuracy under stress.

I remember P. M. S. Blackett (who was then in charge of the newly formed A. A. Command, Operational Research Group), wondering after watching the shell bursts in the night sky and a searchlight-held enemy aircraft, whether it would be possible to determine roughly an operational error distribution with appropriate photo-positioning equipment. I think that we later gave up all hope of estimating the actual aiming errors under operational conditions and made our calculations for a variety of different error combinations, which was often all that was needed in reaching conclusions about the relative merits of different types of shell, etc. It was only towards the end of the war when we were faced with that ideal straight-line-flying target, the V 1 flying bomb, and when using proximity fuses that a rough operational check on the overall adequacy of the model could be made.

6. The fragmentation problem

Before the war, the standard trials for determining the fragmentation characteristics of shell were:

(*a*) Fragmentation in a sand-bag 'beehive', the shell fragments being recovered, passed successively through various sizes of sieve and (above a certain minimum size) counted and weighed.

(*b*) Trials to measure the dispersion and penetrating power of fragments by detonating the shell some 5 ft. above ground, in a surround of 2 in. thick wooden targets, placed in a semicircle of, say, 30, 60, 90 or 120 ft radius. The detonation was either at rest or obtained by firing the shell with appropriate remaining velocities against a light bursting screen.

With the war-time allocation of additional scientific effort onto weapon lethality problems, the number of questions which were posed for answering was greatly increased. The shell and bomb fragment attack on many targets besides aircraft had to be considered.

On the one side it was necessary to have means of projecting individual fragments of various sizes at known velocities, against a variety of targets. On the other it was important to know more about the size-velocity-directional pattern as well as the retardation of the fragments projected by a complete shell burst in flight.

As soon as forward planning is attempted it becomes necessary to generalize the characteristics of a weapon; in the case of A.A. shell the ultimate objective was to be able to predict the characteristics of the fragment distribution from: (i) the drawing board design; (ii) a knowledge of the particular explosive filling to be used; and (iii) for any desired forward velocity of the shell.

It became clear that the old form of trials mentioned in the first paragraph of this section was inadequate. When shells were burst in flight in a wood target surround the resulting pattern of perforations could not be accurately related to the pattern from a static burst, merely by adding the component forward velocity of the shell. Nor was it easy to link the distribution of fragment sizes from the sand-bag collection with the number of perforations in the wood, using any simple assumptions about velocities and retardations. The essential need was for more basic physical experimentation; without this we could not generalize.

Here we were lucky in getting help from a very skilled scientific team at our Safety in Mines Research Establishment at Buxton, who initiated a programme of research which gradually succeeded in disentangling the picture. Shells on which small letters were engraved in successive rings round the circumference were fired at rest, within a surround of strawboard, against which a large number of small velocity measuring screens were placed. Fragments subsequently collected and weighed could be identified with a particular zone of the shell, and velocities estimated either by direct measurement or more crudely from depth of penetration into the strawboard.

It then became clear that the initial velocity of fragments varied very considerably with the part of the casing from which they came and, similarly, that size or weight also varied with position. To some extent this initial velocity could be related to the charge/weight ratio of the section of the shell (perpendicular to its axis) from which the fragments originated. With this information, we began at last to get a surer picture of how fragments would be projected from different designs of shell detonated at any given velocity in free air.

It should be noted that the angle of the fragment zone, in particular the rather sharply defined 'cut-off angle' or semi-vertical angle θ of the backward bounding cone of my Fig. 2 became particularly important with the introduction of proximity fuzes. If the pattern of fuze functioning was not co-ordinated with that of fragmentation the shell might generally burst in positions relative to the target such that fragments were bound to miss the more vulnerable parts of the aircraft.

7. Aircraft vulnerability

In the earliest trials, carried out shortly before the war, an aircraft and an arc of large 2 in. thick vertical wooden screens were placed beyond and on opposite sides of a small burster screen at which the shell (with percussion fuze) was fired at a prescribed velocity. It was in this way possible to correlate the damage done to the aircraft with the density of fragments which perforated 2 in. of wood in a second, similarly constituted fragment stream. By noting and painting round the fragment holes after each round was fired, the same target could be used a large number of times, varying the aspect of attack and distance of detonation as desired.

It was from the observed correlation of density of 'throughs' (fragment capable of perforating 2 in. of wood) and damage that it was possible to introduce into the model calculations a simplified 'equivalent vulnerable target'. This was the first method of attack. At

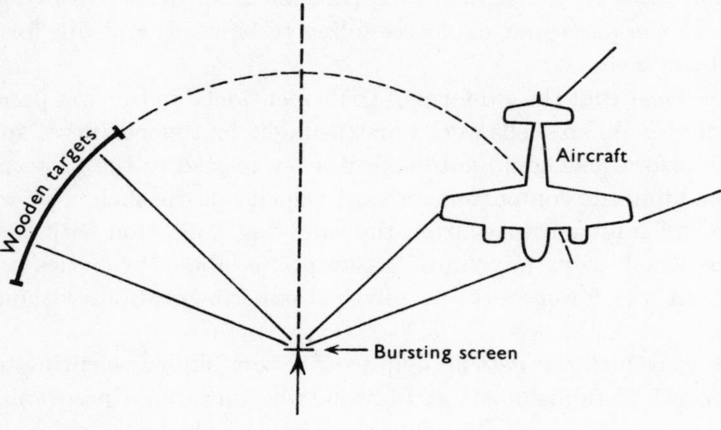

Fig. 3

a later stage after experimental techniques had become more refined and the Royal Aircraft Establishment assessors more experienced, it became possible to dissect the problem still further. The overall vulnerability picture was then built up from information gained by firing from high velocity barrels individual fragments of predetermined sizes, housed in specially designed cups, at a variety of aircraft components, which were screened where necessary by aluminium plate representing wing surfaces or fuselage.

The information so obtained could of course be used directly both in trying to draw conclusions about optimum fragment sizes and velocities and in considering ways of improving the protection of our own aircraft. Viewed in this way the problem may not appear to be statistical at all, but it did assume a statistical character as soon as one had to try and make use of this information in the 'model', with its shells bursting in a probability distribution around an aircraft and each projecting a composite stream of fragments, whose frequency distribution of strikes on equal areas of an intervening target would be roughly of Poisson form.

8. Some conclusions drawn from this survey

Looking back now after a number of years, it seems to me that by 1944 we had really broken the back of the problem. It became possible to make recommendations with some confidence on a number of matters: on the optimum design characteristics of time-fused and of proximity-fused shell; on the relative importance of case thickness and explosive filling; on what might be achieved by using methods to control the size of fragments; on the relative gains to be won by improvement in fire control and in design of shell. Few such questions could have been answered with any confidence in 1939.

It is of course a truism that much of the fundamental research bearing on military problems is only rounded off when it is becoming too late to be of use in the war which provided the stimulus for the effort; and, by the next war, the whole conditions of warfare are changed. This seems particularly true in regard to the ground-to-air weapons. But I think that the work I have been describing brought to the front a number of general principles, a sample of which I will bring to your attention in concluding this account.

The ease with which important factors may be overlooked. A common experience when the human mind starts to investigate the unknown is the way in which important considerations which seem so obvious afterwards are only realized through a process of slow and perhaps painful discovery.

(*a*) We did not for long appreciate the effect of ground ricochet in our firing trials. The influence of ricochet and other factors arising from proximity to the ground on the directional distribution of fragments would be natural operational effects in the case of field artillery or dropped bombs, but were very confusing when we were seeking information about the character of shell-bursts thousands of feet above ground. I know that the American experimenters appreciated this effect before we did and were the first to introduce ricochet traps into A.A. shell trials. Perhaps the most convincing demonstrations of its existence which I recall occurred when we burst a 500 lb. bomb statically, with axis inclined at 30° to the vertical. The target screens showed a striking pattern of holes; a tilted belt like the forward-arm of a V from direct hits and another, like the other arm, from the ground ricochets. As long as bombs or shells were burst with their axes horizontal (or vertical), the effect remained unnoticed.

(*b*) Again, when studying the size distribution of fragments, the amount of secondary break-up on striking the collecting medium after detonation, was only realized when strawboard was used in place of sand and the paths of these pieces, broken on first strike, could be traced through the successive layers of board.

(*c*) Another point not fully appreciated was the effect of emotional stress on the human element under battle conditions. The assessment of its magnitude, especially under circumstances and conditions which cannot be precisely foretold, is one of the hardest problems of the moment.

The place of basic research. In many instances it may not be too difficult to carry out a realistic trial of a particular weapon, against a given target under specified environmental conditions. But a more fundamental knowledge is necessary to assess the performance of weapons, perhaps still on the drawing board, under a wide variety of conditions. It was in this connexion that the detailed experimental work on fragmentation performed to laboratory standards was essential, even if the laws of initial velocity, of size distribution and of retardation which resulted were to some extent empirical.

The value of having something up your sleeve. Observation of the amount of the metal casing which appeared to be broken up into dust or very small fragments,* on detonation, suggested that the destructive power of the anti-aircraft shell might be considerably increased by 'controlling' the size of fragments. It was over this matter that the help of the Safety in Mines Research Establishment was first called on, and by the end of the war this research group had developed a variety of techniques, relatively easily applied, by which it was possible to control the size and shape of shell and bomb fragments to a remarkable

* It was realized later that some of this effect was due to secondary break-up of the large fragments on striking the collecting medium.

degree. These techniques were never used* but they were available to put into operation should any new target have had to be faced, e.g. a tough one against which only large fragments could be effective.

These are some of the still relevant points which I have noted in again coming into contact with problems of weapons research and development after a gap of several years. I am sure there are other lessons to be drawn from these Second World War investigations, and without doubt those scientists who have carried on continuously in government service will have quietly absorbed them, so that they form part of their whole attitude of approach to the problems of today.

9. The position today

There are, of course, many obvious differences between:

(*a*) *The war-time problem*, which was essentially that of trying to establish an understanding of a weapon system in service, in order to determine how its effectiveness could be improved, under conditions which were not expected to change radically from those known to exist.

(*b*) *The problem today*, which is greatly concerned with predictive assessments of the operational performance of future systems, taking many years to develop and to be used against an opponent whose future equipment, weapons and tactics must be to a large extent a matter of guesswork.

In the course of war, even when action has to be taken to meet a new situation, this can be done by working on the basis of information which possesses some element of reality. A good example of this occurred in 1944 with the launching of the V 1 flying bombs against London. Within a few days a complete bomb which had been shot down without exploding was recovered, and immediate steps could be taken to estimate its vulnerability to shell-fire and fighter attack.

As far as I can recall, priority trials were undertaken to determine (*a*) the burst pattern of a proximity fuse around such a target, and (*b*) the nature and extent of its vulnerability to A.A. shell fragments. How quickly we got to the stage of inserting these new parameters into our probability model, I cannot remember; but it must have been soon evident that the V 1 was a target which could be successfully engaged by 3·7 in. anti-aircraft guns with existing shell, provided they were supplied with proximity fuses. The large-scale delivery of American fuses and the appropriate re-deployment of guns, when achieved after some weeks when the fighter aircraft had been forced to take the leading defence roll, played a very large part in countering the menace.

The scientific effort, when it became accepted as of value by the armed services, was quite naturally first directed to the study of the performance of individual weapons or pieces of equipment; the radar set, the proximity fuse, the terminal ballistics of a shell or of a variety of anti-tank weapons. Today there is a special demand for scientific aid in the intractable job of peering into the future. The lead for this activity was of course provided by the Operational Research Sections which were closely associated with various operational commands during the war. In this very difficult field of prediction in which the last war's operational experience becomes less and less relevant, the scientific line of attack must consist in welding together a great number of elements.

* It was found later that the Germans had applied a system of external grooving to some of their A.A. shell, apparently to increase the fragment size.

The following scheme of relationships illustrates what I mean by the many-sided approach:

Mathematical models Paper study	→ ←	Laboratory experiments Simulator trials Range trials
War games Computer games	→ ←	Field experiments Army exercises

The overall inferences to be drawn from the whole build-up are not of course matters of statistics; but the use of the theory of probability and of stochastic processes is implicit in the studies of the left-hand column, while statistical planning plays its part in the laboratory experiments and the range trials—even to some extent in the field trials.

I have already tried to illustrate the great value of a mathematical model in forming the structure against which an evaluation problem may be broken up into parts for separate study. In so doing attention is drawn to the links in the construction where essential information in quantitative form is most needed and perhaps most lacking. Again, and this is important, by permitting a good deal of elasticity in the mechanism and allowing for the introduction of factors which might conceivably operate in a future situation, the model may be used to extrapolate beyond the envelope of engagement conditions tested during field trials or even accepted as likely under present combat conditions.

The application of the model approach to the problem of ground-to-air missile evaluation is the natural successor to the war-time investigations which I have described. The break-up of the problem for study under four headings still remains as before.

(*a*) Engagement geometry. (*b*) Fuse performance.
(*c*) Warhead effectiveness. (*d*) Target vulnerability.

But problem (*a*) has taken a much more complex shape, involving perhaps the use of both analogue and digital computers. The war game has an essential part to play as a research tool in the combined attack on the problem of developing weapons, equipment and tactics for the future. Its main function is perhaps to aid thought and analysis rather than to obtain direct results. By injecting the human decision process into the study, it provides an insight into the complex nature of land battle which it would be hard to get in any other way. In this form of study, as elsewhere, the essential need to formulate rules focuses attention on the limiting conditions which have to be accepted by whatever route we try to make predictions of the performance of future systems.

* * * * * * *

Finally, it may again be asked: what of the statistician? Have I pushed him out of the picture: I think not. You must remember that I have been concentrating on a particular aspect of this matter of research, development and testing—the assessment of operational performance of weapons. In this peculiarly difficult field, the statistician becomes the scientist who must merge his statistical identity into that of a group of men trained in several disciplines, but prepared to give no undue weight to any one of them in searching for answers to the problems in hand. That at any rate has been my personal experience.

APPENDIX

Bibliography of Scientific Papers, etc. published by E. S. Pearson

* These papers have been reproduced above in this volume.
† These joint papers with J. Neyman will be published in a companion volume.

1 1922 (published 1936) Nova Aquilae, 1918. A discussion of the development of the band structure. *Annals of the Solar Physics Laboratory, Cambridge*, **4**, Pt. 3, pp. 130.

2 1922 On variations in personal equation and the correlation of successive judgements. *Biometrika*, **14**, 23–102.

3 1922 On polychoric coefficients of correlation. (With Karl Pearson.) *Biometrika*, **14**, 127–56.

4 1922 Table of the Logarithms of the Complete Gamma Function (to 10 decimal places) for argument 2 to 1200 beyond Legendre's range (argument 1–2). *Tracts for Computers*, **8**.

5 1923 The probable error of a class-index correlation. *Biometrika*, **14**, 261–80.

6 1923 Natural selection and the Age and Area Theory of Dr J. C. Willis. *Biometrika*, **15**, 89–108.

7 1924 Note on the approximations to the probable error of a coefficient of correlation. *Biometrika*, **16**, 196–8.

8 1925 Bayes' Theorem, examined in the light of experimental sampling. *Biometrika*, **17**, 388–442.

9 1926 A further note on the distribution of range in samples taken from a normal population. *Biometrika*, **18**, 173–94.

10 1927 The application of the theory of differential equations to the solution of problems connected with the interdependence of species. *Biometrika*, **19**, 216–22.

11 1927 Further note on the 'linear correlation ratio'. *Biometrika*, **19**, 223–4.

12† 1928 On the use and interpretation of certain test criteria for purposes of statistical inference. (With J. Neyman.) *Biometrika*, **20** A, Part I, 175–240, Part II, 263–94.

13* 1928 The distribution of frequency constants in small samples from symmetrical populations. (Assisted by N. K. Adyanthāya.) *Biometrika*, **20** A, 356–60.

14* 1929 The distribution of frequency constants in small samples from non-normal symmetrical and skew populations. (Assisted by N. K. Adyanthāya.) *Biometrika*, **21**, 259–86.

15 1929 Note on Dr Craig's paper. *Biometrika*, **21**, 294–302.

16* 1929 Some notes on sampling tests with two variables. *Biometrika*, **21**, 337–60.

17 1930 A further development of tests for normality. *Biometrika*, **22**, 239–49.

18† 1930 On the problem of two samples. (With J. Neyman.) *Bull. Polonaise Acad. Sci. et Lettres.* Série A, 73–96.

19† 1931 On the problem of k samples. (With J. Neyman.) *Bull. Polonaise Acad. Sci. et Lettres.* Série A, 460–81.

20 1931 The test of significance for the correlation coefficient. *J. Amer. Statist. Ass.* **26**, 128–34.

21† 1931 Further notes on the χ^2 distribution. (With J. Neyman.) *Biometrika*, **22**, 298–305.

22 1931 Note on tests for normality. *Biometrika*, **22**, 423–4.

23* 1931 The analysis of variance in cases of non-normal variation. *Biometrika*, **23**, 114–33.

24 1932 Further experiments on the sampling distribution of the correlation coefficient. (With Leone Chesire and Elena Oldis.) *J. Amer. Statist. Ass.* **27**, 121–8.

25 1932 The test of significance for the correlation coefficient; some further results. *J. Amer. Statist. Ass.* **27**, 424–6.

26 1932 Distribution of the coefficient of variation. Comparison of A. T. McKay's approximation with experimental sampling results. *J. Roy. Statist. Soc.* **95**, 703–4.

27 1932 The percentage limits for the distribution of range in samples from a normal population ($n \leqslant 100$). *Biometrika*, **24**, 404–17.

28 1933 A survey of the uses of statistical method in the control and standardization of the quality of manufactured products. *J. Roy. Statist. Soc.* **96**, 21–60.

29† 1933 On the problem of the most efficient tests of statistical hypotheses. (With J. Neyman.) *Phil. Trans.* **231**, 289–337.

30† 1933 The testing of statistical hypotheses in relation to probabilities a priori. (With J. Neyman.) *Proc. Camb. Phil. Soc.* **29**, 492–510.

31* 1933 Methods of statistical analysis appropriate for k samples of two variables. (With S. S. Wilks.) *Biometrika*, **25**, 353–78.

32 1933 A note on the distribution of range in samples of n. (With A. T. McKay.) *Biometrika*, **25**, 415–20.

33 1934 Methods of estimating from samples the population standard deviation. (With O. L. Davies.) *J. Roy. Statist. Soc.* Suppl. **1**, 76–93.

34 1934 Sampling problems in industry. *J. Roy. Statist. Soc.* Suppl. **1**, 107–36.

35* 1934 The use of confidence or fiducial limits illustrated in the case of the binomial. (With C. J. Clopper.) *Biometrika*, **26**, 404–13.

36 1934 Analysis of covariance. (Appendix I to a paper by B. H. Wilsdon.) *J. Roy. Statist. Soc.* Suppl. **1**, 178–81.

37 1935 An illustration of the use of fiducial limits in determining the characteristics of a sampled batch. (With A. V. Sukhatme.) *Sankhyā*, **2**, 13–32.

38 1935 The use of range in the place of standard deviation in small samples. (With Joan Haines.) *J. Roy. Statist. Soc.* Suppl. **2**, 83–98.

39 1935 A comparison of β_2 and Mr Geary's w_n criteria. *Biometrika*, **27**, 333–52.

40 1935 *The Application of Statistical Methods to Industrial Standardisation and Quality Control.* British Standards Institution. No. 600, pp. 161.

41† 1936 Contributions to the theory of testing statistical hypotheses, Part I. (With J. Neyman.) *Statistical Research Memoirs*, **1**, 1–37.

42† 1936 Sufficient statistics and uniformly most powerful tests of statistical hypotheses. (With J. Neyman.) *Statistical Research Memoirs*, **1**, 113–37.

43* 1936 The efficiency of statistical tools and a criterion for the rejection of outlying observations. (With C. Chandra Sekar.) *Biometrika*, **28**, 308–20.

44 1936 Statistical method as an aid to control of industrial efficiency. Issued by the Chemical Engineering Congress of the World Power Conference, 1936, K2, 1–24.

45 1936 Statistical method and industry in Great Britain. *J. Amer. Statist. Ass.* **31**, 361–6.

46 1937 Notes on some statistical problems raised in Mr Bayes's paper. (With B. L. Welch.) *J. Roy. Statist. Soc.* Suppl. **4**, 94–101.

47* 1937 Some aspects of the problem of randomization. *Biometrika*, **29**, 53–64.

48 1937 Maximum likelihood and methods of estimation. *Biometrika*, **29**, 155–6.

49 1938 *Karl Pearson: An Appreciation of Some Aspects of his Life and Work.* Cambridge University Press. Pp. vi + 170. (A reproduction with additional Appendices of two articles from *Biometrika* (1936), **28**, 193–257; (1937), **29**, 161–248).

50 1938 Note on some points in 'Student's' paper on 'Comparison between balanced and random arrangements of field plots'. (With J. Neyman.) *Biometrika*, **29**, 380–8.

51* 1938 The probability integral transformation for testing goodness of fit and combining independent tests of significance. *Biometrika*, **30**, 134–48.

52 1938 Some aspects of the problem of randomization. II. An illustration of 'Student's' inquiry into the effect of 'balancing' in agricultural experiments. *Biometrika*, **30**, 159–79.

53† 1938 Contributions to the theory of testing statistical hypotheses. Parts II and III. (With J. Neyman.) *Statistical Research Memoirs*, **2**, 25–57.

54 1939 William Sealy Gosset: 'Student' as a statistician. *Biometrika*, **30**, 210–50.

55 1939 Note on Professor Pitman's contribution to the theory of estimation. *Biometrika*, **30**, 471–4.

56 1939 Note on the inverse and direct methods of estimation in R. D. Gordon's problem. *Biometrika*, **31**, 181–6.

57 1939 (published 1945). The application of the theory of probability to industrial problems. One of a series of papers read before a Conference on the application of the calculus of probability, held at Geneva in June 1939 under the auspices of Institut International de Cooperation Intellectualle.

58* 1941 A note on further properties of statistical tests. *Biometrika*, **32**, 59–61.

59 1941 Tables of percentage points of the incomplete beta-function and of the χ^2 distribution. Prefatory notes. *Biometrika*, **32**, 151–3, 187.

60 1942 The probability integral of the range in samples of n observations from a normal population. Foreword to Tables. *Biometrika*, **32**, 301, 308.

61* 1942 Notes on testing statistical hypotheses. *Biometrika*, **32**, 311–16.

62 1943 Tables of percentage points of the inverted beta (F) distribution. Prefatory note. *Biometrika*, **33**, 73, 88.

63 1943 Tables of the probability integral of the studentized range. (With H. O. Hartley.) *Biometrika*, **33**, 89–99.

64 1945 The probability integral of the mean deviation. Editorial note. *Biometrika*, **33**, 252–3.

65 1946 Tables for testing the homogeneity of a set of estimated variances. Prefatory note. (With H. O. Hartley.) *Biometrika*, **33**, 296–301.

66* 1947 The choice of statistical tests illustrated on the interpretation of data classed in a 2×2 table. *Biometrika*, **34**, 139–67.

67 1948 Note on Professor Haldane's paper regarding the treatment of rare events. *Biometrika*, **35**, 301–3.

68* 1948 2×2 tables; the power function of the test on a randomized experiment. (With Maxine Merrington.) *Biometrika*, **35**, 331–45.

69 1950 Some notes on the use of range. *Biometrika*, **37**, 88–92.

70 1950 Table of the probability integral of the t-distribution. (With H. O. Hartley.) *Biometrika*, **37**, 168–72.

71 1950 Tables of the χ^2-integral and of the cumulative Poisson distribution. (With H. O. Hartley.) *Biometrika*, **37**, 313–25.

72* 1950 On questions raised by the combination of tests based on discontinuous distributions. *Biometrika*, **37**, 383–98.

73 1951 Tables of the 5 % and 0·5 % points of Pearson curves (with argument β_1 and β_2) expressed in standard measure. (With Maxine Merrington.) *Biometrika*, **38**, 4–10.

74 1951 Charts of the power function for analysis of variance tests, derived from the non-central F-distribution. (With H. O. Hartley.) *Biometrika*, **38**, 112–30.

75 1951 Review: R. A. Fisher's 'Contribution to Mathematical Statistics'. *Biometrika*, **38**, 257–9.

76 1951 Moment constants of the distribution of range in normal samples. (With H. O. Hartley.) *Biometrika*, **38**, 463–4.

77 1952 Comparison of two approximations to the distribution of range in small samples from normal populations. *Biometrika*, **39**, 130–6.

78* 1952 The time intervals between industrial accidents. (With B. A. Maguire and A. H. A. Wynn.) *Biometrika*, **39**, 168–80.

79* 1953 Further notes on the analysis of accident data. (With B. A. Maguire and A. H. A. Wynn.) *Biometrika*, **40**, 213–16.

80 1954 *Biometrika Tables for Statisticians*, vol. 1. (With H. O. Hartley.) Published by the Cambridge University Press for the Biometrika Trustees (3rd edition 1966).

81 1954 The distribution of the ratio, in a single normal sample, of range to standard deviation. (With H. A. David and H. O. Hartley.) *Biometrika*, **41**, 482–93.

82 1955 Statistical concepts in their relation to reality. *J. R. Statist. Soc.* B, **17**, 204–7.

83 1955 *Correlated Random Normal Deviates*. (With E. C. Fieller and T. Lewis.) *Tracts for Computers*, no. 26. 3000 sets of deviates each giving 9 random pairs with correlations 0·1 (0·1) 0·9, compiled from Herman Wold's Table of Random Normal Deviates (Tract no. 25). Published by the Cambridge University Press for the Department of Statistics, University College London.

84* 1956 Some aspects of the geometry of statistics. The use of visual presentation in understanding the theory and application of mathematical statistics. (Presidential Address to the Royal Statistical Society.) *J. R. Statist. Soc.* A, **119**, 125–46.

85 1957 John Wishart 1898–1956. An obituary article. *Biometrika*, **44**, 1–8.

86 1957 The distribution of range in normal samples with $n = 200$. (With B. I. Harley.) *Biometrika*, **44**, 257–60.

87 1957 Tests for rank correlation coefficients. I. (With E. C. Fieller and H. O. Hartley.) *Biometrika*, **44**, 470–81.

88 1958 An approximation to the distribution of non-central t. (With Maxine Merrington.) *Biometrika*, **45**, 484–91.

89 1959 Note on Mr Quenouille's Edgeworth Type A transformation. *Biometrika*, **46**, 203–4.

90 1959 Note on an approximation to the distribution of non-central χ^2. *Biometrika*, **46**, 364.

91 1961 Tests for rank correlation coefficients. II. (With E. C. Fieller.) *Biometrika*, **48**, 29–40.

92 1961 *Elementary Statistical Exercises*. (With F. N. David.) Cambridge University Press, pp. 108.

93 1961 Some incidents in the early history of biometry and statistics, 1890–94. Statistical Techniques Research Group, Princeton University. Report no. 45. (Revised and enlarged as no. 109.)

94 1961 Some systems of frequency curves. [As no. 92 above. Report no. 46.]

95 1961 Properties of higher moments and cumulants. Example from the distributions of $\sqrt{b_1}$ and b_2 (or g_1 and g_2). [As no. 92. Report no. 47.]

96 1961 Maximum likelihood and the fitting of curves to observational data. [As no. 92. Report no. 48.]

97 1962 Frequency surfaces. [As no. 92. Report no. 49.]

98 1962 Tests for rank correlation coefficients. III. Distribution of the transformed Kendall coefficient. (With Barbara A. S. Snow.) *Biometrika*, **49**, 185–91.

99* 1962 Some thoughts on statistical inference. *Ann. Math. Statist.* **33**, 394–403.

100 1962 William Palin Elderton, 1877–1962. An obituary notice. *Biometrika*, **49**, 297–303.

101 1962 The goodness of fit tests based on W_N^2 and U_N^2. (With M. A. Stephens.) *Biometrika*, **49**, 397–402.

102* 1963 Some problems arising in approximating to probability distributions, using moments. *Biometrika*, **50**, 95–112.

103* 1963 Comparison of tests for randomness of points on a line. *Biometrika*, **50**, 315–25.

104 1963 Table of percentage points of Pearson curves, for given $\sqrt{\beta_1}$ and β_2, expressed in standard measure. (With N. L. Johnson, Eric Nixon and D. E. Amos.) *Biometrika*, **50**, 459–98.

105* 1963 A statistician's place in assessing the likely operational performance of army weapons and equipment. ARO-D Report 63-2, 1–15.

106 1963 *Tables for Testing Significance in a 2×2 Contingency Table.* Prefatory note and Introduction. Published by the Cambridge University Press for the Biometrika Trustees.

107 1964 The ratio of range to standard deviation in the same normal sample. (With M. A. Stephens.) *Biometrika*, **51**, 484–7.

108 1964 Samuel Stanley Wilks 1906–1964. *J. R. Statist. Soc.* A, **127**, 597–9.

109 1965 Studies in the history of probability and statistics, XIV. Some incidents in the early history of biometry and statistics, 1890–94. *Biometrika*, **52**, 3–18.

110 1965 Tables of percentage points of $\sqrt{b_1}$ and b_2 in normal samples; a rounding off. *Biometrika*, **52**, 282–5.

111 1965 Approximate means and standard deviations based on distances between percentage points of frequency curves. (With J. W. Tukey.) *Biometrika*, **52**, 533–46.

112 1966 The Neyman-Pearson story: 1926–34. Historical sidelights on an episode in Anglo-Polish collaboration. From *Research Papers in Statistics. Festschrift for J. Neyman*, pp. 1–23. Edited by F. N. David. John Wiley and Sons, New York and London.

302546718-